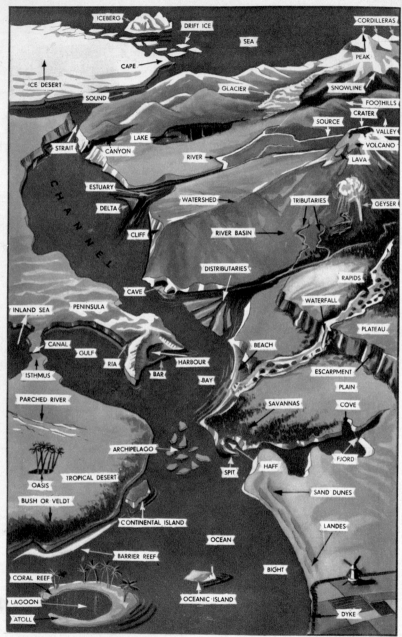

Geographical Terms Pictorially Explained

EVERYBODY'S
BOOK OF FACTS

COMPILED BY
F. L. DUNBAR

EDITED BY
HAROLD WHEELER
HON.D.LITT., F.R.HIST.S.

ODHAMS PRESS LIMITED
LONG ACRE, LONDON, W.C.2

Made and Printed in Great Britain
by Odhams (Watford) Ltd., Watford

CONTENTS

BIRTH OF A WORLD

S INCE man became a thinking being, philosophers and scientists have endeavoured to answer the questions, " Whence did we come and whither are we bound?"

If at night we stand and gaze into the sky at the myriads of twinkling points of light which we know to be suns like the centre of our own solar system, and some of them infinitely larger, and think also of the tens of millions of stars which are so far distant that we cannot see them with the naked eye, we may feel inclined to the opinion that the brain of man is incapable of ever offering an explanation of this wonderful universe, of which our world forms such an infinitesimal part.

In all probability man never will be in a position to offer such an explanation, but within the last few decades scientists have advanced theories which may approximate to the truth. It is a paradox that these discoveries have been brought about, not by the study of the infinitely large universe which lies outside our world, but by the study of the infinitely small particles of matter, called atoms, of which our earth and its atmosphere, as well as the matter outside it, are composed.

IMPORTANT BUT INVISIBLE ATOMS

The atom, which we may imagine as a " knob " of matter too small even to be seen in the most powerful microscope, is capable of being broken up into smaller portions: the proton, which contains a charge of positive electricity, and the electron, containing a charge of negative electricity. The electron revolves around the proton much in the same way as the earth revolves around the sun.

The atom of each element, or substance, of which our universe is composed, contains a number of protons and electrons, the number of which remain constant for each element. Thus the hydrogen atom, which is the lightest, is composed of one proton and one electron; the atom of helium contains four protons and two electrons, all revolving in a complicated manner, and so on for each element.

SPACE IS NOT EMPTY

Another discovery which we need to assist us in our hypothesis is as follows. When we are looking at the stars it seems obvious that the greater part of space is empty; there appears to be nothing between us and the distant stars which interferes with the light which they emit. But space is not so empty as it seems to be. There is a thin content of matter which pervades the whole of space, some of which is thrown out by the sun and the stars by the intense explosive heat that they generate, and there is also much matter from the vast distances of space itself.

Now it has been found by actual experiment that when two atoms or a proton and electron are in the same vicinity, a collision sometimes occurs, and in the same way as when a motor car collides with a bicycle a part of the bicycle is likely to be knocked off, so the heavier atom may knock off a part of the atom with which it comes in contact, and in so doing cause a friction which produces heat.

HOW A NEBULA IS FORMED

Over 250 years ago, Sir Isaac Newton propounded his theory of gravitation, namely that one body or particle of matter is drawn towards another. Although modern scientists have amended this conclusion, it is still fundamentally true enough to assist us in formulating a theory as to the probable origin of the sun.

Let us imagine that out in space two atoms come into contact and coalesce. The joining of these two particles, besides generating an infinitesimal amount of heat, forms an atom which is larger in size than previously, and therefore by reason of its gravitational power, is more easily able to attract small atoms with which it comes in contact.

As the atoms journey on, more and more matter is attracted to them, until after a time they form a "cloud" with atoms racing around each other and colliding, until the amount of heat engendered by the "accidents" is sufficient to set the mass glowing. The heat so generated will in itself cause the electrons to move more quickly, and thus is begun the formation of what is called a nebula, a mass of glowing gases.

BEGINNING OF THE SUN AND ITS FAMILY

AFTER ages of wandering through space, feeding as it were upon every particle of matter with which it comes into contact and increasing in size and heat, the nebula at length becomes a flaming mass of white-hot matter. The more tightly packed parts may coalesce and thus form stars with the outer portions of the nebula still surrounding them, as is the case with some of the great nebulæ visible through large telescopes.

These outer portions of nebulæ will probably themselves form stars in time. Thus is brought into being a system such as our own, which, bounded by the mighty ring of suns known as the Milky Way, is a tremendous "island universe" similar to the great nebula in Andromeda, the nebulæ in the Pleiades, and many others. This, then, is the theory of the formation of our sun from a nebula.

ORIGIN OF THE SOLAR SYSTEM

The theory most widely accepted as to the birth of our planetary system is as follows:—

As the mighty suns of the universe swim through space, it is conceivable that occasionally one sun may pass another so close as to assert its pulling power or gravitational force upon the other. Owing to the colossal distances between the stars, such an occurrence must be extremely rare, but it is believed that far back in time, when the sun was young, such an event did occur.

The passing of the stray sun raised enormous tides in our own sun, and so great was the disturbance that huge flaming masses were violently torn away, not so violently as to take them for ever from the sun's attractive influence, but leaving the torn masses behind in a stream, to revolve round their parent.

The new suns so formed being much smaller than the parent, cooled comparatively quickly and have now become the solid or semi-solid planets which form the planetary system.

DEATH OF THE SOLAR SYSTEM

When the astronomer looks through his giant telescope he finds that the stars differ vastly one from the other. Some are brilliant new suns, burning with intense heat. Others have, as it were, almost burned themselves out, and move through space as great, glowing, red masses of gaseous matter. A third type of sun is still burning with a terrific heat, but throwing out its constituent electrons and protons so quickly that it is contracting rapidly upon itself, and in a comparatively short time the matter of which it is composed will have been dispersed throughout space.

Since it seems likely that all stars must die by reason of their radiation, or the destruction by heat of the matter of which they are composed, and which is thrown out by them, it is obvious that our own sun, which we know to have existed for millions of years, is slowly but surely exhausting its bulk in radiation. It has advanced quite a long distance down its path of life.

It has been discovered that the third type of sun mentioned above, which is called a " white dwarf " and is the heaviest type of star known— its density being some 60,000 times greater than that of water—has not always been contracting so rapidly and dissipating its constituents so prodigally. The rapid contraction seems to occur suddenly when the star has reached a certain stage in its life. It is difficult, however, to say whether a star, when it reaches that stage in its existence, will become a white dwarf, or whether it will retain its original characteristics and continue to use up its energy in the normal manner, and, dying slowly, become one of the " cool red " stars.

Our own sun is approaching this critical period, but it will still be many millions of years before there is any appreciable alteration in its power. Were a sudden change to occur, life would at once become impossible on our earth, just as it will become impossible in the dim, distant ages if the sun dies down to become a red, almost dead globe.

NO IMMEDIATE FEAR OF EXTINCTION

Professor T. J. J. See gave it as his opinion that more than half of the sun's heat from the beginning remains stored up in its colossal mass. " This accumulated heat," he avowed, " in connexion with that yet to be produced by future contraction, assures us a future supply of energy three times as great as that required for the whole past activity of the sun. So far from approaching extinction, our sun is still in its youth, with the zenith of its glory far, far in the future. We need have no fear that it will soon die out and leave our world cold and wrapped in the darkness of everlasting night." Another scientist suggested that 300,000,000 years still remain.

WHEN ALL THE SUNS HAVE DISSIPATED

Modern physics advances a principle which confirms the astronomical theory of the end of all life by freezing in outer space. Known as the second law of thermo-dynamics, this principle states that when all the suns in the universe have dissipated their energy, the matter of which they are composed will be distributed uniformly throughout space at so low a temperature that life will be impossible.

It would seem that life has appeared upon this planet for what must be but a brief minute as measured by astronomical time, only to disappear and return to the atomic structure from which it was formed. It must be remembered, however, that science has as yet opened merely the tiniest peep-hole to the secrets of the universe, and that causes and effects of which we have yet no knowledge may assure for man a longer history that we can at present anticipate.

OTHER PLANETARY SYSTEMS

IT has always been a matter of curiosity to most people as to whether there are other solar systems in the universe similar to our own; whether any of the millions of suns have attendant planets.

We have discussed earlier the probable formation of our sun's planets by the passing of a wandering star, and it would appear that an accident of a similar nature to another star must be of very rare occurrence. Yet it must not be assumed that other such planetary systems do not exist, because no telescope is powerful enough to enable us to perceive a dark body revolving round a distant star unless the planet actually imposes itself between the star and our observer, or unless some peculiar motion of the star itself gives the clue. A dwarf solar system was discovered in 1927 near Spica, in Virgo, the sun of which has a power of illumination 15,000 times greater than our own. The planets which encircle this sun are so small that a man could walk round their equator in half an hour.

CONDITIONS NECESSARY FOR LIFE

In this, or in some other solar system, it is remotely possible that life does exist, but peculiar conditions must be present. Not only must the planet be at such a distance from its sun that it is neither too hot nor too cold, but also there must be an atmosphere round the planet and vegetation which will be capable of supporting life. Moreover the elements from which life obtains its beginnings must be present in such a nicely balanced proportion that living cells can be formed.

Living matter is formed from quite ordinary atoms, but there are few atoms which have the quality of journeying together in large enough numbers to form living cells. From experiments conducted in recent years it appears likely that there is one element alone which, in conjunction with others, supplies the necessary link to form living from " dead " matter, and that is carbon. Why the carbon atom should possess this peculiar life-giving property is not known; it is a secret which nature has so far kept to herself.

From the evidence we have before us it would appear that nature does not go out of her way to produce life; in fact, we must suppose that she is definitely antagonistic to it. From our little globe, smaller in the universe than a grain of sand as compared with the earth, we look out upon the cosmos, and find nothing in its immensity to give us cause to believe that any other world has given birth to life.

TWO STARS THAT LOOK LIKE ONE

Although there is a paucity of evidence regarding other solar systems in our universe, there is an interesting class of stars numbering many thousands, in which one or more stars belong to a single system.

The telescope has revealed that many stars, which to the unaided eye appear as single points of light, are in fact two, or sometimes more, stars which circle round each other. The orbits or paths of double stars have been studied for many years, and in each case have been found to be elliptical in exactly the same way as the orbits of the planets revolving round the sun are elliptical. These stars are not always of the same composition.

WONDERS REVEALED BY THE SPECTROSCOPE

It is possible by means of the spectroscope to examine the constituent matter of a star. The spectroscope is an instrument which splits up the light received from a source, in this case a star, into a broad band of light. The band of light is marked by bars, each bar representing the light emitted when a certain element is burning. One end of the band shows the light of the red rays of long wavelength, and as the bars of colour move across the band the bars represent rays of shorter wavelength, which are the violet rays. The rays of light of the longest wavelength are known as infra-red rays, while those of the shortest wavelength are known as ultra-violet rays.

An instance of suns of different colour is afforded by the constellation of Cassiopeia, in which a violet and a white sun are encircled by a sun of azure blue.

Although the majority of stars in the binary systems, as they are called, are white in colour, yellow, blue, red and green stars, as well as stars of uncertain shades, are found. It sometimes happens that one star of a binary system is in such a position that it is eclipsed by its companion. A star of this type is Algol, which loses much of its light for five hours, then remains at full brightness for nearly three days.

STARS OF MANY KINDS

Our own sun belongs to the class of stars known as dwarf stars, to which the majority of stars belong. The nearest star to our solar system, Alpha Centauri, is also a dwarf sun. The light from this nearest neighbour takes rather more than four years to reach us.

GIANT STARS

The largest star known was discovered early in 1938 by Dr. O. Struve, of Yerkes Observatory, Wisconsin, U.S.A. A companion to the binary star Epsilon Aurigæ, it has a radius of 1,200,000,000 miles, which means that its diameter is about forty times as great as the distance between the earth and the sun.

The star of greatest luminosity ever measured is situated in the Swordfish, and every second it loses some two and a half trillion tons in weight.

VARIABLE STARS

As already noted, the light of some stars varies owing to their lying on the same plane as the earth and thus eclipsing one another, but there is another type of star which shows a true variation of light. These stars are known as Cepheids, and are so named after Cephei, which is a star of this type.

The period of variation of these stars ranges from hours in some cases to weeks in others, and remains constant. They are all of the large type, and show the same characteristic of a quick rise in brightness followed by a slower fall to dimness again. The period of a Cepheid is directly connected with its luminosity, although in exactly what manner is unknown.

There is another type of variable star in which the variation period is much longer than with the Cepheids, but in these cases the period is by no means regular, although the magnitude of the flare-up is many times greater than in the case of the Cepheids.

A third type of variable stars are known as Novæ. Such stars, as a general rule, blaze out brightly as though a terrific explosion has occurred within them, and then slowly recede until they become fainter even than they were originally. They rarely blaze out again.

MAGNITUDE OF SPACE

The stars are situated at enormous distances from the earth. They are so remote that to measure the distance in miles would not only convey little or no meaning to our minds, but would compel us to handle impossibly unwieldy numbers. Consequently, special units of measurements, called astronomical units, are used for measurements beyond the limits of the solar system.

The method of calculating the distance of the stars is by light years.

Light travels at a faster speed than anything else, namely 186,000 miles per second, and a light year consists of the distance which light, travelling at this speed, would cover in a year. Just multiply the number of seconds in a year by 186,000 and you will get the answer.

Our nearest neighbour in space is distant four and one-third light years from us, and from this it is easy to realize why collisions between stars rarely occur.

It may well be asked how it is possible to measure such inconceivable distances with any degree of exactitude. Measurements are obtained by using the well-known fact of the earth's rotation round the sun, the diameter of which rotation is 185,800,000 miles.

MEASURING THE DISTANCE OF A STAR

The star whose distance is to be measured is so far away as to appear stationary in the sky, and even though it may have a motion of its own, this is not perceptible to us. As the earth moves in its elliptical path round the sun we mark the position of the star in the sky in January, then three months later, when the earth has reached a point at a quarter of its orbit, the position of the star is again taken, and so on as each quarter of the orbit is reached.

The star itself will appear to have formed an ellipse on the background of the sky. We thus have two ellipses, one the diameter whose major axis is the diameter of the earth's elliptical path round the sun, and the other an infinitely small ellipse which the star appears to have marked on the background of the sky. The distance of the star will be inversely proportional to the size of the ellipse, and by measuring the angular value of the diameter of the ellipse we are able, since we know the diameter of the earth's path round the sun, to work out the distance of the star. This is called measuring the distance of the star by its parallax.

STAR CLUSTERS

On a clear bright night one may see a broad, luminous band of light which seems to extend like a belt right around the sky. This is the Milky Way. Viewed through a telescope, it consists of thousands of millions of stars. The sun and its attendant planets are situated somewhere near the centre of this great ring, and form part of the enormous star cluster which, bounded by the Milky Way, we call the galactic system.

The universe contains many of these vast globular clusters of stars, which we can liken to continents in the sea of space. All of them are situated enormous distances from us and from each other. It is possible to estimate with a high degree of accuracy the distance of these clusters by using several methods. One method is by studying the Cepheid-type stars within the system, and comparing the apparent magnitude of the Cepheids with their real brightness. The cluster in Centaurus, which is the nearest to us, is 21,000 light years distant.

CLUSTER OF 50,000 STARS

Many clusters are so vast that light sometimes takes hundreds of years to travel from one side of the cluster to the other, and although when viewed through a telescope the stars appear to be packed tightly together, from within the cluster itself, could we but view them in this way, we should find that each star was extremely remote from its neighbour.

The star cluster in Hercules can be seen by the naked eye, and appears as a single twinkling point of light no different from any of its star neighbours. A photograph taken through one of the large telescopes reveals that this point of light is in reality a giant cluster of some 50,000 stars.

SPIRAL NEBULÆ

The spiral nebulæ, like the star clusters, can also be described as island continents in the sea of space, but in structure they are different. They are so called because of their formation, which appears to be that of a streaming mass of matter revolving round a focal point, but continually moving farther away from it.

The nebulæ form the outermost continents of space. Probably the nearest to us is the great nebula in Andromeda, a spiral of flattish shape with the nucleus, as is usual, more condensed than the outer arms. It is believed that most of the matter of which the nebula consists has already formed into countless suns, but certain features suggest that much of the matter may still exist in a glowing, gaseous state which surrounds the bunches of stars, giving them an appearance of a glowing entity rather than of separate points of light.

AT THE OUTER EDGE OF SPACE

There are apparently hundreds of thousands of these vast islands scattered throughout space, and the enormous extent of each island admits of no other possibility than that each one is a separate system. The nearest appear to be about a million light years distant from us, and we are led to assume that these objects are situated, as it were, at the outer edge of space.

Other types of nebulæ, known as planetary nebulæ, can best be described as masses of glowing gases, usually of a bluish colour, and sometimes so small that they can be mistaken for stars. Their true nature only becomes apparent when they are examined in the spectroscope.

ALL THE UNIVERSE IS IN MOTION

Without exception, the whole vast host of stars, planets, clusters, and nebulæ appears to be in motion.

Sir William Herschel (1738-1822) was the first astronomer to study the problem of the motion of the solar system, and to prove that the complete system, while revolving round the sun as a centre, had a motion as a whole through space. He also ascertained that the sun and its attendant planets are racing at a speed of about twelve and a half miles a second towards the constellation Lyra. As each hour goes by the earth is some 20,000 miles nearer to this group of stars, but even at this enormous speed, such is the magnitude of space, it will be many millions of years before there is danger of a collision.

WHY WE DO NOT FEEL THE EARTH'S SPIN

Why are we not conscious of motion as the earth rushes through space? This problem may be explained by taking the analogous case of a passenger in the cabin of a ship moving in a perfectly calm sea. He is unaware of the motion of the vessel while in the apparently motionless confines of his cabin, but were he to go on deck and study the surrounding sea or watch the apparent growth in size of an island on the horizon, he would at once become aware of the ship's motion through the water.

It is by thus studying the firmament outside our solar system that we are able to assure ourselves of the movement of the system, and we find that stars in the constellation of Lyra seem to spread out in the sky, or as it were, grow larger, just as an island in the sea appears to grow larger as the ship approaches it.

The natural sequel to this discovery was the question as to whether the whole of the universe were not in motion. This problem raised many difficulties, because although from our own ship it had been simple for us to check our motion by the objects we approached, it would obviously be difficult to determine whether the other ships which we saw as specks on the distant horizon had a motion of their own, or whether their apparent motion was due to our own.

THE EXPANDING UNIVERSE

Science was able to call in the assistance of the spectroscope in determining the motion of the distant stars and island universes. It was found that when light was received from these distant systems it was displaced towards one end or other of the spectrum, and that the most distant objects had their light displaced towards the red end. What is known as Doppler's principle shows us that when a railway train with whistle blowing passes an observer on a railway platform, the tone of the whistle seems lower after the train has passed. This is because the wavelength of the note emitted by the whistle when it has passed the observer takes longer to reach him, or in other words, the wavelength of the note has increased, and the tone becomes lower as the wavelength increases.

We have mentioned earlier that the red end of the spectrum contains light of the longest wavelength, and we can assume therefore that when the light from an object is displaced towards the red end of the spectrum the object is receding from us, and the amount of displacement being measurable, we can calculate the speed of motion of the object. The results obtained by using this method led to the remarkable conclusion that the universe is expanding at a prodigious speed.

The farther out into space we go to investigate, the more colossal are the speeds attained, and nebulæ which are situated seemingly at the edge of the universe have an apparent speed of motion away from us as great as 15,000 or more miles per second.

The speeds of distant nebulæ appear to be in proportion to their distance from us, and it would seem that at some time in the dim past all matter in the universe must have started in its expanding motion from a point situated near the galactic system.

Were this indeed the case the universe must be younger than we have cause to believe, but more recent researches assign other reasons than motion to the movement of light towards the red end of the spectrum. Light is now believed to be reddened by distance and also by the gravitational power of intervening matter which, as we have shown, consists not only of the stars themselves, but of a tenuous atomic " atmosphere " which pervades space.

It is probable, therefore, that the apparent recession of the nebulæ is to a large extent illusory, although Einstein conceives a universe with a certain amount of curvature of its space and containing matter which is bound to either contract or expand.

FORTY MILLION YEARS TO REACH THE NEAREST STAR

In order to try and gain some conception of the size of our universe, let us imagine the solar system to be the size of a grain of sand in Piccadilly Circus. Then the Milky Way would stretch out to the size of London itself. Were the earth the size of a pea, the nearest fixed star would be as far distant as London is from Sydney, Australia. Were the individual stars in space reduced to the size of pins' heads, each star would still be at an average of forty miles from another.

An express train travelling at a speed of about sixty-seven miles per hour would take nearly 4,000 years to arrive at the planet Neptune and 40,000,000 years to reach the nearest star to the earth.

VISITORS FROM SPACE

The solar system, moving through space towards Lyra, must travel for many millions of years before it comes in contact with a star or with any matter large enough to produce any effect upon our sun or planets. Large conglomerations of matter are apparently very rare in the universe, although there is a school of thought which believes that the moon, the asteroids, the planetary moons, and even some of the planets themselves, are masses of matter which, once floating free in space, have been attracted by the gravitation of the sun and planets.

That the earth comes in contact with a great deal of matter on its journey is evidenced by the meteors, meteorites and cosmic dust which we see entering our atmosphere and find on the earth, and also by the comets, although the last mentioned, together with many of the meteoric showers, are in a rather different category, since many of them are believed to form a part of the solar system.

TRAVELS OF THE METEORS

MANY meteor showers travel in an elliptical orbit around the sun, but their path is very different from that of the planets, whose path is almost circular. The meteoric ellipse is much thinner and longer and one end of its path lies very close to the sun, while the farther end lies far out in space. If we imagine the meteor shower in position at the distant turn in its ellipse, we shall find that its speed of motion is relatively slow owing to the fact that as it recedes from the sun the sun's gravitational pull is lessening, but, having once started on its return journey the speed of the shower increases until it attains its maximum as it rushes round its path nearest the sun.

The path of a meteor shower often cuts across the path of the earth, and since both have regular motions round the sun we are able to assign regular periods for their visitations to our atmosphere.

PRODIGIOUS SPEED OF SHOOTING STARS

One such shower, known as the Leonids, pays us a visit every thirty-three years, when we are given a brilliant display of " shooting stars " for several nights. Meteors generally range in size from a very small pea to a piece of rock weighing several pounds.

They move at prodigious speeds, sometimes at twenty miles a second. In the thin matter of outer space this speed is possible, but as the meteor enters the earth's atmosphere, which is some hundreds of miles thick, the increasing density causes friction which heats the matter of which the meteor is formed until finally it is dissipated into brilliantly fiery vapour which we call a " shooting star."

METEORITE WEIGHING HUNDREDS OF TONS

Very rarely do we find any part of a meteor which has reached the earth, but meteorites are considerably larger and frequently do so. They consist of stone or iron sometimes mingled with other elements, and often cause fear and terror by their fall. It is generally accepted that the large majority come to us from the far depths of space.

Usually the fall of a meteorite is accompanied by a brilliant light and a terrific explosion, and there is evidence that some of them have been truly enormous. In 1908 a meteorite weighing several hundred tons fell in what is fortunately an almost uninhabited part of Siberia. It left a huge crater and penetrated the earth for a considerable distance, while the countryside around was devastated.

VAST CRATER FORMED BY A METEORITE

In the United States there is a crater nearly a mile in diameter, whose existence can be explained in no other way than that it owes its formation to a tremendous meteorite, but although attempts have been made to unearth clear evidence by digging on the spot, the huge object must have buried itself so deeply by its weight and speed that nothing can be found.

When meteorites or fire-balls have been seen to fall, even during the daytime, they emit a bright light, which is sometimes green or coloured.

A meteorite weighing some six tons fell at Quetta, on the north-west frontier of India, during a heavy thunderstorm in 1923.

METEORITE THAT WAS WORSHIPPED

Small wonder that ignorant natives in various parts of the world call meteorites heaven stones. A messenger from the sky fell near Zanzibar in 1855, and was at once regarded as sacred by the natives. They bowed to it, decked it with precious stones, anointed it with oil, and paid it every mark of veneration.

That it was other than a token of special favour never occurred to them until they were attacked by the Masai and defeated. Belief in the luck bringer disappeared almost as quickly as the meteorite had fallen from the sky, and on the first available opportunity the heaven stone was sold to a European trader. It is now in the Munich museum.

COMETS : CELESTIAL WANDERERS

COMETS are hazy, nebulous objects, usually with a rather bright head that constantly changes its size, and a long, transparent tail which is sometimes millions of miles in length. Very few are visible to the naked eye, since they consist of very thin, gaseous matter.

The paths of comets are generally long, thin ellipses, with one end very close to the sun, and the other far out in space. As a comet approaches the sun its head comes first, but after passing round it, the head remains pointing to the sun and the comet travels tail first. Comets do not move towards the sun from any particular part of space, but appear to be wanderers through the solar system, except in so far as one end of their orbit is always round the sun. Many comets, when passing close to the planets, have their direction altered by the gravitational pull of the planet, and in some cases are dispersed or captured entirely. It used to be held that comets portended calamities, but modern astronomers know that there is no possibility of their causing the slightest harm to anything or anybody.

POISON IN A COMET'S TAIL

The idea that comets have their origin within the solar system and are not interlopers from outer space is held by Dr. A. C. D. Crommelin, a famous authority on these celestial wanderers. He also inclines to the opinion that they are clusters of meteors containing a great quantity of gas. Cyanogen, related to potassium cyanide and prussic acid, is present in the head, while carbon monoxide exists in the tail. Both are extremely poisonous.

A few comets make more or less regular visits. Halley's comet, the most famous of them all, returns every seventy-five years approximately. Controlled by solar gravity, comets do not always follow the same orbit, and do not necessarily appear in the same form. They have a tendency to play hide-and-seek. That a comet hit the earth between 100,000 and 1,000,000 years ago is the belief of Dr. F. A. Mellon and Dr. W. Schriever, who hold that on the occasion about 190,000 square miles of the earth were devastated. They base their conclusions on aerial photographs which reveal certain elliptical and parallel depressions in North and South Carolina, U.S.A., some of which are encircled, suggesting a heavy bombardment.

HALLEY'S COMET

Some 600 comets are known, but over 1,000 have been recorded. On the average, four or five comets make their appearance every year, but few are visible to the naked eye. The earliest known picture of Halley's comet is in an old Nuremberg chronicle of 684. It is also featured in the Bayeux Tapestry. When William the Conqueror invaded Great Britain in 1066, the flaming wanderer again made an appearance, and was heralded as a good omen for the Norman, hence its representation. It also showed itself in 1145.

In the famous *Canterbury Psalter*, compiled and illuminated by Eadwine, a monk of Christ Church Priory, Canterbury, there is a drawing of a comet—evidently Halley's—with a very long tail, and in the margin is a note in Anglo-Saxon: "Concerning the star called comet. A suchlike ray has the star known as Comet, and in English it is called ' the hairy star.' It appears seldom, after many winters, and then for an omen." It has been suggested that the Star of Bethlehem was a comet.

PREPARED FOR THE END OF THE WORLD

Halley's comet is named after Edmund Halley (1656-1742) because he saw and described it in 1682. This famous son of a soap boiler worked out the paths of twenty-six comets, no mean accomplishment considering the limited resources at his disposal.

The appearance of Halley's comet has always caused consternation. It was seen in 1456, after the Turks had battered their way through the walls of Constantinople and were busy overthrowing what remained of the Roman Empire. Even in 1910, when the wanderer again flamed its way across the sky, the inhabitants of Teheran prepared for the end of the world, and many Chinese were terror-stricken until the dreaded interloper disappeared. Halley's comet will not appear again until about 1986.

OBSERVATORIES AND TELESCOPES

THE Carnegie Expedition discovered on the hill of Copan, in the land of the Mayas in Central America, the largest and oldest clock in America. It is a sun-clock, formed of pillars at an equal distance from each other. The Maya astronomers posted themselves behind the easternmost pillar to make their sunset observations. It must have been erected about 1,500 years ago, when the culture of the ancient Empire of the Mayas was at its zenith. Tablets fixed to it refer to the annual assemblies of the priestly astronomers.

The Egyptian and the Mexican pyramids, and also the temple towers of Babylon, were doubtless used for astronomical purposes. Besides the division of the celestial equator into thirty-six decades, the Egyptians, as early as 3000 B.C., were acquainted with the ratio between the diameter and circumference of the circle, and reckoned the diameter of the earth at 20,000,000 pyramid metres. On this foundation they calculated the area of the earth's surface, its division into degrees, and determined a series of astronomical standards that have only recently been re-discovered. Astronomical tables were found in the interior of the pyramids. By 550 B.C., the Egyptians were acquainted with the distances of the planets from each other.

FIRST SCHOOL OF ASTRONOMY

The calculations of the Babylonians included a standard that corresponds to the earth's radius, besides figures for the volume and superficial area of the globe. They were acquainted with the periodical eclipses of the sun and the moon, and they calculated the rising and setting of Sirius. Borsippa, near Babylon, had the world's first school of astronomy. It was on their science that the knowledge of the stars possessed by the Greeks was based, but their only contribution was certain improvements in the calendar. By 160 B.C., Hipparchus had determined the positions of 2,000 stars.

Europe has its primitive observatories, such as the prehistoric stone circle of Stonehenge, the so-called Star Court at Gierke in Westphalia (600 B.C.), the stone circle at Ody in West Prussia (500 B.C.), and others, which served also as calendrical observatories for agricultural operations.

In the period from A.D. 200 to 700 astronomy fell into decay. The first medieval observatory was erected in Baghdad in 810, and this was followed in 996 by the famous observatory at Cairo. The use of the terrestrial globe and the celestial chart was taught in the elementary schools of the Arabs. In 1449 an observatory with a large library and a school was founded at Samarkand, capital city of Tamerlane, the Asiatic conqueror, and now in the Uzbek Soviet Socialist Republic. It contained representations of the nine heavens, the seven planets, the sphere of the fixed stars, and the earth with its mountains, deserts, and climates.

At Jaipur, in India, an observatory was built in 1716, equipped with costly astronomical instruments in marble and precious metals, including a gigantic gnomon or sundial that cast so big a shadow that one could follow its movement very easily. Of great fame, too, are the ancient astronomical instruments of the Temple of Heaven at Peiping (Peking), China.

Among the oldest observatories still existing in Europe is the one in the tower of the castle at Palermo, Sicily, which dates from the 12th century. Germany's oldest is the observatory set up by Regiomontanus in 1471, in the house at Nuremberg that was subsequently occupied by Albrecht Dürer, known as the prince of German artists. The Paris observatory was erected in 1667, the Royal Observatory at Greenwich in 1675. Fifty years ago the Vienna University Observatory was considered the greatest in the world, but the American observatories now lead the way.

WORLD'S LARGEST TELESCOPE

The largest telescope is the 200-in. reflector now being erected on Mount Palomar (6,125 ft.), California, U.S.A. Pyrex with a surface coating of aluminium instead of silver was used for the colossal mirror, aluminium being better for reflecting ultra-violet light. Its diameter is 16 ft. 8 in., its thickness 27 in., and its weight 20 tons. The total cost will be about £1,200,000. On the authority of Dr. Edwin Hubble, the instrument will collect about 1,000,000 times as much light as the unaided eye. If it were possible to place a lighted candle in space 10,000 miles away, it would bring it within focus. The molten pyrex was poured into the mould at a temperature of 2,800° F. and allowed to cool very gradually, the process extending for ten months. As a precautionary measure, a second disk was cast. Fixed on a steel bed, this monster inquisitor of the sky will have a tube 55 ft. long, 22 ft. in diameter, and weigh 110 tons. The bearings will weigh about 500 tons. The second largest telescope is the 100-in. Hooker reflector on Mount Wilson, Pasadena, about sixty miles from Mount Palomar. The mirror is 13 in. thick, over 8 ft. in diameter and weighs about 4½ tons.

In 1933 light from the star Arcturus, which had taken forty years to reach the earth, was used to light the lamps of the Scientific Exhibition at Chicago. Six months later the telescope which Galileo made in 1609-1610 was attached to a larger instrument in Italy and focused on the moon. The rays penetrated a photo-electric cell, transformed them into electrical vibrations which travelled by cable and radio to Chicago, and performed a similar feat. The time taken from the moon to the earth was two seconds, and from Florence to Chicago the twentieth part of a second. By a similar apparatus, the light of Sirius was intercepted in Australia and sent to America.

PATH OF WOTAN'S CHARIOT

Besides the sun and the planets, the heavenly bodies most venerated by mankind from the earliest times are the Milky Way and the group of stars which occupy the zone known as the zodiac.

The Sumerians, the original inhabitants of Babylonia, worshipped the Milky Way under the name of the Heavenly Serpent, the Egyptians called it the Heavenly Nile, the Chinese the Silver River, thinking it to be the continuation of the Yangtse Kiang, while the ancient Germans looked on it as the path of Wotan's chariot.

SIGNS OF THE ZODIAC

According to Dr. Norbert Schiller, the ancient Egyptians divided the year into spring, summer, autumn and winter, and assigned to each season three constellations through which the sun passed. To the constellation which the sun entered after March 21, they gave the name of the ram (Aries), because about this time the sheep produce their young. To the constellation that followed in the middle of April, they gave the name of their other domestic animal, the bull (Taurus), on whose strength as a draught animal their agriculture depended.

Next came the twins (Gemini), because the domestic goats usually produce two young ones at the end of May. When the sun came to its turning point, on June 21, i.e., turned back towards the equator, it entered the sign of the crab (Cancer), the animal that crawls backwards. The constellation in which the power of the sun was at its strongest was given the name of the lion (Leo). For harvest time, August, they chose the sign of the virgin (Virgo), gleaning ears of corn, and for the period when day and night are of equal length the sign of the scales (Libra).

As the retreat of the sun in October gives rise to all sorts of diseases, the next constellation received the name of the poisonous scorpion (Scorpio). Then came the hunting time, with the sign of the archer (Sagittarius). On December 21 the sun began to rise higher in the heavens under the sign of the ibex or Capricornus. January, the rainy period, fell under the sign of the water-carrier (Aquarius), while the fishes (Pisces) refer to the time for fishing.

REALM OF THE PLANETS

THE earth and the other planets of the solar system are the children of the sun. From the sun we receive the warmth that keeps us alive, and the radiation that makes our vegetation and the crops that feed us grow. Indirectly it sends us the rain that quenches our thirst.

The sun is a star of a kind similar to the majority of the stars we see in the sky on any cloudless night. In other words it is a normal type of star, middle-aged, and of the kind known as red stars.

It is by far the largest object in the solar system. To get some idea of its size as compared with the planets, if we imagine the sun as a very large Jaffa orange, then the earth is about the size of a pin's head; Jupiter, the largest planet, about the size of a waistcoat button; Saturn, without its rings, rather smaller; Uranus and Neptune about the size of split peas; while Mercury, Venus and Mars can be compared to small grains of sand. Pluto, the outermost planet yet discovered, is about the same size as the earth. All the planets put together are many times smaller in size than the sun.

SPINNING LIKE A TOP

The solar system, like all the other systems of bodies in space, is in motion. Not only is the system as a whole rushing bodily through space, but the planets all circle round the sun in almost the same plane and at regular intervals, while each individual member of the system has a spinning motion of its own. The peculiar thing about the spinning and revolving motions of the sun and planets is that in each case the motion is anti-clockwise, but this law does not apply to all the satellites or moons of the planets.

To us the sun appears as a vast ball of yellow fire with a fiercely bright, unmarked surface, but through a telescope, suitably veiled, of course, it is found that the surface is broken or granulated. This granulation is due to clouds of incandescent vapour of all kinds at different temperatures, of elements such as iron, sodium and tin, which rise from the intensely heated interior.

SUN-SPOTS AFFECT THE EARTH

Sometimes dark patches that we call sun-spots appear on the sun's surface. These spots are the volcanoes of the sun, but as the sun is not a solid body these outbursts take the form of immense whirlwinds, and incandescent matter is shot out of the inner envelope of the sun in great spirals, at a speed far greater than that of a shell from a gun. They appear black to us because we see only the upper portions of the disturbances where the vapours, thousands of miles above the sun's surface, have cooled a little and the atoms of matter, becoming more compact thereby, shut off some of the intense light.

23

These disturbances or storms last considerably longer than our terrestrial storms, and it is by observing their movement across the sun's disk that we have discovered that the solar globe rotates once in twenty-six days at the equator, but more slowly as the poles are approached. Sun-spots occur in eleven-year cycles, and it has been discovered that there is a definite connection between these solar cycles and terrestrial magnetic phenomena. Not only is there a slight but gradual alteration in the position of the magnetic north as the cycle peak approaches, but there is an increase in the number of magnetic storms, and displays of the aurora borealis become more frequent and intense.

WHITE LIGHT OF MANY COLOURS

The light from the sun appears to us to be white, but this white light is in reality a mixture of several colours which, when present singly or in combination, give all the colours of nature. We may see the sunlight being split up in a rainbow, where the tiny particles of water have divided the rays of the sun into the row of colours we call its spectrum.

We get the same effect when we focus the sun's rays on a glass prism. The white rays enter one side of the glass and are refracted by the second side, but since the different rays of light are not refracted equally, we have on the third side of the prism a row of rays of different colours, beginning with red at one end then turning to orange, yellow, green, blue, indigo and finally violet at the other end.

The prism or spectroscope is an invaluable guide in telling us of what elements the sun or any other star is composed, because each element when burning emits a light which, when viewed through the spectroscope, is situated at a particular place on the spectrum.

The gas known as helium, which is so desirable for filling airships owing to its combination of lightness and non-inflammability, was discovered in the spectrum of the sun in 1868, but it was not discovered on the earth until 1894, when Sir William Ramsay came across it during a laboratory experiment.

FLAMES 80,000 MILES HIGH

From the surface of the sun, known as the chromosphere, which is a mass of red fiery flame, great tongues of fire are thrown out which are called solar prominences. These prominences are seen in all their wonder during a total eclipse. Many of them attain heights of over 80,000 miles, and form wonderful patterns, while the velocity with which they leap out of the sun is sometimes as much as 200,000 miles an hour. Also during an eclipse is observed the corona or aureole of light which surrounds the sun. This consists of light reflected from particles of matter and is evidence of the presence of a considerable atmospheric envelope around the solar globe.

Were the density of the matter of which the sun is composed equal to the density of our earth, it would be only a quarter of its present size, but even then it would be enormously larger than the earth. In actual fact the weight of the sun is some 330,000 times greater than that of the earth.

CAUSE OF THE SUN'S INTENSE HEAT

The great energy of the sun is due to the breaking up of the atoms of matter in the centre into the protons and electrons of which these atoms are composed, and it is the actual bombardment of each other by the molecules that gives the sun its intense heat.

The breaking-up process is due to the amazing pressure which exists at its centre, a pressure which is never relaxed owing to the fact that as the sun throws out energy in the form of light and heat, it is contracting upon itself. This contraction must in time cause a diminution of the sun's energy, but it is extremely unlikely that there will be any appreciable difference to us for millions of years to come.

In one minute the sun provides the earth with sufficient heat to raise 37,000 tons of water to boiling point. If a crust of ice thirty-eight yards thick enveloped the earth, the sun would melt it in a year. Its brilliancy is 570,000 times greater than that of the full moon; in other words, it is equal to the light of 1,000 quadrillion candles (a quadrillion is a unit followed by twenty-four noughts).

The weight of the sunshine that strikes the earth during a hundred years is approximately equal to the weight of a heavy shower of rain falling from the sky for one-fiftieth of a second. The pressure of the light-ray was measured by Prof. James Clerk Maxwell in 1873.

HARNESSING THE SUN'S POWER

The utilization of the sun's power, as of that of the tides, has hitherto proved complicated and expensive. A couple of pounds of coal provides in the period of a minute as many thermal units as are cast by the sun, shining from a clear sky, on an area of 22,750 square feet.

One of Edison's co-workers wrote sixty years ago: " If we utilized the solar radiation on that area of the United States that is unsuited to agriculture, and reckoned its effectiveness at only ten per cent, we could even then obtain a power production of 13,000 million kilowatts."

At a scientific congress held at Bologna in Italy, Dr. Giacomo Ciamician envisaged a time when the sun would do most of the manual labour of the world. Many attempts have been made with this idea in view, particularly in countries where the sky is not normally overcast by clouds. At Meadi, in Egypt, a solar engine using mirrors to focus the sun's rays on boiler-tubes was built for pumping purposes just previous to the outbreak of the World War. By catching the rays in a device containing over 1,700 mirrors, each two feet long and three inches wide, and reflecting them on a cylinder holding about 100 gallons of water, it was found possible to raise 150 lb. of steam pressure in an hour. The apparatus was set up in California, where it was used for working a pump capable of raising some 1,400 gallons of water per minute.

A low-pressure engine was run by heat obtained from the sun acting on a shallow pond covered with glass at Needles, California. Dr. C. G. Abbot, of the Smithsonian Institution at Washington, invented a solar cooker by storing the sun's heat in oil, catching the rays by means of an aluminium mirror. Bernard Grossman, a graduate of the College of the City of New York, invented a "heat-canning plant" which focused sun rays on a test tube of water and from the resulting steam operated a miniature engine. It was recently announced that scientists were at work at Tashkent, capital of the Uzbek Soviet Republic, on a solar power-plant having a capacity of some 30,000 kilowatts.

THE SUN AS SEEN FROM THE PLANETS

Neptune is thirty times as far from the sun as the earth is, and the average amount of sunlight it enjoys is only 1/900th of that received by the earth. From Saturn the sun looks ninety times smaller than it does to us. When half the sun's disk is covered in an eclipse, the earth receives the same amount of light as does Mars.

As the sun is 570,000 times as bright as the full moon, and Neptune receives only 1/900th of the amount of our sunlight, the brightness of the sun on Neptune is 633 times greater than earthly moonlight, although the sun appears to Neptune as a disk of only about one-sixtieth of an astronomical degree in diameter. On Neptune one would therefore still be able to read print by sunlight. From Uranus the sun looks twice as large as Jupiter does from the earth. Pluto receives from the sun 1,600 times less light and heat than the earth does.

MERCURY: THE SMALLEST PLANET

Mercury, which lies nearest to the sun, is the smallest of the nine large planets. So close to the sun does this little planet lie that its path is always low upon the horizon and it is seldom seen. In spite of this, records of its appearance go back to remote antiquity. Mercury can be observed best in the British Isles in spring, and at about an hour after sunset, when the elevation of the planet above the horizon is greatest. Seen by the naked eye Mercury is a beautiful object, since, being close to the sun, it reflects the sunlight very brightly.

PERPETUAL DAY AND PERPETUAL NIGHT

Like the moon to the earth, Mercury presents always the same face to the sun. Thus one side of the planet enjoys perpetual day and the other perpetual night. The brightness of the surface prevents us from discovering much about this little world, but there are certain general assumptions which are safe to make.

Firstly, the surface exposed to the sun must be a scorched waste owing to its closeness to the fiery globe. The orbit of Mercury round the sun is much more elliptic than that of any of the outer planets. At its most distant point, known as aphelion, it is some forty-three million miles distant, while at its nearest, called perihelion, it approaches to within twenty-nine million miles of the sun, but even at the most distant point the sun's power is some four times greater than is felt on Earth, while at its nearest the intensity of the sun increases to nine times greater than the solar radiation received by us. Not only is this surface of Mercury so heated, but the seasons pass much more quickly. The planet completes its orbit or path once in eighty-eight days, and from midsummer to midwinter is only a little over six weeks.

The other side of the planet opposes itself always to the dark, frozen outer space, and, since there is believed to be little atmosphere present on Mercury, there is practically no possibility of life existing on its surface. Life as we know it might perhaps be sustained in the narrow twilight belt between the two halves of the sphere, but the almost total absence of atmosphere makes even this highly improbable. Spectroscopic observations indicate that there is a certain amount of water vapour present around the planet.

TRANSIT OF MERCURY

The speed with which Mercury encircles the sun is about twenty-nine miles a second. This speed seems enormous to us, but if we compare the speed of a rifle bullet with that of the planet we find that there is not such a vast difference.

Since Mercury lies between the earth and the sun, and on almost the same plane, it sometimes happens that the planet passes directly between us and the sun's disk. This is called the transit of Mercury. Occurring about thirteen times during a century, it is useful in assisting us in our computations of the movements of this little planet.

DESERT WORLD OF VENUS

THE planet Venus, which is situated in the solar system between the earth's orbit round the sun and that of Mercury, is known generally as the evening star. Its orbit round the sun is almost circular, and it is situated at about 67,000,000 miles distant from our luminary.

ONE FACE ALWAYS TO THE SUN

The year of Venus lasts 224.7 days, and its speed is about twenty-two miles per second. At intervals of nineteen months Venus appears at sunset low in the west, a brilliant gem that transcends in brightness even Jupiter and Sirius, and as night follows night it mounts higher and higher in the heavens until after some weeks its lustre begins to decline. Then, before the sun rises in the morning, a "new," brilliant star appears in the east. It is Venus once more, which has moved from one side of the sky to the other.

Like Mercury, Venus presents a crescent shape to us, and it is believed also that it has a speed of rotation that causes it to turn one face always to the sun. It is difficult to obtain any certain knowledge of the surface owing to the heavy clouds and dust which fill the atmosphere around it. By studying this atmosphere in the spectroscope we find that the preponderating gas in the atmosphere is carbon dioxide. This fact tells us a great deal, as we can deduce from it that there is probably little or no life on the planet. Plant life of some kind is the first that is likely to appear, but plants absorb carbon dioxide while growing and set free oxygen. There is then little likelihood of there being vegetation on the planet, the absence of free oxygen in the atmosphere leading us to imagine the surface of the planet as dry desert, probably disturbed constantly by violent dust storms.

Occasionally the clouds have cleared a little and given astronomers an indistinct glimpse of the planet's surface, but beyond slight discolorations and apparent irregularities at the ends of the horns of the crescent, little can be distinguished.

ALMOST THE TWIN OF THE EARTH

We are sometimes able to see Venus in transit across the face of the sun, but this event is much more rare than in the case of Mercury, as the transit of Venus occurs only twice every century, these two occasions being at an eight-year interval. The next transit takes place in 2004 and will be followed by another in 2012.

Venus is almost the twin of the earth in some details. Its diameter is 7,700 miles or 218 less than that of the earth, but a computation of its mass shows us that the matter of which it is composed is not quite so dense as that of the earth. It has no moon, and makes its journey round the sun each year a lonely, dead world.

MOTHER EARTH

MOVING outwards from the sun, and taking the planets in order, we find that the earth comes third on the list. Life is plentiful on it now, but it was not always so. In astronomical time, life has existed on this planet for a very short space, and thinking man for a very, very much shorter space.

It is impossible to determine exactly when life began, although many estimates have been made. We can, however, say quite safely that life started in the sea many millions of years ago, when the climate of the world was much warmer than it is now, and tropical forests and seas stretched to where the Arctic ice now is. We find evidence of these forests in the coalfields of the United Kingdom and coal is plentiful in parts of the Arctic.

The earth itself in those times had not cooled so much as now, and it is probable that the heat escaping from inside the cooling earth had a great deal to do with the widespread warm climate that prevailed. The earth is still losing heat from its interior, as is evidenced by the still active volcanoes and hot springs with which it is dotted in various places. In many northern latitudes, Iceland for instance, geysers are common.

LIFE FIRST MANIFESTED AS A WATER PLANT

Life probably manifested itself as a water plant, and it must have been many millions of years before this simple structure became at all complex in character. From it evolved more complicated forms, more luxurious water plants, and life endowed with the faculty of motion. The forms were still of the type which had to live in water to continue their existence, and more millions of years passed before the raising of the land surface and its consequent drying up forced plant life to accustom itself to the strange new conditions.

It was again plant life only that first established itself on the dry land. Not until about twenty million years ago did the lizard fish of the era, living in shallow waters, begin to develop limbs that enabled them to travel on dry land, but from that time the evolution of life from the lower forms has been comparatively rapid.

The evolution of man within the last five million years has probably been the most rapid transformation of any form of life to a higher plane.

BULGE AT THE EQUATOR EXPLAINED

The earth spins on its axis once in twenty-four hours, and encircles the sun in a fraction over 365 days. The earth is about 93,000,000 miles from the sun, and it is this situation that gives a climate that enables us to live in comfort. Were we to move closer to the sun, the heat from it would increase until life would be burned off the earth, while farther out in space we should very soon freeze.

The earth is globular in shape, as are the other planets, but there is rather more of a bulge around the equator than is the case with Mercury and Venus. This bulge is explained if we go back to the time when the earth was in a semi-solid and gaseous state. Then the quick rotation of the earth on its axis, much more rapid than the speed of rotation of Mercury and Venus, tended to make the outer part of the globe round the equator expand and caused a flatness at the poles. As the outer crust of the earth solidified the bulge remained, and thus the diameter of the earth is slightly greater from equator to equator than from pole to pole.

We see evidence of the earth's roundness when we watch a ship at sea receding from us. The lower part of the ship has disappeared long before the funnels, and even after the whole ship has gone from sight the line of smoke from its fires is still visible.

EARTH'S OWN SATELLITE

THERE is one respect in which our planet is unique when compared with Mercury and Venus, and that is in the possession of an accompanying body, the moon. The moon plays a big part in all our lives. Were the moon to be suddenly transported elsewhere a chaotic state of affairs would begin in ocean transport. Ports visited by luxury liner and rust-stained tramp alike would be closed to them, because it is the moon's attraction that gives us the tides upon which so many large ports rely for deep water.

If the whole surface of the earth were uniformly covered with water, all the points on a meridian would have high tide simultaneously, and the waves, coming from north and south, and following the course of the moon from east to west, would encircle the globe in twenty-four hours. Undeflected on an open ocean surface, as on the Pacific, the flood varies between three and a quarter feet at neap tide, and thirty-nine feet at spring tide, i.e., the times of the full moon and the new moon, when the direction of the moon's and sun's attractions coincide.

The flood waves of the tides are dangerous where there are obstructions and races, especially near Sumatra and the mouths of the Amazon, Mississippi and Dordogne. Near Mont St. Michel in Normandy, the flood tide is extremely violent and at times reaches a height of more than forty-five feet. Recent measurements in the Bay of Fundy, between New Brunswick and Nova Scotia, have fixed the height of the tide at forty-three feet. Every tide, therefore, brings some one-and-a-half billion cubic yards of water into the bay, an amount of water equal to a week's rainfall in the whole of the United States.

The highest flood, known as the spring tide, and the lowest ebb, called neap, occur one or two days after the new moon and the full moon. In conjunction with gales blowing towards the land, spring tides become storm floods, such as may have created the Zuyder Zee and in ancient times are thought to have caused the emigration of the Teutons and Cimbri tribes from Schleswig-Holstein.

LAND TIDES OF THE EARTH

Scientists at the University of Harvard have discovered by means of wireless signals that the distance between America and Europe varies in a single day by sixty-five feet. This means that the influence of the moon makes itself felt on the earth's crust as well as on the sea, for the former is to a certain extent elastic, rendering an expansion and contraction of land possible.

The globe itself rises and falls daily to the extent of as much as fifty feet, owing to the attraction of the sun and moon. They are constantly producing two vital " hills " of water or land which, situated opposite each other, encircle the equator once daily in an east-west direction. When one elevation is in the longitude of Greenwich, the corresponding depression is near Calcutta; if the other depression is in the latitude of Chicago, the corresponding elevation is near the Fiji Islands. Three hours later the first " hill " has reached Rio de Janeiro.

THE MOON HAS NO ATMOSPHERE

The moon is only 239,000 miles from the earth. Its nearness and its lack of atmosphere accounts for the brilliancy with which it reflects the sun's light. It is considerably smaller than the earth, the diameters being 2,160 miles and 7,914 miles respectively. The entire absence of atmosphere on the moon can be easily understood, because, knowing what a strong pull the moon exerts on our oceans, the earth's greater gravitational attraction on the moon must long ago have robbed the moon of any gaseous envelope.

The moon remains at a constant distance from the earth, which means that it must have a movement round the earth, for were it to stand still, it would soon begin to move towards us.

The moon encircles the earth almost, but not quite, on the same plane as the earth encircles the sun. This fact is easily proved by watching the different phases of the moon, which is full when at the opposite side of the earth to the sun, but invisible when between us and the sun. On occasions the moon comes directly in front of the sun along a thin line of the earth's surface, and it is then that we have an eclipse of the sun. When the moon is in opposition to the sun the earth's shadow is thrown across the moon and we have a lunar eclipse.

When watching a lunar eclipse it is noticeable that when the moon has entered the earth's shadow it still continues to glow with a subdued coppery light. This is due to the sunlight which, entering the earth's atmosphere, is refracted, or bent by it, and reaches the moon in this way, but much reduced in illuminative power. The moon turns always the same face to us, the reason being that it takes almost exactly the same time to revolve on its axis as it does to perform one revolution round the earth.

BIRTH OF THE MOON

Ranges of mountains, great craters and large circular plains cover the whole visible surface of the moon. Some of the mountains are obviously extinct volcanoes, but many of the features of the moon are of far greater dimensions than similar objects on earth. The diameter of one large crater is sixty miles, the bottom of the crater lying about 2,500 feet below the surrounding plain, while one mountain peak towers 40,000 feet above the valley below. The reason why we see no evidence of volcanic upheavals taking place is because the moon must have dissipated all its internal heat long ago.

The lunar mountains and the ground surface are extremely rugged and rough, for there is no rain, no wind, no wearing agent of any kind on the moon to alter its natural features.

It is debatable whether all the craters owe their existence to volcanic action, and many scientists think that some at least are caused by giant meteorites striking the surface. Since there is no atmosphere to impede the approach of a meteorite, such a visitor would simply bury itself in the ground, throwing up soil and rocks all round it in the form of a crater.

The origin of the moon has been accounted for in the most varied ways. Fauth-Hörbiger, the German astronomer, considers it a captured neighbour-planet, like the moons of Jupiter, Saturn and Uranus. Even Mars and Venus are liable to be captured by the earth when at their perigee and to becomes its satellites. Sir George Darwin, on the other hand, thought that the moon was a fragment of the earth, from which it is receding in ever widening spirals. He held that it flew off fifty or sixty million years ago owing to the speed at which the earth was then rotating. The region of the Pacific Ocean has been suggested as the point of separation.

Fauth-Hörbiger asserts, however, that the moon is not the first planet that the earth has captured. In every geological period some heavenly body or other has come too near the earth and finally descended upon it in the form of debris. That this debris is to be identified with loess, so frequent in many river-valleys, has been disproved.

THE MOON MAY SPLIT INTO MANY MOONS

If the earth and moon system had a common centre of gravity, the end of the moon would be an approach to the earth in a narrowing spiral course until its mass fell into the equatorial belt of the earth in the same manner as in the possible case of the fall of the planets into the sun. The moon would take hardly a minute to fall directly upon the earth, as its distance from us is only sixty times the length of the earth's radius.

" According to calculation," to quote Dr. Harley Shapley, " the moon will ultimately return to the earth, and in the dimly remote future its fate will be disruption by the tidal forces of the earth and transformation into a ring system of myriads of moons such as that now observed around Saturn. This process may fail of completion if in the meanwhile the sun's stores of energy have become exhausted and our oceans have become frozen, stilling the tides which are evolved in the evolution of days and months. The irregularities are probably due to pulsations of unknown origin in the earth's crust."

DID MEN SEE THE MOON'S CAPTURE?

Legends exist of pre-lunar times and of the first appearance of the moon. A kind of substance is given to these legends by the stories of the colossal inundations that caused the disappearance of Atlantis and by observations made during his Andean explorations by Professor Kies, who discovered primitive buildings, work on which had been suddenly interrupted, and also enormous quantities of bones of animals and men embedded in the grey-white clay. He connects his discoveries with the floods caused by the capture of the moon, which gave rise to cataclysmic earthquakes and brought into existence the great lakes of the Andes.

According to Delparte, the French astronomer, the earth can only capture a body whose speed, at the time when it is passing close to the edge of the earth's atmosphere, does not exceed seven miles a second. If at a greater distance, this relative speed of the approaching body must be much smaller still for capture to be possible. This is the reason why the earth did not make a second moon out of the planetoid Adonis on February 12, 1936, the time of its nearest approach to the earth.

EARTH

VENUS
(THE EVENING STAR)

URANUS

JUPITER
(THE LARGEST PLANET)

SATURN
(THE RINGED PLANET)

NEPTUNE

MERCURY
(NEAREST THE SUN)

MARS
(THE RED PLANET)

PLUTO
(THE FURTHEST PLANET)

Relative Sizes of the Major Planets

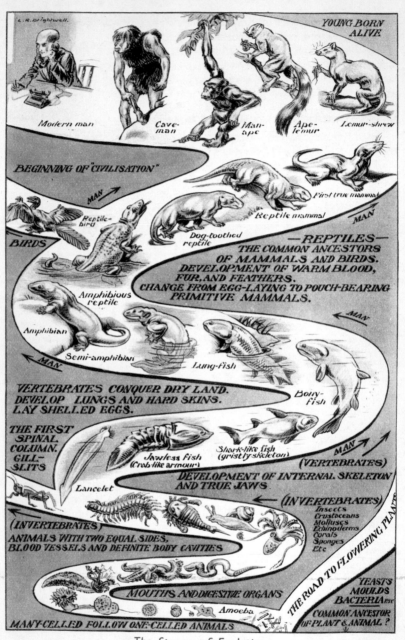

The Stream of Evolution

Although the diameter of Adonis is only five-eighths of a mile, its speed is some seventeen miles a second.

Sir James Jeans is of the opinion that the moon in the near future —that is to say in about 20,000 years—will split into two, and then into four fragments, while its core, after a certain lapse of time, will be surrounded by the debris, as Saturn is by its rings.

MINERAL WEALTH FROM THE MOON

So far as we can tell, the moon is composed of similar materials to the earth, and deposits of minerals must exist on or beneath its surface.

Though we should probably find metals and certain chemicals in abundance, we should not expect to find all terrestrial minerals. Coal, for instance, is formed from age-old deposits of vegetable matter, and the absence of an atmosphere on the moon excludes the possibility of its having at any time supported surface vegetation.

Were we able to reach the moon, we might find we could replenish our supplies of iron and steel, of which there is a threatened world shortage. Apart from atmospheric difficulties, working the mines ought to be easier than on earth, owing to the reduced weight of all materials.

HEARING THE SOUND OF MOONLIGHT

The moon's rays were made audible in a Czech observatory in 1935. The moonlight was converted into sound-waves, and the result was a long-drawn, harmonious, increasing and fading sound in the pitch of A. The waves were recorded at the same time and broadcast.

MARS, THE RED PLANET

MARS is our next neighbour amongst the planets. Its orbit is very interesting owing to its eccentricity. It is not always visible to us since at its most distant point it appears to rise and set with the sun, but when it approaches the earth it is clearly seen. At this time it is some 35,000,000 miles away, and has a red tinge of colour which is due to its atmosphere. The Martian year is 687 days long, nearly twice as long as our own, and it is about 141,000,000 miles from the sun. Mars is much smaller than the earth, its diameter being only 4,200 miles.

COMPLICATED NETWORK OF " CANALS "

The planet is rich in markings of various colours, some verging on green, others yellow or orange, while some parts are brown or white. The polar caps are easily distinguished, and their increase and decrease in area as summer passes to winter and winter to summer leads astronomers to conclude that similar conditions exist upon Mars as upon the earth, as far as the changes in the seasons are concerned. The green portions have been taken for seas, and the orange portions for continents.

In 1877 Professor Giovanni Schiaparelli detected the long, thin markings or " canals " which issue from the green portions and traverse the continents in a complicated network. He later astonished astronomers by announcing that many of the canals had become double since he first detected them. It has subsequently been discovered that this doubling of the canals is of a periodic character and is produced at the time that the planet passes through its equinox.

The double canals are from 30 to 350 miles apart, but another puzzling feature of them is that while one of them is almost always in the same place, the second sometimes appears on the opposite side to that on which it was previously seen. Larger and more modern telescopes than that used by Schiaparelli have resolved the canals into a series of spots and dashes which gives the illusion of a line, but no satisfactory explanation of their character is forthcoming.

POSSIBILITY OF LIFE ON MARS

Mars has an atmosphere similar to our own but of about half its density, while there appears to be very little more than one-thirtieth the amount of water vapour in the air that there is on the earth. It is possible that life of some kind can exist there in spite of these differences and also of the greater distance of Mars from the sun. Indeed, Mars has reached a stage in its history which is more advanced than our own, and if beings exist there it may be that they have reached a greater degree of civilization than ourselves. On the other hand, they may have disappeared.

"Life probably flourished on Mars millions of years ago," says Dr. H. Spencer Jones, Astronomer Royal, "but has been dried up by the atmosphere, and has probably by now become almost impossible." "We see in Mars," asserts Dr. W. H. Steavenson, "a very dry, cold world, in which some sort of vegetable life could, and probably does exist, but in which human beings like ourselves would most certainly perish. We cannot, of course, rule out the possibility of some form of animal life specially adapted to the conditions obtaining on the planet, but such speculations are outside the province of the astronomer, as such." Camille Flammarion, although admitting that conditions were inhospitable, not only supported the idea of life on Mars but went so far as to assert that eventually we shall communicate with its inhabitants. We have every reason to believe that vegetation grows upon Mars, as is evidenced by the presence of oxygen in the atmosphere.

MOON IN A HURRY

Mars has two moons, whose revolutions are unique. The Martian day is about the same length as ours. The inner moon, Phobos, journeys round Mars in just over seven and a half hours, which means that it revolves three times round the planet while Mars revolves once, and as far as we know this rapid motion is unparalleled in any other case.

Phobos rises in the west and sets in about five hours, while Deimos, the outer moon, rises in the east and sets, after two days, in the west.

Both moons are extremely small, having diameters of less than thirty miles, and are so close to the planet that neither is visible from the poles.

MINOR PLANETS BY THE HUNDRED

BETWEEN the orbits of Mars and Jupiter there is a considerable space which does not appear to fit in with a curious rule known as Bode's law. This law establishes that there is a definite proportion existing between the distance of the planets from the sun, the proportion being as follows. Taking the series of numbers 0: 3: 6: 12: 24: 48: 96 and adding 4 to each we get 4: 7: 10: 16: 28: 52 and 100, which numbers are all practically proportional to the distances of the planets. There is, however, no planet existing to represent the number 28 in this list, and it was not till the end of the 18th century that it was discovered that not one, but hundreds of tiny planets or asteroids inhabit this portion of our system.

EARTH'S NEAREST NEIGHBOUR IN SPACE

The first of the minor planets to be discovered was Ceres—by Ginseppe Piazzi, in 1801—and it was quickly followed by the finding of many others. In the next few years the total had increased to nearly 600, and at the present time over 1,000 have been listed.

The paths taken by these planets round the sun are wide, and in many cases very irregular. One of them, Eros, which is not globular but wedge-shaped, when at its nearest to us, comes much closer than Mars, and is indeed our nearest neighbour in space.

The exact character of these small planets cannot be ascertained since they are too small to allow of any detailed inspection by the most powerful telescopes. It is very probable that they are composed of the same material as the earth, and it has been suggested that they may be the remains of a much larger planet that has at some time, and by some cause which we cannot know, been broken up into many fragments.

JUPITER: LORD OF THE SUN'S PLANETS

JUPITER is in size the lord of the sun's planets. Its diameter is 86,500 miles, and it is 1,309 times larger than the earth. Jupiter's year lasts as long as twelve of ours, and it rotates in the short time of nine hours fifty-five minutes, the period of daylight being less than five hours.

HIDDEN BY CURTAINS OF CLOUD

Jupiter, like all the other planets, is visible to us by reflected sunlight, but we have never seen anything of the surface because it is always hidden behind thick curtains of cloud. The amount of heat received by Jupiter from the sun is only one twenty-seventh that received by the earth, but it seems to be much brighter than would be the case if we saw it by reflected light alone. From this fact it has been concluded that Jupiter is not a solid body but in a red-hot, or even a white-hot state.

There is evidence for this conclusion inasmuch as the earth itself has cooled down through many millions of years until it has passed from a gaseous through a semi-solid to a solid state. A vast body the size of Jupiter would naturally take far longer than the earth to cool, and thus we might conclude that Jupiter is still in an early stage of its existence. Still further evidence is supplied when we determine the weight of the planet. It is much lighter for its size than it would be were it a solid body like the earth.

A recent observation, made in 1935 by Professor Jeffries, is opposed to these conclusions. He holds the theory that Jupiter has a crust of rock covered to a depth of 11,000 miles with ice, the cloud formations being coagulations of frozen carbonic acid gas.

JUPITER'S GREAT RED SPOT

The farther away from the sun a planet is situated, the slower is its motion round the sun. Not only has it much farther to go, but its rate of progress is slower. Jupiter takes about 4,333 days to complete its circuit round the sun.

Owing to the great velocity with which this planet revolves upon its axis, it shows a very considerable bulge around the Equator and flatness at the poles, so that the diameter of 86,500 miles must only be taken as a mean.

There are certain indistinct markings to be seen. One is known as the great Red Spot, situated in the southern hemisphere, and there is also a series of bands which run parallel to each other around the planet. The band effect is probably caused partly by the speed of revolution, but there are no permanent markings observable, and the bands appear constantly to change in position.

ACCOMPANIED BY NINE MOONS

Jupiter has nine moons. The nearest of these is small, the next four being larger, but all appear to revolve round the parent in one plane, and one or more are frequently invisible behind the planet when viewed through a telescope. The third moon is the greatest, having a diameter of about 3,560 miles.

The four outer satellites are very much smaller and stretch far out into space. The outermost moon has a peculiar motion since it revolves around Jupiter in the opposite direction to the others. It is thought that this moon may be a body from outer space which has been captured by the attraction of the great planet and drawn into its orbit, so that it is now forced to remain a part of the system.

Life would not be possible on Jupiter itself, but there is a possibility of its existence on one of the satellites. The distance is so great that no positive proof of the conditions which exist on them can be obtained.

SATURN AND ITS RINGS

Saturn travels on its orbit round the sun at a distance of 886 million miles. It is vastly larger than the earth, but not nearly so great a body as Jupiter, having a mean diameter of about 71,000 miles. Saturn, like Jupiter, is in a seemingly semi-liquid condition and covered by thick cloud. It circles round the sun in twenty-nine and a half years.

FORMED OF THOUSANDS OF LITTLE BODIES

The great interest of Saturn is in the system of rings and satellites which attend the planet. Their movements are highly complicated. At intervals of fifteen years they seem to disappear, but the reason for this is that the astronomer is viewing them edgewise through his telescope. It follows that they must be very thin, and it is thought that their thickness is no more than about fifteen miles.

When viewed at their widest, the rings form two belts around the planet and are divided by an almost black concentric space. Outside the two bright rings a third has been discovered of a rather different nature from the inner ones. This third ring is believed to be only semi-solid in nature, but it is universally accepted that the two bright inner rings are formed of thousands of little bodies all revolving round the parent planet.

At first this theory of the revolution of the rings was very difficult to accept, since it would be necessary for the outer edge of the rings to revolve more slowly than the inner, but by studying the rings through the spectroscope it has been established that the rings do actually revolve around the planet, the inner edge of the ring at about thirteen miles an hour and the outer edge at about ten and a half miles an hour. These rings are unique, as far as we know, in the whole universe.

COURT OF NINE SATELLITES

Besides the rings, Saturn has nine satellites, the sixth of which, Titian, is the largest, with a diameter of about 2,700 miles. The most distant of these moons, like the outermost satellite of Jupiter, does not revolve from west to east but from east to west, and it is possible that this, too, is a captured body.

URANUS

In ancient times, Saturn was believed to mark the boundary of the solar system, but in 1781 Sir William Herschel, a Hanoverian musician who had settled in England, discovered by means of a new telescope which he had built, an object in the sky which showed the distinctive disk of a planet where no planet had been known to exist before. This momentous discovery brought wide fame to Herschel. George III conferred upon him the title of King's Astronomer, and established him in an observatory at Slough.

IN A GASEOUS STATE

Uranus is situated 18,000,000,000 miles from the sun, and makes its majestic orbit once in eighty-four years. Its diameter is about 30,000 miles, but it is so far distant that even the most powerful telescopes can reveal little of its surface character. The spectroscope shows that it is in a gaseous state and that it contains elements that do not appear to exist on earth. Of all the planets, Uranus revolves at the greatest speed, its day being only seven hours long.

Uranus is accompanied by four satellites, which revolve in exactly the same plane round the parent, but are inclined almost at right angles to the plane of the orbit of Uranus, a circumstance unknown elsewhere, and which we cannot explain.

The most distant of these moons completes a revolution in nearly thirteen and a half days, while the nearest goes around in about two days fourteen hours.

NEPTUNE

THE discovery of Uranus was a romantic one, but the finding of Neptune was just as romantic, although made in an entirely different way. Two men shared the honour, one an astronomer of some note, the other a student at St. John's College, Cambridge.

CALCULATING WHERE A PLANET OUGHT TO BE

It is known by Newton's theory of gravitation that every body attracts another. In our solar system every planet is attracted by the sun, but all the planets are also attracted by each other, and the amount of attraction exerted by all the bodies in the system upon any other determines the path that the body takes in its journey round the sun.

When Uranus was discovered, its orbit was carefully recorded and measured, and it was found that there were certain perceptible deviations which could not be explained by the attractive powers of the known planets. As it happened, these measurements were being made by two scientists at the same time and unknown to each other. They were J. C. Adams, an Englishman, and U. J. J. Leverrier, a Frenchman. These astronomers worked out by complicated mathematics the path that should be described by a planet if it were to explain the deviations in the orbit of Uranus, and they were able to calculate the mass of the supposed body as well as its distance.

With the help of colleagues, the skies were studied in the place where the new planet would appear. The calculations of both proved correct, and the planet was found.

Leverrier was the first to publish his discovery, and bitter controversy arose when it was followed by the publication of Adams's parallel discovery a few days later. Happily, when the two claims were investigated, both were found to be justified, and both astronomers are entitled to the highest praise for their brilliant success.

NOT A SOLID GLOBE

Even with the most powerful telescope, Neptune is not visible as a disk, owing to its enormous distance—2,800,000,000 miles—from the sun, but in spite of this its diameter has been measured and found to be about 35,000 miles. Like Jupiter and Saturn, it is not a solid globe, for its density is only about one-fifth that of the earth. Travelling at three miles a second, it voyages round the sun once in 165 years.

Neptune is accompanied by one moon, which travels in the opposite direction to the planet. Like the moons of Uranus, its path is an inclined plane, compared with the paths of the majority of bodies in the solar system.

PLUTO

Aᴏᴛᴇʀ the discovery of Neptune, it was found that the path of Uranus still showed discrepancies for which Neptune could not be entirely responsible, and some years ago Percival Lowell began a series of calculations to find out if it were possible that an even more distant planet was present in our system. By taking photographs of the heavens and studying them by means of a microscope, he discovered in 1930 a faint star which moved in such a manner as a planet beyond Neptune might move. It proved to be a ninth planet, situated about forty times farther away from the sun than the earth, and taking 250 years to encircle the sun once.

Pluto has no atmosphere, as we can tell by the brilliance with which it reflects the sun's rays, although the light which reaches the planet from the sun is 1,700 times weaker than the light we receive on the earth. It may be that Pluto is the farthest-flung member of the sun's family, but astronomers are always working and calculating, and at any time we may hear of yet another planet circling solemnly round the sun far out in space.

TRAVEL TO THE PLANETS

It is interesting to speculate on the possibility of man's being able to travel in the future from planet to planet by some such means as rocket-plane.

The difficulties attending even a journey to the moon are seemingly insuperable, but science has in the past enabled us to perform miracles formerly thought to be impossible.

Among the outstanding problems is that of finding a fuel sufficiently powerful to lift the rocket from the earth at a speed sufficient to overcome the force of Earth's gravity. This fuel must also be light enough and small enough in bulk to allow of a sufficient quantity being carried. There are also the questions as to whether the human body could stand the enormous speeds which would be achieved in space, and whether a machine could be constructed capable of such rapid transit and of withstanding the temperatures of outer space.

If we suppose these questions to have been solved, and the travellers to have arrived on the moon or another planet, there is the necessity of their having portable air-containers, since the moon has no atmosphere, and several of the planets have little or none. Suitable clothing would be required, to stand extremes of heat and cold unknown on Earth.

Then comes the question of moving about on any body reached. A man on the moon would experience the greatest difficulty in learning to walk. The gravitational pull of the moon is far less than that of the earth owing to its smaller size and the lack of the weight of any atmosphere, so that ordinary-sized steps would be turned into great leaping bounds on the surface of the moon.

It is very doubtful if the human body could contend with all these difficulties of pressure, temperature and gravitation, yet in spite of these problems, which are only a few of those to be tackled before we can visit the moon or one of the nearer planets, it is not safe to say that scientists will not solve them.

JOURNEY LASTING SIXTY YEARS

In contemplating a visit to one of the outer planets, say Jupiter, even greater difficulties loom ahead. Jupiter is, when at its nearest to us, some 390,000,000 miles away. To reach the planet in a lifetime of sixty years, a man would have to travel continuously at a speed of about 740 miles an hour.

Jupiter is over 13,000 times larger than the earth. Its gravitational attraction is so great that it is difficult by the farthest stretch of imagination to conceive of a man-made machine capable of a braking power sufficient to enable it to make a landing on the surface of Jupiter. Even then it is extremely doubtful whether the surface of the planet is in such a state as would enable a landing to be made.

It would seem that the only safe assumption at the moment is that we may possibly find a way of becoming more closely acquainted with our immediate neighbours in the solar system.

HOME OF MANKIND

For long the sun was believed to be the only star in the universe to have revolving round it a series of planets. Recent discoveries point to the existence of other planetary systems, but so far very little is known of them. It is not impossible that on some or all of them there may be some form of life, though this is not considered likely. In the present state of knowledge, the planets which revolve round the sun are the only known heavenly bodies possessing such surface conditions as will permit the existence of life.

Not even all the sun's planets offer such conditions. It is generally agreed by astronomers that on none of the outer group, consisting of Jupiter, Saturn, Uranus, Neptune, and Pluto, can there be any life. The thousand or more planetoids, or minor planets, most of which revolve between Jupiter and Mars, are also considered lifeless. It is only on the planets of the inner group that life may be expected; and despite the most diligent research, no certainty of its existence has been established outside Earth.

POSSIBILITY OF LIFE ON THE PLANETS

Mercury, which revolves nearest to the sun at a mean distance of thirty-six million miles, has a very thin atmosphere, or possibly none at all, and its orbit or path is such that one half of the planet has perpetual day, the other perpetual night. The half exposed to the sun's rays is intensely hot, the half in darkness intensely cold. If there is life on this planet, it can exist only—at least in such form as we can understand—on the twilight borderland which divides the hemisphere of day from that of night.

Venus, nearest of the planets to Earth, and sixty-seven million miles distant from the sun, is literally veiled in mystery, for it is surrounded by a heavy cloud-filled atmosphere which so far has effectively prevented any certain knowledge being gained of its surface.

Because of the nearness of this planet to the sun, its temperature is much higher than that of the earth. It is above the boiling point of water, so water cannot exist there in liquid form. The atmosphere of Venus contains much carbon dioxide; this suggests that the planet has no plant life. If there were plants, they would absorb most of the carbon dioxide, as they do on Earth.

MARCONI ON RADIO SIGNALS FROM MARS

Concerning the possibility of life on Mars there has been a vast amount of speculation, much of it purely fantastic, but some based on very considerable scientific knowledge.

Some years ago Marconi stated that he had noted effects on his radio set resembling signals of great wavelengths coming apparently from somewhere in space. This remark was regarded as suggesting that the mysterious sounds might have come from Mars. The famous scientist, in a later reference to the matter, said that "they might be caused by magnetic disturbances in the sun; they might come from Mars or from Venus even." He added, however, that the effects had been less noticeable of late, and he hoped that this would not be interpreted that he had asserted that "the Martians, in despair at receiving no reply to their signals, had given up the attempt, probably thinking that our state of civilization is so low that they had better wait several thousand years before repeating the attempt."

The balance of opinion appears to be that, if life exists on Mars, it is in a form different from that known on Earth. The idea, which has been more than once popularized in romances, of a very advanced civilization, may not be without reason.

ORIGIN OF THE EARTH

THE earth, like the other planets, was born of fire, and had to condense, possibly from a gas to a liquid, and then cool from a liquid to a solid —or, rather, a body with a solid exterior—before it could become a fit home for life. At least, that is the supposition that has been held in the past by orthodox people.

Many theories have been advanced as to the origin of the earth, but only one has so far commanded anything like general acceptance from modern scientists. This is what is known as the tidal theory, which was first stated by the French mathematician and astronomer, Pierre Simon, Marquis de Laplace, between 1799 and 1825. According to this theory, at some time in the infinitely remote past a large star passed so near to the sun that by gravitational attraction it caused filaments or long streams of incandescent matter, to be drawn out of it.

These filaments must have had a forward movement given to them by the grazing star. The attraction of the sun kept them from flying off, and their forward movement kept them from falling into the sun. Thus they were compelled to travel round the sun in elliptical orbits or paths. A swirling movement was also given to the filaments themselves, so that they condensed in globular masses. This was the origin of the major planets of the solar system.

A comparatively short period sufficed to cool the gaseous mass, which was to become the earth, into a whirling sphere of liquid. A longer period elapsed before there began to form on the surface of this sphere a solid crust or shell. Once that crust was formed, the earth, though still very hot, was cool enough to condense the water vapour in the atmosphere which had formed round the globe.

Descending as rain in storms of a violence barely imaginable today, this water vapour not only rapidly increased the rate of cooling of the outer rocks, but also commenced upon them the process of denudation, or wearing away, by which is accumulated the soil upon which man and all land animals are dependent for their existence.

THE PLANETESIMAL THEORY

The belief that the earth was first gas, then liquid, then solid outside with a molten interior was challenged in the early years of the present century by Professors T. C. Chamberlin and F. R. Moulton, of the University of Chicago, who developed what is known as the planetesimal theory. Accepting the tidal theory of the origin of the solar system, they contended that the result of the passing star's gravitational pull upon the sun left that body the centre of a spiral nebula untold millions of miles long, and containing in its length innumerable knots of solid matter. All these knots were revolving round the sun in intersecting elliptical orbits. This type of revolution meant that in course of time larger and smaller knobs were bound to collide; when they did the larger absorbed the smaller, and so added to its mass.

According to this theory, the earth began as a solid, not a gaseous body. It had probably only about one-tenth of its present mass, but it kept adding to this by absorbing " planetesimals," which also modified its orbit, slowed its rate of revolution about its axis, and increased its gravity. This increase of mass compressed the interior of the earth and is largely responsible for its great heat.

CALCULATING THE AGE OF THE EARTH

How long ago did the birth of the earth take place? We do not know. The most we can say is that in all probability it happened between 1,500,000,000 and 3,000,000,000 years ago. Even this degree of precision has only been achieved since the discovery of radio-activity, which provides us with by far the most accurate means of estimating the age of the earth.

Three hundred years ago, men reckoned the age of the earth only in thousands of years. In 1650-54, James Usher, or Ussher, Archbishop of Armagh, published a celebrated work in which he included a scheme of chronology for Biblical events, beginning with 4004 B.C. as the date of the Creation. This date is still printed in copies of the authorized version of the Bible.

LORD KELVIN'S ESTIMATE

By the middle of the 19th century, Usher's estimate had been multiplied more than a thousandfold; the 20th century has left the 19th almost as far behind as the latter left Usher. Lord Kelvin, who as William Thomson became in 1846 professor of natural philosophy at Glasgow University—a post he was to hold for fifty-three years—and whose reputation as a physicist was unrivalled throughout the second half of the 19th century, early in his career estimated that the earth cooled from a molten to a solid state at some time between 20,000,000 and 400,000,000 years ago, probably, he thought, about 100,000,000 years ago.

Professor Peter Guthrie Tait, who held the chair of natural philosophy at Edinburgh during the greater part of Kelvin's reign at

Glasgow, and who collaborated with his great contemporary in a notable volume on natural philosophy, would not allow more than 20,000,000 years as the span of the earth's existence.

With both these estimates the geologists disagreed violently. They believed the earth to be far older than either Tait or Thomson said; but they were unable to find any flaw in the latter's reasoning. That flaw was not discovered until the early years of the 20th century.

Thomson (who in 1892 became Baron Kelvin of Largs), based his calculations on the conduction and radiation of heat, and worked out how long it must have taken for the earth to cool from a molten state to its present condition. There was no error in his calculations; the error lay in imagining that the earth had cooled steadily and uninterruptedly, "losing its primitive heat like a loaf taken from the oven," as he put it.

RADIO-ACTIVE ROCKS AS TIMEKEEPERS

In 1896, M. Henri Becquerel discovered the radio-active properties of uranium; two years later M. and Mme Curie announced that they had extracted radium from pitchblende. In 1903, M. Curie discovered that radium is always giving out heat, and shortly afterwards Lord Rutherford established that radium is found widely distributed throughout the rocks.

These discoveries led to the abrupt abandonment of Kelvin's theory. The earth had not cooled "like a loaf taken from the oven"; it contained within itself a source of heat which must have rendered the process of cooling immensely slower than had previously been imagined.

As a result we find the well-known popular biologist, Sir Edwin Ray Lankester, writing in 1906 that the physicists are "now willing to give us, not merely a thousand million years, but as many more as we want." A quarter of a century later, Sir James Jeans, whose mathematical genius has been responsible for a number of original theories concerning the nature of the universe, gave his opinion of the age of the earth as approximately 2,000,000,000 years. Life had existed on the earth, he thought, for some 300,000,000 years, while man appeared upon it about 300,000 years ago.

HOW RADIO-ACTIVITY GIVES THE EARTH'S AGE

The calculation of the age of the earth from the radio-activity in its rocks is based on what is called the transformation theory, which was stated in 1903 by Rutherford and Professor Frederick Soddy. In brief, the theory is that the heat given out by radium is the result of a continuous series of explosions in its atoms. These explosions expel with tremendous violence alpha and beta particles, and consequently each explosion means that an atom has decreased in mass.

Now no element can continue to change the constitution of its atoms and remain the same element. Consequently, as time goes on, part of any given specimen of radium must cease to be radium, its explosions having transformed it into a different kind of matter. Actually, radium is transformed into a heavy gas called emanation, which in turn becomes in rapid succession radium A, B, and C. The process continues, radium D, E, and F being produced. Radium F is exactly the same as polonium, the first radio-active substance which Mme Curie obtained, and which she named in honour of her native country, Poland.

Ultimately, radium becomes a substance identical in all respects with lead, except that its atomic weight is different. Now, since scientists have been able to work out the times which these various transformations (of which only an outline is given here) take, it becomes possible by examining the products of radium which are found in the rocks, to say how long the breaking up of the atom has been going on.

URANIUM, THE PARENT ELEMENT

It was discovered that radium is not an original element, but itself the product of the breaking up of the atoms of other elements. The parent element was found to be uranium, which disintegrates into an element called ionium which in turn produces radium.

The rate at which these elements disintegrate depends on the quantity present. We have a " half-life period " for each element. Thus half of any quantity of radium disintegrates in 1,700 years, half of the remainder in the next 1,700 years, and so on. The half-life period of ionium is probably 76,000 years, and even this figure pales into insignificance before the calculated half-life period of uranium, which is 6,000,000,000 years.

The alpha particles ejected by radio-active elements are nuclei of the inert gas helium, which is found in rocks containing the radio-active elements. Such rocks have been examined, and the proportions of the radio-active elements and their products, including the stable elements helium and lead, have been found. This gives a means of finding how long the disintegration has been going on, and thus a measure of the age of the rocks, and consequently of the solid crust of the earth. The most probable estimates are those already given, that is, between 1,500,000,000 and 3,000,000,000 years.

HOW THE WORLD MAY END

CONCERNING the future of the earth, scientists do not as yet know enough to make any certain prediction. The general opinion seems to be that it will be a long one, that the earth is still young, and that thanks to the constant generation of heat by radio-activity she may expect to live to a ripe old age.

Unless, of course, some entirely unforeseen and cataclysmic disaster overwhelmed her. Various gruesome speculations as to the nature of such disaster have been made from time to time. The sun, for example, might without warning suddenly expand or explode. The event is not considered likely; the theory is based on the comparatively numerous instances, observed since antiquity, of stars that, for reasons concerning which nothing is certainly known, become suddenly far more brilliant than they have ever been before. These stars are called novæ or " new " stars.

STAR VISIBLE AT NOON

It is said to have been the appearance of a nova in 134 B.C. which caused the Greek astronomer, Hipparchus, to compile the first catalogue of stars. As a general rule novæ fade out again very quickly, but in A.D. 173 a nova which appeared in the constellation Centaurus remained visible for eight months.

The most brilliant nova on record appeared in November, 1572. This was the famous Tycho's star, so called because it was the subject of observation by the celebrated Danish astronomer, Tycho Brahe. This star could actually be seen with the naked eye at midday, and during the first three weeks of its brilliance it shone more brightly than either Jupiter or Venus. After that it began to fade, turning from white to red in colour, and later becoming " pale with a livid cast," until by March, 1574, it had disappeared from sight.

Thirty years later one of the pupils of Johann Kepler, the famous German astronomer who to a large extent paved the way for Sir Isaac Newton, saw a brilliant " new " star suddenly blaze forth in the constellation Ophiuchus. This nova remained visible even longer than Tycho's star.

It was not until February, 1901, that another nova rivalling either of these two appeared. This star, which twinkled in the constellation Perseus, was within two days the brightest in the northern hemisphere. A further very brilliant one appeared in 1918.

The appearance of a nova means that the star in question has swelled to many times its normal size. In 1925 Nova Pictoris was seen to expand to 214 times its ordinary size. Incidentally, so great is the distance of this star from Earth that the inflation actually took place in 2573 B.C. The light from this colossal explosion, though travelling at 186,000 miles a second, had taken 4,498 years to reach Earth.

In 1927, a star in Aquila grew to an enormous size, only to fade away within a month. In December, 1934, a nova was observed in the constellation Hercules; and it has since been established that as a result of its explosion this star broke into two, and that the two new stars thus formed are steadily moving away from each other.

THE STAR OF BETHLEHEM

Some astronomers believe that the Star of Bethlehem, which the wise men saw rising in the east, and which guided them to the cradle of the Child Jesus, was a nova. Another theory is that the star was really Halley's comet, which is known to have approached the earth in 11 B.C., and to have " stood over where the young child " was born at Bethlehem.

Any such violent explosion or inflation of the sun as takes place when a nova appears would of course bring the earth to an abrupt end. If it were to expand even to 200 times its present size it would completely swallow up Mercury and Venus, and its corona—the gaseous envelope which surrounds it—would reach the earth's orbit. Even assuming the sun remained at its present heat, this would mean the end of all life upon Earth; but actually any such expansion would mean an incredible rise in temperature. An ordinary nova achieves a brightness from 10,000 to 100,000 times that of the sun, while super-novæ such as Tycho's star become 10,000,000 to 100,000,000 times as bright.

IF EARTH CEASED TO REVOLVE

Another interesting theory concerning the end of the earth suggests that the orbits of the planets which revolve round the sun will gradually become narrower and narrower until the force of gravity will draw the planets back into the sun whence they originally came. The argument is that as the planets were whirled out of the sun, they will be hurled farther and farther from it by centrifugal force; and then, when that force is exhausted, will similarly be drawn back.

Other authorities on this interesting if highly speculative subject say that the earth is spinning ever more slowly on its axis and must ultimately cease to revolve. That would mean, as on Mercury, one hemisphere of eternal day and one of eternal night; the hemisphere in darkness would be too cold for life, that in light might be too hot. Estimates of this slowing in the rate of revolution vary from one-tenth of a second in 100 years to a second a year.

CATASTROPHIC FORCES HELD IN LEASH

Lord Rutherford, who in 1919 disintegrated, or "split" the nucleus of the atom of nitrogen by bombarding it with alpha particles, once jokingly remarked that "if a proper detonator could be discovered, a wave of atomic explosion might be started through all matter which would transmute the whole mass of the globe, and leave but a wrack of light gas behind." How improbable such a catastrophe is held to be we may judge from the words of Sir J. J. Thomson, the distinguished Cambridge physicist, who said, "If I woke up one morning and found that the earth had swung out of her course, and the sun did not rise, I should be less amazed than over the discovery that the atom was breaking up."

Another possible cause of the destruction of all life upon the earth is said to lie in the invisible, exceedingly shortwave rays discovered by the American scientist, Dr. R. A. Millikan. These can penetrate lead plate fifty-nine inches thick, and are highly pernicious to all forms of life, being capable of burning up animal tissue in a tenth of a second. The universe, it is said, is full of these rays, and only the atmosphere encircling the earth prevents them from exercising their deadly effect on our bodies. If this protective envelope were withdrawn, every living thing would automatically perish. Happily, this withdrawal seems extremely unlikely, though some people do appear to think that its constitution will in time be radically altered, because of the amount of carbon dioxide which vegetation is constantly extracting from it.

The distinguished Polar explorer, Lincoln Ellsworth, has pointed out that if by any chance the South Pole were to swing vertically under the sun, the melting of the huge ice-cap of Antarctica, which is 7,000 feet thick, would drown the entire world surface with the exception of the summits of a few of the highest mountains. This would not mean the end of the earth, but it would certainly mean the extinction of life upon it.

EARTH'S SIZE AND SHAPE

THE modern method of calculating the weight of the earth is by making a comparison of its " pull " or gravitational attraction, upon a small sphere at its surface with that of an exactly-weighed larger sphere upon the same small sphere.

This method was first used in 1797-98 by the English physicist, Henry Cavendish, though the experiment was planned and apparatus designed for it by the Rev. John Michell, inventor of the torsion balance. Cavendish, who reconstructed Michell's apparatus after the latter's death in 1793, determined the attraction of a ball of lead, twelve inches in diameter, upon another leaden ball, two inches in diameter, by use of a torsion balance. The result he obtained was extremely accurate; no one bettered it for a century.

WEIGHT OF THE EARTH

Before this there had been a number of attempts to measure the mass of the earth, the earliest being made by Pierre Bouguer, about 1740, and the most celebrated in 1774 by the British Astronomer Royal, Nevil Maskelyne, who measured the deflection of a plumb line by the mountain of Schiehallien, in Perthshire. The method was, simply, to hang a plumb line on either side of a steeply sloping " hog's back " hill, to note the angle made by the plumb line from the line between a fixed star on which it was trained and the centre of the earth (to which, if there were no force of gravity, it would point), and then calculate the mass of the mountain. From these data the pull of the earth could be determined, and from that its density. Two independent calculations have given the mass of the earth as 5.98×10^{21} metric tons. As a metric ton, which is 1,000 kilograms, equals 0.9842 British tons, this has been calculated in full as 5,885,516,000,000,000,000,000 British tons.

Mathematically-minded folk have estimated that to load up the earth on the trucks of a goods train would take 378,000,000,000 years, that the length of the train would be 160,000 times the distance of the nearest fixed star from the earth, and that a ray of light which passed from the locomotive to the last truck would be 500,000 years on the way.

DENSITY OF EARTH, SUN AND MOON

The density of the earth as a whole is just over five and a half times as great as that of water; that is to say that if a representative sample of Earth could be placed on one of the scales of a weighing-machine, rather more than five and a half times the volume of water would have to be placed on the other scale to make an exact balance. Twice as much granite or zinc would balance the Earth sample, while only half the volume of lead would be required.

The density of the sun is only about a quarter of that of the earth, but its mass is 332,000 times as great. The moon is three-fifths as dense as the earth, but its mass is only one-eighteenth. Because of its small mass, the moon has a surface gravity only about one-sixth that of the earth; that is, a man who weighs twelve stone on Earth would weigh only two stone, or twenty-eight pounds on the moon. The densities of the stars range from 1/10,000th of the earth's atmosphere to that of a white dwarf star recently discovered by Sir James Jeans which has an average density about 6,500,000 times as great as Earth.

PROVING THE EARTH A GLOBE

Despite the opinions of its greatest mathematicians and thinkers, mankind in general continued, until a few centuries ago, to believe that the earth was flat. In the 6th century B.C., Pythagoras declared it to be a sphere. Three hundred years later, Aristotle put forward in favour of its globular shape the arguments found in every geography book today: that when a ship sails out of harbour towards the horizon it does not disappear from sight as a whole: that during an eclipse a circular shadow appears on the moon or the sun: and that as one journeys about the earth some stars disappear, while new ones make their appearance. About 250 B.C., the Greek astronomer, Eratosthenes, measured a degree of latitude and from that calculated the circumference and the diameter of the earth.

But it was not until Magellan, Francis Drake and other explorers had actually sailed round the earth that the ordinary man was convinced that it was a globe. The majority of the Greek philosophers, and almost everyone in the Middle Ages, remained faithful to the popular idea of a "disk surrounded by the world-sea." One medieval monk told his contemporaries that he had crawled to the edge of the world and looked over it—and most people believed him.

There is said to be a sect in North America which still holds to the idea of a flat earth, while other people declare that the earth and the firmament are inside the cavity of a great ball. Another idea is that the earth in its cooling-off process assumed the shape of a whipping-top.

In 1930, Captain A. W. Stevens, of the United States Army, took in South America photographs from an aeroplane which showed the curvature of the earth's surface. With the aid of special plates, he secured pictures of a range of the Andes and a section of the pampas which were quite invisible to him but which revealed a distinct bend.

FLATTENED AT THE POLES

Quite apart from gross errors, even when we say that the earth is a sphere or a globe we are not giving the exact literal truth. Its shape most nearly resembles that of an oblate spheroid, which is the figure traced by an ellipse which is rotating about its shortest diameter.

In simple language, the earth is very slightly flattened at the poles. Its diameter from the North to the South Pole is about twenty-seven miles less than its diameter at the Equator. This difference, slight though it may seem (the earth's diameter being about 8,000 miles) has its effect upon the " pull " of gravitational attraction. A man who weighs sixteen stone at the Equator is a pound heavier at the North Pole; a bar of gold weighing two pounds three ounces at.Singapore weighs .011 lb. more in Spitsbergen.

According to one learned professor, even the Equator is not a perfect circle, but an ellipse, its greatest diameter being just over 300 yards longer than its shortest. The longest diameter passes precisely through the meridian of Greenwich, the shortest from the Galapagos Islands in the Pacific off Ecuador to near Sumatra, an island in the Indian Ocean.

IS THE EARTH SHRINKING?

For hundreds of millions of years the forces of Nature—rain, frost, wind—have been wearing away the land surface of the earth. Streams and rivers have carried away the result of this weathering and deposited it as sediment on the beds of the oceans.

Had this process not been retarded in any way, the continents must long since have vanished beneath the waves, and the human race and all land animals would have disappeared. But the very process which, so to speak, planes down the surface of the land, leads to the continents being uplifted again.

As surface material is removed from them the land areas become lighter, while the sea areas, because of the sediment they continuously receive, become heavier. The rocks which form the earth's crust have an enormous power of resistance against strain, but in time the strain grows too great even for them. The material in the interior of the earth begins to shift, and the crust to sink.

It does not sink all over to an equal degree. The rocks beneath the oceans are slightly denser than those beneath the continents, and the weight of the sediment on the ocean bed further increases the pressure. Consequently the parts beneath the oceans sink more, and the pressure caused by their contraction tends to push upwards the lighter continental areas. This pressure, when, as often occurs, it is horizontal, is naturally greatest on the edges of the continents, and the result is seen in the ridges of folded mountains to be found on the margins of the continents. The most noticeable example is the vast Andes-Rockies chain along the west coast of America.

This sinking of the earth's surface, and consequent shrinkage of the earth's diameter, takes place—fortunately for us—on a very minute scale and over a very long period. It is calculated that the diameter of the earth has shrunk only some thirty miles since the beginning of the world.

WHAT THE EARTH CONTAINS

IF a tube could be bored through the earth, and the centre of gravity shifted from the centre of the earth to the far end, a weight would fall through the tube in forty-two minutes twenty-two seconds. If a railway train could be run through the tube at an average speed of sixty miles an hour, its journey would take about five and a half days. Neither weight nor train would, as a matter of fact, survive the journey, because of the intense heat that would be met.

EARTH'S HEART OF METAL

Opinions differ as to whether the central portion of the earth is liquid or solid, though it is generally agreed that this core consists largely of iron, or iron and nickel. One theory of the structure of the earth gives it an outside layer of sedimentary rocks averaging up to four miles in depth, beneath which lie, first a layer of granite about twice as thick, and then one either of basalt in a glassy condition, or of diorite, a crystalline rock half-way between basalt and granite. This layer is probably about twelve miles thick.

After these thin surface layers comes an immensely thick one, probably 1,800 miles in depth, consisting of a rock called dunite, which is only very rarely met on the earth's surface. This encloses the liquid core, which is something under 2,200 miles in diameter.

Man has penetrated only an infinitesimal distance towards the heart of the earth; his deepest boring—a mine in South Africa—goes less than two miles down. But he has calculated the temperature at various depths far beyond this. He knows that during the first half-mile or so the temperature rises approximately $1°$ Fahrenheit every seventy feet. At a depth of about twelve and a half miles the temperature has probably risen to something over $1,000°$ Fahrenheit, at 200 miles down to over $2,000°$ Fahrenheit, and at 400 miles to over $3,000°$ Fahrenheit.

MAKING USE OF EARTH'S INTERNAL HEAT

According to J. L. Hodgson, the heat stored in the hot rocks of the earth's interior is 30,000,000 times that available in the world's coal reserves. In various places this reservoir of heat has been tapped. Some of the hot springs in Iceland are used for cooking and laundry purposes, and the hospital at Reykjavik, the capital, is warmed by what may be termed natural central heating. Enthusiastic gardeners use the same sources for the purpose of rearing plants under glass. The Maori housewives of Whakerewarena, New Zealand, also employ a similar economical hot-water supply.

Experimental bore-holes at Larderello and Big Sulphur Creek, near San Francisco, delivered 37,500 lb. of steam per hour at a pressure of 75 lb. per square inch. A steam vent in Geyser Canyon, California, was used to work an engine that developed 1,500 h.p., while power plants are run by similar means at Volterra and Larderello, Italy. Sir Charles A. Parsons, inventor of the modern turbine, and a man not given to picturesque imaginings, proposed that a shaft twelve miles deep should be sunk, for he was firmly of the opinion that it might be a means of " solving our power problems for ever and also revealing new and valuable chemical elements and metals."

NATURE'S SAFETY VALVES

IT used to be thought, not so very long ago, that volcanoes were outlets for the molten material which is believed to occupy the central portion of the earth. As so many volcanoes are situated close to the sea, the theory arose that water soaked through cracks in the earth's crust, came into contact with the molten interior, caused a terrific explosion, and the result was the clouds of what appears to be steam and the streams of lava one sees when a volcano is in eruption.

The discovery of active volcanoes hundreds of miles from any seaboard has discredited that theory, though such seeping through of water may very likely increase the violence of an eruption. The terrible explosion at Krakatoa in 1883 was probably due to this cause.

MODERN THEORY ABOUT VOLCANOES

It is now believed that each volcano, or group of volcanoes, has, so to speak, its own furnace, and that this furnace is at most a few score miles beneath the surface of the earth. These " furnaces " are created by the enormous pressure of the overlying rock upon substances existing in gaseous form. When there occurs a shifting or fracture in the earth's surface, these gases escape through a break or a weak spot. Strength is given to this theory by the fact that earthquake shocks almost invariably precede serious eruptions. The molten matter which is erupted, so it is said, is not molten at all, but a solution, produced from previously solid material, of minerals and gases at a very high temperature. This solution, called magma, rises very slowly to the surface of the earth, and not by any means all of it is erupted as lava. A great deal gets cooled on the way and remains beneath the layer of sedimentary rocks as granite or similar igneous rock.

We usually think of a volcano as an ordinary mountain doing extraordinary things. This is quite wrong. Though one volcano may tower to a height of nearly 20,000 feet, like Cotopaxi (18,163 feet) in Ecuador, or Orizaba (over 18,000 feet) in Mexico, another will look just like a huge crack in the crust of the earth, and be flat as a pancake. Most volcanoes build themselves up by the overflowing of lava-rock wholly or partly melted. The sloping layers harden and a cone or funnel is formed, the basin-like interior of which is called the crater. One of the most remarkable instances in the world is Mauna Loa in Hawaii, which has an enormous flat cone nearly 14,000 feet high.

Another common error is that dense smoke and brilliant flames are emitted. What is mistaken for the former is watery vapour, cinders, or fragments of rock, perhaps all combined, and the latter is generally the reflection of the molten lava on the clouds of steam. Lava is often so hot that a large quantity falling into the sea has been known to make it boil for a considerable distance from the shore.

VOLCANOES THAT BLOW THEIR HEADS OFF

Fortunately Nature usually gives warning when she is about to use one of her safety-valves. Low rumblings, and sometimes earthquakes, herald the outbreak. Explosions caused by gases, probably generated with the help of water which finds its way by cracks and cavities into the heated interior, then take place. Afterwards the lava rises and flows over the edge of the crater. If the pressure is too great in the pipe, huge rents are torn in the sides of the volcano, and more cones are gradually built up. Etna, in Sicily, affords examples of this process. It has some 200 cones in addition to the main crater.

Occasionally the head of the volcano is blown off, and a new cone is created inside the old crater. This is what happened in the case of Vesuvius. The fiery furnace had slept so peacefully for centuries that trees and flowers grew on its slopes, and three splendid cities, Herculaneum, Stabiae, and Pompeii were built nearby. Nature gave her first danger signal in A.D. 63, when an earthquake struck terror into the hearts of poor and rich alike. Many of the fine buildings and monuments were damaged. Further warnings were uttered from time to time, but little notice seems to have been taken. At last, on August 24, A.D. 79, the threatened eruption broke forth in appalling fury.

WHEN POMPEII WAS DESTROYED

Pliny the Younger, who was fortunate enough to escape, says that during the earthquake just before the final disaster, the earth shook so violently that chariots rocked on level ground, the sea went back a considerable distance, and ashes began to fall. In the pitch darkness, he tells us, " you might hear the shrieks of women, the screams of children, and the shouts of men; some calling for their children, others for their parents, others for their husbands, and seeking to recognize each other by the voices that replied; one lamenting his own fate, another that of his family; some wishing to die, from the very fear of dying, some lifting their hands to the gods, but the greater part convinced that there were no gods at all, and that the final night of which we have heard had come upon the world. It now grew rather lighter, which we imagined to be rather the forerunner of an approaching burst of flames, as in truth it was, than the return of day; however, the fire fell a distance from us, which we were obliged every now and then to stand up to shake off, otherwise we should certainly have been crushed and buried in the heap."

Of the 20,000 or 30,000 inhabitants of Pompeii, some 2,000 were unable to get away, and perished. The eruption, and others that followed it, buried the city twenty feet deep. Nearly 1,600 years later, this appalling tragedy was repeated. On December 16, 1631, after six months of earthquakes, floods of destruction poured from Vesuvius and killed, so it is said, some 18,000 people. A death-dealing storm of lava, from twelve to forty feet in depth and nearly 1,200 feet wide, poured down the sides of the volcano in 1794 and made its way to the sea. Further serious outbreaks occurred in 1872 and 1906. In 1906 a great rent a mile deep and a mile wide was made in the valley separating the two summits of Vesuvius, causing immense damage. A titanic flood of mud, carrying with it everything that stood in its path, crashed through the masonry built by the government as a protection against eruptions.

EXPLORING THE FIERY THROAT OF VESUVIUS

Greatly daring, Professor Malladra, of the Vesuvius Observatory, with a guide, descended more than 1,000 feet into the depths of the fiery throat. Although they were met by jets of poisonous gas, avalanches of large and small stones, and scorching heat, these bold adventurers returned safely. "Gurglings, splashings, dull and loud blows," could be heard by placing the ear against the rocks during moments of quiet, evidence of the restless, seething cauldron boiling away in the bowels of the earth.

Unlike Vesuvius, Stromboli, which sailors call "the lighthouse of the Mediterranean," is in constant activity.

ERUPTION THAT ALTERED THE MAP

Towards the end of the 19th century a volcanic eruption altered the map and made itself known all over the world. One explosion was heard 3,000 miles away. It occurred at Krakatoa, an uninhabited island in the Sunda Straits, between Java and Sumatra. For two hundred years the volcano had been quiet. Then, in the last week of August, 1883, with earthquakes as a prelude, a series of appalling explosions blew away eight square miles of Krakatoa. New islands were born, and waves nearly 100 feet high flooded Java and Sumatra, dealing death to thousands of unhappy people. When the water receded, a warship was found stranded three miles inland. So great was the disturbance of the sea that the effects of the disaster were noted in the English Channel. The ashes, becoming tiny specks of dust, travelled round the globe and caused brilliant sunsets that defied every artist who tried to reproduce the effects on canvas.

Early in 1902 a great rumbling came from the volcano of Mont Pelée, on the island of Martinique. Towards the end of April, volcanic activity began, and on May 2 and 3 there was a serious eruption. But the inhabitants of St. Pierre, the chief commercial city, were reassured when they heard that eruptions were occurring on the neighbouring island of St. Vincent. Suddenly, on the morning of May 8, the city was overwhelmed; flames, lava and ashes poured on it, and a dense, black cloud came from the heart of the crater and travelled towards the city at the rate of a mile a minute. Did this cloud contain poison gas, liberated as liquid, which vaporized? This may well have been the case, although authorities consider that its deadly effect was due mainly to the very fine, hot dust it contained. It suffocated thousands who might otherwise have escaped. Of the 40,000 people, it is said that one man, a prisoner in an underground cell, alone escaped alive from this dreadful calamity. In the following July, Mont Pelée again waxed angry and wrought further destruction.

DESOLATION AT ST. PIERRE

"What remains of St. Pierre," writes Professor Angelo Heilprin, who visited the city after the first outbreak, " is a wilderness of rock and plaster, with pieces of walls standing out in long lines, and looking like patches of ancient aqueduct rising from a ruined field. There is not a building that carries a roof, not a chimney to tell where formerly there was a glad fireside. For two miles or more the ruins continue; you know the streets by their standing walls, you recognize some of the houses by what the walls still carry. Here is the corner of the cathedral, there the municipal building, and farther to one side the wall of the military hospital. . . .

" We followed clumps of charred tree trunks along what was the ocean promenade," continues the professor, " and from thence passed to the central square, or Place Bertin, where, in the shade of its lofty trees and around its attractive fountain the populace met for recreation and business. What is there today? Great tree trunks stretched in line, their branches buried in dust and turned almost to coal, their roots pointing to the mountain that brought such devastation. We found twisted bars of iron, great masses of roof-sheeting wrapped like cloth about the posts on which they had been flung, and iron girders looped and festooned as if they had been made of rope."

IN THE LAND OF ICE AND FIRE

In 1783, Mt. Laki, in Iceland, burst into furious activity. A great crack was rent in the earth over twenty miles in length, from which floods of lava and clouds of vapours burst forth. The molten matter covered the countryside, dried up rivers and filled their beds until, on the authority of Dr. Arthur Holmes, there was sufficient rock " to have petrified the whole of London in a stony, winding-sheet fifty feet in thickness." This, the largest single outflow of lava yet recorded, covers an area of 218 square miles. In Iceland there is also a lava field, the result of eruptions from more than twenty volcanoes, which covers in all 1,700 square miles. A chasm 500 feet deep was made by an outbreak of Tarawera, New Zealand, in 1886. This eruption, from a mountain never previously known to have been active, also caused a lake to subside. Some of these titanic safety-valves are less lusty than others. Kilauea, in Hawaii, emits floods of lava in quite a peaceful manner. In its enormous crater is a plain over two miles wide, in the centre of which is a restless lake of steaming lava. Maui, also in the Sandwich Islands, possesses a wonderful extinct volcano called Haleakala, or "House of the Sun." Its crater is 2,700 feet deep and twenty miles in circumference. Even this is small beside the gigantic crater of Aso-san in Japan, which is estimated at 100 square miles.

Over 300 large, active volcanoes are known, many of them on the shores of the Pacific and the mountain backbone of Central America. Geysers, which throw up fountains of hot water, and hot springs, are also evidence of volcanic activity. They are found principally in Iceland, New Zealand and the Yellowstone Park region of the United States. Closely allied to geysers and frequently found near them are mud volcanoes, which throw up muddy water instead of clean.

WHEN BRITAIN HAD VOLCANOES

Though no active volcanoes have been known during historical times in the British Isles, this region along with much of north-west Europe was once the scene of intense volcanic activity. Volcanic rocks are to be found in many places in south-west Scotland and north-east Ireland, the basalt columns of Staffa and of the Giant's Causeway being well known; in England in Charnwood Forest, the Lickey Hills near Birmingham, and in Shropshire; in Wales in Merionethshire and the Breidden Hills.

When lava cools quickly under low pressure it forms a dark, glassy rock called obsidian. This is found in quantities in the Lipari Isles, on Pantellaria, in Iceland, and in New Zealand, where the Maoris use it for making tools and weapons. Near deposits of obsidian, pumice is also usually found; this is volcanic rock which has cooled so rapidly that it had not time to crystallize, and which the gaseous contents swelled at the time of cooling into a species of rocky froth. After the Krakatoa eruption, pumice was found floating on the sea, many square miles of which were covered, in places to depths of four or five feet.

CONTINENTS OLD AND NEW

JUST as there are conflicting theories about the origin of the earth, so there are about the origin of the continents. One school of thought would attribute them entirely to earth movements during the remote past, and their continued existence, in spite of weathering, to further earth movements which, using the existing coasts as levers, push them up again when they seem likely to be submerged beneath the waves. Many land surfaces, which were originally beneath the ocean, have been levered up; the chalk hills in south and south-eastern England, for example, are formed of the bones of minute shellfish. On the other hand, surfaces which are now beneath the sea were once dry land. It is generally believed that the British Isles were at one time a part of Europe. In this case the hollows now filled with sea were, in part at any rate, carved by glacial action.

CONTINENTS FORMED OF DUST

The scientists who uphold the planetesimal theory explain the origin of the land surfaces differently. They say that in the earliest days, when the earth was adding to its bulk by attracting innumerable hosts of planetesimals, while the larger of these bodies fell more or less uniformly all over the earth's surface, the smaller, which in many cases were no larger than specks of dust, were deposited in far greater quantity upon areas where rain was abundant than where it was slight. This process tended to become cumulative, for as the areas of land rose above the areas of water, by means of their more rapid reactions to changes of temperature, they attracted to themselves rain-bearing winds and so more of the planetesimal dust. This theory has been used to explain why the rocks on the sea bed are heavier than those beneath the land.

Geologists are still not agreed as to whether the present continents and oceans are to be regarded as permanent features of the earth's surface. Opinion inclines to the belief that the Pacific Ocean is very old, but that the Atlantic and the Indian Oceans were formed in relatively recent times. The Austrian geologist, Edouard Suess, who made outstanding contributions to our knowledge of the earth's surface, showed that there are vast areas where the sedimentary rocks are still lying in horizontal layers. One of these is in Canada, another in Russia; a third in South America, a fourth in Africa and a fifth in peninsular India. He suggested that the first and second originally formed a continuous stretch, as did also the third, fourth and fifth, and that at some time in the past portions sank, to form the Atlantic and Indian Oceans.

ARE THE CONTINENTS FLOATING?

Suess, in common with many other geologists, believed the earth's crust to be entirely covered with lighter rocks, beneath which is a layer of heavier rocks of the basalt class. The German meteorologist, Alfred Wegener, who died in 1930 on his way to the coast of Greenland from a station on the ice cap, believed that while the continents were formed of the lighter rock, or sial as it is called, the beds of the oceans are composed of sima, the heavier rock, and that the continents are, so to speak, floating on the sima.

It must not be imagined that the sima is a liquid in the sense that we understand the word; but as also it is not solid, to speak of floating continents seems perfectly reasonable. According to Wegener, the continents are not only floating but also constantly on the move : they are for ever changing their relative positions. Professor John Joly, the Irish geophysicist, also holds that the continents are sheets of sial floating in a sea of sima, but contends that movement and displacement are not continuous but recurrent.

RISE AND FALL OF LAND MASSES

Both sial and sima, he says, are radio-active, and therefore perpetually generating heat. The heat generated by the sima which is below the continents moves upwards and in time (since sial has a higher melting point than sima) melts the lower part of the sial. Then, naturally, the continent sinks, pressing down upon the molten mass beneath. Since sima expands on melting, it must find an outlet somewhere, and consequently it bursts through weak spots in the ocean bed. Once this happens it begins to cool, and a reverse process starts; the contracting sima gradually sinks. The sial sinks also, but to a lesser degree, thus retaining the land surface at a higher level than the ocean. Eventually the pressure, which is the result of all this contraction, grows too great. Something has to give. Usually this is the lighter sial, and so mountain ranges are formed by folding of the land surface.

FABLED LAND OF ATLANTIS

Throughout history, from the time of the ancient Greeks right down to the 18th century, there persisted the legend of an island, called variously Atlantis, Atalantis and Atlantica, situated in the Atlantic Ocean west of the Straits of Gibraltar. This legend was first related in detail by Plato, who records how Egyptian priests told Solon, the Athenian lawgiver, of its vast size and great military power.

According to his account, its armies were alleged, about 8,500 B.C., to have conquered all the states in southern Europe, Athens alone excepted. Its government, also described by Plato, was regarded as ideal. The story passed into the hands of the Arabs during the period when Arabia led the world in the sciences, and by them it was returned to Europe, where throughout the Middle Ages it was universally accepted as true. Even as late as the 18th century the usually sceptical Voltaire was half inclined to believe it.

Alongside this legend there grew up numerous others of vanished islands in the Atlantic. Homer tells in the *Odyssey* of the fabled islands of the Phæacians; the lost land of Lyonnesse off the Cornish coast and the Welsh Avalon figure in the story of King Arthur and his Knights of the Round Table, while the Greek Isles of the Blest and the Portuguese Isle of Seven Cities were celebrated in many a song and story. The entirely legendary Portuguese Green Island actually remained marked on British navigation charts as late as 1853.

While all these stories may be regarded as either the product of man's imagination, or as based on the actual existence of islands, such as the Canaries and Madeira, known to the ancients but " lost " until they were rediscovered by the explorers of Renaissance days, the fact remains that geologists believe it most likely that at one time Africa and South America formed a continuous land mass.

The rocks and the fossils found in them bear similarities too striking to be ignored. Similar fossils are found also in India and Australia, a fact which Wegener used to support his theory that originally the land formed a continuous stretch covering about a third of the earth's surface.

CONTINENTS OF THE PAST

From a variety of evidence some inquirers into the earth's past have surmised that approximately 200,000,000 years ago there were five continents very differently placed from the present ones. The largest stretched from where Buenos Ayres now stands to the Himalayas, and was separated by the broad straits of Bengal from a continent which extended from Mongolia in the north to New Zealand in the south. The third and—as it still is—the second largest continent, was the so-called "Old Red Northland," now known as North America; but in those days it stretched from Utah in U.S.A. to Norway, and was separated by the straits of Iceland from a northern continent the size of Australia. The fifth and smallest continent, no larger than Asia Minor with Arabia, was an island comprising much of what is now called Turkestan, in the western half of Central Asia. This continent had two eastern bays, Tarim and Tibet, facing the coasts of the Mongolia-New Zealand continent.

Where today the long, low chain of hills called the Ural Mountains divides Europe from Asia, lay at that time a small Ural island, the size of Great Britain, in the middle of a Siberian sea. Europe consisted of a group of islands. There were twelve larger ones including Spain, Brittany and Ireland, and numerous smaller ones, among which were Bohemia, Scotland and England.

In those days one could have walked from Rio de Janeiro in South America to Colombo in Ceylon, from Chicago to The Faeroes, or from Peking to Melbourne. If there was a Gulf Stream then, it may quite probably have flowed in much the same direction as it does today, for the central sea which separated the "Old Red Northland" from the South America-Africa-India continent had a width as great as the distance between Sicily and Denmark. The southern continent contained a huge oval bay which occupied the whole of the western half of the present Indian Ocean, and was bounded on the south by Madagascar. This bay was so situated and shaped that Mecca, the Holy City of the Mohammedans, would have been a seaport at its head, facing Bombay on the other side.

SIX CONTINENTS AND FIVE OCEANS

This picture is largely conjectural, based on the rock formations found on the earth's surface. It is interesting to compare it with the present disposition of the world's land masses.

There are now six continents: Europe, Asia, Africa, America, Australia, and Antarctica. Some geographers regard Europe and Asia as a unit, to which they give the name Eurasia, but this is not generally followed. Europe, the most densely populated of the great land masses, has an area, stated in round figures, of 3,500,000 square miles; Asia, the largest of the continents, 17,250,000 square miles; Africa, 11,450,000 square miles; America, 16,000,000 square miles; Australia, 2,974,500 square miles; and Antarctica, 5,000,000 square miles.

The seas cover an area of about 140,000,000 square miles. The area of the Pacific Ocean is 67,000,000 square miles; of the Atlantic, 34,000,000 square miles; of the Indian Ocean, 18,000,000 square miles; of the Arctic Ocean, 5,400,000 square miles; and of the Antarctic Ocean, 10,200,000 square miles. The saltest water is that of the Red Sea. Although in some parts the Pacific is 30,000 feet deep, the lowest depth in water descended by man is 3,028 feet. This was reached by Dr. William Beebe, in a steel ball which he called a bathysphere. The deepest mine is at Johannesburg, South Africa, 8,500 feet.

NAMING OF THE CONTINENTS

The origin of the name Europe is lost in the mists of time. Most authorities hold that it is of Semitic origin and signifies the land of the setting sun. Herodotus, the famous Greek historian and traveller, bluntly dismisses the subject by avowing that no mortal can give the meaning of the word. It is not mentioned in any of the works ascribed to Homer, and appears for the first time in a hymn to Apollo.

The Assyrians called the adjoining continent Asu, the land of the rising sun. It has been suggested that the name Asia was originally derived from a Semitic term signifying central, or from a Sanscrit word meaning dawn. Africa was known in antiquity as Libya, the designation being later borne by the Italian colony of Tripoli in North Africa. The name of a Berber tribe may have been the source of the Roman name Afrikia. America was called after Americus Vespucius, a Florentine merchant and navigator, the suggestion being made by a German, Martin Waldseemüller, who in a book published in 1507, incorrectly wrote: " Another fourth part of the globe has been discovered by Americus Vespucius. So I do not see why anyone should rightly object to calling it America, after its discoverer Americus." The belief that there was a Terra Australis, or South Land, was prevalent long before Australia was discovered.

EARTH'S UNSTABLE SURFACE

IN the year 1768, a Scottish doctor of medicine, James Hutton by name, who had given most of his time to the improvement of farming, retired from practice and devoted himself to the study of rocks and soils. Seventeen years later, he read to the Royal Society of Edinburgh a paper entitled *Theory of the Earth, or an Investigation of the Laws Observable in the Composition, Dissolution and Restoration of Land upon the Globe.*

For ten years scarcely anyone took any notice of what Hutton had said. He himself worked on patiently, elaborating his theory, and in 1795, only two years before his death, he published the greater part of his researches in two volumes.

Then at last geologists began to sit up and take notice. Some eagerly embraced Hutton's doctrine; others attacked it fiercely. In 1800 a critic declared the doctor's theories to be " not only hostile to sacred history, but equally hostile to the principles of probability, to the results of the ablest observations on the mineral kingdom, and to the dictates of rational philosophy."

EARTH'S SURFACE IS ALWAYS CHANGING

What were the theories which evoked so wholesale a condemnation? They sprang from Hutton's observation that every day, all over the world, the surface of the earth is changing. Not even the hardest and most solid rocks can resist the disintegrating power of frost, rain and wind: they are slowly but surely broken up and eventually reduced to earth, sand, clay or dust. This pulverized matter is washed by rain into streams and rivers, which carry it to the ocean and there deposit it.

As Hutton pondered the possible results of this ceaseless process, the conviction grew upon him that if only it lasted long enough the entire land surface must in time be worn down to sea level. In the same time the oceans, in part at least, must be filled up with deposited matter.

That was the basis of Hutton's theory. He turned to the rocks for evidence in support of it, and found confirmation everywhere. The rocks, it could be seen, had been formed in strata, as they would be by the ceaseless deposition of mud in layers. They had hardened into rock under the influence of enormous pressure, such as would be found on an ocean bed. And they were full of fossils, that is petrified remains or impressions of marine animals.

WEATHERING VERSUS CONVULSION

A number of questions presented themselves to Hutton's mind. The strata were rarely horizontal, as they ought to be if they had remained undisturbed. Nor were they continuous: they were usually tilted, broken by stretches of different kinds of rock, and frequently mixed with this other rock. And how had they been uplifted from the ocean bed to form dry land—in many cases to form mountains and hills?

To Hutton the answer was clear. Heat from the interior of the earth. Heat which had melted the rocks underlying the bed of the ocean, forced them and the strata of sedimentary rocks violently upwards to form new lands, and had left them exposed as jagged, broken and uneven prominences consisting of mingled sedimentary and igneous, or fire-produced, rock.

This process Hutton conceived as having taken place over and over again. The surface of the globe had been made and remade many times, and was still being re-fashioned by the two processes of weathering and convulsion.

The theory, with modifications in detail due to increased knowledge, is today universally accepted, but it provoked one of the bitterest of the many scientific controversies of the 19th century. The main opposition to Hutton's teaching came from Abraham Gottlob Werner, known as the "father of German geology," and his followers. Werner, though he made very real contributions to geology, held an altogether erroneous theory as to the formation of rocks. He believed that "in the beginning" all the solid matter, which later formed the earth's crust, was dissolved in a universal hot ocean, from which, as the waters cooled, it was precipitated in successive layers. He and his followers were dubbed Neptunists, from Neptune the god of the sea, while those who adhered to Hutton's theory were styled Plutonists, after Pluto, the deity of the infernal regions, which were popularly supposed to consist of a raging, fiery furnace.

COASTS THAT RISE AND FALL

Both theories explained the strata of the rocks, but Hutton's also explained volcanoes, which Werner's did not, or only very inadequately. Werner was forced to declare that he considered volcanoes accidental phenomena, due probably, he thought, to the setting alight of coal layers beneath the surface of the rocks. Hutton's followers, on the other hand, made the existence of volcanoes one of the primary arguments in favour of their theory.

Hutton himself believed, and his earlier disciples agreed with him, that the changes in the formation of the earth's surface took place with volcanic violence, but only every now and then. In between, there were long periods without change. Charles Lyell, the Scottish geologist, who invented the now well-known names Eocene, Miocene, and Pliocene to describe certain prehistoric eras, challenged this belief, declaring that these changes in the level of strata have been going on all the time, and are still proceeding, but that they are very gradual, and that their most violent form is seen in earthquakes.

Lyell travelled to Sweden to confirm claims which had already been made that the coastline of that country is rising at a rate of from a few inches to a few feet every hundred years. He quoted Darwin as evidence that Patagonia in South America is also rising, and other scientists that Greenland is sinking.

This "uniformitarian" theory, which saw the continental masses slowly oscillating, rising and falling as waves on the ocean, explained a number of points which had hitherto puzzled geologists. It explained why there could be alternate layers of rock containing fossils of sea and freshwater animals, and why coal layers were found between layers that had been laid down under the sea. It also explained the enormous thickness to which the sedimentary strata could attain. Before Lyell's theory, this had remained a mystery, for these strata exceeded by many times the depth of the deepest ocean. A slowly sinking ocean bed, with the phenomenon often repeated, made any thickness possible.

DISCOVERY OF THE ICE AGE

It seems strange today to think that Hutton's idea that frost, rain and wind could, if uninterrupted, in time plane all land surfaces down to sea-level, was only very slowly accepted. Yet for half a century or more it was disputed, even by leading geologists, who clung to the upheaval theory to explain the irregularities of the earth's land surface.

Even when these geologists found massive boulders, weighing hundreds of tons, miles away from and, still more awkward, hundreds of feet higher than the formations to which they belonged, the early 19th century geologists were content to believe either that they had been shot there, like shells from a howitzer, or that they had been washed there by the Flood.

Lyell got on to the track of the right idea, though his conception of it was wrong. He said that these boulders had been carried down by glaciers. The ends of the glaciers broke off as icebergs, which when they melted deposited the boulders on the ocean bed. The ocean bed gradually rose, and in time there were the boulders high and dry on the mountain slope.

It all sounded very plausible, and indeed many people accepted the theory. But, though Lyell did not yet know of this, it had already been proved inaccurate.

AN ALPINE HUNTER'S IDEA

Some fifteen years before Lyell propounded his " uniformitarian " theory, an Alpine chamois-hunter, Perraudin by name, began to wonder about these "erratics," as the boulders found distant from their formations are called. He, like Lyell later, concluded that they had been broken off and carried away by glaciers; but he saw quite clearly that such glaciers as he knew and lived amongst could not have done it. The glaciers, he reasoned, must have been far huger than anything he knew. In fact, the entire Alps must once have been covered by an enormous glacier.

It was an amazingly simple idea. So simple that all the learned geologists had overlooked it. So simple that they could not accept it even when it was presented to them. Perraudin carried his idea to the foremost geologist he knew of, Jean de Charpentier, who had studied under Werner, and had had as fellow pupils the celebrated German scientists, von Buch and von Humboldt. Charpentier laughed at him for his pains.

It was ten years before Perraudin could get anyone to listen to him. Then a civil engineer took up the theory. He read a paper on it which attracted Charpentier's attention. This time the latter decided to look into this novel theory, with the result that he became converted to it. In turn he passed the idea on to Jean Louis Rodolphe Agassiz, a young naturalist who had already achieved great fame as an ichthyologist, or student of fish forms. Agassiz, after a period of doubting, took up the matter with his usual indefatigable thoroughness. He built a hut on the Aar glacier for himself and his fellow workers, whence they studied the movements and structure of the glacier.

Four years later, in 1840, Agassiz published the results of his researches. These showed that, in his opinion, the whole of Switzerland had, in a comparatively recent geological era, been covered by an immense sheet of ice. He went further; he declared that "great sheets of ice, resembling those now existing in Greenland, once covered all the countries in which unstratified gravel is found." This meant that the ice-cap must have covered the whole of the higher latitudes of the northern hemisphere. The Ice Age, now so familiar to every student of the remote past, had been discovered.

EARTHQUAKES THAT ALTER LANDSCAPES

There is no more terrifying or destructive manifestation of Nature's power than the earthquake. Avalanches, typhoons, volcanoes—all these pale into insignificance before the earthquake, which can in a few seconds of time kill thousands of people and crash to destruction the noblest and most enduring works of man.

What is an earthquake? It is the result of strain in the earth's crust. The pressure among the rocks grows too great; a weak part breaks and other strata rush into the gap, thus causing further breakages and displacements. The actual faulting, as this breakage is called, usually takes place some distance beneath the level of the ground; what happens on the surface is the result of shock carried through the rocks by wave motion. This wave motion accounts for the quaking, or vibration, of the earth which is a characteristic feature of earthquakes.

An earthquake is usually preceded by a rumbling sound which has been variously described as like an express train, a heavy lorry, or distant thunder. Then comes the first tremor, usually comparatively feeble, but quickly merging into the "principal portion" of the earthquake, in which the vibrations become very much greater in extent, and then die away in a long period of lesser vibrations. In highly destructive earthquakes the ground moves as a whole; then, no building of any sort survives the shock.

EARTH'S SURFACE TORN ASUNDER

The displacement caused by an earthquake may be horizontal or vertical, or both. Occasionally, as in Sicily in 1908, the earth's surface is warped instead of torn asunder. When the displacement is horizontal, cracks varying in width from a few inches to over twenty feet are found on the surface; when it is vertical, a portion of the surface drops below, or is lifted above, the surrounding surface. In the Assam earthquake of 1897, drops or uplifts were in some places as great as thirty-five feet; two years later there occurred in Alaska the greatest uplift yet measured— one of forty-seven feet.

Earthquakes frequently take place under the sea; when this happens, or when the point of origin of the earthquake is sufficiently near the

Conquest of the Mountains

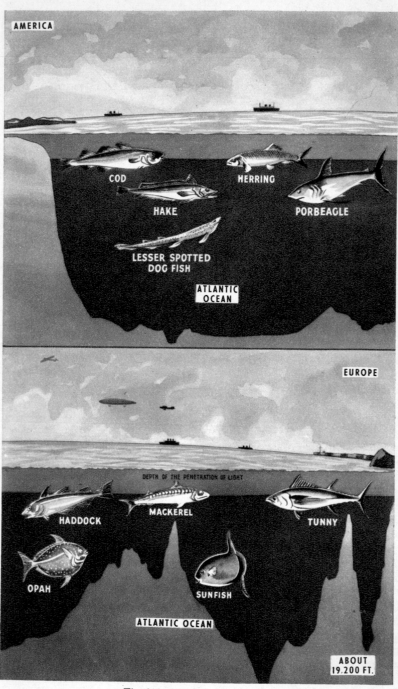

The World of the Underseas

sea to cause disturbance there, a huge sea wave—often called a tidal wave, though it has nothing to do with tides—ensues, which frequently does nearly as much damage as the earthquake itself. This sea wave may reach an enormous height—that in the earthquake at Sanriku, in Japan, in 1896, was almost 100 feet—and travel huge distances, waves having been registered 10,000 miles from their points of origin.

EARTHQUAKES FOUR TIMES A DAY

It is well known that earthquakes are very largely confined to certain well-defined areas of the earth. F. de Montessus de Ballore, who plotted a world earthquake map, based on a catalogue he had compiled of nearly 160,000 earthquakes, enunciated the following law: The earth's crust trembles almost only along two narrow bands which lie along great circles of the earth, the Mediterranean or Alpino-Caucasian-Himalayan circle, and the circum-Pacific or Ando-Japanese-Malayan circle.

At some points along these bands earthquakes are as frequent as showers in England. Over a period of eighteen years, Japan averaged 1,447 shocks a year, or almost four a day. The majority of these were no more than slight quiverings, sufficient perhaps to rattle the crockery, but Kyoto, once capital of Japan, was, during the 1,000 years of its existence, shaken by 1,318 earthquakes, of which 194 were strong, and 34 absolutely destructive.

It has been calculated that any Italian who lives to be seventy will be certain to have experienced one serious earthquake and two slight ones. Records show in this country 300 earthquakes in three years. The ancient town of Guatemala, in South America, was destroyed seven times between 1541 and 1775, while Valparaiso was severely damaged five times between 1731 and 1908. Concepcion in Chile was in 1939 laid in ruins for the fourth time in 300 years.

EARTHQUAKES MOST FREQUENT IN WINTER

Many attempts have been made to show that earthquakes occur at regular intervals and at certain times. In 1831, P. Merian observed that they take place more frequently in winter than at any other season. Other students have attempted to show that they reach their greatest frequency at intervals of eleven, twenty-two, thirty-three and nineteen years. Destructive earthquakes tend to happen in groups; in one period of 103 years, between 1601 and 1881, there were in Italy 182 destructive earthquakes, but in the remaining 178 years there were only 27.

Alexis Perrey, a distinguished French student of earthquakes, laid down three laws concerning the occurrence of these phenomena. He said that they are most numerous at new moon and full; when the moon approaches most nearly to the earth, and when the moon crosses the meridian of the place shaken. Though he published these laws over one hundred years ago, they have not yet been shown either to be false or true, though the third is very much doubted.

B.O.F.—C

TOLL OF THE EARTHQUAKE

The most terrible earthquake in recent years occurred in 1923, when the Japanese cities of Tokyo and Yokohama were almost destroyed and the killed and missing reached the appalling figure of 142,800. (The total Japanese casualties in the war with Russia in 1905 were no more than 167,402.) The number of injured was 103,733. Nearly 2,000,000 people were left homeless by the destruction of over 500,000 houses. The loss of treasure was estimated at £550,000,000. In 1915 over 370 towns and villages were damaged in Central Italy, and some 30,000 lives were lost. In the south of the country an earthquake in 1908 shook Sicily and Calabria, almost wiped out Messina and neighbouring towns, killed 77,283 inhabitants and injured 95,000. The coastline was altered by a tidal wave that rose to a height of forty feet. Two years before, nearly 700 people met violent deaths in San Francisco, U.S.A., by reason of a similar but less violent shock, which left 200,000 citizens without shelter. Widespread damage was done by fire.

A catastrophe which filled Europe with dread was that which shook Lisbon three times on a November day in 1755. The city was virtually destroyed, and again a huge tidal wave added to the destruction. Those were not the days of exact statistics, and the figures of the death-roll are stated at from 30,000 to 60,000. The whole tragic happening was over in eight minutes. It is estimated that from 1783 to 1857 the kingdom of Naples suffered the loss of 111,000 subjects, including 12,300 who perished in the latter year.

THOUSANDS KILLED IN TWO MINUTES

India has suffered grievously from earth movements. An earthquake killed 300,000 people in 1737, and in 1935 a disaster in the neighbourhood of Quetta, Baluchistan, caused a toll estimated at 56,000 killed and injured. The tragedy occurred at 3 a.m. and lasted for two minutes. The devastation followed another, less than eighteen months before, in Bihar, when an area as large as Scotland and with five times its inhabitants was affected. Twelve towns with populations varying from 10,000 to 60,000 were wrecked, and over 6,000 people killed. An area of 18,000 square miles was smothered in sand, in some places four feet in depth. Experts gave it as their opinion that the probable cause was the thrust of the whole peninsula northwards against the Himalayas.

In the Chinese province of Kansu, an area 100 by 300 miles in extent suffered catastrophe in 1920. The appearance of many districts was completely altered. Towns were covered by landslides, rivers were blocked, and hills slid into valleys. It was estimated that nearly 200,000 people were buried or disappeared. With strange irony, the disaster that wrought so much havoc saved the province from another misfortune. At the moment it occurred, a Moslem fanatic and some hundreds of his followers were in a cave planning a holy war. An avalanche sealed the mouth and immured them for ever. A sentry who was stationed at the entrance alone escaped.

Another disaster occurred in the same province in 1927. Serious as this unquestionably was, the calamity was small when compared to the Chinese earthquake of 1556, when more than 830,000 people are said to have lost their lives. It is believed that during the past 4,000 years about 14,000,000 people have died as the result of earthquakes, either through being killed outright, from injuries received, or through heart failure due to fright.

EARTHQUAKES IN BRITAIN

After much patient research, Major de Montessus de Ballore compiled a catalogue of nearly 160,000 shocks, both major and minor, extending over half a century. Italy headed the list with 27,672, followed by Japan with 27,562; Greece, 10,306; South America, 8,081; Mexico, 5,586; Pacific coast of the United States, 4,467; Asia Minor, 4,451; Sicily, 4,331; Switzerland, 3,895; France, 2,793; Central America, 2,739; Spain and Portugal, 2,656; West Indies, 2,561; Holland and North Germany, 2,326; Java, 2,155; and New Zealand, 1,925. The Atlantic islands totalled 1,704 shocks, followed in decreasing numbers by the Atlantic coast of the United States, India, Scandinavia, Russia, and Australia and Tasmania.

In the British Isles, 1,139 tremors occurred, nearly half of them in Perthshire. The earthquake referred to in *Romeo and Juliet,* " 'Tis since the earthquake now eleven years," is thought to be that which happened in London in 1580. More recent shocks were felt in 1750—a visitation, according to the Bishop of Salisbury, for the sinful lives led by the people of London—1884, 1896, 1901, 1906, 1915, 1923, 1924, 1926, 1927, 1931, 1933, 1935, 1936, and 1938.

According to Professor A. C. Lawson, of the University of California, " the most plausible theory of earthquakes is that deep in the earth the rocks, while remaining hard and very dense, act like a fluid and tend to flow from one part of the earth to another, carrying the upper crust with them. The strains that produce earthquakes at the surface are caused by these deeper movements." Violent volcanic eruptions are also apt to cause shocks.

NEW ISLANDS DUE TO EARTHQUAKES

Earthquakes occur beneath the sea. It is believed that many of the most violent earthquakes in Japan have originated along the western slope of the Tuscarora Deep, off the east coast, the bottom of which is five and a quarter miles below the surface. It is so called because it was surveyed by a United States warship of that name in 1874. A few years ago an earthquake was felt in mid-Atlantic by the commanders of two steamers, seventy miles apart, who each confirmed the other's story.

New islands occasionally appear as a sequel to these disturbances. The island formerly known as Bogosloff I, and now Castle Island, in the Bering Sea, made its advent in 1796 and was witnessed by a Russian trader named Krukoff. A column of smoke, followed by flames and a shower of stones heralded this addition to the land surface of the globe. Bogosloff II, since called Fire Island, came out of the sea in 1883, and was followed by Bogosloff III in 1907. The gradual rise of a new submarine range beneath the Pacific, extending from the vicinity of Valparaiso to the Aleutian Islands that stretch between Alaska and Siberia, is regarded by some geologists as probable.

EARTH'S VAST DESERTS

IF you look at a physical map of the world you will discover three big areas of barren lands. Two of these are rendered unproductive by excessive cold; they are the regions of perpetual ice and snow which surround the North and South Poles. The third stretches across the centre of the greatest aggregation of land masses in the world, the continents of Africa and Asia with Europe. Beginning on the west coast of Africa, the Sahara Desert lies right across the breadth of that vast continent. Broken only by the narrow waters of the Red Sea, the desert belt is continued in Syria, Iraq and Arabia, and across the almost equally narrow inlet of the Persian Gulf, in the Great Salt Desert of Iran, the deserts of Afghanistan and Baluchistan, and the enormous empty waste called the Desert of Gobi or Shamo. This desert belt is, with the exception of Gobi, the result of excessive heat.

The cold deserts of the North and South Poles have, so far as we know, existed since time immemorial. The hot deserts include regions which within historical times were fertile and prosperous. It is believed that formerly much of the Sahara, which still contains many large oases, was open grassland similar to that of the steppes. In Iraq and Central Asia, the ruins of many once famous cities, such as Babylon, Nineveh, and Ur, testify to the existence of advanced civilizations in what are now desert or semi-desert regions. Even the Gobi, most desolate, arid and uninhabited of all large deserts, has produced evidence that primitive man found means of sustenance there for thousands of years.

THE DESERT AREA IS GROWING

The total extent of desert area has grown enormously within historic times: and many scientists believe this to be a sign that the earth as a whole is drying up. Its store of water, they say, is gradually disappearing in the form of vapour, which escapes through the atmosphere into the limitless emptiness of space. It is said that the level of the ocean is slowly sinking, and it is known that the great inland seas are drying up.

The desiccation, or drying up, of a land area may proceed for centuries without making much difference to the lives of the human beings and animals living thereon. As time goes on, there are rather fewer showers of rain, the rivers carry, decade by decade, a slightly decreasing flow of water to the ocean, the levels of the lakes sink ever lower. But so slow is the process that it is barely if at all perceptible to the inhabitants.

Suddenly there comes what is known as the " capsizing point," and then the climate and the land change in character remarkably within a relatively very short period. The level of the subsoil water, which gives birth to the springs, has fallen too low to continue to supply the streams and rivers of the area. Consequently, the streams and rivers dry up; less and less moisture passes into the atmosphere to fall as rain; the land becomes increasingly parched, and dust and sand storms begin their terribly effective work of erosion, excavation and burial.

BURIED IN WIND-DRIVEN SAND

Even in the temperate climate of western Europe one may, in various places, study the catastrophic effects of wind-driven sand. On the Norfolk coast the church of Eccles was, in 1839, buried up to its belfry tower. Some hundreds of years ago the entire parish of Forvie, in Aberdeenshire, was overwhelmed. The disaster was attributed by a zealous Protestant to the fact that the parishioners were " Papists and grossly ignorant." For 700 years, until 1835, when it was dug out, the church of Constantine, in south Cornwall, remained entombed in sand. From the Baltic to the Pyrenees there are places where the sands of the seashore every year swallow up a depth of from three to twenty-four feet of fertile land.

If such changes can be effected in temperate climates, where winds are normally gentle, one can imagine the colossal devastation wrought in lands subject to extremes of temperature with consequent fiercely raging winds, hurricanes and tornadoes. The sunny island of Bermuda is swept by sandstorms which bury fields and even woods. Along the north-west coast of Africa the wind has piled sand in dunes 400 to 600 feet high. This constant stream of sand, which is carried across the Sahara towards Cape Bojador and Cape Blanco, blots out oases and has been said to bury whole caravans on the desert routes. Around Lake Michigan, in North America, swamps, forests and even hills lie buried under masses of sand.

Sand not only buries; it files down obstacles and excavates territory. In Devon and Cornwall you may see cliffs, rocks and hills worn to weird shapes by the constant scouring of wind-driven sand. On the lonely island of Kerguelen, in the Indian Ocean, rocks exposed to the strong west winds are deeply grooved from west to east by the sand stream.

PROPOSAL TO FLOOD THE SAHARA

Although the average height of the Sahara Desert is 2,000 feet, there are already areas in Tripoli and Algeria which are below sea-level. The prevailing winds being north-east, the surface of these regions is persistently being carried away to the south-west. Fresh supplies of sand are constantly being ground by erosion from the sandstone and other rocks which form the floor of the desert. In time the entire Sahara will be excavated to below sea-level. It has already been suggested many times that the northern area should be flooded by canal from the

Mediterranean; but so far no responsible authority has ventured to put in hand this costly and possibly profitless project.

MILLIONS OF MILES OF DESERT

The Sahara which, including Tripoli and Fezzan, has an area of nearly 3,500,000 square miles, is the world's greatest desert. Almost as large as Europe, it is still growing. The excessive heat of the day, rising at times to 140°F., is followed by a steep drop in temperature at night; and these perpetually recurrent changes cause the barren rocks and hills to crumble. Into such soft and friable material the wind, carrying with it untold millions of grains of rasping sand, cuts deeply. The desert still contains ranges of mountains with peaks towering thousands of feet high, yet even these are being worn down, slowly but irrevocably, by the wind-swept sand which hurls itself against them.

On the face of the desert the skeleton of what was once a river system can be discerned. Today, occasional boulder-strewn valleys show where once the rivers flowed. Oases are shrinking, and water holes which formerly were worth more than gold to camel caravans, are disappearing or giving out. Deserted cities stand as memorials to their defeat by the desert. Agades, capital of the Tuareg people, once housed 50,000 inhabitants; its population has dwindled to a few thousands.

So quickly does the contour of the desert change under the incessant sandstorms, that dunes which today have slopes of forty-five degrees may be as flat as a table top tomorrow. This fact constitutes a major objection to the building of a railway across the Sahara. Such a project was drafted by the French Ministry of Public Works in 1932. The line was to run from a port on the Mediterranean to the River Niger, and the estimated cost of construction was £20,800,000.

Captain A. H. H. Haywood, who in 1911 made a remarkable journey from Sierra Leone to Algiers, pointed out the insuperable difficulty of keeping the track from being buried. The strong, gusty winds, he argued, would quickly cover them with sand many feet deep.

THE SAHARA CONQUERED BY CAR

On the other hand the journey across the desert is today being almost regularly made by motor car. The Citroën expedition, consisting of five cars equipped with caterpillar wheels, took only three weeks to travel from Touggourt in the north to Timbuktu in the south, a distance of over 2,000 miles. Arab caravans usually take seven months over this journey. M. Dalpiez travelled from Touggourt to Tozeur, a distance of 186 miles, in a specially designed car having six pairs of wheels, in a sixth of the time usually occupied by camels. In December, 1938, the motor explorer, Humphrey Symons, covered the 2,260 miles from Algiers to Kano, in Nigeria, in three days four hours, thus setting up a world record.

Twice a year two caravans of 5,000 camels each set out from Gao, on the River Niger, and once the capital of the former great negro empire of

Songhai, to carry food and other necessaries to the salt-miners of Taoudeni. They return laden with the product of the mines, which are still worked by slave labour.

In 1932, seven men in two motor cars set out from Reggan, a French military post, to cover the 500 miles of desert that separated them from the salt city, which is situated on a plateau known as Hamada-el-Hariche. Subjected to almost incessant sandstorms, and perpetually scourged by the stinging, sandy " shrapnel " of the desert, the party accomplished its mission after a gruelling experience. Not a single blade of grass or a tree was seen on the way.

In skirmishes in the desert, according to Professor O. Olufsen, " it is sometimes impossible for infantry to lie down; they stand up, preferring the risk of being killed by bullets, rather than that of allowing themselves to be burned to death on the sand."

According to Dr. James Henry Breasted, the distinguished American historian, who between 1905 and 1920 led a number of archæological expeditions into Asia Minor and North Africa, the Sahara was at one time covered by dense forests. Before that, as has been shown by the sinking of artesian wells at various points, the area was a vast sea. Evidences of marine life similar to that found in the lakes of Palestine have been brought to the surface. According to André Berthelot, during the time that the great Ice Age buried Europe under a vast ice sheet, the Sahara was a steppe, through which flowed large rivers. Here many of the refugees from the frozen north made their home.

OTHER DESERT ENCROACHMENTS

Deserts are found not only in North but also in South Africa. The Kalahari Desert, which extends over 120,000 square miles in British Bechuanaland Protectorate and South-West Africa, was in 1878-79 the scene of a pitiful tragedy. A company of Boers, with their wives and children, set out from the Transvaal across the desert to Ngami and thence to Angola. They reached their destination, but at frightful cost; it is said that 250 men, women and children, and 9,000 cattle, died of thirst.

General J. C. Smuts stated recently that the problem of soil erosion in South Africa was even more urgent than the solution of political problems. In several parts of the Union of South Africa and in South-West Africa it is possible to observe a steady deterioration of the pasture land and a fall in the level of the subsoil water. The rise of the African continent, said to be still going on, tends to increase the impetuosity of the rivers and to cause them to wash away their beds ever more rapidly and to greater depths, thus increasing the desiccation of the highlands.

WORLD'S MOST DESOLATE AREA

The Gobi Desert is a continuation of the series of deserts that make great empty and worthless stretches from the Atlantic frontier of the Sahara to Mongolia. One thousand miles across, 600 miles from north to south, and in places 5,000 feet above sea-level, it is one of the world's most desolate areas. How appallingly desolate is shown by the requirements of the Third Asiatic Expedition of the American Museum of Natural History, which consisted of a caravan of five motor cars, two one-ton lorries, and a four-footed service station of 125 camels carrying 3,500 gallons of petrol, and food supplies. In no other way could the wants of man and of machine be supplied. Even this convoy seems small when compared with that of Dr. Sven Hedin, who was accompanied on one occasion by 392 camels.

In the Gobi, Dr. Roy Chapman Andrews discovered relics of the time of Neanderthal man, and on the shores of ancient lakes, fireplaces, flint scrapers and other evidence of dune-dwellers who lived and perished 20,000 years ago. Moreover, he found a nest of twelve dinosaur eggs, approximately 10,000,000 years old. The same intrepid scientist and explorer is of the opinion that man made his appearance on the Mongolian plateau from half a million to one million years ago, when the now desolate waste " was a well-watered region with a stimulating climate."

In one part of the Gobi is a stretch of sand known as the Sand Mountain, which extends for six dreary miles. " We knew," writes Anna Louise Strong, a recent traveller, " that if our wheels sank through the crust made by recent rains (and no one knew how strong that crust might be) we would wait, lost in some cup of the sand hills under the sunset, till help could be summoned from the wandering tribes beyond." Melons, apricots, peaches, grapes, plums and pomegranates flourish in certain oases, but the south-western quarter is absolutely waterless. It is this part which has earned for the Gobi its Chinese name of Sha-mo, " sand desert," and Han-hai, " dry sea."

LOST OASES OF LIBYA

The Libyan Desert, which is really part of the Sahara, is mainly of interest by reason of several recent expeditions undertaken to discover real or legendary oases of bygone days. Hassaneim Bey, for instance, found Owenat and Arkenu in 1923, and in 1924-25 Prince Kemal el-Din and Dr. John Ball came across Merga (Nekheila). Dr. Ball had already found, in 1916, hundreds of earthenware jars, but how, why and when they got there remains a mystery. An attempt made by motor cars in 1926 to locate Lagia resulted in the explorers having to be rescued by aeroplanes. W. J. Harding King, who set out in 1874 to reach the Kufara oasis, found the sandhills insurmountable, and only a few years ago an aviator reported two enormous ramparts of sand that ran north and south about twenty miles east of the oasis of Baharia. No tracks were to be seen. Elsewhere, sandstone cliffs a thousand feet high stretch for seventy miles. Cave paintings of cattle and people, believed to have been executed at least 10,000 years ago, have been brought to light. In 1932, Dr. Junker, of the German Institute at Cairo, discovered the site of a Byzantine settlement at Kashem el Gaud.

MAN-MADE DESERTS

Not all deserts are the result of changes in climate. The slight but continuous increase in height of the Himalaya and Trans-Himalaya mountains partially accounts for the barrenness of much of western China, because this progressively cuts off the supply of moisture-bearing winds; but the primary cause of the desiccation of the land is the cutting down of the forests. Neglect and destruction of protective vegetation by the Turks is said to be the reason why Iraq, Syria, and Palestine, once "lands flowing with milk and honey," became in great part arid and barren.

The most modern, and in some respects the most terrifying, examples of man-made deserts are to be found in North America. During the 19th century, when settlers streamed westward across the Continent in an endless flood, lumbermen and farmers felled vast stretches of forest to make way for homesteads and farms, little dreaming that they were destroying Nature's rampart against drought.

For years all went well; the increasing dryness of the soil passed unnoticed, while golden harvests were reaped from the rich, virgin earth. But gradually the bitter spring winds and the parching heat of summer did their work. The level of the subsoil water grew ever lower —in places it has fallen six and a half yards during the past 100 years— and the top soil became increasingly dry.

DUST STORMS THREE MILES HIGH

Within the past twenty years the result of forest destruction has become terribly evident. In 1920, 2,000,000 tons of loose soil in Colorado, Wyoming, Kansas, and Nebraska were lifted thousands of feet high and carried by a gale to the neighbourhood of the Great Lakes and the St. Lawrence, where they were deposited during a snowstorm which lasted two days. In 1925, an area of 172,900,000 acres was devastated by dust storms, and in 1934 a dust storm extending for 1,500 miles reached at times a height of three miles. Soil swept from the western prairies invaded the streets and houses of New York.

In twenty states some 400,000 families had to receive relief from the Federal authorities, £105,000,000 being in one session voted by Congress for this purpose. Millions of cattle had to be slaughtered or removed long distances; thousands died of disease.

In the following year, 2,000,000 acres in Colorado and Kansas were devastated by dust, which in places formed miniature mountains six feet high. The dust forced down aeroplanes or prevented them from going up. What was termed "dust pneumonia," and congestion of the lungs took a deadly toll of victims. Masks were hurriedly made, and worn both indoors and out. The wind-driven soil threatened to bury farmhouses, some of which were covered up to the roof. Orchards were blotted out. Day took on the appearance of night.

Dr. Rex Tugwell, Under-Secretary for Agriculture, gave it as his opinion that, if action were not taken, the Middle West would one day be as barren as the interior of China, and Dr. O. E. Baker declared that since the settlement of America, surface soil equal to the total area of cultivated land in Germany had been removed. Another eminent authority maintained that if the rate of denudation continued the country had "less than one hundred years of virile, national existence."

These warnings have had their effect; the United States Government is now fully alive to the danger, and though effective measures of defence have yet to be devised, it is certain that ere long they will be. A rampart of trees 100 miles wide and 1,000 miles long is now being planted across the United States from Canada to Texas, and experiments are being carried out in the planting of soil-binding grasses. The Boulder Dam, completed in 1935, is intended to store water for the irrigation of some 1,000,000 acres of desert land in the lower Colorado basin. This is only one of several vast projects for the reclamation of barren areas in the United States.

IS EUROPE DRYING UP?

Europe as a whole is singularly fortunate as regards climate. The prevailing winds come from the south-west, that is, from the ocean, and consequently bring much moisture. They also keep the Continent cool in summer and warm in winter. Though the annual rainfall varies enormously, from sixty inches or more in places along the coast from Norway to Portugal, down to twenty inches or less in parts of the Russian plain, it rarely drops anywhere for long below the safety margin, though every now and then periods of prolonged drought are experienced.

The drought which in 1933-34 spread its influence over much of continental Europe, the British Isles, the United States, Canada, and South Africa was the worst for at least eighty years, though the droughts of 1887, 1893, 1911 and 1921 were severe enough to be serious. At the beginning of June, 1934, the flow of the Thames above Teddington Weir fell by 100,000,000 gallons a day, the normal daily average for the month being 819,000,000 gallons.

DROUGHT WHICH DRIED THE THAMES

It is said that towards the end of the 7th century "for the space of three years before the coming thither of Bishop Wilfrid, there had fallen no rain from the air within that province of the South Saxons." In 1113-14, the Thames at London was sufficiently dry for children to wade across it "between the bridges and the town." The weather repeated itself in this respect in 1281 and again in 1716. Further droughts serious enough to be noticed by historians took place in 1236, 1241, 1252, 1260, 1591-92, 1681, 1864 and 1870.

THE GAS WE ALL BREATHE

ILLIONS of years ago, when the glowing, metallic vapours of the earth cooled off on the surface, the heavy elements, including platinum, gold, silver, copper and iron sank towards the earth's centre, while the lighter ones, including helium, hydrogen, oxygen and nitrogen remained on the surface and slowly amalgamated to form the so-called atmosphere. It has been estimated that the total weight of the air layers that envelop us is about 6,000 billion tons.

TREMENDOUS WEIGHT OF AIR CARRIED BY MAN

Air has the capacity to expand, a fact that was discovered about 100 B.C. by Hero of Alexandria, the Greek philosopher, who may be considered the Einstein of antiquity. The pressure of the air was investigated by Evangelista Torricelli, an Italian and a pupil of the great Galileo, who invented the mercury thermometer.

Each person supports an air column weighing twenty-five cwt. On the whole surface of the earth the air's pressure exerts a force of 5,100 billion tons; the load on each square inch at sea-level amounts to 14.7 lb. This may seem a crushing weight for a person to bear, but it is evenly distributed, and the pressure within the human body is the same as that outside, thereby equalizing what would otherwise be an impossible burden.

HOW AIR IS CONDITIONED

Pure air is so essential to human welfare that increasing attention is being given to what is termed air-conditioning, which is entirely independent of the usual means of ventilation by windows and air bricks. Humidity, or the degree of dampness in the air, is extremely important, for damp air holds a greater quantity of heat than dry, and it is the over-dry atmosphere in a house which is responsible for many chills and much depression noticeable in winter, when fires and central heating are in evidence.

An air-conditioning plant draws air from the outside of a building, cleans it, and gives it a cooling or warming shower as required. Sometimes a certain proportion of ozone is added before the air is pumped to various outlets in rooms and corridors. It has been found by means of exhaustive experiments that 55°F. is the healthiest temperature for brain workers. At Broadcasting House, London, the amount of air handled by the conditioning plant per hour is approximately 260 tons, which is distributed to 180 rooms.

"Artificial atmospheres of desired temperature and humidity," notes a report of the American Chemical Society, "permit delicate processes to be carried on in factory and laboratory regardless of weather conditions, eliminating losses to owners and workers resulting from seasonal schedules of production." Although air conditioning has not been generally introduced, railways, stores, banks, hotels and offices which have tried it report a considerable reduction of illness and loss of time among employees, and increased efficiency. In many processes, such as the manufacture of cotton, tobacco and films, control of the moisture in the air is of the utmost importance.

POLLUTION OF CITY AIR

It is stated that the purest air in a city is about twenty-six feet above ground level, and therefore the healthiest rooms are those situated at that height. The air of a great city contains as many as 10,000,000 deposit nuclei, on which water particles are able to collect. When there is no wind, the city is covered with a haze stratum which absorbs the sunlight and the short-wave space rays a hundred times more than pure air does.

The amount of pollution in the air in the neighbourhood of big cities and towns is almost unbelievable. On the authority of Dr. R. Lessing, 1,500,000 tons of flue dust are distributed throughout Great Britain annually. Greater London alone contributes 500,000 tons of noxious sulphur every twelve months.

WHAT THE AIR CONTAINS

Dry air consists of 78 per cent of nitrogen, 21 per cent of oxygen, 0.93 per cent of argon, and 0.03 per cent of carbon dioxide. Six other gases are present in small quantities. If the oxygen content falls to 18½ per cent a candle is extinguished; if it falls to 17.2 per cent a human being is rapidly suffocated.

EARTH'S LUNGS

The earth's left lung is Canada, and the right lung Northern Siberia. In the winter these lungs absorb enormous quantities of warm air and in turn reject the old cold air.

In summer the process is reversed: the warm air rises and is replaced by an influx of cold air from the Pole.

EARTH'S COSMIC FUR

THE atmosphere has rightly been termed the "cosmic fur of the earth." It resembles the glass roof of a conservatory, for a glass roof lets through bright and not dark heat, such as the heat of a tiled oven and of rays reflected from the earth.

REGION OF CONSTANT TEMPERATURE

About forty per cent of the sun's heat is absorbed by the atmosphere. While the temperature of the interior of the earth increases 1°C. for every 100 feet we descend, the temperature of the air decreases by ½°C. for every 300 feet we ascend.

The decrease in the temperature of the atmosphere does not continue indefinitely. A region of constant temperature, at least twenty-five miles thick, envelops the earth. Known as the stratosphere, it begins at a height of about ten miles above our heads. The region next to the earth is called the troposphere.

HEAVENLY BODIES THAT POSSESS ATMOSPHERES

According to the theory of the mobility of the various kinds of gases, the lightest gases consist of molecules that have great velocities and can therefore only be prevented from escaping into space by the exercise of very powerful gravity-force on the part of the heavenly body which they surround. The earth, for instance, has not got a sufficiently powerful force of gravity to retain within its atmosphere any very considerable quantities of hydrogen and helium.

The moon once had an atmosphere composed of gases, but these have long since been dissipated into space. Mercury, whose mass is twenty times smaller than that of the earth, has no atmosphere comparable to ours. Mars is gradually losing its atmosphere. Venus, on the other hand, would appear to be surrounded by a comparatively dense atmosphere, such as that surrounding our globe. It has even been suggested that it would be possible for a human being to breathe without artificial aids on Venus.

FLATTENING OF THE ATMOSPHERE

The degree of oblateness of the earth (i.e. the flattening at the poles) is far less than that of the oblateness of the atmosphere. The height of the troposphere—the lowest layer of the atmosphere—above the Equator is about ten miles, but it falls to about half that amount at the poles.

HOW HIGH ARE THE CLOUDS?

The warmer the air that supports them the higher the clouds. For instance, if cirrus clouds at the Equator are six miles high—none rises higher—they will not be much more than half a mile high in the colder temperature of Greenland. In Northern Europe, dome-shaped cumulus or fine-weather clouds are usually from half a mile to two miles high; nimbus rain-clouds half a mile to one and a quarter miles high; the stratus, an elevated and continuous horizontal sheet of vapour, from a third to three and three-quarter miles; while the veil that forms haloes round the sun and the moon is three and three-quarters to eight miles high. The cirrus clouds, that portend good weather, and are called " mares' tails " by sailors, are from three to five and a half miles up, but the cumulo-nimbus or thunder-clouds move at a height of from two to four miles. The same height is reached by the cirro-cumulus or mackerel clouds which, when light-hued, indicate the coming of good weather, but which when dark portend the opposite. Squall clouds frequently come as low as 550 yards, and so do wind-torn cumulus clouds.

THREE HUNDRED MILES UP

The highest altitude ever reached by man—14 miles—was attained by the Americans, Capt. A. Stevens and Capt. O. Anderson, on Armistice Day, 1935. In the following year the German scientist and explorer, Professor Alfred Wegener, sent a sounding balloon up to a height of well over twenty miles.

At a height of 45,500 feet the temperature was $-63°C$. Between twelve and a half and twenty miles up is a warm layer, rich in ozone, in which, as Professor Wegener discovered in 1934, sun rays are absorbed and by which sound is reflected back to the earth. The curve of the shells from " Big Bertha," the German long-range gun that bombarded Paris during the World War, reached a height of nearly twenty-two miles, and lava ejected in the eruption of Krakatoa, in the Sunda Sea, in 1883, a height of over thirty miles.

At that height the density of the air is only one-thousandth that of its lowest strata. At fifty miles, the height of the glimmering night-clouds that consist of ice crystals or volcanic or cosmic dust, and the limit of meteors or shooting stars, there rages an east wind with a velocity of 175 miles an hour, because the atmosphere at this level ceases to take part in the earth's rotation. At an altitude of sixty miles the air is possibly a million times less dense than at sea-level. It is there that we see the Northern Lights, or Aurora Borealis, at heights varying from 40 to over 600 miles. This phenomenon may be caused by frozen particles of nitrogen which have phosphoresced at a temperature of $237°C$. below zero; or it may be due to discharges of electricity which direct themselves towards the magnetic North.

The great whirlwinds on earth are said to be caused by air currents at a height of 250 miles. Recent research has shown that at an altitude of 300 miles, scattered molecules of hydrogen and nitrogen are still present. Professor E. V. Appleton asserts that in the ionosphere, between 60 and 140 miles up, great heat prevails; that between 600 and 1,200 miles up the heat of a summer's day on earth prevails, but that at 1,560 miles up the temperature is $-56°C$.

GASES MORE VALUABLE THAN GOLD

Of all substances precious gases are the most valuable : more so than gold and platinum, for they possess the greatest power of resistance to weather and to chemical and physical influences—they are completely inert. Not even the greatest heat has the slightest effect on them.

The proportions of precious gases in the air are 0.93 per cent argon, 0.0018 per cent neon, 0.0005 per cent helium, 0.0001 per cent krypton, and 0.000009 per cent zenon. Moist air contains a comparatively larger proportion of precious gases. The yield can be increased still further by utilizing the treasures of sea water, for air dissolved in sea water contains three times as much precious gases as atmospheric air. Neon gas is used for advertisement light-signs, and helium is used, among other things, for inflating airships.

PRECIOUS GAS FOR AIRSHIPS

Helium, which is non-inflammable, is the lightest of known gases. It is one-seventh the weight of nitrogen. It will not combine chemically with any other element and is derived from natural gas by a process of elimination. The United States has the largest source of supply, although Russia, and Ontario and Alberta, in Canada, have wells. In Alberta there is a well with a flow of 15,000,000 cubic feet of natural gas a day, but the helium content is small compared with over seven per cent obtained in Colorado. The gas is also obtained in Utah and Texas. The presence of helium in the sun was discovered in 1868 by a party of astronomers in India, who had gone to observe an eclipse of the sun, and the name given to the gas was derived from the Greek word for sun. Its existence on the earth was definitely proved by Sir William Ramsay in 1894, a few days after Dr. W. F. Hillebrand had discovered it but mistaken it for nitrogen. Its source of origin remains a puzzle to scientists. Some think that it was brought from the sun and imprisoned in the interior when the globe was cast off from the parent body. Others believe that it is a by-product of radio-activity. In 1908, Professor Kamerlingh Onnes produced helium in liquid form, and in 1926 Professor Keeson, of Leyden University, succeeded in solidifying it.

Helium is extracted from natural gas by a process similar to those by which oxygen is extracted from the atmosphere. There is a large plant at Fort Worth in the United States which is capable of handling 44,000 cubic feet of natural gas an hour.

The first airship to use the gas was the *C-7* of the United States Navy, which was filled with 176,400 cubic feet. Following the destruction of the *Hindenberg* airship by fire, the Germans wished to obtain helium for their Zeppelins, but the request was refused by the United States Government on account of the possibility of the aircraft being used for military purposes. The gas is now being used for the relief of asthma and other ailments where breathing is difficult.

CARBON DIOXIDE THE LIFE-PRESERVER

Although the proportion of carbon dioxide in the air is only about 0.03 per cent, the temperature of the earth's surface would fall 20°C. if it were to vanish completely. The alternation of tropical and glacial periods in the earth's history depends on variations in the carbon dioxide content of the air. During the cold periods all volcanic activity was at a standstill.

The carbon dioxide content is increased by volcanic activity, by the industrial consumption of coal, and by the breathing of human beings and animals. It is diminished by the decomposition of carbon dioxide in sea water and by growing plants. Of the two billion tons of carbon dioxide in the atmosphere, the plant world consumes about 59,000,000,000 tons yearly. If the carbon dioxide content were not recruited from other sources, the supply would be completely used up in thirty-five years, and life on earth would come to an end

TEMPERS OF THE WIND

A T the poles the air particles are driven twice as quickly by the rotation of the earth as in tropical regions. The formation of great tornadoes is connected with the air currents that prevail at a height of about 250 miles. Characterized as the shortest and most vicious type of storm, it is fortunate that many tornadoes spend their force in the upper air. Notwithstanding this, they are of frequent occurrence in the United States.

HURLED TO DEATH BY TORNADOES

About 130 tornadoes strike the United States every year, usually from March to June inclusive, with an average annual loss of 310 men, women and children. Travelling at a speed varying from 25 to 500 miles an hour, the whirling funnel seldom concentrates on one spot for more than a minute, though it may last an hour before it exhausts itself.

A series of tornadoes caused death and destruction from Louisiana to Virginia in 1924, leaving over 100 dead and 400 injured, some of whom were "whisked through the air like straws." No fewer than nine States were affected. Three years later St. Louis, which in 1896 had been visited by a tornado which wrecked property valued at £2,000,000, again suffered the loss of many lives in addition to the wrecking of some 5,500 buildings. In 1928 a tornado in Florida exacted a toll of nearly 1,200 dead, and 1,270 people were killed in Guadeloupe.

HOUSES THAT EXPLODED

On many occasions houses have literally exploded during the passing of a tornado, the vacuum at the centre of the wind-tunnel and the natural pressure—fifteen pounds to the square inch—of the air inside the buildings causing the walls to collapse outwards. In Europe, cyclones are comparatively rare, but in 1923 the hamlet of Longuenne, in France, was blown away, and 50,000 trees were uprooted in the forest of Andaines.

A tornado which strikes the water is a waterspout. Such a visitor appeared in Toulon eight years later (1931), capsizing small boats, drowning many of their occupants, and discharging so fierce a fusillade of hail that damage was done to the extent of some thousands of pounds sterling.

HAVOC OF THE HURRICANE

Hot air above the warm waters of the equatorial current meeting the cold northern and eastern trade winds causes the disastrous hurricanes which so often visit the beautiful islands of the Caribbean Sea and the neighbouring mainland. A hurricane struck Palm Beach and Miami, famous resorts in Florida, in 1926, killed at least 1,200 inhabitants, injured thousands more, rendered 40,000 people homeless and did damage estimated at £25,000,000.

In 1930 a similar storm left only 400 houses standing in Santo Domingo, capital of the republic of that name, while twelve months later Belize, British Honduras, was devastated. Some 1,500 inhabitants were killed, chaos was created in the city, and the cathedral was torn down. Vessels were carried inland by a tidal wave, which flooded the town but probably prevented a series of disastrous fires. On Swan Island, 300 miles south of Cuba, the United States and Cuban governments keep trained meteorologists from July to November to take barometrical and wind readings and report by radio to Washington and Havana, from whence storm warnings are issued.

WINDMILLS ARE STILL USEFUL

Tradition has it that the windmill was introduced into England by the Crusaders. Recent investigation goes to show that its original home was Persia, and that the idea was brought to Europe by the Northmen and introduced by them into the Netherlands. At Liége, in Belgium, the oldest windmill in the world, believed to have been built in the 12th century, is still turning. Bury St. Edmunds, Suffolk, is known to have had a windmill as early as 1191. It was erected by one Hubert the Dean, and later pulled down by the abbot's orders. The last windmill at Pulham St. Mary, Norfolk, was demolished in 1910; it is said to have had predecessors for a thousand years. The oldest dated windmill in England is Bourn Mill, in Cambridgeshire, which was in use in 1633; a post or peg-mill, built in 1688, stands at Brill, Buckinghamshire. The windmill at Ringmer, Sussex, had been in use for 225 years before it ground its last sack of corn in 1921, four years before it collapsed. Friston Mill, " a diadem of the Sussex hills," was blown down in 1926, and the windmill at Rye was destroyed by fire.

Holland's 2,500 windmills drain the polders, cut hay, saw timber and render other useful services. It is stated that each windmill used for the purpose drains an average of 310 acres. In China, towerless windmills consisting of seven massive sails on poles, rotate on geared shafts and pump water from wells to irrigate the fields. They look like gaunt merry-go-rounds.

POWER FROM THE AIR

Modern technology envisages gigantic apparatus which will make it possible for power to be derived from the air by means of electric air turbines. The average temperature in the tropics, up to a height of half a mile, is 30°C. M. Dubos planned to create an equalization of heat by means of a concrete tube, half a mile high and sixty-six yards in diameter. In this tube the ascending heat and descending cold would create an enormous vortex. The interposition of a turbine would convert this strong air current into electricity, which could be conducted to any desired distances from the upper end of the tube.

The first wind-power station was erected at Duisburg in 1935, and consists of a tower 100 feet high with four sails, estimated to produce seventy horse-power. The wind tunnel at Meudon, near Paris, used to test the air resistance of aircraft, produces an air current with a velocity of 110 miles per hour.

RAIN AND FOG

RAINDROPS are larger in summer than in winter. Their maximum diameter in summer is between three-twentieths and three-tenths of an inch, and their minimum diameter a very small fraction of an inch. The larger drops come from greater heights than the smaller ones, which are reduced to about one five-hundredth of an inch diameter in fog.

WEIGHT OF A RAINDROP

An average drop of rain weighs about 0.2 grams. On its way from the cloud to the earth it covers about thirteen feet a second, and a large drop falls as fast as twenty-five feet a second. In thunder rain the drops are negatively charged; the charge and tension are from ten to thirty times as great in the case of thunderstorms as in ordinary rain.

The British Isles have a mean annual rainfall of just over twenty-two inches; but as much as 247 inches fell in Carnarvonshire during 1923, which is 211 inches less than the annual rainfall in Cherra Punji, Assam; while during 1921 Margate received only nine inches. The average for London is twenty-five inches; the Lake District has over four times that amount. Forests, fields, gardens, and meadows are content with an eight per cent share of all the rain that falls in the country; man uses only one per cent for drinking and for domestic and industrial purposes; the greater part runs into rivers and lakes. An inch of rain means slightly more than 100 tons to the acre. Various districts in the British Isles receive their maximum rainfall at different periods of the year; in London, for example, October shows the highest average, but in Edinburgh July tops the list.

MAN CANNOT MAKE RAIN

In 1923, seven natives were found guilty at Salisbury, Rhodesia, of the murder of a member of their tribe. They had burnt him as a sacrifice to the rain goddess in order to break a severe drought. Attempts to make rain on more scientific principles have been tried from time to time, usually without success. While experiments carried out in England to produce a downpour by heavy gunfire have failed, similar means have achieved slight success in the United States and South America. In the Middle Ages the ringing of church bells was believed to bring about precipitation.

A number of Dutch aeroplanes dropped powdered ice on clouds above the Zuider Zee and caused a shower, and rockets charged with explosives are used for the same purpose by vine growers in Switzerland and France, but these devices cannot be regarded as solving the problem of creating a steady rain over a wide area.

FOG COSTS MILLIONS

Mist is a cloud at ground level, and is normally white and clean. It is only when the vapour particles of which it consists absorb smoke, soot and other impurities that it becomes fog. A pall such as this hung over the greater part of England for five days just previous to Christmas, 1904, and cost the country about £10,000,000. In 1921 the British Meteorological Office gave the atmospheric pollution during a dense fog in February as 11 lb. per 1,000,000 cubic yards maximum and 0.5 lb. minimum. On seven consecutive days in November of the following year, London had only six minutes of sunshine, and the death rate during the period rose to 13.3 per 1,000. In 1936, on a day in February, practically the whole of Europe was enveloped in fog. Shipping was paralysed, train services were disorganized, and many air services were cancelled. It has been estimated that in Great Britain 25,000,000 working hours are lost every year through fog by railway passengers alone.

According to Captain James Bisset, of the Cunard White Star Line, banks of mist in the North Atlantic frequently measure over 1,000 miles long and 400 miles wide. He adds that in the neighbourhood of the Newfoundland Banks there is double the amount of mist during summer that there is in winter. The mists are caused by air from warmer parts becoming chilled by the cold Labrador current and condensing, just as steam turns into minute particles of water when it escapes from the spout of a boiling kettle. On one occasion, the commander of a liner spent sixty-nine hours on the bridge bringing his ship into Cherbourg Harbour when the air was blanketed in this way.

WHEN THUNDERSTORMS RAGE

A CLOUD is a cause and not an effect. The more rapidly a cloud formation takes place, the sooner a cloud becomes a thunder-cloud. The course of events is much as follows. Through the prevalence of two winds blowing in opposite directions, a sultry calm sets in. Finally the cold wind, breaking in from above, penetrates the warm air, the cooling-off of which produces a rain formation. After one or two hours of sultriness there usually appears the so-called cirrus screen, followed by the blue-black cumulo-nimbus thunder-cloud at a height of about 3,300 feet. Dust-eddies occur; light yellow clouds approach rapidly below the thunder-cloud. Soon the first large drops—or often hail—begin to fall, and then the thunder rain starts.

SIXTEEN MILLION THUNDERSTORMS YEARLY

It has been calculated that every year there are 16,000,000 thunderstorms on the earth; about 44,000 storms and about 600,000 flashes of lightning daily. During a storm the average number of flashes is about 200 an hour. Lightning is an enormous spark, in which differences of tension between a cloud and the earth or between two clouds are discharged. For the most part the flash goes from the earth to a negatively charged thunder-cloud; the amount of current may be as much as 5,000,000 ampères.

Lightning discharges itself in one-millionth of a second, has as much as 500,000,000 horse-power, and moves at the speed of light, namely 186,000 miles per second. Each flash, according to the length of the spark and the density of the air, uses up a current of from 2,000,000 to 10,000,000 kilo-volt ampères, i.e., on an average 8,000,000 kilowatt hours. The last figure given represents about one three-thousandth of the amount consumed by Great Britain in a recent year.

WHERE THUNDERSTORMS ARE MOST FREQUENT

Thunderstorms are most frequent in the tropics. Abyssinia and the Cameroons each have an average of 214 thundery days in the year. Thunderstorms are unknown in the Antarctic and are few and far between in the Arctic, though they occur occasionally in Greenland, Spitzbergen and other northern places. They are common in Java and Mexico; rare at Algoa Bay and in Peru. To the east of Trondhjem (Norway), Königsberg (Germany) and Budapest (Hungary) there are no winter thunderstorms, which become more frequent as one approaches the Atlantic, and are not uncommon in Iceland. A census of thunderstorms revealed that Java had 223 each year, central Africa 150, southern Mexico 142, Panama 136, central Brazil 105, and Madagascar 95.

LIGHTNING AS ENEMY AND FRIEND

Lightning is both enemy and friend. On the credit side of the account it produces some 100,000,000 tons of fixed nitrogen yearly, which is brought down with rain and supplies valuable fertilizer to the soil. On the other side it is probably responsible for more forest fires than any other cause, and the hail that frequently accompanies it does damage estimated at £40,000,000 per annum. In a given twelve months, 713 persons were killed or fatally injured and 973 hurt in the United States alone. No fewer that 729 buildings caught fire and 5,527 were otherwise damaged. The reason why trees are often struck is because their spreading branches and roots form excellent conductors. Contrary to popular belief, lightning often strikes twice or more in the same place. This has been proved by trees which bear marks of several flashes. Cattle lying near wire fencing are apt to be struck. In Scotland, eighteen were killed together in this manner.

Lightning sometimes leaves its autograph on sandy soil. A fulgurite, or lightning tube as it is sometimes called, melts the grains of sand and fuses them into tubes of vitrified quartz. These delicate formations were regarded as the "fruit of subterranean fires" by their first-known discoverer, Pastor Hermann, who unearthed a specimen near Masseh, in Silesia, in 1706. It was not until a century later that a scientist associated them with lightning. Fulgurites take all manner of strange forms, including zig-zag, knots and loops.

Thunder was once regarded as a portent of future events. If it occurred on Sunday it foretold the death of a great man, on Monday of a famous woman, on Tuesday and Thursday good harvests, on Wednesday bloodshed, on Friday war, and on Saturday pestilence. Until 1783, when George III suppressed the custom, church bells were rung during a thunderstorm.

BELATED THUNDER

Thunder takes three seconds to cover five-eighths of a mile. By means of a telephone you can hear a clap of thunder twice, first through the telephone, and again, at a distance of just under four miles, eighteen seconds later. The zig-zag flash of lightning is the origin of the rune ᛋ which represents the letter S, because we instinctively associate lightning with a hissing sound. As the conductivity of air is diminished by burning incense, it used to be thought that the lightning god was propitiated by this ritual. The roll of thunder is due to echoes, which sometimes last as long as fifty seconds. They are mainly caused by layers of air at different densities and temperatures.

TOWER OF LIGHTNING

In 1935 there was built at Nuremberg, Germany, the "Tower of Lightning," a laboratory for research into high-tension electricity. Thirty condenser batteries, each charged with 100,000 volts, are connected up with a lightning generator, placed in a scaffolding of porcelain pillars, forty feet high, and produce a current of 3,000,000 volts and flashes of lightning twenty-three feet in length. At the Paris Exhibition of 1937 an electrical machine capable of producing flashes sixteen feet long attracted great attention.

OBELISKS AS LIGHTNING CONDUCTORS

The fact that lightning has a partiality for metal was known to the ancient Egyptians, who placed copper tips on the obelisks in front of their temples. Solomon's temple, a very inflammable structure, had two brazen columns as lightning conductors; these had lily-shaped tops, were linked together with chains, and connected with a water basin that served as an earth.

The modern lightning conductor was invented by the American, Benjamin Franklin, in 1752, when he was engaged on experiments to prove the electrical nature of lightning. The scientist, Conti, made a lightning conductor in 1790 that was not of metal but of graphite and clay. Much research has gone to the improvement of lightning conductors, particularly since Sir Oliver Lodge demonstrated that there are two kinds of lightning discharges. The first type, when no cloud intervenes between the earth and the electrically charged cloud, can be protected against; but when a cloud does intervene the flash takes a most erratic course, against which it is most difficult to afford protection.

CLIMATE'S MANY CHANGES

Climate means the sum total of the physical conditions of the atmosphere above a given area—a section through the weather on a long series of days. Temperature, degree of moisture, light radiation, air movement, aerial electricity, chemical qualities of the air, all these factors together constitute the climate.

Climate is roughly classified in zones, though there are many exceptions to this somewhat rough-and-ready method. Heat and torrential rain make up the equatorial or middle zones. Then come, both north and south, a band of desert with little rain but extremes of temperature, the temperate zone, and the polar regions. The Equator receives most heat because the sun's rays fall perpendicularly; at the poles they have a wide slant and are therefore less powerful.

RACE AND CLIMATE

The average temperature of the earth is 16°C., but it can rise to + 75° (in Turkestan) and fall to − 90° (in Greenland). Man and the dog are the only animals that are able to any considerable extent to acclimatize themselves, but not all the races of mankind have this faculty in a uniform degree.

The white race is the most successful in this respect, then the yellow, the black, the brown Malays, and last of all the Redskins, who are the most sensitive to a change of climate.

CHANGES IN THE WORLD'S CLIMATE

" During the glacial period," writes Dr. Mildner, of the Geophysical Institute at Leipzig, " the temperature fell only 5°C. below the present mean, but during the Stone and Bronze Ages it was 2° higher than now. About 4000 B.C. the climate of Europe gradually became more temperate. The influence of the ocean made itself more felt. The winters were mild, the summers cool, and the rainfall plentiful. In the farthest north, in Greenland, Iceland, and Scandinavia, plants flourished that cannot exist there any longer.

" Then came a drier, more continental climate. In Western Europe great forests sprang up in districts that were previously moorland. About 1800 B.C. (roughly at the end of the Bronze Age) another rainy period set in, which lasted till about 500 B.C., and forced the Germanic tribes to emigrate from Scandinavia. It was at its height from 450 to 250 B.C., and it is noteworthy that the Greek and Roman civilizations were at their zenith in that period. After 250 B.C., the rainfall decreased, and many rivers were converted into marshes, the breeding-place of mosquitoes and malaria.

" North Africa, Asia Minor, Persia, and Syria," adds Dr. Mildner, " were thickly populated by agricultural tribes in the classical, rainy epoch. The springs gave out at the end of the classical age, the Roman aqueducts collapsed, and the desert spread far and wide. It has been found possible to trace in trees even slight variations of climate right back to A.D. 500. A more plentiful rainfall began again about A.D. 1000, reaching its maximum between 1350 and 1400. This was followed by another dry period, about the year 1500, after which the present climatic conditions gradually asserted themselves."

CONQUEST OF CLIMATE

It would appear that changes of climate can take place rapidly and even within the lifetime of a single generation. The United States is apparently getting drier. In six years North America experienced three serious droughts, culminating in a prolonged spell of heat in 1936 that ruined for a time 500,000 square miles of rich farm land in Mid-Western Canada and the United States. On the other hand, aviators state that since the building of the Boulder Dam, between Nevada and Arizona, and the creation of an immense lake 115 miles long, the air above the reservoir is definitely cooler.

By patient experiment man is learning to overcome some of the difficulties imposed on him by climate. Vilhjalmur Stefansson lived for months without supplies other than what he obtained in what he refers to as the " friendly Arctic." A third of the territory of Soviet Russia lies within the Arctic Circle, and much has been done during recent years to develop trade routes that may eventually release some of the immense wealth of Siberia. This includes not only vast forests but rich deposits of platinum, gold, silver, copper, tin, coal and other minerals. Corn and vegetables now grow where it was once believed that only reindeer moss would thrive. Throughout the world experimental stations are at work producing seeds and plants which will resist the cold, heat, diseases or pests which have hitherto prevented their introduction to new districts.

CAUSES OF VARIATIONS IN CLIMATE

The true causes of climatic variations are not known with any certainty. In the first place, the state of the sun is probably a decisive factor. Solar radiation is almost the sole source of the energy that feeds the vast thermal machinery of our atmosphere. The rate at which the machinery works depends on the quantity of fuel that is fed to it. More powerful radiation means greater evaporation and more plentiful rainfall.

Unfortunately, there is no reliable information available concerning the state of the sun and the number of sunspots for more than a few centuries back, so that it is impossible to determine their relevance with regard to the great climatic fluctuations of the past. For the last 100-150 years, however, a whole series of important connexions between the sun's activity and the weather can be established with absolute certainty. In 1935 a special apparatus for measuring solar radiation was constructed on Mt. Evans, in Colorado, in order to determine the bearing of cosmic rays on climatic variations.

WILL THE EARTH LOSE ITS ATMOSPHERE?

The moon has lost its envelope of air because of its small power of attraction. It could not retain its gases, whose molecules, superheated by the sun, were set in violent motion and were gradually lost in space.

The great attractive power of the earth, which is six times as strong as that of the moon, keeps all substances on it, including its atmospheric gases, firmly attached. It is only when the earth's crust becomes thicker and the earth gets colder and colder that the atmosphere will turn into liquid and then pass into a solid condition.

WORLD-SUMMER AND WORLD-WINTER

The extent of the earth's orbit or path fluctuates within a period of 91,800 years. The inclination of the earth's axis towards the sun's equator is subject to a periodical change. In every 25,800 years it executes a regular turbinate movement. This " platonic world-year," as it is called, like the earth's ordinary year, alternates between a world-summer and a world-winter.

The cause of the earth's five glacial ages (the last of which, a world-winter, comprised in its turn eleven different glacial periods in 600,000 years) is not that our solar system passes in its course sometimes through areas rich in stars and at other times through areas poor in stars, but that displacements of the earth's centre of gravity cause a shifting of its poles. The distribution of land and water has constantly altered in the various epochs of the earth's history. The Gulf Stream, for instance, once flowed into the Pacific, and at one time the Indian and Atlantic Oceans were one.

In the Permian and Carboniferous Ages, about 175,000,000 years ago, the North Pole was situated in 30° N. lat., and 45° W. long. Traces of the glaciation of that period are still to be seen in India, South Australia and America. In the Tertiary Age, about 50,000,000 years ago, the North Pole was situated in 70° N. lat., and 60° W. long., and Alaska and North Siberia began to freeze up. In the last glacial period the southern limit of the ice zone extended from Scotland along the coastline of England, via Cologne, the Harz Mountains and the Giant Mountains to Moscow. Some 70,000 years ago Europe was covered with polar ice, and North America, as far south as Baltimore, lay under a sheet of ice 3,200 feet thick.

WEATHER IN THE MAKING

CLIMATE may be regarded as a serial story, of which the various states of weather are the chapters. Forecasting was not recognized as a scientific possibility until 1861, when Admiral Fitzroy, of the British Board of Trade, began to issue reports. They were discontinued in 1865 and recommenced in 1879. Now hundreds of stations co-operate in the task, and millions of people would feel aggrieved if they did not get their daily weather forecast.

ALL QUIET—OR OTHERWISE—ON THE WEATHER FRONT

According to Dr. G. C. Simpson, an eminent authority, weather is the result of great masses of air from the polar and tropical regions being brought together by the circulation of the atmosphere. They do not readily mix, and form what may be termed " fronts " of cold and warm air respectively.

" As warm air slides up over cold air, or cold air cuts into warm air," Dr. Simpson adds, " cloud and rain are formed, so that ' fronts ' are long and usually narrow strips of bad weather, and it is the motion of the ' fronts ' which is now the chief concern of the forecaster. The recognition of ' fronts ' has given the forecaster a powerful new tool for the study of what is actually taking place in the atmosphere, and has greatly improved the short-period forecasts, especially those for aviation." Many meteorologists believe that variations of weather occur in a more or less rhythmical way.

LOWEST AND HIGHEST TEMPERATURES

The lowest temperature on earth, $-130°F.$, is reckoned to exist in the interior of Greenland. The lowest actually recorded was $-94°F.$ at Verkhoyansk, in Siberia. In Whale Bay, in the Antarctic, $-47.25°F.$ was recorded in August. The greatest heat ever recorded up to 1935 was $133°F.$, in Death Valley, South California, which is 179 feet below sea-level. The thermometer has risen to only one degree less in the interior of New South Wales. Temperatures of up to $125.5°F.$ prevail in the desert of Arizona and on the frontier between Baluchistan and India.

TEMPERATURE EXTREMES IN BRITAIN

The highest temperature experienced in recent times in Britain was $100°F.$ in the shade four feet above the ground. This was recorded on July 15, 1881, at Salisbury, and on August 9, 1911, at Greenwich. The lowest temperature was $-23°F.$, recorded on December 4, 1879, at Blackadder, Berwickshire.

DRIEST AND WETTEST PLACES

The driest place on earth is Khartoum, the capital of the Anglo-Egyptian Sudan, with an average humidity of only twenty-eight per cent, while the wettest place is probably the foot of the Cameroon Mountain, West Africa, with a constant monthly average of ninety-three per cent. The cloudiest place is the Russian Kola Peninsula, where nine-tenths of the sky is constantly clouded over. Over the town of Calama, in Chile, in $22°S.$ lat., the sky is always unclouded, for which reason a special solar observatory was erected there in 1934.

The largest number of rainy days, 336 yearly on an average, is returned by the Jaluit Islands in the Marshalls, while at Wadi Halfa, on the Nile, there is often not a drop of rain for ten years. On one of the Cape Verde Islands it only rains once in six years. The rainiest spot is said to be Waialeale, in Hawaii, 5,525 feet above sea-level, with an annual mean rainfall of over 580 inches. This mountain lies in the course of the wet subtropical trade winds; its winding ravines catch the sea breezes, although only eleven and a quarter miles to the east a desert climate prevails. What is called the day of the Big Rain was January 14, 1930, when rain fell over practically the whole of the United States and Canada, a most unusual occurrence. The heaviest rainfall in twenty-four hours was measured at Baguio, in the Philippines, where forty-six inches were registered. Previously Sura, in the Fiji Islands, had held the record with twenty-six inches.

ABNORMAL WINTERS AND SUMMERS

From the 3rd century A.D. comes a report of a sheet of ice on the Nile. In 401 and 673 the Black Sea was frozen over, and the Lake of Constance eleven times between 1277 and 1870. In the winter of 1306 trade was carried on by means of wheeled traffic between Estonia and Gothland, by way of the Aaland Islands. In 1423-24 the Baltic Sea froze over. In 1607-08 the whole of Europe, including Spain and Italy, was covered with a vast mantle of snow, and skating was still possible at Danzig on May 15.

In 1740, the year of Frederick the Great's accession, the thermometer is said to have recorded −65°F. in Berlin. People's noses were frostbitten, the dead could not be buried, and the River Havel was still covered with ice in April. Vine growing in Brandenburg was ruined. It was the longest winter known, for it froze continuously from October 24, 1739, to June 13, 1740. In 1833 it snowed in Lower Egypt, and at the beginning of October, 1936, in Sicily, ruining the vintage.

St. Gregory of Tours writes of the mild winter of A.D. 584, when roses in France bloomed in January. In January, 1301, the trees in Germany burst into leaf. In 1186 the fruit trees blossomed in January, and the apple trees were already bearing small fruit in February. Harvest came at the end of May, and in August the grapes were pressed. In 1624 and 1720 the cherry trees were in bloom almost the whole winter through. The winter of 1822-23 was extraordinarily mild throughout Europe, and even in Siberia it only rained instead of snowing. The year 1930 was the first in Berlin for 150 years in which the freezing point had not been reached by December 1.

The French chroniclers relate that in A.D. 627 all the wells gave out, and in 933 the trees in the fields caught fire from the heat. In 1303 the Rhine, Danube and Seine were passable on foot. Nearly all the cattle died of drought in 1603, and meat, it is said, was cooked in the sun in 1705. From June, 1838, to September, 1839, not a drop of rain fell in Southern Europe, and in 1479 and 1718 no rain fell between April and October. In 1911 the thermometer rose to over 86°F., fissures a yard deep appeared in the earth's surface, and even the oil paintings in the Nuremberg gallery began to crack. During 1936 the prairie provinces of Canada suffered terribly from lack of rain, which did not fall in Saskatchewan till July.

MOST BENEFICIAL TEMPERATURE

The most beneficial temperature is that which puts least strain on the heat-equalizing apparatus of the human skin. Dr. Ellsworth Huntington, who investigated 2,500 workers on the effect of climate and weather on efficiency, found that for most mental workers 55°F. was best, and for physical workers between 55° and 65°. April and October were maximum months for output.

HEAT RECEIVED FROM THE SUN

The total radiation of the sun, compared with the amount received by the earth, is as seventy-four years to a second. The other planets and moons receive in the aggregate only about ten times as much as the earth, and the rest is lost in space.

Only forty per cent of the sun's rays that approach the earth ever reach its surface; twenty per cent is absorbed in the atmosphere, which it warms, and the other forty per cent is immediately reflected by the air strata, without imparting any of its heat to the atmosphere. Of the forty per cent that reaches the earth, about twenty-five per cent is utilized for the evaporation of water, which warms the atmosphere still further and descends in the form of rain. If the heat of the sun, which is believed to be some 10,000°F., were reduced by ten per cent, the temperate zone would freeze.

SHARING THE SUNSHINE

London has an average of 1,309 hours of sunshine every year, while Hastings enjoys 500 hours more. Forty million tons of coal, costing £85,000,000, are consumed in British domestic grates every year. They give out 4,000,000 tons of smoke, which shut off a great deal of sunshine. Berlin uses so much coal that it only gets forty per cent of the sunlight to which its climate and situation entitle it. In New York, 275 days in the year are too cold, too hot, or too wet, while in Athens the sky is only covered by clouds on twenty-five days in the year.

The annual amount of sunshine in Europe varies between 900 hours at Fort Augustus, Scotland, and 2,900 hours in Madrid. The sun shines on an average about three hours a day in Scotland, four and a half to five and a half hours in Germany, five to seven hours in Austria, seven to eight hours in Spain, and eight and a half hours in Cairo. The lowest sunshine figures are for the west coast of Norway, where double as much rain falls as in Central Europe.

SUNLIGHT DESTROYS GERMS

The modern practical appreciation of sunlight is really the resurrection of a very old and legitimate belief. Solaria, or sun-rooms, were architectural features of ancient Rome, where public buildings were set apart for the open-air treatment of gout, insomnia, nervous diseases and skin troubles. The Indians of Central America believed in the effectiveness of the sun's rays in such ailments as rheumatism and tuberculosis, and the Spanish colonists were not slow to appreciate what the " heathen " taught them.

" The sun's rays are Nature's best weapons to destroy germs," says Dr. Randle C Rosenberger. " Most germs are not able to stand the direct action of the sun's rays for more than a few minutes." Sunlight helps to build up a resistance against cold, pneumonia and consumption, and prevents and cures rickets. Sir Bruce Bruce-Porter states that there is one slum area in London where there is no rickets because the people were so poor that their children had hardly any clothes. This meant that the sunlight got through to their skins. It is estimated that, on the average, a town has at least twenty per cent less sunshine than the open country. After the prohibition of soft, and therefore smoky, coal in New York, there was a marked decline of rickets in children; the sun was able to carry on its beneficent work as a healer.

" Excessive exposure to light rays," according to Dr. Watson Smith, " whether natural or artificial, entail fatigue and exhaustion, but it also produces early degeneration of the skin, such as may be seen in sailors. The external ears, the lower half of the face, and the backs of the hands degenerate so as to exhibit a skin become thin, atrophied, and pigmented, upon which are grafted warty growths which, later, may assume a malignant form. Because of immediate and remote risk of over-radiation, caution should be advised in the use of the sun bath and of artificial light baths. But, properly and prudently used, sunlight is of inestimable value." The first clinic for the treatment of surgical tuberculosis was opened in 1903, in Leysin, Switzerland, by Dr. A. Rollier, who avows that sunlight, by absorption in the blood, becomes a reservoir of circulating energy, reinforcing the defensive powers of the body. Living on high mountains has a marked effect for good on some kinds of anæmia. It causes a rapid increase in the number of red blood corpuscles because there is less filtration of the sun's rays by the atmosphere.

FATHER NEPTUNE'S KINGDOM

WATER covers nearly three-quarters of the surface of the globe. The old Babylonian idea of the world as a mountain in the middle of an ocean was not altogether fantastic, for the oceans actually form a continuous sheet of water surrounding the four great land masses.

Of this sheet of water, over 140,000,000 square miles in total area, forty-three per cent lies in the Northern Hemisphere, where it covers sixty-one per cent of the surface. The other fifty-seven per cent is in the Southern Hemisphere, where the total land area amounts to less than one-fifth of the surface.

ROBBING THE SEA OF WATER

The oceans form the world's reservoir. Every year evaporation robs the sea of a layer of water thirteen feet nine inches thick. Taking the aggregate area of sea surface at the round figure of 140,000,000 square miles (actually it is rather more), this means that the volume of water evaporated annually is over 53,000 billion cubic feet. A cubic foot of water weighs sixty-two and a half pounds, so the seas lose annually 1,500 billion tons of water through the power of the sun's heat. This loss is compensated by rainfall and the inflow of rivers.

Vast reserves of water remain locked up as ice in the Arctic and Antarctic regions. A sudden and complete thaw in these regions would submerge the entire land surface with the exception of a few of the highest mountain peaks. As it is, only an infinitesimal fraction of this ice becomes water each year, chiefly through the dissolution of icebergs.

GREATEST ICEBERG FACTORY

The greatest iceberg factory in the world is Greenland, from whose vast frozen cap, in some places 6,000 feet thick and covering perhaps 400,000 square miles—the exact area is unknown—it is estimated that 1,000,000,000 tons are discharged into the sea every twelve months. Labrador and Spitzbergen are also fruitful sources of supply. Great or small portions break away as the glaciers gradually reach the water, some to float for a time and melt, others gradually to drift as floating menaces to ships traversing the traffic lanes of the Grand Banks off Newfoundland.

On an average about 420 icebergs drift southward, some as far as 2,000 miles, but in 1929 over 1,300 were officially reported. Even this was fewer than in 1914, when in July there were estimated to be 2,000 bergs in the Labrador current. The largest berg ever seen was about 65 feet high and some 1,700 feet long; its weight must have been several millions of tons. Until the institution of the International Ice Patrol, following the loss of the *Titanic,* in 1912, almost every year ships mysteriously disappeared, in all probability due to collision with ice.

Although many attempts have been made to break up icebergs by gunfire and exploding mines, they have always ended in failure. On one occasion five powerful mines were exploded, resulting in a hole fifteen feet deep and twenty feet long, but the berg remained in being much as before minus the loss of a few tons' weight. A charge of 210 lbs. of trinitrotoluene (T.N.T.) was placed on another berg and fired by electricity. It made practically no impression on the vast, floating mountain. A berg floats with about seven-eighths of its bulk below water, but once it reaches the warm waters of the Gulf Stream it speedily disintegrates. It then becomes a growler, and the gradual disappearance of the mass below the surface renders it liable to capsize without warning.

WILL THE OCEANS DRY UP?

The possibility of the oceans drying up suddenly is remote. It is as unlikely that the seas would be by some supernatural force sucked heavenward as that the earth should open and swallow the water or convert it into steam. A gradual diminution of the world's supply of water seems more possible.

It has been suggested that some of the water taken from the seas by evaporation is never returned, but passes away into space. Other people have worried lest the enormous weight of the ocean should break through the ocean bed. An American astrophysicist has endeavoured to prove that infiltration of the sea into the interior of the earth, due to the formation of crystals which need water for their structure and to the wearing away of watertight rocks on the sea bed, is taking place to such an extent that the level of the ocean must be falling nearly ten inches a year.

If this theory be correct, then all the oceans will be dry within 12,000 years. But an Austrian scientist declares even one three-hundredth of such a fall to be quite out of the question, as no loss of water from the earth's store can be traced over the past 10,000 years.

THE WORLD'S OCEANS AND SEAS

GEOGRAPHERS recognize three major divisions of the world's water surface: the Pacific, the Atlantic, and the Indian Oceans. The name ocean is also given to the stretches of water surrounding the North Pole and the continent of Antarctica; while some map makers prefer to regard the continuous belt of water formed by the southern portions of the Pacific, Atlantic, and Indian Oceans as a separate ocean, which they name the Southern or Great Southern.

THE MIGHTY PACIFIC

Of the three great oceanic divisions the Pacific is the largest and the deepest. It extends from the Bering Strait in the north to Antarctica in the south, a distance of 8,350 nautical miles, or 9,630

land miles. East to west it is bounded on the one hand by North and
South America, on the other by Asia and Australia. Between Panama
in Central America, and Mindanao in the Philippine Islands, lie 9,300
nautical miles (nearly 10,600 land miles) of water unbroken by any
land.

The average depth of the Pacific is 2,342 fathoms, or just over
14,000 feet. East of the meridian 150° W. the depth is remarkably
uniform, but the western half of the ocean contains numerous " deeps "
or " trenches." In these are found the greatest depths of water ever
plumbed.

Off the coast of South America, and running roughly parallel with
it are four small deeps, respectively 18,592, 19,251, 22,529, and 25,048
feet in depth. But these are comparatively shallow compared with the
enormous depths which have been discovered in the western Pacific.

In 1927 the German cruiser *Emden* made a sounding of 35,300
feet east of Mindanao, in the Philippines. If Mount Everest, the world's
highest mountain, were placed in this submarine depression, which is
known as the Philippine trench, and Ben Nevis, the highest peak in
Britain, were placed on top of Everest, the water would still be nearly
2,000 feet deep. H.M.S. *Penguin*, exploring what is known as the
Kermadec-Tonga trench, north-east of New Zealand, dropped the line
to 30,879 feet, while the United States cable ship, *Nero*, found south-east
of Guam a depth of 31,774 feet.

These deeps form in extent an insignificant fraction of the total area
of this mighty ocean. Only two-hundredths of the Pacific has a greater
depth than 23,000 feet, but more than a quarter of it is between 16,500
and 20,000 feet deep. An interesting and unique feature of the deepest
trenches is that they are almost all found on the outer side (that is, facing
the open ocean) of chains of volcanic islands.

OCEAN OF EXQUISITE COLOURS

The traveller, voyaging across the Indian Ocean from South Africa
to India, will frequently be rewarded by the most exquisite play of light
upon the water, resulting in a range of colours the beauty of which
beggars description. It is another story when the monsoon winds lash
the ocean into fury and pile up enormous and hungry-looking waves.

This ocean has an average depth of 2,167 fathoms, or almost exactly
13,000 feet. This is twenty fathoms (120 feet) more than the average
depth of the Atlantic. None of the other stretches of water on the globe
has anything approaching these depths. The Arctic, with an average
depth of just under 4,000 feet, is shallower on the whole than the
Mediterranean, which averages about 700 feet more.

The shallowest of the seas is the Persian Gulf, which averages only
eighty-four feet. The Baltic is rather more than double this, being about
twelve feet shallower than the English Channel and the Irish Sea, which
average 192 feet. Besides these last, the North Sea, with an average of
312 feet, seems comparatively deep.

MOUNTAINS BENEATH THE WAVES

The beds of the oceans have their mountains and valleys, their hills and plateaux, as have the continents. Where the mountain ranges are higher than the ocean depth we get islands. Thus the Galapagos Islands off Ecuador are the peaks of a submarine ridge which runs south-west from the Isthmus of Panama. Westward from the coast of Chile there runs another ridge, which unites with the first, the range then turning south and running to the Antarctic. The mass of islands in the western Pacific affords clear evidence of numerous mountain ranges beneath the waves.

In the North Atlantic, a ridge, some 1,300 feet below the surface, links Scotland with Iceland by way of the Faeroes, and Iceland with Greenland. How this ridge must tower above the surrounding ocean bed is shown by the fact that depths exceeding 9,500 feet are numerous off the coast of Norway, while Fridtjof Nansen made a sounding of 12,628 feet in the Arctic Ocean. In 1937 Soviet scientists measured a depth of 14,750 feet at the North Pole.

The tiny island of Rockall, which lies nearly 500 miles west of the Hebrides in Scotland, marks the track of another submarine ridge, which runs south-west from the Faeroes. A third runs in a roughly parallel direction from Iceland. The famous Grand Banks of Newfoundland, site of one of the world's greatest fisheries, are less than 700 feet beneath the surface. Between the Banks and Iceland is what has been named the Telegraph Plateau, because of the number of transatlantic submarine cables which it carries. Though called a plateau, this area of the ocean bed shows depths varying from 1,500 to over 13,000 feet.

SUBMARINE RANGE 7,000 MILES LONG

All the submarine ranges in the North Atlantic are relatively insignificant when compared with the immense central Atlantic rise. This prodigious mountain range, which begins south of the Telegraph Plateau, continues its majestic way south until it reaches Bouvet Island in the South Polar Regions, where it turns east towards the Indian Ocean. Its position along the greater portion of its length of approximately 7,000 miles is clearly indicated by the islands of the Azores, the islets of St. Paul's Rocks, which lie some 540 miles east of South America and just north of the Equator, and the lonely outposts of Ascension and Tristan da Cunha.

The range lies generally between 6,500 and 10,000 feet below the level of the ocean with, on either side of it, valleys 16,000 to 20,000 feet below sea-level. In the Azores the range rises to 7,613 feet above sea-level, in Tristan da Cunha to 7,640 feet. Although the channels which separate the three islands of the Tristan da Cunha group are only twenty miles and ten miles broad respectively, they reach in places a depth of 6,000 feet.

The central Atlantic rise, having turned eastward at latitude 50°S., runs across the Indian Ocean to meet a submarine plateau in the Antarctic, near Kaiser Wilhelm Land. Its route can be plotted by the Crozet Islands and the island of Kerguelen. The island of Madagascar is linked with Africa by a submarine ridge nearly 9,000 feet below sea-level; the Laccadive and Maldive Islands, and most of the islands of the Chagos Archipelago are projections from another ridge, while the Seychelles rise from another.

A most remarkable feature of the bed of the Indian Ocean is found in the parallel ridges and valleys west of Sumatra and south of Java. First comes a valley 4,800 feet deep between Sumatra and the Mentawei Islands, and 9,000 to 12,000 feet deep off Java. This is followed by a ridge exactly parallel with it, and then by a second valley, also strictly parallel, but 15,000 feet deep off Sumatra and 21,000 feet deep off Java.

OCEAN TEMPERATURES

The surface of the sea is never still; the water is both on the move and rising and falling. Consequently its temperature varies little throughout the twenty-four hours; less than a degree in tropical seas, and less than a quarter of a degree in cool, temperate climes. During the day time it may be anything up to a degree cooler than the air above it; during the night it remains a degree to a degree and a half warmer.

The heat of sea water is derived almost entirely from the sun, though some small amount of it must come from the interior of the earth. What proportion is due to this latter source has not been determined, nor is it yet known to what depth the sun's rays penetrate. One observation showed that on a bright, sunny day, without wind, the temperature of the water sixty-five feet below the surface of the Mediterranean Sea rose about one-sixth of a degree Fahrenheit.

Countless measurements of ocean temperatures have been taken, at the surface and down to depths of over 12,000 feet. At the Equator, in mid-Atlantic, the temperature on the surface averages 79.2°F.; at a depth of 300 feet it has dropped to 63°F., at 3,000 feet to about 40°F. But whereas in the first 3,000 feet the temperature falls 30°, in the following 9,000 feet it drops only 5°.

The temperature of the water does not everywhere decrease with depth; in the Arctic and Antarctic it increases. The surface water, chilled by the ice and the intense cold of the overlying air, is from two and a half to three and a half degrees cooler than that found lower down. At the North Pole, according to the observations of the Soviet expedition of 1937, a warm layer of water from the Atlantic is found at depths between 825 and 1,975 feet. Below the latter level the temperature falls gradually until a depth between 8,250 and 9,850 feet is reached, after which it rises again slightly.

Ocean temperatures at a depth of 12,000 feet vary little in different latitudes. At the Equator the average temperature is about 35°F.; at 60°S. it is approximately 31.3°F., though on the surface there is a difference of 50° between these latitudes.

HOTTEST SEA WATER

The hottest sea water in the world is found in summer in the Persian Gulf, where the temperature reaches 96°F. The Red Sea is almost equally hot, 94°F. being recorded. The Bay of Bengal and the equatorial belt of the Indian Ocean rise in May—just before the breaking of the monsoon—to between 84°F. and 86°F., while the hottest parts of the Indian Ocean and of the western Pacific show mean annual temperatures of 82° to 84°F. In these districts 90°F. is frequently recorded.

The range of temperature here is slight, but the seas north-east of Japan have been known to be as cold as 27°F., and as hot as 83°F. This extreme range, the greatest yet recorded, is due to the successive advance and retreat of cold and warm currents.

A curious situation is often found in the North Sea where, after a storm, in which the water has been thoroughly churned up, the temperature will be the same from surface to bed. In very deep, enclosed seas it is usual to find no change in temperature below the level of the rim which separates the basin of the sea from the open ocean. In the Central American Sea there is a huge depression called the Bartlett Deep, which is over 20,000 feet deep. But the temperature of the water in this deep is nowhere lower than that of the ocean bed beyond the sea, though that bed is less than 6,000 feet below sea-level.

Because of the salt which it contains, sea water freezes at a lower temperature than fresh. The more salt it contains, the lower the temperature at which it will freeze. What may be termed averagely salt water freezes at 28.6°F., but unless it is in actual contact with snow or ice, sea water can fall quite considerably below this temperature without freezing.

When sea water freezes, part of the salt is driven out, though as a rule from one-third to a half remains in the ice, which is consequently not fit for drinking purposes. Generally the expelled salt sinks to the water below the ice, but in polar regions it may sometimes be seen as crystals on the surface of the ice.

HOW SALT IS THE SEA?

Sea water is a very complex mixture. Of the ninety known elements, more than one-third have been found in solution in the sea. Among these latter are silver and gold, but in such minute proportions that any hope of making a fortune by recovery of the precious metals from the sea is out of the question.

What may be termed average sea water contains 35 parts per 1,000 of salts. The great bulk of this is common salt, or sodium chloride, which accounts for over 27 parts. There are nearly 4 parts of magnesium chloride; magnesium sulphate (Epsom salts) and gypsum, or calcium sulphate, make up another three parts, the remaining part being composed of potassium sulphate, calcium carbonate and magnesium bromide.

The Atlantic is the saltiest ocean, the Indian Ocean coming next. In each of the three oceans the most saline belts are in the tropics. The equatorial belt is less salt, while the polar regions are least salt of all.

Some of the enclosed seas are more salt than the open ocean, others are less. Among the former are the Persian Gulf, the Red Sea, and the Mediterranean; among the latter the North Sea and the Baltic. This last at its eastern and northern extremities, the Gulfs of Finland and Bothnia, consists of virtually fresh water.

MAKING THE OCEAN FIT TO DRINK

Death from thirst while surrounded by water is not unknown even to modern navigators. Recently, long research at the National Physical Laboratory, Middlesex, ended in the triumphant discovery that by a relatively simple process the salts could be extracted from sea water.

A certain amber is made synthetically from formalin and formic acid. Of this amber, tubes are constructed. From anilin, in combination with formalin, a synthetic resin is prepared. Of this a second set of tubes is manufactured. The salt water which is to be made fresh is forced to flow first through a set of amber tubes. These extract the metals and alkalis present, and the water is then passed through the resin tubes, which rob the water of its acids.

COLOUR OF THE SEA

To speak of the " deep blue sea " is literally correct, though from the coast the water rarely appears this shade. When viewed from above, shallow water is always green, this colour being due as a rule to sand in suspension in the water. In mid-ocean patches of green are due to swarms of plankton, the minute organisms which form the chief food of smaller fishes.

The purest blue is to be found in the North Atlantic, the Sargasso Sea, and tropical and sub-tropical areas of the Pacific and Indian Oceans. Generally speaking, the farther north one goes from the Equator the greener the water is.

The North Sea is almost pure green, though under a blanket of cloud it will appear dirty grey. The blue of the Mediterranean is famous, but actually the western half is rather green, the pure blue being observed only in the eastern basin.

There is a close relationship between the colour and the transparency of sea water. The bluer it is the more transparent it tends to be. To test the transparency, disks painted white are dropped into the water and allowed to sink out of sight.

The greatest recorded transparency is that of the Sargasso Sea, where a disk six feet ten and a half inches in diameter remained visible to a depth of 216 feet. In the North Sea, on the other hand, the disk disappears from sight in calm weather at between 60 and 100 feet, in rough at 30 feet.

Tests have also been made to see how far below the surface light penetrates. One experiment in the Mediterranean traced the effect of sunlight only down to 1,200 feet, but in mid-Atlantic photographic plates have turned dark at nearly 5,000 feet. When Dr. W. Beebe descended in his bathysphere 3,028 feet below the surface he was in total darkness after 2,000 feet. This was at a spot six miles off the coast of Bermuda.

WAVES AND TIDES

WHENEVER moving air in the form of a gust of wind strikes a calm sheet of water it sets the surface of that water in motion. Innumerable wavelets appear, their crests running transversely to the direction of the wind and their lengths pressing forward, or appearing to press forward, in response to the pressure of the wind.

Actually the water to leeward of each wavelet is pushing back against that wavelet, so that on the surface there is a constant backward and forward movement. This continues until either the wind drops or it becomes steady and strong enough to carry the whole surface forward.

WAVES OF THE OCEAN

It is only on the open ocean that one can see waves at their full stature. No lake on earth is large enough to allow of full growth, but across the vast spaces of the Pacific, the Atlantic or the Indian Ocean, the wind, blowing with tremendous force and unhindered constancy, causes the waves to pile up to huge size and to travel in enormously long crests.

Many exaggerated estimates have been given of the height of waves, while a popular turn of phrase describes some as "mountain high." This exaggeration is due largely to the fact that during gales and squalls the waves follow fast after each other, so that three or four are all that can be seen from a ship, and that flying spray and rain haze the atmosphere and give an impression of great size.

Actually, in a strong gale or heavy swell, the height of the waves does not usually exceed forty and fifty feet, though considerably greater heights have been observed. In December, 1922, the liner *Majestic* recorded waves more than seventy feet high during a storm in the North Atlantic.

Admiral Robert Fitzroy experienced waves sixty feet high during a heavy gale in the Atlantic not far from the Bay of Biscay. "I never saw such seas before," he notes, "and have never seen any equal to them since, either off Cape Horn or the Cape of Good Hope, during two circumnavigations and many years of foreign service." As a general rule the height of waves in a gale is ten feet to eighteen feet, in a strong gale eighteen feet to twenty-eight feet, in a hurricane a little over twenty-eight feet. The sixty-foot high crest cited by Fitzroy is seldom reached other than as the consequence of a tidal wave.

William Scoresby, far-famed as an Arctic explorer, gave the maximum height of Atlantic waves as forty-three feet from trough (hollow) to crest. He calculated that waves thirty feet high are 600 feet from crest to crest. During the *Challenger* Expedition of 1872-76, waves twenty-two feet high and 480 feet long were observed.

Abnormal waves are encountered on occasion. In the spring of 1928 the *Leviathan* was struck by a wave which wrecked the searchlight on the foremast, eighty-five feet above the water line, smashed four lifeboats and did other damage. Waves were calculated by the commander of the *Bremen* to have reached a height of sixty feet in a terrific storm in 1929, when the wind attained a force of over 115 miles an hour.

TERRIFIC FORCE OF WAVES

If a wind begins to blow in the same direction as that in which an ocean swell is moving, and exceeds the swell in velocity, it piles the waves up to great height, but the waves formed during a great storm are not usually so high as those created by a gale of only moderate force, but longer duration.

There appears to be little relation between the speed of the wind and that of the waves. Sometimes one group of waves will overtake another; after a succession of storms or squalls several such groups may be racing one after the other across the ocean. During December, 1898, 139 large breakers fell on one shore within forty-five minutes, that is, one every nineteen seconds. Their speed across the ocean was sixty-six and a half miles an hour. In February, 1899, breakers were observed travelling at seventy-eight and a half miles an hour, while speeds exceeding 100 miles an hour have been recorded. Such velocities, however, have been recorded only for a few seconds at a time.

The power of the waves is particularly great on steep coasts. Extremely violent and continuous surf, even in the calmest weather, is to be seen on the coasts of Sumatra, the Cape Verde island of Fogo, and in the Gulf of Benin. Fogo, the name of which means "fire," is an almost circular mass of volcanic rock, 190 square miles in extent, which rises to about 10,000 feet in the active volcano Pico do Cano. The island is exposed to the full force of the north-east trade winds.

A pressure of three and a half tons per square foot as a wave is breaking has been registered in the Atlantic and the North Sea, and a ground-swell roller has been calculated to fall with a pressure of about a ton on every square foot. On the south coast of England, a Martello tower near Hythe, erected as a fortification during the threatened invasion of England by Napoleon I, was split into three giant pieces by a wave, and afterwards completely demolished by a series of batterings by the sea. In 1864, over 300 feet of Wick Harbour breakwater was swept away, despite the fact that it was built of blocks weighing from five to ten tons. Eight years later a mass weighing 1,350 tons was shifted, and in 1873 material weighing 2,600 tons was swept away whole.

INVASION OF THE LAND BY THE SEA

The ravages of coast erosion throughout the world are enormous. While the sea builds up in some places, it tears down in others—a perpetual game of give-and-take in which, over a period of thirty-five years, Great Britain surrendered 6,640 acres and gained 48,000, though it should be added that the latter figure includes reclamation by engineers. The east coast of England is paying heavy toll to the North Sea. Millions of tons of material disappear every year, particularly where the coast is exposed to the full fury of gales.

The " white cliffs " of Dover are gradually being undermined, and a fall of 5,000 tons of chalk is not a rare occurrence. Ancient Dunwich, once the capital of East Anglia, is beneath the waves. " Walls and gates enclosed a king's court, a bishop's palace, a mayoral residence, fifty-two churches, as many windmills, a spacious harbour, and houses to make up such a noted city." Thus John Stow, the chronicler and antiquary, describes the once populous place.

Reculver, in Kent, and Ravenspur, in Yorkshire, where Bolingbroke landed before he overthrew Richard II and became Henry IV, have disappeared. Even rock-bound Cornwall, which boasted 2,400 square miles in the 14th century, is now reduced to 1,357 square miles. Corton, near Lowestoft, is said to have lost 1,000,000 tons of beach in a stormy three days in 1924. A forest is buried under the Wash. Romney Marsh, one of the finest sheep pastures in Great Britain, is in peril of being engulfed. At one point the sea is encroaching at the rate of about fifty feet a year.

According to tradition, the infamous Goodwin Sands, at the entrance to the Straits of Dover, on which many a noble ship has been wrecked, are the remains of an island once the property of Earl Goodwine, the great 11th century statesman. The South Bull, an island in Dublin Bay, is now no more than a spit of sand. It cost Fleetwood, in Lancashire, £60,000 to build a sea wall 1,940 yards long. Selsea is being washed away at the rate of from ten feet to fifteen feet a year. Three centuries ago, the foundations of St. Wilfrid's Monastery and the Saxon cathedral were visible at low water, which is proof of the sea's appetite in the neighbourhood of the headland known as Selsea Bill. Between Brighton and Newhaven the average rate of erosion was calculated to be 3.17 feet per annum over the period 1897-1930. The ruins of the old parish church of Walton-on-Naze, Essex, which was engulfed in 1798, suddenly emerged from the sea in 1928, thanks to an exceptionally low tide.

THE SEA IS NEVER STILL

What keeps the sea perpetually in motion? First and foremost, the tides, the rhythmic ebb and flow of the water on the face of the earth as the result of the gravitational pull of the moon. Generally speaking, twice every twenty-five hours there is at any seaside place a high tide and a low tide. The average interval is twelve hours and twenty-five minutes, though in some places the interval is as little as twelve hours, while in others it may exceed twenty-four hours. Southampton, standing at the head of two narrow channels, has four high tides a day; other places have four low tides.

The range of a tide, that is, the difference between the height of the water at high and low tides, varies from less than two feet in the Mediterranean and some island regions of the Pacific to fifty feet or more in the Bay of Fundy in North America. At the head of this long, narrow bay a range of sixty-two feet has been recorded.

A second important cause of the sea's motion is found in the marine currents, which are of two kinds, surface and depth. The surface currents are created chiefly by wind; they affect the water only down to a depth of 1,000 feet. The depth currents are the result of differences in salinity and temperature.

The most famous surface current in the world is the Gulf Stream, which is the result of the piling up in the Caribbean Sea of water driven westward by the Atlantic trade winds, north and south of the Equator. This water finds an outlet between Florida and the Bahamas, and in the strait flows at a rate of five feet a second.

It is incorrect to speak of the Gulf Stream off the coasts of Europe, because the actual stream ceases off the Newfoundland Banks, but the drift of warmer water from the Gulf Stream, carried eastward by the winds, certainly has a powerful influence on the continent of Europe. It keeps the west coast of Greenland free from ice for nine or ten months of the year, and the south and west coasts of Iceland entirely so. It is the cause of the humid climate of western Scotland, and of the relatively mild climate of west Norway and Spitzbergen.

Many attempts have been made to discover the origin of this great river bounded by an ocean. It was once thought that its source was the Mississippi. Difference in densities of the water, caused by evaporation, may account for the variation in temperature, while trade winds and the sun have also been held responsible. Some scientists even go so far as to say that the importance of the Gulf Stream has been vastly overrated, that it loses itself in the Atlantic and has no influence on the climate of the British Isles. The late Lord Rayleigh, Sir Richard Gregory and Dr. Fridtjof Nansen were of this opinion.

WEALTH FROM THE SEA

A FLASHLIGHT photograph has been passed by the scientists to industry to indicate the possibilities of using the magnesium in the ocean. Magnesium can be made into sheets and bars, into beams and pillars; and cities built of magnesium is the vision science has in mind. Cities gleaming in the sunshine, with every tower and steeple, every roof and house front made from magnesium recovered from the ocean.

From approximately one-two hundred and fiftieth of the ocean's content, so runs an American calculation, there could be extracted nearly

6,000,000 tons of magnesium, 117,000,000 tons of salt, 94,000,000 tons of silver, 35,500,000 tons of sulphuric acid, 3,000,000 tons of gold, and very considerable quantities of bromide and iodine.

CORALS TO WARD OFF EVIL

Among the sea's treasures are corals. It used to be thought that the living creatures became petrified when touched. They are worn in some parts of India as a protection against storms, lightning and ghosts; and in Rome they are hung round children's necks to ward off evil spells. The ancient Gauls adorned their weapons with coral.

Beginning life as little creatures hatched from eggs and at liberty to go here, there and everywhere, most corals soon lose their power of freedom and attach themselves to a colony. Then they begin to build a skeleton with secretions of lime. More polyps form, and gradually the whole mass may become a vast collection such as the Great Barrier Reef, off the north-eastern coast of Australia, which is over 1,000 miles long and varies from ten feet to ninety miles in breadth.

Corals take many shapes, some resembling fans, others gnarled trees, organ pipes, stags' horns, and the underside of a mushroom. The species most sought after for ornamental purposes live mainly in the Mediterranean.

PEARLS OF GREAT PRICE

Many of the finest pearls are found near the Bahrein Islands, in the Persian Gulf, though beautiful specimens are recovered in the Torres Straits, between Australia and New Guinea, the Pearl and Hermes reefs in the Pacific, so called because two British ships of that name went aground on them in 1822, the Spice Islands, Ceylon and elsewhere. It being difficult to trace the existence of a pearl in a fresh oyster, it is usual to allow the animal to decompose before an attempt is made at discovery.

The iridescence for which the gem is noted, and which alone makes it valuable, is no more than skin deep. If the tiny wrinkles and folds, spaced at about one fifty-thousandth of an inch apart, which cause the effect, are removed, nothing remains but limestone. Benvenuto Cellini, the Italian goldsmith and sculptor, who lived in the 16th century, avowed that " Pearls are not gems but fishes' homes, which in the course of time must lose their lustre."

In ancient Rome, pearls first became known through the victory of Pompey over Mithradates VI, in the 1st century B.C. Walls were inlaid with pearls. The Servilia pearl, given by Cæsar to Brutus's mother, was worth over £35,000 in present-day money. No less than £64,000 was given for a pearl by the Shah of Persia in 1633. Nine pearls grown together and forming a perfect cross were found off Roeburn, Western Australia, in 1874. Of world fame are the half-black pearls in the treasury at Munich, and the pearl necklace which Anne of Austria brought with her to France as a dowry and which Louis XV gave to Marie Antoinette.

A pearl as big as a plum was worn by Mary of Modena, wife of Charles II, in her hat. In the Green Vault at Dresden are four necklaces of 177 Saxon and 218 Oriental pearls, and in the museum at Arles, in France, there is a large, oval, gold-coloured pearl. A pearl necklace, numbering 145 specimens, once owned by Mme A. Thiers, wife of a former President of the French Republic, was sold for £140,000 in 1924.

Artificial pearls were known even in antiquity. In pre-Mycenæan times they were made by melting together lime, magnesium and carbonic acid and colouring the product. Another form of artificial pearl was invented by Jacquin, in 1680, and has since become very popular. Japanese pearls are made out of the scales of the ketei fish, the so-called "essence d'Orient." To produce a pound of pearl essence costs the lives of 20,000 of these lovely fishes.

INLAND SEAS AND LAKES

THE greatest inland sea in the world is the Caspian, which covers an area of approximately 170,000 square miles, or rather more than that of the Baltic. Originally it was far larger, for it was united with the Sea of Aral (26,000 square miles), and filled the whole of the great depression between these two seas. In those days the level of its surface was approximately that of the present level of the Black Sea. To-day the Caspian has shrunk to the deepest part of the depression, and its surface is eighty-five feet below the level of that of the Black Sea.

The largest freshwater lake in the world is Lake Superior, in North America, which has an area of 31,810 square miles. This is considerably larger than Lake Victoria, in Africa, though this is over 26,000 square miles in extent.

HEIGHTS AND DEPTHS OF LAKES

What is believed to be the world's highest lake was sighted by the British airmen who flew over Mount Everest in 1933. This stretch of water has not yet been explored, and is in any case very small. The highest lake of considerable size is Lake Titicaca, in South America, which is 12,500 feet above sea-level, and in addition the largest lake in the continent.

The Yellowstone Lake in the United States is 7,741 feet above sea-level, Lake Victoria is 3,720, and Lake Superior 601 feet. On the other hand, the Sea of Galilee is 682 feet, and the Dead Sea 1,292 feet below sea-level.

The deepest lake is Lake Baikal, in Siberia, which has an average depth of nearly 2,300 feet. In places this depth is doubled, and one sounding of only just under 5,000 feet has been taken. Lake Tanganyika, in Africa, which has also the distinction of being the world's longest freshwater lake (450 miles), comes next. It is in places over 4,700 feet deep. As the surface is 2,536 feet above sea-level, the floor is at the deepest 2,172 feet below it.

Europe's largest lake, Ladoga, which forms part of the boundary between Russia and Finland, is 7,000 square miles in extent, but being comparatively shallow—on an average 250 to 350 feet, with a greatest depth of 730 feet—it contains, for its size, far less water than many other lakes. It is remarkable in being supplied by seventy rivers.

GREAT RIVERS OF THE WORLD

THE longest river system in the world is the Missouri-Mississippi, though some half-dozen other rivers, including the Amazon, the Nile, and the Congo, exceed in length the Missouri, and more than a dozen the Mississippi.

The Missouri is 2,950 miles long, the Mississippi 1,250 miles, giving the system a total length of 4,200 miles. The Amazon and the Nile are each approximately 4,000 miles in length, the Congo in Africa, the Yangtze, the Lena, and the Amur in Asia, approximately 3,000.

AMAZON'S HUGE BASIN

The Missouri-Mississippi drains an area of nearly 1,250,000 square miles, or rather more than a third of the United States. This is less than half the size of the Amazon basin. That river, with its numerous tributaries, drains an area of 2,722,000 square miles, and bears to the sea a greater volume of water than any other.

Ocean-going steamers can penetrate 2,300 miles up the Amazon; small steamers can go nearly 500 miles farther. The average depth of the river is 120 feet, and the current flows at an average speed of three miles an hour. Inland, the river varies from one to six miles in breadth, though during the rainy season it overflows its banks in many places and becomes, as it were, a gigantic reservoir up to 500 miles broad.

At its mouth the Amazon is over 200 miles broad. The last 100 miles of its course is full of low islands and sandbanks. The Mississippi is as narrow at its mouth as the Amazon is wide. Over the latter part of its course it decreases in width, until at the head of its delta it is only 800 yards wide.

MOTHER NILE

Perhaps the most famous of all rivers, the Nile is, according to one estimate, the second longest in the world. It has the longest of all basins, 2,450 miles, but a smaller drainage area than that of the Congo.

The source of the Nile was disputed from antiquity right down to the 19th century. The Nile proper emerges from Lake Victoria, whence it follows a course of 3,473 miles to the Mediterranean. But Lake Victoria has itself to be fed by rivers, and modern explorers have traced the source of the Nile back via the Kagera, the most important feeder of Lake Victoria, to the three streams which unite to form the Kagera, the Nyavarongo, Akanyaru, and Ruvuvu, and the still lesser mountain streams which unite to form each of these three.

In former days most remarkable stories were circulated concerning the origin of the Nile. Perhaps the strangest of these was originated by Juba II, King of Mauretania, in North-West Africa, during the lifetime of Christ. He made the Nile rise in a lake in his kingdom not far from the Atlantic, flow underground for many miles to another lake farther east in Mauretania, dive underground again and continue a subterranean course for twenty days' journey until it rose to the surface again in the borders of Abyssinia.

Out of this story probably arose the theory, widely believed by Arab writers of the 12th and 13th centuries, that the Nile and the Niger had a common origin in a great inland lake. This theory persisted until the beginning of the 19th century. The problem of the source of the Nile was solved by J. H. Speke in 1862.

RIVERS THAT ALTER THEIR COURSES

The Mississippi, noted for its disastrous floods, frequently alters its course in detail on the flat, alluvial plain it has created north of the Gulf of Mexico. In its 1,700 miles of wanderings across this plain of 600 miles long, its banks can never be relied upon to remain stable. The river will cut through a peninsula, turning it into an island, or flooding the area intervening between the old and the new bed; or leave a relatively straight channel to make an extensive and frequently tortuous detour.

The Hwang-ho, or Yellow River, of North China has altered its course several times. In 1852, after having for more than 500 years entered the Yellow Sea south of the highlands of Shantung, it switched 250 miles to the north. One of the names given to it in China is " The Ungovernable." Another, far better known, is " China's Sorrow," an all too well merited appellation, seeing that the Hwang-ho has caused through its floods probably more loss of life and destruction of property than any other river.

MOUTHLESS RIVERS

Some rivers never reach the sea. The most notable example is the Tarim, which drains the vast basin (over 350,000 square miles) of the same name, lying between the Kun Lun and Tien Shan mountains of Central Asia.

The Tarim begins as a strong and vigorous stream. It is joined by a number of tributaries, and not until it has made a course of some 400 miles does it begin to fight a losing battle against the sand dunes of the Gobi Desert. Then it branches off into northern and southern channels, and forms a number of shallow lakes. Emerging from these it recovers for a while, but breaks up again and finally peters out altogether in the shallow and shifting Lop-nor lakes, which lie between the Altyn Tagh and the Kuruk Tagh, in the Gobi Desert. During the last part of its course it flows so slowly that the sediment of its water cannot remain in suspension but falls to the bed.

HIGHEST AND WIDEST WATERFALLS

THE world's highest waterfall is in Venezuela. It was discovered in 1938 by Mr. J. Angel, an American airman, after he had crashed in the Caroni region. It is estimated to be a mile high, and may be the one referred to by Sir Walter Raleigh in his *Discovery of Guiana*, published nearly three and a half centuries ago. "Wee saw it afarre off," he writes, "and it appeared like a white church-tower of exceeding height. There falleth over it a mighty river which toucheth no part of the side of the mountaine, but rusheth over the toppe of it, and falleth to the ground with so terrible a noyse and clamour, as if a thousand great bels were knockt one against another. I think there is not in the world so strange an overfall, nor so wonderfull to behold."

IN INDIA AND BRITISH GUIANA

The Gersoppa or Jog Falls, in the Western Ghats of India, are 830 feet high. They are on the Sharavati River and fall into a pool 132 feet deep. Kaieteur, in British Guiana, discovered by Barrington Brown in 1871, has a height of 822 feet, of which 741 feet is a perpendicular fall, the remainder being cascades. The Kalambo Falls in Northern Rhodesia, near the south-east end of Lake Tanganyika, have a sheer drop of nearly 900 feet. As the volume of this stream is small, the water reaches the bottom only as spray.

Among the widest waterfalls are the world-famed Niagara Falls, which have a length along the crest of 4,000 feet. An island separates the Horseshoe or Canadian Fall, 2,600 feet broad, from the American Fall. The height of the former is 155 feet, of the latter 165 feet.

KNOWN TO THE NATIVES AS "THUNDERING SMOKE"

Rivalling Niagara in magnificence, but utterly different in shape, are the Victoria Falls on the Zambesi River in Central Africa. At a point where the river is 5,580 feet wide, it falls suddenly into a chasm from 256 to 343 feet deep. So narrow is this chasm that the water strikes the opposite wall, which is equally high, sending up a perpetual vast cloud of spray and vapour. Hence the native name for the falls, "Thundering Smoke."

The Yosemite Falls in California, situated in one of the world's most beautiful and picturesque valleys, drop 2,600 feet in three leaps, the longest being a sheer drop of 1,430 feet, while another is 320 feet. The Sutherland Falls in New Zealand are 1,904 feet high; the Gavarnie Falls in the Pyrenees, 1,515 feet.

MOUNTAINS AND CLIMBERS

THE principal elevations of the earth's surface are almost as great as are the greatest depths, namely about five and a half miles. The highest mountain, Mount Everest in the Indian Himalayas, is calculated to be 29,141 feet in height; a sounding made near Mindanao, Philippine Islands, by a survey ship showed a depth of considerably over 35,000 feet.

SHRINKAGE THRUSTS UP MOUNTAIN RANGES

Mountains occur in places where, during the earth's shrinking from a molten state, masses of the cracked crust have been pressed against each other, their edges being bent up in the form of permanent waves, a process that can be observed on a small scale on the banks of a frozen pond. While the central sheets of ice are firm and undisturbed, or at most show radiating cracks, those near the banks pile up; small icebergs form, broken lumps sink under and let the water well through.

In just the same way, disturbed areas have developed round the edges of the continental land masses. Here are situated most of the volcanoes which permit the more fluid interior of the earth to well up. Mountains that date from early geological periods of the earth's history, when the continents had different limits, are now worn down into plateaux or hill ranges, such as the Urals, Salisbury Plain, and the Black Forest region. The Himalayas, the Andes, the Cordilleras and the Alps are much more recent formations.

Lincoln Ellsworth, the Polar explorer and geologist, makes the interesting point that, in the neighbourhood of the North Pole, deep-sea soundings which he took on one of his expeditions indicated an approximate depth of 12,500 feet, which is about the height of the mountains near the South Pole. "It seems," he writes, "almost as if a great fist had struck the earth at the North Pole during a malleable age, denting it in two miles or more and causing a corresponding bulge at the opposite end of the axis." The depth of water at the North Pole is now known to be 14,750 feet; Antarctica has peaks up to 15,000 feet.

WHY THE EARTH QUAKES

As a mass of molten matter solidifies, cracks and fissures naturally appear on the surface. Terrestrial rock is in a state of constant tension, owing to the shrinkage of the globe, this tension giving rise to fractures. The more mobile portions of the earth's crust split up into separate slabs, or rise up in huge lumps, and the consequence of this process is an earthquake or seismic wave. Other causes of earthquakes are, firstly, explosions in the magma, or hot, semi-liquid stratum under the crust, giving rise to volcanic eruptions; and, secondly, the collapse of underground cavities.

EARTHQUAKES BELOW THE SEA

Centres of seismic disturbances are rarely deeper than thirty-seven and a half miles. Submarine earthquakes have given rise to tidal waves some 130 feet high, geological evidences of which may be seen in the Jordan basin and in the huge Tanganyika Rift Valley in East Africa, in the obstruction of river mouths like that of the Zambesi in Africa, and in the damming up of other rivers into lakes.

The oldest volcanic region, according to Professor Haas, of Kiel University, is the Urach district in Württemberg, Germany.

GREAT EXPLOSION OF THE KRAKATOA VOLCANO

Earthquakes are registered almost daily in Hawaii in the North Pacific, and in the Central American state of San Salvador, while in Japan they are even more frequent. Other areas subject to frequent shocks include Italy, Greece, Mexico, Southern Italy, Spain and the Eifel district of Germany. Scotland and the east coast of England are also on the earthquake line, slight tremors being occasionally felt.

The greatest volcanic earthquake and eruption of modern times took place in 1883 on the volcano island of Krakatoa in the Sunda Straits, when masses of lava were hurled to a height of thirty miles. An area as large as France was buried under volcanic ash. Finally the volcano blew out its " plug " of lava, and the explosion was heard 2,250 miles distant. Tidal waves overwhelmed parts of Java and Sumatra, and even in Europe a disturbance of the sea's equilibrium was noticed. In July, 1935, the volcano ejected lava to a height of 6,500 feet.

THE ALPS ARE "MODERN" MOUNTAINS

According to recent research, in the early Tertiary Age, about fifty million years ago, the Alps were merely a modest hill district, their height being the work of subsequent vertical upheavals. Their massive mountain folds have brought rock to the surface from a depth of twelve and a half miles at most.

If the modern continent of Europe was once a sea of islands, as many geologists believe, the Eastern Alps and the southern part of the Western Alps formed the north boundary of the Africa of that time, which would be dammed up on the north side by the deposits of a primitive Mediterranean. Mont Blanc (15,782 feet) and the Jungfrau (13,670 feet) were, according to Professor Collet, the southmost pillars of Europe. Looking thence over the Valais Alps, we are thus seeing the flat expanse of ancient North Africa, crumbled against the bulwark of the Jungfrau.

GERMAN PLATEAU THAT IS MOVING

Geologists have stated that, owing to further upward folding of the Alps, the distance between Munich and the Zugspitze (9,738 feet) has diminished within the historical period; also that the whole of the

Bavarian-Swabian plateau is moving westwards by about ten feet every eighty-five years. This is evidenced by the courses of the rivers Iller, Lech, Isar and Inn, all of which, in their central reaches, describe a decided arc in a westward direction.

WHEN SWITZERLAND WILL BE FLAT

The Alps and other mountains that came into being at the same time have probably reached their full height. It has been calculated that in seven and a half million years the Aar glaciers in Switzerland will be completely worn down and levelled, and that in ten million years the last boulder will be ground to sand. That is, of course, provided that no earth movement occurs to uplift these districts again.

The enormous weight of the mountain masses is another reason for their eventual annihilation. Loads of 4,500,000 pounds rest on each square yard of the earth's floating crust. Owing to this enormous pressure, the earth a few miles below the surface gradually becomes so soft that it is ready to give way under the weight. The reason why mountains do not sink is that they are already deeply embedded; moreover, being of lighter material, they float in the magma rather like icebergs in the sea.

When certain portions of the mountain become heavier owing to superimposed matter, further subsidences to the extent of several hundred yards take place. Former valleys sink in, become filled with water, and form mountain lakes.

On the other hand, millions of tons are washed away annually by rivers and streams, and thus the weight is decreased. For instance, 250 cubic yards are calculated as the amount washed out annually from the Swiss district of the Reuss, on the St. Gothard. The reaction in the marginal districts takes the form of an upward thrust, with slight earth tremors.

MOUNTAINS ON THE MOVE

Dr. Robert Campbell notes that the gradual crumbling of the mountains of Scotland is caused by the freezing of moisture in the cracks of the rock, while sudden changes in temperature are responsible for the process in hot climates. Human activities occasionally bring about extensive falls. Slate quarrying at the base of Plattenbergkopf, in Switzerland, caused great rents in the mountain, with the result that in 1881 the village of Elm was destroyed by a partial collapse. Ten million cubic metres of rock crashed and killed 120 people.

Three of the peaks of Motto Arbino, in the same country, tottered and fell in 1928, destroying some two square miles of pasture and forest, and blocking the Arbedo Valley. In the same year fissures developed in Nantymynydd, in the Rhondda Valley, Wales, and caused a landslide. In 1934 the mountain at Troedrhiwfuwch, also in Wales, twisted and cracked owing to heavy rains following a dry summer. Ten years before one of the Sierra Nevada range, in southern Spain, moved in the direction of the Monachil River, engulfing vineyards and olive gardens. In Savoy, where it is situated, Mount Pourri is called " the rotten mountain " by reason of its unstable qualities.

SOLID ICE RIVERS THAT SCOOP VALLEYS

Glaciers are the ice rivers of the high mountains; the snow, which melts in the sun, freezes again into solid ice. The greatest glacier districts of the Alps are in the Canton Valais, where they cover an area of 221 square miles, or equal in size to the Lake of Geneva. In the Bernese Oberland there are 184 square miles of glaciers, or about the area of Lake Constance.

In the last Ice Age the Rhône Glacier left traces extending as far as Lyons, and the glacier which carved out of the mountain-side the trough now filled by the Lake of Garda stretched into Lombardy far beyond Peschiera. The Aletsch Glacier, which is the largest in the Alps, is fifteen and five-eighths miles long, and the Zemu Glacier in the Himalayas occupies a basin 112 square miles in area.

In a recent year, of 102 Swiss glaciers 79 were retreating, 12 were stationary, and 11 were advancing. Among the receding glaciers were the Gornier, the Rhône, and the Aletsch, the most marked retrogression being the 180 feet of the Tiatscha. Those which showed progression included the Lower Grindelwald, a comparatively small glacier, the Lenta, and the Damma, the last of which advanced 75 feet. In some countries glaciers are enlarging in volume. Those of French Savoy have been moving from 70 feet to 150 feet a year and have gained in volume from 15,000,000 to 250,000,000 cubic feet.

The erratic boulder near Lützen (where Gustavus Adolphus fell in the battle of that name in 1632) was carried to its present position by a glacier of the Ice Age, which must have taken about 200 years to travel from the former Wärmland mountains of Sweden to Saxony.

The vast ice-top of Antarctica is receding at a rate estimated at about one-tenth of a mile a year. According to one authority, if nothing interrupts the process, this means that in 7,000 or 8,000 years the great continent of 5,000,000 square miles will be as habitable as Great Britain.

MADE WILLS BEFORE CROSSING THE ALPS

The Romans had a knowledge of the Alps through Hannibal's invasions and the incursions of the Cimbri tribes; but they, like all the civilized southern peoples, felt only a strange horror of the inhospitable world of towering peaks. Even in the Middle Ages men used to make their wills before crossing the Alps. They believed their heights and ravines to be inhabited by demons.

Conrad Gessner, at the beginning of the 16th century, was the first traveller to enjoy the sublimity of nature in his wanderings through the Alps. In consequence of the wars of religion, which chiefly occupied the following century, no advance was made in either scientific investigation or aesthetic appreciation of mountains; and in 1620 the

Belgian savant, Daniel Eremita, asserted that the inhabitants of the Alps had become as beasts and lost the power of speech. Rousseau, the famous French philosopher and autobiographer, who was born in Geneva, contributed largely to the growth of a taste for nature and the conception of the " noble savage." He admired mountains, and from the Swiss cantonal governments drew many of the ideas for his political philosophy in the *Contrat Social*, published in 1761.

"NOTHING BUT HIDEOUS MOUNTAINS"

The artists who considered flat, bare landscapes "beautiful and cheerful" had no feeling for the charms of Alpine scenery, though exception must be made in the case of Salvator Rosa (1615-73), and of the Dutchman, Jan Hackaert, who in 1656 painted the mountains of Schams, in Switzerland.

In 1705 it was opined that the unhealthy Alpine air made people uncouth and dumb, and Dr. Johnson, in his dictionary of 1755, described a mountain as a " vast protuberance," and a mountaineer as " a savage, a freebooter, or rustick." As late as 1780, J. C. Fussli, in his description of the Engelberg Valley, could write: "What do we find there? Nothing but hideous mountains, bare pastures and no gardens, fields, or fruit trees."

The Alpine world found its first enthusiastic singer in Albrecht von Haller, although his poem *The Alps* (1729) is mostly a description of their human inhabitants, couched in a moralizing and political vein.

ALPINE CLIMBERS OF 1128

Mountain climbing is quite a modern sport, although the first recorded mountain climbers were ten Swiss, who in 1128 are said to have gone over the St. Bernard Pass with the Bishop of Liège. They used alpenstocks and climbing irons. Ascents outside Europe gave the first stimulus. It was not long after C. M. de la Condamine had explored the Cordilleras, in America, and Baron von Humboldt had climbed their highest peak, Chimborazo (20,500 feet), that Dr. Paccard and the Swiss guide, Jacques Balmat, climbed Mont Blanc (15,782 feet) for the first time. This was in 1786, and the scientist, de Saussure, followed in the next year with barometer and thermometer. The first woman to make the ascent of Mont Blanc was Mlle Henriette d'Angeville, in 1838. Henceforth she was nicknamed La Fiancée de Mont Blanc. The youngest mountaineer to accomplish the feat was Miss Pamela Wilkinson, who climbed the peak in 1931, when she was eleven years of age.

Outstanding events in Alpine history are the ascent of the Jungfrau (13,670 feet), 1811; that of the Wetterhorn (12,165 feet) by Sir Alfred Wills, 1854; next year's climb of Monte Rosa (15,217 feet); and Edward Whymper's conquest of the almost perpendicular Matterhorn (14,784 feet), 1865, which closed the main period of Alpine conquest. During it a corps of professional guides had been formed, and the foundation of the London Alpine Club (1857) had been followed by similar institutions in other countries. Between 1890 and 1896, Weilenmann scaled 1,500 peaks, forty of over 13,000 feet.

4,900 FEET UP A SHEER ICE FACE

Later Alpine feats have included the notable ones of G. W. Young, who with various companions ascended the Bruillard ridge of Mont Blanc in 1911, traversed the western ridge of the Grandes Jorasses, and climbed the Mer de Glace face of the Grepon and the west ridge of the Gespaltenhorn. In 1923, Oliver and Courtauld mastered the south face of Mont Blanc, and in 1925 Weizenbeck and Allwein clambered up the northern face of the Dent d'Herens. Three years later, Dr. Dorothy Lloyd made the ascent and descent of the Eiger (13,042 feet) by the formidable Mittellegi Ridge in one day.

In 1935 the 4,900 feet sheer ice face of the Leschaux Glacier on Mont Blanc was scaled by Peters and Meyer, of Munich, and in 1938 a hitherto unscaled face of the Eiger was conquered.

BRITISH PIONEERS OF WINTER SPORTS

Not until a hundred years ago were mountains in winter " discovered " as resorts for health and sports.

Switzerland's first winter patient was Mayr, a manufacturer suffering from asthma who, in 1834, was on his way to Naples but stayed on in St. Moritz, finding that its glorious winter climate had an excellent effect on his complaint. It was only in 1864-5, however, that Johann Badrutt accommodated two patients during the winter at St. Moritz. A year later, Dr. Spengler induced the first consumptives to winter in Davos.

The pioneers of winter sports were the British. The first ice rink at Davos was opened in 1876, and the first toboggan run in 1877, tobogganing being the original winter sport in Switzerland, whereas snowshoeing and skiing were introduced from Norway in 1883. An ice rink measuring some 27,000 square yards was constructed at Davos in 1885, and in the same year the first " Grand National " was held on the artificial toboggan run at St. Moritz, called by the British the Cresta Run.

The first ice hockey match was held in 1888, the first ski race in 1893. In 1901 an Englishman, Bott, introduced the sliding-seat toboggan on the Cresta Run, and in 1904 ski-kjöring (the skier being towed by a pony) was introduced, likewise at St. Moritz.

CONQUESTS AND DEFEATS IN MANY LANDS

MOUNTAIN exploration simultaneously went on in other parts of the world. Ramond, Peake, Russell and others had climbed the main heights in the Pyrenees; D. W. Freshfield, between 1868 and 1888, operated in the Caucasus. In the New Zealand Alps, where Harold

Porter in 1923 and 1925 performed some remarkable feats, the Rev. W. S. Green had climbed successfully in 1882, the same explorer ascending the Selkirks in North America in 1888.

Recent feats in the Canadian Alps include the ascent of the Rockies' highest point, Mount Robson (12,972 feet), in 1913, by A. H. MacCarthy and W. W. Foster, and that of Mount Logan (19,850 feet) by a Canadian-American party led by A. H. MacCarthy in 1935. Aconcagua (22,877 feet) in South America was scaled in 1897 by Zurbriggen. Trapetsia (19,520 feet), in the Pamir Mountains, Central Asia, was climbed by a party of Soviet soldiers in 1935.

AFRICA'S ROCKY GIANTS

The two mightiest mountains in Africa were both conquered in 1889, Kilimanjaro (19,720 feet) in Tanganyika Territory being climbed by Dr. Hans Meyer, and Mount Kenya (17,040 feet) in Kenya Colony by J. E. S. Mackinder. The ascent of the former was also made in 1927 by Miss Sheila Macdonald, of London. The peak of Ruwenzori (16,800 feet), in Uganda Protectorate, was scaled by H. J. Moore in 1900, the Duke of Abruzzi's expedition exploring the range generally in 1906, reaching several heights of over 16,000 feet.

FIFTY TERRIBLE PEAKS IN THE GRIM HIMALAYAS

Asia has claimed the limelight with the Everest expeditions in recent years. Omitting these for the moment, it is notable that the Asiatic heights were extensively surveyed before they were climbed. The Himalayas, 1,563 miles in length, have over fifty summits more than 25,000 feet high, mostly impossible to scale by present methods; only one, Mount Kamet (25,447 feet) has been successfully climbed. Kanchenjunga and K2 are next after Everest, and are both about 28,150 feet. The Schlagintweit brothers were surveying pioneers who in the course of their work reached 22,329 feet on a lesser peak of the Kamet group; I. S. Pocock erected a plane table not far away at 22,700 feet.

In 1849 Sir Joseph Hooker explored the Sikkim valleys of Kanchenjunga and attempted Kangchenjau (22,700 feet) and Pauhunri (23,180 feet). Sir Martin Conway in 1892 explored the Karakoram Himalayas, near the Baltoro Glacier, as did Sir Francis Younghusband, who first crossed the Karakoram Pass. The Duke of Abruzzi's party reached 25,000 feet on the Bride Peak. A. F. Mummery was lost in a final effort to reach the summit of Nangaparbat. D. W. Freshfield first circuited Kanchenjunga, exploring the Nepal side, in 1899. Gurkhas, Sherpas and Bhotias were meanwhile being trained as mountain porters by Brig.-Gen. the Hon. C. G. Bruce.

With this help, Dr. and Mrs. B. Workman made many expeditions in the Karakorams, 1911-12, including climbing a Nun Kun peak of 23,300 feet. W. W. Graham, with Swiss guides, ascended Kabru (24,000 feet).

MOUNT KAMET SCALED

Dr. A. M. Kellas, at the beginning of the present century, made remarkable climbs, including Kangchenjau, Pauhunri and Chomiomo, reaching 23,500 feet on Kamet with H. T. Morshead in 1920. Numerous attempts have been made upon Kanchenjunga, the first in 1905. An American explorer, E. F. Farmer, was killed in 1929, in which year Paul Bauer led a Bavarian party which reached 25,000 feet. In 1930, Professor G. Dyhrenfurth's party was repulsed, but ascended peaks including the Ramthang Peak (23,200 feet) and the Jonsong (24,344 feet). Bauer tried again in 1931, failing at a greater height; and in the same summer, F. S. Smythe's British party reached the Kamet summit (25,447 feet), the highest peak but one of those scaled by man.

Nangaparbat has been the object of two recent expeditions under Dr. Merkl, of Munich, in 1932 and 1934, both being unsuccessful, the latter with the loss of nine lives. In 1934 also all four peaks of Queen Mary, in the Karakorams, were climbed by Dyhrenfurth's expedition.

ATTEMPTS UPON THE WORLD'S HIGHEST POINT

Mount Everest (29,141 feet by latest calculation), the highest mountain in the world, has attracted repeated attempts since 1920, when the Dalai Lama of Tibet first gave permission for attempts from the Tibetan side. It was named in honour of Sir John Everest, an officer of the Indian Army and Indian Survey. A preliminary reconnaissance expedition under Colonel C. K. Howard-Bury, shaped plans for future efforts in 1921, reaching 22,860 feet; upon this journey Dr. Kellas died.

The first serious attempt was that of 1922, under General Bruce, which reached 27,235 feet. This, the highest point then reached, was overpassed in 1924 when, on Bruce's second expedition, Lieut.-Col. E. F. Norton and Dr. T. H. Somervell reached 28,200 feet. G. L. Mallory and A. C. Irvine set off for the final climb and were not again seen.

In 1933 Harris, Wager and Longland, of the Hugh Ruttledge expedition, reached 27,400 feet at Camp 6; F. S. Smythe alone managed to reach about the same elevation, but also had to retreat. In this year also an aerial survey of the mountain was made, led by Major L. V. Blacker.

In 1934 a solo attempt on Everest was made by Maurice Wilson. His body was found in 1935 by E. F. Shipton's party at 21,000 feet. The Shipton Expedition proved that in the monsoon seasons Everest was definitely impracticable, which confined the time each year for possible climbing to a very few weeks.

The 1936 expedition was again led by Hugh Ruttledge, and included the veteran climbers Shipton, Smythe and Wyn Harris. It reached only the same height as the first expedition of 1921, namely 22,860 feet. In the same year, W. H. Tilman stood on the 25,645 feet summit of Nanda Devi, the highest mountain top reached to date.

The 1938 expedition was led by Tilman, the party again including

Shipton and Smythe. It reached 27,000 feet, but was defeated by the early monsoon, Tilman and others being nearly killed by an avalanche.

FIVE MEN ON THE ROOF OF THE WORLD

The highest permanent habitation is at an elevation of 19,500 feet on the Donkiala Pass, where five men, living in a stone hut, guard the important road from India to Tibet.

MOUNTAINS AS CENTRES OF RELIGION

CERTAIN mountains that dominated the countryside with peaks that towered into the heavens have been considered to be sacred altars and dwelling places of the gods The stone temple towers known as ziggurats, erected on the wide plains of Mesopotamia, were artificial sacred mountains, designed to impress. Such was the Tower of Babel (Babylon) and such perhaps also the Pyramids, though these were primarily tombs of the Pharaohs. On these heights, which dominated the surrounding plains, although they were of no great elevation, people felt themselves nearer to the gods.

IN BABYLON AND PALESTINE

The Babylonian tower was a seven-storied, pyramidal structure, some 300 feet high. A spiral staircase ascended to the top, which was furnished with a golden couch and table and was guarded by a virgin priestess.

On Mount Moriah, in Jerusalem, David set up the tent with the Ark of the Covenant. Since the return of the Jews from the Babylonian exile, 537 B.C., the summit of the hill of Gerizim has been occupied by the temple of the Samaritans, who boast of possessing the oldest roll of laws. Sinai is a granite mountain shaped like an altar. A cross was set up in 1927 on its highest point, Mount Horeb (8,656 feet). Jeremiah is said to have carried the Ark of the Covenant to the sacred mountain of Nebo.

The Syrian people gave their sun-god Baal the form of a pointed cone, and set it up for worship on the tops of mountains, where the first rays of the sun could strike it. Among such were Mount Carmel and the holy mountain of Casius in Syria, which the Emperor Hadrian (76-138) ascended in order to see the spectacle of the sunrise.

SACRED MOUNTAIN OF THE BENEDICTINES

Helios, the Greek god of the sun, also had his throne on sacred mountains. Owing to the similarity of name, these places are now dedicated to St. Elias, venerated by the Greek Church. Monte Cassino, the mountain on which Apollo, the god of light, was once worshipped, is associated with St. Benedict and the monastic movement initiated by him there when he founded his Rule and Order in the year 528.

About 15,000 Benedictine monasteries arose in Europe, mostly situated on hill tops, to which paths lined with figured Stations of the Cross usually ascended.

In the Oeta mountains of Thessaly was the mountain of sacrifice on which Heracles, the half-human hero of the Hellenic world, met his transfiguration. When he burnt himself on the mountain top, the sun is said to have been darkened. His soul was freed from earthly dross by this baptism of fire, and a cloud carried it, amid the crash of thunder, up to heaven, where his father, Zeus, received him.

From the holy mountain of Athos (6,350 feet) Zeus is supposed to have destroyed the Persian fleet in 493 B.C. The site of his gigantic statue has been occupied for centuries by the Church of the Assumption of the Virgin Mary. Mount Olympus (9,754 feet) was the dwelling of the Greek circle of gods, the goddess Athena had the temple-covered hill of the Acropolis which dominated ancient Athens as her home, and from the hill of the Capitol in Rome, Jupiter swayed the Roman world at his feet.

HOLY HEIGHTS OF JAPAN AND CHINA

Fujiyama (12,395 feet) and Ontake (10,450 feet) are the sacred mountains of Japan, just as Taishan (4,875 feet) is the Olympus of China. Taishan is the highest mountain in Shantung, always wrapped in a mysterious cloak of mists and thunderclouds. Confucius (about 550—479 B.C.), the Chinese moral teacher, was born in its shadow. Before his time the Chinese were a nation of nature-worshippers; the weather mountain of Taishan, on which good harvests and famine depended, was their god. Each emperor made the sacrifices on its summit which marked him as the Son of Heaven. Up there, amid clouds and thunder and lightning, the Chinese ruler was installed and received autocratic power.

On this mountain, too, the light-radiating gods of life and the heavenly mother had their homes. A flight of 6,000 steps led to the summit. At the top the Gate of Heaven, composed of gigantic blocks of stone, gave on a plateau a mile and a quarter long, dotted with temples and altars.

PARADISE MOUNTAIN OF THE BUDDHISTS

The Buddhists believe in the Paradise Mountain of Meru (14,955), the original home of mankind and the seat of the gods, above which are the vaults of the successive heavens. The holy mountain of the Tibetans is Kailas (19,900 feet) among the Himalayas of Tibet, which, as the throne of the god-king Shiva, is sacred also to 300,000,000 Hindus. The Peruvians of Incan times worshipped the water-giving spirit on the sacred mountain of Illimani (20,830 feet).

Among the holy mountains of the Germanic tribes were the Kyffhäuser, the hill of the ancient Norse deities; the Bielstein in the Harz Mountains; and the Donnersberg (or Donersberg).

EARTH'S STORE OF MINERALS

MINERALS are the hard skin of Mother Earth. Without them a mechanized age such as our own would be impossible. They are seldom simple elements. Perhaps the most important minerals are the metals, which are usually divided into those which are base or common, and those which are precious or uncommon. Metals may be soft, hard, brittle, tough, heavy or light, and most of them are found with other metals and have to be extracted.

TO ONE GRAMME OF RADIUM: £24,750

Metals are valued according to the law of supply and demand. Silver was once more valuable than gold, iron dearer than gold or silver. The most expensive substance is now radium, discovered in pitchblende in 1898 by Marie Curie, a Polish refugee doing research work in Paris, and obtained from Joachimstal in Bohemia. In 1926 one gramme of radium cost £24,750. By 1928 the price had fallen to £14,440 because in the meantime radium had been discovered in the Belgian Congo, and also in Canada and Colorado, U.S.A., in the so-called carnotite stratum, which contains a small percentage of uranium, although only 3.3 parts of radium can be obtained.

In 1928 potassium was also discovered to be radio-active, and so the most valuable substance diminished in price. Radium rays can penetrate lead plates half an inch thick. In order to obtain a single gramme, 4,000 tons of earth with uranium content, enough to fill 400 goods trucks, are needed. The richest ones contain no more than five to ten grammes in 100 tons.

Professor Mysotsky, of the Radium Institute of Leningrad, tested in 1935 an apparatus for the production of artificial radium, by a process entailing the use of high tension to the extent of 15-18,000,000 volts. The apparatus includes the largest magnet in the world, capable of lifting a weight equal to the tare of several goods trains, as its magnetic power is sufficient to overcome a weight of 150 tons. Another research worker claims to have extracted radium from kitchen salt.

Mesothorium possesses the same biological effect as radium. One gramme of this substance cost £6,000. Some 200 tons of monazite sand from India are required to make one gramme of mesothorium.

PLATINUM AND RHODIUM: LUXURY METALS

Platinum, a pound of which today costs £85 to £90, is found in Russia, Africa and the United States. Three-quarters of the production is used for jewellery and dental purposes. It is nearly twice as heavy as lead, and was once regarded as of so little worth that coins of small value were minted of it by the Russian Government.

In 1936, at his laboratory in the University of California, a scientist converted platinum into gold by means of his cyclotron apparatus.

Rhodium is closely related to platinum, but is still more expensive. It was formerly found in proportions of from 0.3 to 0.5 per cent in platinum ore from the Ural Mountains. When a pound of platinum cost about £43 10s., rhodium cost £435. Recently, nickel ore has been found to be another source for the extraction of rhodium.

NICKEL AND ALUMINIUM AS "NEW" METALS

Lead has been discovered in ancient Egyptian tombs, and pipes of it have been dug up in the buried cities of Herculaneum and Pompeii in a state of perfect preservation. Both these places were destroyed in A.D. 79. In the natural state lead is found in the form of galena combined with sulphur, or with silver in silver mines. At present a quarter of the world's production comes from the United States. Although soft lead is the fourth heaviest metal, it offers a greater resistance to rust than iron, and for this reason it is used in the form of paint to protect the more corrosive metal. Vast quantities are made into water pipes, and it is a constituent of solder.

The youngest child of the great family of metals is aluminium, which fifty years ago was as expensive as silver, just as silver was once more precious than gold, and iron more valuable than either. The first to isolate it was the German chemist, Friedrich Wöhler, in 1827. Napoleon III used an aluminium spoon at state banquets, and had a set of buttons for his uniform of the same substance. It then cost about £109 a pound. In 1880 only seventy pounds were produced annually; in 1885 thirteen tons; in 1926 some 200,000 tons; now even cooking-vessels are made of aluminium.

The metal is never found by itself but always in combination with other elements, including clay. The United States is the chief producer, although it is believed that aluminium worth about £288,000,000 is available in the Gold Coast Colony. The largest night sign in the world is made of this metal. It graces the R.C.A. building in Rockefeller Centre, New York, is twenty-four feet high and outlined in neon lighting.

Nickel first became known in 1751, through the work of the German scientists, Cronstedt and Bergmann. Canada is the largest producer.

TURNING WASTE INTO WEALTH

A deposit of phlogopite mica in a mountain near Libby, in Montana, U.S.A., was regarded as quite useless commercially until it was subjected to a high temperature. It then revealed a light, flaky material that turned a rich gold colour.

Put to further tests, it was discovered that zonolite, as it was named, was fireproof up to 2500°F. This led to the finding of many uses for the newly discovered substance, including insulating packing for such articles as safes and incubators, the making of a particularly attractive gold-bronze paint, and decorative material for plastered walls.

MELTING POINTS OF VARIOUS MINERALS

Wolfram melts at 5576°F., platinum at from 3092°F. to 3272°F., copper at 1922°F., bismuth at 514°F., lead at 617°F., and tin at 440°F. Potassium melts in hot water at 145°F. An alloy of bismuth, cadmium, tin, lead and indium melts at 116°F.

HOTTEST MINES IN THE WORLD

The tin mines of the Malayan Peninsula are the hottest in the world. Fortunately a great deal of the mineral is now dredged from the river beds. Another method is by playing a stream of water at a pressure of 200 lbs. on to a cliff where tin stone is known to abound and tearing it down. Malaya is the principal tin-producing country, followed by Bolivia, the Dutch East Indies, Siam, China, Nigeria, Australia, Tasmania, and Great Britain.

In 1800 the Duchy of Cornwall was producing 80 per cent of the world's output, and an average year meant the raising of 15,000 tons of ore. Once there were 300 mines active, with 100,000 miles of galleries, many of them beneath the bed of the sea, and some 1,600 feet deep. The terrible scourge of phthisis, caused by the dust of the rock settling in the lungs, is now held in check, thanks to the use of drills which project water through their tips. Before this humane invention was introduced the average life of a Cornish miner was no more than thirty-five years.

A considerable amount of the metal is used in connection with the canning industry, and the feverish race for armaments has led on occasion to a rise of nearly £60 per ton in the course of a week. The normal consumption of tin in Great Britain is about eighty tons a day.

PEWTER MAY TURN TO DUST

Metals are subject to deterioration. There are fatigues of tin, lead and bronze. Long ago the Roman historian, Plutarch, complained of the ruin of many valuable works of art in metal through such phenomena.

The collection of pewter vessels and plates at Schloss Karneid in the Tyrol collapsed into grey powder overnight. Pewter is an alloy of tin and lead.

The largest quicksilver or mercury mines are at Almaden in Spain and Idria in Italy, which yield 3,650 tons annually. The former mine is said to have been opened about 800 B.C. Besides its meteorological and medicinal uses, quicksilver is also employed to drive certain types of turbine.

It is the only known metal that is fluid at ordinary temperatures.

ELECTRIC CURRENT AS DIVINING ROD

The *caduceus* or staff of Hermes, the messenger of the Greek gods, is believed to represent a divining rod. Water finders accompanied the Roman armies in order that drinking water should be available at short notice in case of necessity. In Algeria many ancient borings, 650 feet deep, have been discovered, and these the French have put in order.

Since it is often impracticable to examine the composition of the soil by borings and deep digging alone, methods were invented for the exploration, without disturbing the surface, of the qualities of the soil, the position of the various strata, the presence of ores, subsoil water, and so on. By the so-called seismic method, working with apparatus that registers the most delicate shocks, artificial tremors are produced, and calculations based on the fact that different strata conduct the tremor at different speeds. Calculations of this nature can also be made by the magnetic method.

The electrical method is particularly interesting. We can either measure the electric currents that are engendered naturally by the chemical composition between subsoil water and beds of pyrites, for instance, or we can send a current into the ground and, from its conductivity, make far-reaching deductions as to its internal structure. A very small amount of power current directed into the earth can determine the constitution of the soil down to depths of 3,250 feet.

In the search for ore and salt deposits, and for water in desert places, modern science uses the alternating current process, in order to determine their exact position, extent and depth.

AGES OF MANKIND NAMED AFTER METALS

In the long story of mankind, metals have played an important part. The Stone Age was followed by the Copper Age, the Bronze Age by the Iron Age, and the Iron Age by the Steel Age—that in which we live. Some of these periods overlapped, and various parts of the world have not yet emerged from the Stone Age.

MINING IN THE TRANSVAAL, 3,000 B.C.

As early as the close of the last Ice Age, there were copper utensils in Egypt. Analyses made by Professor R. Dart, of Johannesburg, showed that the metals used in the bronze for the statues of the ancient Egyptians came from mines in the Transvaal, which must, therefore, have been worked as long ago as 3000 B.C.

In Egypt the Stone Age was followed by the Copper Age. Later on, the copper was mixed with ten per cent of tin, and bronze was obtained, which was at first cast in the form of stones. In Babylonia, 3000 B.C., copper was mixed with lead and zinc to make brass. About 2000 B.C. the Bronze Age reached Central Europe through the medium of the then inhabitants of Italy.

Owing to Phœnician imports of tin from the Cassiterides or Tin Islands of the English Channel—perhaps the Scilly Islands or islands off the coast of Brittany—bronze became the commonest metal. About 1900 B.C. it came into use in Scandinavia.

Bronze soon came to be manufactured wherever supplies of tin and copper were available. Of special repute was the bronze from the Greek island of Delos, which Polyclitus, the great Greek sculptor of the 5th century B.C., liked to use for his statues, while the equally celebrated Myron obtained his bronze from the workshops on the island of Aegina, near Athens. At the fire of Corinth in 146 B.C., accident produced a bronze mixture that afterwards became famous.

BRONZE USED BY KING SOLOMON

In Japan there does not appear to have been a Bronze Age. Bronze was introduced to the Chinese not earlier than 500 B.C. by the Scythians, who inhabited the districts around the Caspian Sea and exploited the metal deposits of the Altai Mountains in Central Asia. The Phœnicians were masters of the craft of casting and working bronze. The bronze used by King Solomon in large quantities in the building of his temple was cast for him by Hiram, the Phœnician King of Tyre, who flourished about 1000 B.C.

In Northern Europe, where the Bronze Age started about 1900 B.C., daggers, swords, and shields were made of bronze, and so were such ornaments as safety pins, combs, finger rings, armlets and necklets. About the same time the first towns appeared in Central Europe where previously there had been only villages, and the plough began to take the place of the axe. The well-known Celtic copper mine of Mitterberg, near Salzburg, is of vast antiquity. The Bronze Age then merged into the Iron Age, at first in Southern and Central Europe (about 1000 B.C.), then, about the 7th century B.C., in Northern Europe.

Traces of copper are evident in both earth and sea, but it is poisonous in other than minute doses. This is why vegetation seldom grows where the mineral is found, although there is a herb called copper grass which flourishes on copper outcrops in Australia, and is regarded as a reliable indication of the presence of copper by prospectors.

COPPER RECEIVED ITS NAME FROM CYPRUS

Just as England was the tin island of the Bronze Age, Cyprus was the copper island, and the metal is still produced on a small scale. The goddess of the copper mines was the ancient Asiatic divinity Astarte, afterwards known to the Greeks as Aphrodite. As early as 1500 B.C. there was a lively trade in the barter of bronze from Cyprus with ivory from Egypt and Syria. The name of Cyprus in Greek is Kupros, and the word "copper" is derived from it. In Spain, the mines of Rio Tinto, still the richest copper mines in the world, were exploited in very early times. Copper was mined by the Scythians in the Altai Mountains, and by the Celts in the Eastern Alps.

Owing to world-wide electrification, the use of copper has recently experienced an enormous impetus. The Americans have already extracted 1,000,000 tons of copper from the lava of the mountains near Lake Superior, the Calumet and Hecla mines being the most important. The site was first visited in modern times by General Louis Cass in 1819, although the American Indians were well acquainted with it and had mined the metal in a primitive way by burning bonfires where there was a bed, dousing them with water, and breaking off the cracked lumps. One of the earliest white men to describe the deposits was Father Claude Allouez, who in 1665 wrote: " One often finds at the bottom of the water, pieces of pure copper of ten and twenty livres' weight. I have several times seen such pieces in the savages' hands; and, since they are superstitious, they keep them as so many divinities, or as presents which the gods dwelling beneath the water have given them, and on which their welfare is to depend. For this reason they preserve these pieces of copper, wrapped up, among their most precious possessions. Some have kept them for more than fifty years; others have had them in their families from time immemorial, and cherish them as household gods."

IRON TOOLS IN TUTENKHAMON'S TOMB

In 1928, a chest containing model tools of iron was discovered by Dr. Howard Carter in the farthest tomb-chamber of Tutenkhamon, Pharoah of Egypt 1,350 years before the advent of Christ. Although iron is fairly common in the eastern desert of Egypt, and the working of copper and bronze demands a much greater metallurgical skill than iron, yet there is no authentic proof of the use of iron before the time of Tutenkhamon. Even under the next dynasty, iron objects are extremely rare.

In 1926, Professor Hrozny deciphered a Hittite king's letter of about 1400 B.C.—the Hittites were a dominant Indo-European people of Asia Minor—in which the Pharaoh was promised iron from the mines on the Black Sea.

IRON ONCE AS PRECIOUS AS GOLD

Iron reached Southern Europe about 1000 B.C. The Greeks and Italiots had no previous knowledge of it, and its value is shown by the fact that many hundred years later an ordinance was made that no iron should be used in the building of Cyzicus, an ancient Greek city on the coast of Asia Minor.

On the other hand, an iron coinage was introduced among the Spartans as early as 800 B.C. Iron was not allowed to be used in the annual reconstruction of the Pons Sublicus, that ancient wooden bridge in Rome, and the cult utensils of the Vestal Virgins could not be of iron. But the ring of a general who was granted a triumph, and Roman wedding rings, were of iron, a sign of how costly iron had once been among the Romans.

The Iron Age began in Gaul and Switzerland about 1000 B.C., and by 700 B.C. it had reached the Baltic. In 1899 two iron nails, dating from about 1200 B.C., were discovered in a prince's grave at Seddin, a few hours east of Berlin, and in an urn found near Stade in 1931 were two shield-boss rivets of iron. As this urn-grave is thought to date from the 16th century B.C., these pieces of iron must be looked upon as great rarities imported from the south. As late as 1370, Edward III of England, when taking stock of his treasury, reckoned his iron utensils among the plate.

Today the world production of pig-iron amounts to 72,000,000 tons per annum, and the steel production (ingots and castings) to about 98,000,000 tons.

RUSTLESS IRON IN INDIA IN 350 B.C.

The Aztecs of Mexico made their ceremonial vessels of a chemical mixture of iron and clay, the secret of which was lost in the conquest of Mexico by the Spaniards. At Delhi, the capital of India, there stands to this day a wrought-iron column erected in 350 B.C., which weighs 12,600 pounds. It was constructed by skilled craftsmen in small sections, and is rust-proof. The column is as completely free from rust as if it were of modern rustless steel.

The Romans at first employed the pure smelting process when they exploited the rich deposits of iron on the island of Elba, still being worked today. The Chinese were acquainted with cast-iron as long ago as 700 B.C.

The first cast-iron furnaces in Europe were built in Alsace in 1490. The process of making steel from cast-iron has been known since 1722. Pig-iron has been smelted with coal in blast furnaces since 1766; crucible steel appeared about 1851; steel has been obtained by the Bessemer converter as a second combustion of pig-iron from 1856. Electrical production of steel was invented in 1900.

MAKING A PERFECT STEEL WEAPON

Steel is a combination of iron, usually with carbon. Without it civilization would not have taken on the harsh, mechanical texture it has done. Much of the world's business is carried on in buildings with steel frames that house steel machines; humanity is transported in steel motor cars and steel railway coaches by a steel locomotive over steel bridges, under which steel ships pass and above which aeroplanes with steel frames fly With steel guns, offender and defender hurl death and destruction at enemies they probably cannot see; with steel scalpels the surgeon patches up the maimed. Perhaps no appliance in the armoury has been manufactured with greater skill and care than the inlaid sword blades of Damascus, famous 500 years ago. There were no elaborate laboratory and inspection tests in those days. A simpler method was adopted, light on which is shed by a contemporary document discovered by Professor von Eulenspiegel.

"Let the high dignitary," it runs, "furnish an Ethiop of fair frame, and let him be bound down, shoulders upward, upon the block of the god Bal-hal, his arms fastened underneath with thongs; a strap of goatskin over his back and wound twice round the block; his feet close together lashed to a dowel of wood, and his head and back projecting over and beyond the end of the block.

"Then let the master workman, having cold-hammered the blade to a smooth and thin edge, thrust it into the fire of the cedarwood coals, in and out, the while reciting the prayer to the god Bal-hal, until the steel be of the colour of the red of the rising sun when he comes up over the desert toward the east, and then, with a quick motion, pass the same from the heel thereof to the point, six times through the most fleshy portion of the slave's back and thighs, when it shall have become the colour of the purple of the king. Then, if with one swing and one stroke of the right arm of the master workman it severs the head of the slave from his body, and display not nick nor crack along the edge, and the blade may be bent round about the body of a man and break not, it shall be accepted as a perfect weapon sacred to the service of the god Bal-hal, and the owner thereof may thrust it into a scabbard of asses' skin, brazen with brass, and hung to a girdle of camels' wool dyed in royal purple."

SILVER AND GOLD

THE word silver is said to be of Basque origin. The metal is often found in association with lead and copper, and when these are smelted silver is usually obtained as a by-product. The Egyptians brought it from Abyssinia and Nubia, the Phœnicians from Spain. Until 1600 B.C., it was worth more than gold in Egypt, and articles of gold were often silvered. Its use as money, according to a Chaldean inscription, dates from 4500 B.C., and the Patriarch Abraham bought a burial ground with it.

FIRST TO MINT SILVER COINS

The Etruscans were the first to mint silver coins, in 550 B.C.; their example was followed by the Romans in 270 B.C. The Athenians possessed silver mines in the Laurion Mountains of Attica and in Epirus. In the Middle Ages the silver mines at Kremnitz in Austria, which had been worked by the Romans, were reopened.

Rich deposits of silver were discovered in 1169 near Schneeberg, in Germany, and in 1623 near Kongsberg, Norway. A veritable flood of silver from the mines of Cerro de Potosi, in Bolivia, was distributed through Europe by the agency of the Spaniards, and quickly lowered its market value. Silver has also been found in Australia in modern times, and a nugget weighing nearly three tons was displayed by Canada at the British Empire Exhibition in 1924.

"SILVER" THAT IS NOT SILVER

German silver, sometimes called nickel silver, is an alloy of copper, zinc and nickel. It was discovered by Gritner in 1812. The so-called " silver paper " used for wrapping cigarettes and sweets is usually aluminium foil, lead foil, or tin foil. There is nothing silver about it other than the name.

HALL-MARKS ON SILVER

The English hall-mark on a piece of silver dates back to the 15th century, when it was made compulsory by law to prevent fraud. The lion has been used as one of the devices by London since 1545, and until 1740 every silversmith had his own symbol, which was registered at the assay office. The date letter, which first appeared in 1478, is changed each year. The letters are used in cycles of twenty from A to U or V, excluding J, and are never repeated in the same way.

The term hall-mark originated from the fact that in early times each article was assayed in the hall of the maker's guild. If it was of the required standard the warden punched the piece with the official mark.

GOLD COLLECTED IN SHEEPSKINS

The first gold mine was opened in 1500 B.C. by the Pharaoh Thutmose III. Rings of gold of standard weight preceded coined money. The oldest papyrus map in the world, dating from 1100 B.C., shows the way to the Egyptian gold mines of Koptos, which were probably situated in the gold district of Ophir, on the Red Sea.

Since then gold has been found in almost every country in the world, in rivers, and also in the sea. In the River Pactolus in Asia Minor they used to collect the gold in sheepskins; this was probably the origin of the fable of the Golden Fleece. Gold has also been found in the rivers Po and Rhine, hence the legend of *Das Rheingold*; and in North Wales. A nugget weighing sixty-six grammes was found in the mud of the River Moselle.

New gold and silver mines were discovered in 1936 at Ouray, Colorado. The largest gold mine in Europe is in Transylvania. It produces 2,250 pounds annually. The deepest is the Morro Velho, Brazil, which is over 6,100 feet below the surface, and the most important gold-mining centre is Johannesburg, South Africa.

WORLD'S GREATEST GOLD MINES

The principal source of gold is South Africa, which now produces about 11,735,000 fine ounces annually; its production at this rate is said to be likely to last only till 1950. After that date it may no longer be capable of fulfilling the world's demands. Canada provides about 4,055,000 fine ounces yearly.

Gold-mining flourished in California following the "gold rush" of 1848, but that district now produces only alluvial ore, which is found in sand or mud in streams and lakes and is recovered by washing. One ton of ore yields .0038 troy ounces of gold, worth 7d. Shortly before 1900 there were gold rushes to the Klondike in Alaska, and to Kalgoorlie in Western Australia. The first gold to be discovered in the Dominion was found in 1851 at Summer Hill Creek, New South Wales. Within twelve months there were 200,000 prospectors at the diggings. In 1903, Australia produced 3,898,000 fine ounces; but this figure was reduced to 1,380,000 ounces, worth £12,000,000, in 1937.

The world's annual production of gold is estimated at 35,500,000 fine ounces, worth approximately £265,000,000 sterling. The British Empire produces just over half of the total amount, and South Africa alone, about one-third of the total. Soviet Russia, producing about 6,000,000 fine ounces a year, ranks next to South Africa. Then come the United States of America, with 4,090,000 ounces, and Canada with 4,060,000 ounces. The only European countries, besides Russia, that produce gold in quantity are Sweden and Rumania.

GOLD IN GREAT BRITAIN

The earliest gold workings in Great Britain of which there is record were carried on by the Romans in Carmarthenshire. The precious metal has been discovered in Devon and Cornwall, where miners "streaming" for tin occasionally come across it. Nuggets weighing from seven to twenty-two ounces have been discovered in Ireland, and one of twenty-seven ounces in Scotland. A mountain on the borders of Wicklow and Wexford gave 945 ounces in two years, but in 1840 the Commissioners of Woods and Forests forbade further prospecting owing to a dispute. In 1875-8 some 720 ounces were produced near Dolgelly, in Wales, and 741 ounces in 1910; from 1888 to 1911 some 104,049 ounces of pure gold, valued at £368,847 were recovered. In 1910, 1,668 ounces were taken from the Gwyn mine in Merionethshire. The Prince Edward gold mine at Trawsfynydd was sold to a London syndicate in 1934 for £20,000. The wedding rings of Queen Mary, Queen Elizabeth and the Princess Royal are made of Welsh gold.

There was a gold rush in Scotland in 1868, when a vein was struck at Kildonan, in Sutherlandshire, and there was a smaller rush in 1911. Goldfields were worked at Glenconner, Crawfordmuir and Wenlock in the 16th and 17th centuries.

THINNEST GOLD

An ounce of gold produces 2,500 gold leaves three and a quarter inches square. Gold leaf is used for decorative purposes, and was so employed by the ancient Egyptians. Gold-beaters' skin is part of the intestine of an ox, and was given its name by goldsmiths of the Middle Ages. They discovered that by putting gold, which is the most elastic metal, between strips of the material it could be hammered without damage or loss. There is nearly £1,000 worth of gold leaf on the railings of Buckingham Palace.

Gold is used in medicine in treating phthisis, tuberculosis of the skin, lupus, leprosy and other diseases. Many experiments have been made to manufacture gold on a commercial basis. Of recent years several charlatans have been rewarded for their pains by terms of imprisonment.

The World War, the cause of immense material losses, brought about a fundamental change in the distribution of the world's stock of gold. Gold flowed out of the countries at war into the neutral states. Large sums in gold left Germany after the war in the form of reparations. By the end of 1923 only 100,000,000 marks in gold currency were left in Germany, which before the war had possessed over 4,000,000,000.

According to one estimate, the belligerent states of Europe lost about one-third of the stock of gold that they possessed before the conflict, while the United States and the European neutrals doubled their gold reserves. During its civil war, Russia lost the greater part of its gold holdings.

In the interests of international trade, America re-established European credit by means of the Dawes Plan, and by the end of 1928 the aggregate European gold holdings were for the first time since the war larger than those of the United States. Notwithstanding this, the gold holdings of the United States in 1937 were about five times as great as those of France.

LARGEST NUGGET OF GOLD IS IN ENGLAND

The largest nugget of gold ever discovered was found in Victoria, Australia. It is the " Welcome Stranger," brought to light in 1869. It weighs 2,520 ounces and is now in England. The " Welcome " nugget weighs 2,217 ounces. A nugget discovered in Larkinville, Western Australia, weighs 1,136 ounces, and a slab of gold was once found which turned the scales at 630 pounds.

TREASURE THAT HAS DISAPPEARED

WHERE are now the treasures of Crœsus, of Solomon, of Cyrus, and of Sesostris? Where are the hoards of the Nibelungs, the treasures of Attila, and those of which Nadir Shah despoiled the Great Mogul of India? Where are now the tons of gold that for thousands of years have been washed out of rivers and dug out of mines in all parts of the world?

A huge quantity of treasure has been buried and forgotten. The value of the Charon coins, which the Greeks and Romans were wont to place in the mouths of their dead to pay the fee of the fabulous ferryman who piloted the souls across the murky Styx to the land of the shades, reckoning the period up to A.D. 300, is computed at about £100,000. The custom is still prevalent among the Chinese.

BURIED TREASURE OF THE INCAS OF PERU

In 1935 an American investigator instituted systematic excavations at Visby, the chief town of the Baltic island of Gottland. He followed the precedent established in an attempt to salve the treasure of the Incas. Visby, from A.D. 1250 to 1299, was one of the centres of the powerful Hanseatic League, and to its harbour were brought countless treasures from all parts of the Old World. As many as 5,000 Roman gold coins were found.

In order to discover the treasures of the Inca kings, the sacred lake of Guatavia, in Peru, 11,375 feet above sea-level, was drained off, with the result that £5,000 worth of gold and precious stones were found. These had been thrown into the lake as votive gifts to the deified kings.

JEWELLERY AND COINS FROM TOMBS

Untold treasure is still piously preserved in royal graves of every period. Many tombs, such as those of the Egyptian pharaohs, the French kings, and the Russian tsars, have been rifled, as a few years ago were the last resting places of the emperors of China. In the tomb of the Empress Tsi-li objects to the value of several million taels were recovered. The grave of Genghis Khan, the great Mongolian ruler, near Karakoram in Mongolia, contained jewellery of enormous value.

TREASURE CHESTS OF MONTEZUMA AND NAPOLEON

Another famous treasure was that of Montezuma, the last emperor of the Aztecs, who is believed to have buried in 1520 treasure valued at £1,000,000 in the temple of Mokachahan, in present-day Guatemala.

One successful search was that undertaken in 1933 to salve the crown treasury of the Emperor Maximilian (shot in 1867), which President Diaz took with him on his flight in 1911, and which was lost on a ship that sank near the Virginian coast.

In 1935, descendants of the soldiers of the Grand Army, led so disastrously into Russia in 1812, searched for Napoleon's war chest on the banks of the River Niemen, near Kovno, and excavations were made near Sobelu on the Danube in the hope of finding the royal treasure of the Dacians, who inhabited Rumania in the time of the Roman Empire.

MILLIONS THAT GO UP IN SMOKE

THE treasures of the earth include coal deposits. In 1800 some 277,000,000 tons of coal were hewn; and in 1937 the figure was 1,446,000,000. Europe, which mines more coal than any other continent, has an annual output of approximately 823,000,000 metric tons, of which 210,000,000 tons are lignite, or brown coal. Great Britain alone annually produces 244,000,000 metric tons, 185,000,000 of which she consumes herself. North and South America together produce 460,000,000 tons, but 442,000,000 tons are produced by the United States alone. The production of Asia amounts to 133,000,000 tons; of Australasia to 16,000,000 tons; and of Africa to 15,000,000 tons.

Sixteen of the principal countries of Europe consume 650,000,000 tons a year; Canada and the United States consume 454,000,000 (of which the United States accounts for 430,000,000); the Soviet Union, 118,000,000 tons; Asia, exclusive of the U.S.S.R., 90,000,000 tons; and Australasia and the Union of South Africa each 12,000,000 tons. The coal reserves of North and Central America are estimated at 2,220,000 million metric tons; those of Asia at 1,345,000 million; those of Europe at 780,000,000,000; and those of Africa at 22,000,000,000.

IMMENSE COAL SEAMS OF AMERICA AND INDIA

The thickest coal seam in the world is at Shenandoah in the United States. It is 215 feet thick, and almost unlimited in extent. Other thick seams are those between the Godavari and the Ganges, which rise to the surface of the earth. The South Staffordshire coalfield has a seam with an average thickness of twenty-four feet. The purest steam coal, or anthracite, comes from primeval beds of seaweed. Such beds are extensively found in South Wales.

In the seams of greater age are found roots showing 2,000 rings of annual growth; these are relics of swamp cypresses such as still grow in China; remains of antelopes and other tropical animals are also found.

WHAT A TON OF COAL CONTAINS

Out of a ton of coal is obtainable some seven and a half pounds of liquid gas, from which explosives, artificial manures, and artificial ice can be manufactured; 462 pounds of gas for lighting, cooking, etc.; 1,568 pounds of coke, with dyes, briquettes, greases, and cleaning materials as by-products; and 175 pounds of tar. Chemical experts have now perfected a process of suspending coal particles in oil, and thus producing a fuel of high merit which can be distributed by means of pipes; it has been adopted for use in the British Navy.

The first graphite pencils were made in England in 1665, and the first coke was produced in the same country in 1713.

COAL-TAR'S PROLIFIC FAMILY

Coal-tar vaporization at different temperatures condenses in various by-products. The first fraction of the four divisions in which this distillation is generally carried out yields benzene and toluene; the second fraction phenol (carbolic acid), naphthalene; the third creosote or heavy oil; and the fourth anthracene.

After various processes, first, second and fourth fractions provide some 300 by-products. About seventy-five per cent of the 1,500 materials manufactured from these are dyestuffs, twenty-five per cent drugs, perfumes and explosives. A mauve coal-tar dye was first produced by Sir W. H. Perkin in 1856, but German exploitation gave Germany a practical monopoly in Great Britain until the 1921 Import Restrictions Act. German aniline dyes are based on benzene mixed with nitric and sulphuric acids, these forming nitro-benzene; they include an indigo blue (produced by Baeyer, 1870, and later manufactured from naphthalene) and a picric yellow from benzene and phenol.

The explosive T.N.T., or trinitrotoluene, is also produced from a benzene base. Benzene itself was discovered by the famous English chemist, Michael Faraday, in 1825; its fat-dissolvent power at a low temperature (it boils at 176°F.) makes it invaluable in dry-cleaning processes.

Phenol, as well as being used practically unaltered as carbolic acid, produces aspirin and wintergreen oil. Naphthalene, discovered in 1820, is the white moth-ball substance, and is the basis for various dyes Anthracene yields turkey-red.

Amongst other coal-tar products are roofing felt, ink, artificial silk, soaps, substitute amber, motor spirit (two and a half gallons from the tar in a ton of coal) and vulcanite.

ROMANCE IN OIL

JUST as coal is the result of the decay, produced by bacteria, of vegetable matter, so petroleum is probably the result of the decay of animal matter, although some scientists are of the opinion that it is composed of both animal and vegetable matter.

USED TO EMBALM THE DEAD

Petroleum was known to the ancients. Thus we read in *Deuteronomy* and *Job* of oil running out of rock. It was used for embalming and medicinal purposes. Herodotus, Pliny, Josephus and other writers refer to it. Marco Polo, the famous Venetian traveller of the 13th century, tells of how people came from vast distances to fetch oil from Baku. Pitch, which is crude petroleum that has lost its volatile qualities owing to exposure, was used in the building of Noah's Ark, which was "pitched within and without with pitch." The little ark of bulrushes in which the infant Moses was cradled on the Nile was rendered waterproof by the same means, and the "slime" used in the building of the Tower of Babel was pitch.

The oil wells along the River Irrawaddy, in Burma, are among the oldest in the world, although the Chinese were obtaining oil from artesian wells long before the birth of Christ. The Temple of Jupiter in Rome was lighted by oil from the petroleum springs of Sicily.

OIL WEALTH OF THE WORLD

Every year 280,000,000 metric tons of oil are extracted from the earth. The richest oil wells, giving over half of the world's production, are owned by the United States. Other oil districts are Soviet Russia, Mexico, Venezuela, Persia, the Dutch East Indies, and Rumania. From petroleum we obtain fuel principally, and also light oils, lubricating oils, greases and paraffin.

The modern discovery of petroleum took place towards the end of the 18th century, in the west of the United States, when salt springs were being exploited. The brine was pumped from the earth and allowed to evaporate, so as to collect the salt crystals that it contained. On occasions, however, an oily substance mixed in the brine rendered the spring useless. This was petroleum or rock oil.

In 1831 a rancher named Mandal was out shooting with some friends near a salt spring, and brought down several stags. Mandal spent the night alone in the forest. While he was asleep, his gun went off accidentally, the bullet ploughing the ground. On the following morning, Mandal saw a strong-smelling oily substance oozing from the hole. The bullet had hit a small petroleum well. When he made a fire, some of the sparks were blown on to the oil and caused a tremendous blaze.

Two years elapsed before Ferris, another American, recognized the economic significance of the occurrence. By 1851 he had invented a process for refining crude petroleum so that it would not explode and would lose the strong smell it emitted while burning. A company was formed in New York to bore petroleum wells. After a few failures the prospectors succeeded in extracting sufficient to fill several barrels a day. The rush for oil then became as great a rage as the rush for gold. Many very productive wells were discovered, some of which yield more than 50,000 barrels a day.

HAVOC IN THE OILFIELDS

Terrible havoc has been caused by violent discharges called gushers and by fire in oilfields. In 1926 damage estimated at £3,000,000 was done by lightning striking the oil tanks at San Luis Obispo, California. The Moreno well in Rumania blazed for three years before it was extinguished. It was finally got under control by pumping out a considerable quantity of the natural gas which had caused the disaster.

Men clad in special clothing and mica masks succeeded in screwing a two-ton nipple die on a gusher after it had threatened to overwhelm Oklahoma City, U.S.A. Flames sixty feet high rose from the North Canadian river, but fortunately the wind was not blowing in the direction of the town. A newly-drilled well near Silsbee, East Texas, caught fire, illuminating the countryside at night for fifty miles. After a two-months' fight the outbreak was got under control, but not before the loss had reached a total of approximately £50,000. A spark from a hammer set an oil well alight in Texas and burned fourteen men to death.

Ten men, each remunerated at £20 an hour, succeeded in capping a well at Long Beach, California, when it was hurling the equivalent of 15,000 barrels of oil 120 feet high into the air every twenty-four hours. It was an appalling risk, but the volunteers took it and won, although they were partially blinded for a time by the rain of oil.

PRECIOUS STONES IN RICH VARIETY

SINCE the dawn of history man has collected precious stones of many varieties, both for decorative purposes and as treasure. Today the value of gems in human possession runs into many millions of pounds sterling.

King Mithradates of Pontus (about 132-63 B.C.) had a valuable collection, which was taken from him by his conqueror Pompey, the Roman general, who deposited it in the treasure chamber of the Capitol.

Julius Cæsar had six collections which he bequeathed to the Temple of Venus in Rome.

Three-quarters of the present world's production is made into jewellery, while the rest is used for technical purposes. The art of cutting precious stones, known from antiquity, declined during the earlier centuries of the Christian era, but was revived at the Renaissance. The art of faceting dates only from the 18th century. The style of diamond-cutting was fundamentally altered about fifty years ago.

CRYSTALS ALMOST LIVE

Crystals are among the most wonderful geological creations. In a diamond formed under the pressure of 30,000 atmospheres and in a heat of as much as 2,900° F., the atoms of carbon are arranged at symmetrical intervals. If we break a point off a crystal and put the crystal into a nutritive solution, the point slowly grows again, but before it is fully grown the other points have become blunted of their own accord.

The crystal behaves almost like a living, centralized organism that retracts its feelers when danger threatens.

DIAMONDS FALLEN FROM THE SKY

Certain diamonds are regarded by some scientists as presents from space. According to them they are products of small meteorites which have fallen into the " pipes " of Kimberley, where the principal diamond mines of South Africa are situated. The molten iron of meteors, when suddenly cooled, contracts its substance; the carbon is changed from density 2 to density 3 5, and is transformed into diamonds.

Kimberley diamonds are washed down by the Orange River right to its mouth. Smaller diamonds have been carried 200 miles by sandstorms from eastern Namaqualand, in South-West Africa, to the coast. The rubies and sapphires found in the river valleys of Burma and Assam originally came from western Tibet.

ANNUAL PRODUCTION OF DIAMONDS

In recent years the world's annual production of diamonds has amounted to about 8,000,000 carats, worth approximately £8,000,000. In 1936 the Belgian Congo produced 4,800,000 carats; the Gold Coast 1,489,410; and South Africa 624,000 carats, worth £3,200,000.

Until sixty years ago, only 126 pounds of diamonds were found every year, and these came from India and Brazil; twice as many rubies were found, and six times as many sapphires. Then chance led to discoveries in several dry river beds in the Orange Free State, and at the height of the diamond fever the Kimberley mines were discovered.

The diamonds lay in the top stratum, in ancient volcanic craters permeated with the precious stones. Within twenty years, surface work had to be abandoned, and since 1889 deep mining has taken its place at Kimberley.

WORLD'S LARGEST DIAMONDS

The Cullinan diamond, found in 1905, is still the largest diamond known. Discovered in the Premier mine, near Pretoria, it was originally 3,106 carats, and was presented by the Transvaal Government to King Edward VII in 1907, and next year cut into nine main stones; two of these, of 516½ and of 309 3/16 carats, are the largest known brilliants or faceted diamonds. The first of these, known as the Star of Africa, is mounted in the British monarch's sceptre. A carat, the unit of diamond measurement, is 3.17 grains (English), or .2053 grammes (cubic). The second largest diamond is the Excelsior, 969½ carats when found, and since cut into ten stones. Its nearest rival is the President Vargas, found at Minas Geraés, Brazil, in 1938.

The fourth largest diamond could not be sold. It was the flawless white Jonker, found in 1934 in South Africa at Elandsfontein, three miles from the Cullinan find. It weighed 726 carats, and was eventually cut into twelve stones in New York. The name perpetuated that of Jacobus Jonker, a Boer farmer on whose claim the brilliant was discovered.

The Great Mogul is a somewhat legendary stone, estimated at 787 carats before cutting, and reduced to 287½ carats owing to unskilful workmanship. Tavernier, the famous French dealer, saw it in the Mogul Emperor Aurangzeb's treasury in 1666; the Emir Jumla gave it to Shah Jehan. The stone so reported may be that at present in the Teheran treasury in Iran (Persia), which the shah tried to sell in 1924 in exchange for a railway system.

Speculations, which seem unfounded, have attributed two other famous diamonds, the Orloff and the Koh-i-noor, to parts of the original Great Mogul stone. The Orloff is believed to have been stolen by a French soldier from an idol in a Hindu temple. It was eventually given to the Russian Empress, Catherine II, and weighs 194¾ carats.

TRAVELS OF FAMOUS DIAMONDS

The Koh-i-noor (" Mountain of Light ") passed into the hands of the British East India Company from those of the Rajah of Lahore, having originally been mounted on the sarcophagus of Akbar the Great. It was presented to Queen Victoria in 1850, being then 186 1/16 carats, later cut to 106 1/16 carats.

The Pitt or Regent diamond was discovered in 1701 in the Parteal mine. It was bought by William Pitt, Governor of Madras, and from him by the French Regent, the Duke of Orleans, at the reputed price of 2,000,000 francs; he had it cut to 136 14/16 carats. It was stolen during the French Revolution, but later recovered. Napoleon had it mounted in the sword which he wore at his coronation.

Other stones with romantic stories are the Akbar Shah, of 116 carats, cut to 71, bought by the late Gaekwar of Baroda for £35,000; the Nizam, a 277 carat stone said to have been part of a stone weighing 440 carats; and the Sancy, 53 12/16 carats, which belonged in turn to Charles the Bold, de Sancy, Queen Elizabeth, Queen Henrietta Maria, Cardinal Mazarin, and Louis XIV of France. After being stolen during the French Revolution, it is said to have been owned in succession by the King of Spain, Prince Demidoff, and an Indian prince.

TURQUOISE MINES OF IRAN

Fine rubies occasionally fetch five times as much as diamonds of the same size. A four-carat ruby may sell for £12,000, and a ten-carat ruby for a similar amount. The wonderful turquoise mines of Iran (Persia), employing 1,500 hands, are thirty-one miles from Nishapur and from 4,800 to 7,650 feet above sea-level.

CURATIVE STONE OF ABRAHAM

Tradition has it that precious stones exercise a beneficent influence on man's most valuable possessions, his life and his health. Consequently in olden days people used to choose a different stone as a talisman each month.

According to the Talmud, Abraham wore around his neck a precious stone that cured sick people who looked on it. Pope Clement VII, it is said, was given a powdered diamond that, instead of healing him, hastened his death, probably designedly.

Sapphires and emeralds rubbed on the eyelids are supposed to make the eyes bright, the turquoise to lose colour when its owner is threatened with illness. There is, in fact, no end to superstitions about jewels. The so-called birthday stones are as follows: January, garnet; February, amethyst; March, bloodstone; April, diamond; May, emerald; June, agate; July, cornelian; August, sardonyx; September, chrysolite; October, opal; November, topaz; December, turquoise.

ARTIFICIAL PRECIOUS STONES

Paste jewels and dyed topazes have been found in ancient Egyptian tombs. The Roman historian, Seneca, tells us that there were factories in Rome engaged in manufacturing false jewellery. In these a favourite practice was to mix lead with the glass paste to give it a beautiful colour and brilliance.

In 1893, Moisson, a Frenchman, claimed to have succeeded in producing by artificial means diamond splinters .01968 inches thick, and Sir William Crookes made a similar statement. In 1927, Moisson's fellow-countryman, Basset, manufactured diamonds by using a pressure of 56,000 pounds to .3937 inch square, and in 1935, Dr. Karabacek made rough diamonds, .1968 inches in diameter, in a furnace heated up to 2,730°F. with the help of a hydraulic pressure of 1,500 atmospheres and sudden cooling. Sir Charles Parsons once confessed that he had spent £20,000 on unsuccessful experiments with the same object in view.

"One of the most simple and beautiful crystals is the diamond," Sir William Bragg points out. "It consists only of carbon atoms arranged in a very symmetrical way. Every carbon atom has four others spaced round it. The symmetry of the structure is such that the atoms are most difficult to displace, for which reason a diamond can be used as a tool to cut any other substance, because the atoms of the other substance give way before the rigidly set atoms of the diamond."

AMBER HOLDS CREATURES OF A BYGONE AGE

Amber is not a precious stone, although it was regarded as such in past times. It is the fossilized resin from vanished forests of the Tertiary period, with which a former land-bridge stretching to Scandinavia was covered. At Palmnicken, in East Prussia, as much as 840,000 pounds of amber are extracted annually. A cubic yard of blue earth contains about four and a half pounds of amber. The Amber Museum at Königsberg, which is unique of its kind, displays specimens of amber which contain long-extinct animals and plants now found only in Eastern Asia.

Amber was known to the Phœnicians through dealers on the Black Sea, who obtained it from the Baltic coast. The Emperor Nero sent a Roman knight specially to Prussia in order to purchase large quantities of amber, and the largest piece he brought back with him weighed eight and a half pounds. Homer mentions amber under the name of elektron, namely sunstone.

The Greek philosopher Thales, in the 6th century B.C., recognized the electrical properties of amber. This inexplicable quality made it a " wonder stone " to the Greeks. It was put into the mouths of children for them to bite when teething. Even today amber necklaces are worn as a cure for rheumatism.

HIDDEN IN TEMPLES AND TOMBS

To store up in treasure-chambers the earth's most valuable products has been customary since the earliest civilized times. The tombs of the Pharaohs and other princes are museums of the valuables of their period; some still await discovery, although many of them have been rifled by robbers. The most notable recent find was the tomb of Tutenkhamon, who died about 3,300 years ago. It was brought to light by the Earl of Carnarvon and Mr. Howard Carter in 1923-24. Hundreds of articles of great value were revealed, including the mummy case of the Pharaoh, covered with a sheet of solid gold. State treasures were carefully guarded, being mostly kept in temples sacred to the gods.

In the uncertain Middle Ages, most rulers provided themselves with treasure-chambers against " a rainy day," and these gradually became safe deposits for crown jewels and all kinds of gems. All that is left of the regalia of France is now exhibited in the Apollo Salon in the Louvre, including the crowns of Louis XV and Napoleon I, the sceptre of Charles V, a coronation sword of 1150, and the coronation ring of the Capetian dynasty of France.

At Monza, in Italy, the iron crown of Lombardy is kept in safe custody, as well as two silver loaves presented to the cathedral's treasury by Napoleon I after his coronation.

In the Munich treasury are the crowns of the Emperor Henry II and his queen (1010), and the crown of Frederick of the Palatinate, the "Winter King" of Bohemia, captured in Prague in 1620. The Vienna treasury still contains the regalia of the old Holy Roman Empire, saved from Napoleon by being taken out of Nuremberg hidden in a manure cart. In the Green Vaults, at Dresden, are the onyx cameo, an enormous semi-precious stone covered with bas-reliefs made to the order of the Roman Emperor Augustus, and the valuable Green Diamond.

The Polish State treasure is kept in the Palace Church at Cracow; that of the former Spanish world-empire used to be kept in the Armeria (arsenal) at Madrid. The Danish crown jewels are exhibited on a velvet-covered pyramid in an obelisk-shaped glass case which can be let down under the floor; they include an amethyst the size of an ostrich egg.

BRITAIN'S PRICELESS CROWN JEWELS

The priceless crown jewels of the British Empire are on view in the Tower of London, and are so well guarded that there is a saying: "If a thief can steal them, he deserves them." They include the Imperial State Crown, made for Queen Victoria's coronation in 1838 and remade for Edward VII; amongst its gems are 2,818 diamonds, one being a Cullinan cutting, 297 pearls, and a great uncut ruby given in 1367 by Don Pedro the Cruel to the Black Prince and worn by Henry V at the Battle of Agincourt.

Also to be seen is the Imperial Crown worn by King George V at the Delhi Durbar, 1911, containing a thirty-four-carat Indian emerald, 6,170 diamonds and other jewels. St. Edward's Crown was made for Charles II's coronation, from whose time much of the existing regalia dates.

The Russian crown jewels are kept in a secret place closely guarded by officers, while the private treasures of the tsars are stored in the strong-rooms of various London and Paris banks. The Italian regalia are under military guard in underground vaults on an island in the Tiber. Bulgaria keeps its treasures in a small castle on the Danube.

GAS-GUARDED VAULTS FOR GOLD

Not only kings and nations possess treasure-chambers; museums and churches contain objects of enormous intrinsic and artistic value. The newest treasure-chamber is that constructed for the $22,000,000,000 (£4,400,000,000) of the Federal gold reserve in a lonely spot in the Rocky Mountains. The treasure vaults at Fort Knox are constructed of various thicknesses of steel, the spaces between which are filled with a special powder. When heated it gives off deadly gases.

The fort is strongly guarded and entirely surrounded with a wire network charged with high-voltage electricity.

BRICKS OF THE UNIVERSE

I F we take a house to pieces we find that it is composed ultimately of
bricks and a little cementing material. The bricks are all more or
less alike, so nearly alike that we ignore any differences. Yet we can
build up out of similar bricks as many houses as we wish, and no two of
the houses need be alike. We have to think of the universe in the same
way, as built up of bricks; every substance we know of is made up of
these bricks arranged in different ways and fastened together in different
ways.

MOSES AND CLEOPATRA AS ALCHEMISTS

Scientists have always been prying into matter, searching for the
ultimate bricks out of which it is built up. The ancient alchemists
sought to transmute or change the baser metals into gold. Such a
process could only be possible if the different metals were composed of
the same basic substance, and the alchemists must have believed that.

Alchemy originated in Egypt; indeed the name is derived from
"Chimia," the old priestly name for Egypt. Moses and his sister
Miriam are supposed to have studied alchemy, and so also did Job and
Cleopatra. Alchemy had a great vogue in the Middle Ages, when
ignorant people were ready to accept any fairy tale. It persisted till the
end of the 18th century.

ALCHEMY GAVE PLACE TO CHEMISTRY

When the old and carefully guarded mysteries were cleared away
from alchemy there remained the wholesome kernel, chemistry.
Chemistry transmutes, not base metals into gold, but raw materials
into ruby glass, porcelain, and a host of other useful and beautiful
things. Chemistry is indeed the new alchemy.

The old alchemy still has its believers. We are apt to smile at the
credulity of the Middle Ages. Yet, as recently as 1928, it was reported
from Douai, in France, that gold had been made, in the best style of the
old alchemists, by baking together silver, arsenic and sulphur.

PARTICLES THAT CANNOT BE DIVIDED

The ancient Greeks devoted little attention to alchemy, but they
arrived at another of the fundamental ideas of matter. They imagined
matter divided into minute fragments. By crushing brimstone we can
reduce it to a fine powder; in flowers of sulphur the particles are smaller
still; in milk of sulphur the particles are extremely small, but still
separately visible. We can imagine sulphur divided into smaller and
smaller particles, until at last we reach the almost inconceivably small
atom, the particle that cannot be further divided, the " indivisible."

The old Greek idea of the atom was reinvented by John Dalton
(1766-1844) about the end of the 18th century, and it became the basis

of 19th century chemistry. In the new chemistry which Dalton began there were about ninety different kinds of atom, though they were not all discovered at once. Each kind of atom was different from any of the others; each was one of the ultimate bricks out of which the universe is built up. Thus we got the idea of ninety or so elements, none of which could be further broken up into any other kind of matter. Water was split up into the two gases, oxygen and hydrogen, but by no chemical process could either of these gases be further split up; oxygen and hydrogen are elements.

TRACKING DOWN THE ELEMENTS

At the beginning of the 19th century twenty-seven of the elements were known, and throughout the century element after element was added to the list. It is not easy to track down and isolate an unknown element. Few of the elements occur naturally in a free state. Oxygen and nitrogen and other elementary gases are found free in the air; gold is found as grains of native gold; sulphur is found in the neighbourhood of volcanoes; charcoal consists largely of uncombined carbon, and diamonds are almost pure carbon. But most of the elements are combined with other elements in substances which are utterly different from the elements themselves. We know now, for example, that chalk is composed of a soft, silver-white metal called calcium, carbon, and oxygen—a white metal, a black solid, and a gas.

In tracking down the elements, chemists used the heat of Bunsen burners, blowpipes and furnaces; they passed electric currents through compounds which they meant to break up; and they had acids and alkalis and other reagents—the detectives of science which discover the presence of other substances—to help in their researches. More recently they have had the powerful aid of the spectroscope, which enables minute traces of an element to be found even when it is combined with other elements. By examining light passed through the heated vapour of a substance, the spectroscope enables us to identify the elements of which it is composed.

Some of the elements with which we are all now familiar were discovered comparatively recently. Iridium, which tips the points of our gold nibs, was discovered in 1804; aluminium made its first appearance as an element in 1827, though it was not till long after that it was used commercially; the discovery of inert gases in the atmosphere began with argon in 1894. In 1898 came the discovery of radium. The search for two remaining, and very elusive, elements still goes on.

SERIES OF ELEMENTS

Scientists were not content with this idea of ninety or so different kinds of bricks—ninety or so elements. The age-old notion of the alchemists that all matter was ultimately composed of the same basic materials still persisted. The idea that the elements were totally different in kind was given up slowly and reluctantly.

It began to appear that some at least of the elements could be arranged in series. There was no doubt that sodium and potassium, for example, are similar in their properties. They are both soft metals, they both burn on water, they form similar compounds which have a soapy feeling when dissolved in water. Groups of elements were arranged in " periodic " series. In these series properties varied from element to element in a particular order, and this order was invariable for any series.

ARRANGING THE ELEMENTS

Fluorine, chlorine, bromine and iodine form one of these series. Fluorine boils at an extremely low temperature, $-187°C.$, chlorine boils at $-34°C.$, bromine at $59°C.$, and iodine changes to a gas at $184°C.$ Thus we have a periodic rise of the boiling point from element to element. Other properties run through this series of elements in the same order. There is a deepening colour, for example, from the pale greenish yellow of fluorine to the deep violet of iodine. These are only examples of the properties which run through the series of elements, always increasing or decreasing in the same order. There could be no reasonable doubt that the four elements were related in some way.

Other series of related elements were noticed, and some sort of haphazard arrangement of the elements began. The matter was suddenly taken out of the realm of the haphazard in 1869, when Dmitri Ivanovich Mendeleyev (1834-1907), a Russian chemist, produced his famous " periodic table."

WHAT ATOMIC WEIGHT MEANS

Every element has a number attached to it called its atomic weight. If we take a mass of hydrogen and an exactly similar mass of oxygen, we shall find that the oxygen is always sixteen times as heavy as the hydrogen. Thus we arrive at the idea that an oxygen atom is sixteen times as heavy as a hydrogen atom. We call the atomic weight of hydrogen one, since hydrogen is lightest of the elements; then the atomic weight of oxygen is sixteen. The atomic weight of carbon is twelve, that is, a carbon atom is twelve times as heavy as a hydrogen atom; the atomic weight of sulphur is thirty-two, that is, a sulphur atom is thirty-two times as heavy as a hydrogen atom; and so on up to uranium, which has an atomic weight of 238.

The atomic weights give the proportions in which the elements unite. The proportions are always simple multiples of the atomic weights. Water is composed of hydrogen and oxygen; the proportions are : twice the atomic weight of hydrogen to once the atomic weight of oxygen, that is, two parts by weight of hydrogen to sixteen of oxygen. All pure water has the two elements combined in those proportions.

Common salt is formed by the union of sodium and chlorine : once the atomic weight of sodium combined with once the atomic weight of chlorine. And so on with all other compounds; we may have 1 to 1,

1 to 2, 1 to 3, 2 to 3—always simple multiples of the atomic weights. In chalk we have 1 : 1 : 3, that is, once the atomic weight of calcium to once the atomic weight of carbon and three times the atomic weight of oxygen.

IMPORTANCE OF ATOMIC WEIGHTS

Before Mendeleyev's time some of the elements had been arranged in " triads "—groups of three similar elements. (The Three Bears of nursery lore were just such a triad, the Mother Bear having properties midway between those of the Big Bear and the Little Bear.) It was noticed that in each of the triads the atomic weight of the middle element was halfway between those of the outside elements. Apparently the properties of an element depend in some way upon its atomic weight.

Mendeleyev arranged the whole of the known elements in order of their atomic weights. He observed that certain properties ran through the elements, changing gradually from element to element; at a certain distance down the list of elements the properties began again. The first element in the second group was similar to the first element in the first group, the second to the second, and so on. Still further down the list of sequence of properties began once more, and so on.

THE PERIODIC TABLE

Thus there was a periodic recurrence of properties. For this reason the groups of elements are called " periods." In a modern form of the periodic table, hydrogen and helium stand at the top. Then come the " first short period " of eight elements, the " second short period " also of eight elements, two " long periods " each of eighteen elements, the " third long period " of thirty-two elements, and finally the beginning of a " fourth long period."

Each period begins the sequence of properties over again. Thus, the first elements of the periods are : lithium, sodium, potassium, rubidium, cæsium—all soft alkali metals with properties changing progressively from lithium to cæsium. The second elements in the periods form a similar progressive series, and so on. The last elements in the periods are : helium, neon, argon, krypton, xenon, emanation—all inert gases which do not form compounds with other elements. (The relationship of the elements in the periods is rather more complicated than this, because of the larger numbers of elements in the long periods, but this need not be considered.)

GAPS IN THE TABLE

Mendeleyev found it necessary to interchange three pairs of elements, because their properties indicated that they should be placed in the reverse order. This was a small thing, though it was not overlooked, in comparison with what Mendeleyev had achieved. His table as originally published contained a number of gaps, and Mendeleyev declared that these gaps would eventually be filled.

He went on to predict the properties of some of these unknown elements from their positions in the table, and to suggest methods of detecting them. In 1871 he predicted the properties of gallium; the metal was actually discovered in 1875, and its properties corresponded closely with those predicted.

STRUCTURE OF AN ATOM

IF the atoms of each element were composed of matter entirely different from that of all the other elements, there would seem to be no particular reason why the elements should resemble one another or why there should be progressive differences amongst them. A few casual resemblances might be ascribed to chance, but Mendeleyev had brought the whole range of elements into his periodic table. The idea that an atom is indivisible had to be given up.

An atom can still be regarded as the smallest fragment of an element that has the properties of the element; an atom of iron, for example, we regard as a minute bit of iron. In that sense the atom can still be regarded as indivisible. But the atom itself has a structure; it is built up of still smaller particles which are not iron at all. These ultimate particles are common to all the elements. The particles which compose an atom of uranium are the same as those which compose an atom of hydrogen. It is the number of the particles and their arrangement in the atoms that make the important difference between one of the heaviest of the metals and the lightest of the gases.

DISCOVERY OF THE ELECTRON

The first of the ultimate particles to be discovered was the electron; it was investigated by Sir J. J. Thomson towards the end of the 19th century. When an electric discharge is passed through a tube from which most of the air has been pumped out rays are emitted from the cathode (or negative electrode); these rays are known as cathode rays; they are used in television receivers to form pictures on a fluorescent screen. Thomson showed that the cathode rays are streams of minute particles each carrying a small negative electric charge; he called the particles electrons. He showed also that electrons are the same from whatever source they are derived, and thus that they are constituents of all kinds of matter.

MEASURING ELECTRONS

The next step was to measure the size of an electron, and this was achieved by Dr. Robert A. Millikan in a very ingenious way. He sprayed electrons with a very fine spray of oil. One or more electrons would adhere to each drop. The drops were very fine, but still large enough to be seen through a microscope, and their rate of fall, which was very slow, could be measured.

Millikan then applied an electric field to the falling drops. Any drops without a charge would be unaffected; those with one electron would be drawn toward the positive pole and their speed would be changed. Those with two electrons would be drawn with twice the force, and so on. By watching individual drops, and measuring their rates of fall, Millikan was able to detect which drops had one electron, which had two and which had more. The pull of the electric field gave him a measure of the size of an electron; he found that an electron has a mass equal to the 1/1840th part of a hydrogen atom.

THE ATOM AS A TINY UNIVERSE

The charge on an electron is extremely minute, but since each atom of a substance has one or more of these minute charges we might expect the whole body of a substance to have a considerable charge. This is not so; it is only in exceptional circumstances that bodies are electrified. There must therefore be positive charges in each atom sufficient to neutralize the effect of the negative charges on the electrons. Lord Rutherford (1871-1937) showed that the positive charges are concentrated on a minute nucleus at the centre of the atom.

Rutherford's picture of the atom was based on our knowledge of the solar system. We know that the solar system has the sun as a centre, and nine major planets revolving round it in elliptical orbits or paths—Mercury in scorching proximity to the sun, then Venus, Earth, Mars, Jupiter, Saturn, Uranus and, in cold, outer obscurity, Neptune, and even beyond Neptune the small, newly-discovered Pluto. We have to imagine an atom, in spite of its diminutive size, as a little universe in itself. Each atom is a minute planetary system with the electrons revolving about a nucleus, like planets revolving about a sun.

The number of electrons varies from element to element, beginning with hydrogen, which has a single electron revolving about its nucleus, then helium with two electrons, lithium with three, and so on, adding the electrons one by one till we reach uranium with ninety-two electrons.

VALUE OF THE ATOMIC NUMBER

The positive charge on the nucleus balances the combined charges on the electrons, and thus we see that this charge also increases unit by unit, from a single unit on the nucleus of the hydrogen atom up to ninety-two units on that of the uranium atom. H. G. J. Moseley showed, in 1913, that the number of charges on the nucleus is an important characteristic of an atom. He was able to mark each element with an atomic number—the number of charges on the nucleus.

The use of atomic numbers instead of atomic weights has cleared up the last discrepancies in Mendeleyev's table. Each element is now put definitely into the place indicated by its atomic number; there are now no awkward and unexplained anomalies. The positions of gaps in the table are known with certainty. All the elements except two have been detected, and we know definitely that there are only these two still to be found, unless there are more elaborate elements with atomic numbers higher than ninety-two.

SUN OF THE ATOMIC PLANETARY SYSTEM

Attention was now directed to the nucleus, the sun of the atomic planetary system. We know how the great mass of the sun controls the solar system. The sun has a mass 750 times as great as that of all the planets put together; it is this great mass at the centre that holds the planets in their orbits or paths and prevents them from flying off. In the solar system we have the force of gravity to hold the system together. In the atom we have the attraction between the positively charged nucleus and the negatively charged electrons.

The electrons do not fall into the nucleus for the same reason that the planets do not fall into the sun; in each case the forward movement prevents them falling to the centre towards which they are attracted. The nucleus of an atom is extremely small, but massive. We have seen that the mass of an electron is only the 1/1840th part of the mass of a hydrogen atom. The remainder of the mass is concentrated in the nucleus

STRUCTURE OF THE NUCLEUS

It was to be expected that the nucleus would reveal some kind of structure, otherwise we should be driven back on the idea of ninety-two different kinds of bricks. We should have avoided that difficulty in the electronic part of the atom, only to meet it again in the nucleus.

The method used in experiments on the nucleus is to bombard the element with high-speed particles. We cannot expect a great number of direct hits. The nucleus is extremely small; it is surrounded by rapidly moving electrons, and these have to be broken through before the nucleus can be reached; and finally the nucleus is surrounded by an electric field sufficient to divert one of the minute projectiles used in bombardment. Fortunately we are able to bombard with billions of particles, and there are sufficient direct hits to give observable results.

The method of bombardment revealed that the nucleus of an element contains at least two kinds of particle. One of these particles has a positive charge equal to the charge of an electron; this kind of particle is called a proton. The other kind of particle has the same mass as a proton, but it has no charge either positive or negative; for this reason it is called a neutron. When the physicists of Columbia University, U.S.A., in 1939 split the atom of uranium, they did so by bombarding it with neutrons.

Recently a fourth kind of particle has been detected. This is a positively charged particle. Its mass is equal to that of an electron; its charge also is equal to that of an electron, but of course of opposite sign. It is sometimes called a positive electron and sometimes a positron.

The position of the positron in the scheme of things is still doubtful. Positrons definitely form part of the nucleus, since they have been ejected from nuclei during bombardment. One possibility is that a proton may be a combination of a neutron and a positron; the neutron would give the required mass and the positron the required charge.

MINUTE BUT MIGHTY PARTICLES

These then, so far as we know, are the ultimate particles out of which the universe is built. There are two light particles—the electron and the positron—which seem capable of no further division; their masses are equal; their charges are equal and opposite. There are two heavy particles which supply almost the whole mass of matter; these are the proton and neutron.

All the infinite variety of the universe, of so-called " dead " matter and of all types of life, consists in the last resort of varied arrangements of these four particles.

YUKONS FROM OUTER SPACE

The Japanese scientist, Yukawa, suggested a few years ago that another kind of particle, the yukon, may occur in the nuclei of atoms. The yukon is a heavy electron; it has the same charge as an electron, and a mass one hundred and fifty times as great.

Yukons were first observed in connexion with cosmic rays. These rays have great penetrating power; they appear to reach the earth from outer space. It has been shown that they contain streams of yukons. Yukawa suggests that yukons may play a part in the splitting up of atomic nuclei, but it is difficult to see how the mass of fifteen can be made to fit in with the other observed masses.

THE NUCLEUS IS A GAS

Professor Neils Bohr, the famous Danish physicist whose name is closely associated with work on the atom, considers that the nucleus is not to be regarded as a solid. It is in the condition of a gas, with the various particles in constant agitation, and constantly colliding.

When a nucleus is hit during bombardment its temperature goes up to a level that has been calculated at 40,000,000°C. The nucleus loses this stupendous heat by emitting particles and rays.

STRIPPING AN ATOM

The electrons of an atom are not unalterably attached to the nucleus. We have to think of them as spinning round the nucleus, some of them in orbits comparatively close to the nucleus, and others farther out.

An atom may be stripped of one or more of its electrons, or it may have electrons added to it. Hydrogen atoms, for example, may be stripped of their single electrons by passing an electrical discharge through the gas in a rarefied condition. If an electron is added to an atom, we have an atom with a negative charge; in this state the atom is called an ion. The removal of an electron (that is, of a negative charge) is equivalent to the addition of a positive charge; as though one of the charges on the nucleus were unbalanced, and so became effective. Thus we can have ions with positive charges, as well as ions with negative charges. An ion with a negative charge is called a cathion; an ion with a positive charge is called an anion.

ELEMENTS IDENTIFIED BY NUMBER

An atom which has lost an electron does not change its identity; it is still an atom of the same element, a charged atom but still the same element. Equally, if an atom gains an electron it remains an atom of the same element.

This is not true of the nucleus. The atomic number, that is the number of positive charges on the nucleus, identifies the element. Zinc, for example, has the atomic number thirty; it is identified by the fact that it has thirty charges on the nucleus. If by any means we could expel a proton (with its positive charge) from the nucleus of an atom of zinc it would cease to be an atom of zinc; it would become an atom with atomic number twenty-nine, that is an atom of copper.

BOMBARDING THE ELEMENTS

THE dream of the alchemists was to transmute or change the baser metals into gold. In the days when the ninety or so elements were regarded as distinct and unrelated entities, the dream of the alchemists appeared to be an idle dream. Now we are not so sure. What we do know is that elements have actually been transmuted.

THREE KINDS OF AMMUNITION

In order to effect the transmutation of elements we have to bombard them with fast-moving particles. There are three kinds of particle that can be used. There are what are called alpha-particles; these are emitted by radium. They come from the nuclei of radium atoms, and they have two positive charges. Each alpha-particle is therefore equivalent to two protons, and is the same as the nucleus of a helium atom. When they are emitted by radium they have a speed of about 10,000 miles per second. They have, therefore, the properties necessary for successful bombardment: small size, large mass and high speed.

We can also carry out bombardment experiments with fast-moving protons. A hydrogen atom consists of an electron revolving about a proton. We can get rid of the electrons by passing an electric discharge through a tube which contains traces of hydrogen. We want the protons to move at a considerable speed, and so we attract them by means of a strong negative charge. The pull of the electric charge gives the protons an extremely high speed. Ordinary hydrogen atoms could not be used because they have no charge and cannot therefore be accelerated in an electric field.

Neutrons are the third kind of particles which can be used in bombarding the elements. When beryllium is bombarded with alpha-particles neutrons are emitted. They are ejected with so high a speed that they can be used effectively in the bombardment of other elements. In some experiments slow neutrons are used; they are slowed down by letting them pass through solid paraffin. Some elements absorb slow-moving neutrons.

CHANGING BORON INTO CARBON

The actual transmutation of the elements has so far been achieved on a very small scale. Boron atoms have been bombarded with alpha-particles and converted into atoms of carbon, the next higher element on the atomic scale; during the process protons are emitted. It is evident that when there is a direct hit the boron nucleus captures an alpha-particle and emits a proton, that is, it gains two positive charges and loses one. The net gain of one positive charge raises the atom one place in the scale.

Other things may happen during a bombardment. An alpha-particle may pass so close to a nucleus that it disturbs it, so that it emits a proton without capturing the alpha-particle. There is a loss of one positive charge to the nucleus; an atom of boron moves down one place and becomes an atom of beryllium.

When beryllium is bombarded with alpha-particles a direct hit results in the nucleus capturing the alpha-particle and ejecting a neutron. The nucleus gains two positive charges, and so the atom of beryllium moves up two places and becomes an atom of carbon. The ejected neutrons have no charges, and so do not affect the identity of the atoms.

MERCURY BECOMES GOLD

If we wish to manufacture gold the most hopeful metal to start with is mercury. Gold is element 79, and mercury is element 80; so that if we can expel one proton from the nucleus of an atom of mercury we have transmuted it into an atom of gold. The process is difficult because an atom of mercury has eighty electrons; eighty orbits have to be broken through, as well as the electric field round the nucleus. The experiment was, however, successfully carried out at the Physical-Technical State Institute at Berlin. The bombarding particles were given a high speed by means of a field of 30,000 volts, and a small, but observable, quantity of gold was produced from quicksilver.

We have no means of knowing whether these minute laboratory transmutations can ever be reproduced on a commercial scale. Further knowledge of the structure of the nucleus may show whether large-scale transmutations can be carried out at a sufficiently low price. For the moment we know that elements can be transmuted—but only just.

WHAT AN ISOTOPE IS

Another point of great interest emerges from these bombardment experiments. When we are bombarding with neutrons the nuclei of bombarded atoms may capture some of the neutrons, which have the same mass as protons but no charge. A nucleus captures a neutron; its mass increases by one unit, but its charge remains unaltered. We know that the identity of the atom depends on the charge; thus the gain of a neutron changes the weight of an atom without changing the properties which make it an atom of a particular element. We can, therefore, have two samples of an element which differ in weight but which are alike in other ways.

These varieties of an element are called isotopes. When two isotopes of an element are mixed it is extremely difficult to separate them because their properties are alike. They dissolve to the same extent in water and other liquids; they form exactly the same chemical compounds. The differences that we usually rely on to separate one substance from another are missing.

HEAVY HYDROGEN

Nevertheless, isotopes have been wholly or partially separated. The most spectacular success occurred with hydrogen. Any sample of pure water from any part of the world has exactly the same composition and the same properties as any other sample; it has the same boiling point, the same melting point, it dissolves the same proportions of the various solids and so on. It can be decomposed in the same way by passing an electric current through it, and there is no observable difference between one sample of hydrogen given off and any other sample.

It turns out, however, that there are two kinds of hydrogen, but they are so thoroughly mixed that all samples of hydrogen are alike. There is a large amount of hydrogen with one proton as the nucleus of each atom, and a very small amount with a proton and a neutron as a nucleus; there is only one part of the latter in 6,000 parts of hydrogen. The latter form of hydrogen has about twice the weight of the former because of the added neutron, but the same properties (apart from those dependent on weight) because each has a single positive charge on the nucleus.

When an electric current is passed through water, the water is split up into oxygen and hydrogen. These gases are given off, but the lighter hydrogen is given off more rapidly, in proportion to its quantity, than the heavy hydrogen. If the electric current is left running for weeks and months there is a slow concentration of heavy hydrogen in the small amount of water that is left. Almost pure heavy hydrogen, free from the lighter isotope, can be obtained in this manner.

HEAVY WATER

Heavy hydrogen can be separated from ordinary hydrogen in the way described, because there is a great difference between the densities of the two isotopes; one has twice the density of the other.

Heavy water, composed of oxygen and heavy hydrogen, differs considerably from ordinary water in some of its properties. These properties are those that depend on weight. It is more viscous or sticky than ordinary water, it melts at a higher temperature ($3.8\,^{\circ}$C. instead of $0\,^{\circ}$C.), and boils at $101.4\,^{\circ}$C. instead of $100\,^{\circ}$C. Oddly enough, heavy water appears to have poisonous properties; tadpoles die in it and seeds do not germinate. It does not, however, add another to the list of poisons that can endanger human life. If taken internally it would be quickly diluted by water in the body and become harmless.

SEPARATING OTHER ISOTOPES

It is much more difficult to separate the isotopes of other elements because there is comparatively little difference between their densities. Chlorine, for example, has two isotopes with atomic weights 35 and 37; ordinary chlorine is a mixture of these two, and has an atomic weight of 35.46. The difference in density between the two isotopes is two parts in thirty-five, or about six per cent as compared with 100 per cent in the case of hydrogen. Isotopes have, however, been partially separated in various ways; the separation is shown by the fact that one sample of the element is heavier than another sample because it contains a bigger proportion of the heavier isotope.

The isotopes of neon were partially separated by allowing the gas to diffuse through a clay pipe. The lighter isotope diffused more quickly through the porous clay, and a distinct difference was found between the weight of the neon outside the tube and of that inside it.

KNOWN AS A MASS SPECTRUM

We have seen how the isotopes of some elements can be separated, wholly or partially, in quantities that can be measured by ordinary means. Professor F. W. Aston devised a means by which minute quantities of isotopes can be separated from one another.

The atoms of the element are ionized, that is, each atom is given an electric charge by submitting the element to a stream of electrons. The charged atoms are caused to move at a high speed by electric attraction. They are allowed to pass first through an electric field and then through a magnetic field. The charged atoms are deflected, lighter atoms being deflected more than heavier atoms. The streams of atoms are allowed to fall on a photographic plate, and each stream makes a line on it. Thus there is a separate line corresponding to each isotope. The atomic weights are given by the positions of the photographic records on the plate. A record of this kind is a mass spectrum. Mass spectra have enabled the isotopes of elements to be discovered, even where it is not possible to separate them in quantities that can be measured by ordinary means. It is the mass spectrum that enable us to say that chlorine has two isotopes, and that their atomic weights are 35 and 37.

HOW ATOMS AND MOLECULES MOVE

Two atoms of hydrogen unite with one atom of oxygen to form a molecule of water; the three atoms are held together by their outer electrons. A molecule of water is the smallest fragment of water that is water. If a molecule of water were further divided it would be, not water, but the two gases, oxygen and hydrogen.

The molecules of water are in a state of constant agitation. Molecules at the surface may leave the water and form water vapour in the air; other molecules leave the air and return to the liquid. The hotter the water is the more violently are the molecules agitated. When water boils, the upward pressure of molecules trying to leave the liquid is equal to the downward pressure of the air, and so molecules of water leave the liquid in great quantities and become steam.

Not only do the molecules interchange with one another; the atoms also interchange. An atom of hydrogen may leave one molecule and join on to another. There is a constant interchange amongst these lively particles.

One of the early experimenters with heavy hydrogen incautiously stored his supply of it over water. In most circumstances that is a good way of storing a gas. But when the experimenter came to use his store of heavy hydrogen all he found was a supply of ordinary hydrogen. He had forgotten that atoms are constantly interchanging. The atoms in his little store of heavy hydrogen had interchanged with hydrogen atoms in the much greater mass of water over which the gas had been stored.

ISOTOPES WERE MIXED WHEN THE EARTH WAS YOUNG

The interchange of atoms should explain why isotopes are seldom found unmixed. There has been ample time in the many millions of years of the earth's history for complete mixing. Molecules are most active in the gaseous state, less active in the liquid state, and least active in the solid state. The complete mixing of isotopes appears to have taken place at an early stage in the history of the solar system, when the elements were in a gaseous or liquid condition. Samples of iron from all sources, for example, prove to have exactly the same atomic weight. Occasionally meteorites fall on the earth from outside space. Samples of iron from these meteorites have the same atomic weight as terrestrial iron. This suggests a common origin, and a very thorough mixing of isotopes, at any rate in the colder parts of the solar system.

The only exceptions are found amongst the radio-active elements and their products. Ordinary lead has an atomic weight of 207.2. Lead from radium minerals has an atomic weight of 206, and that from thorium minerals 208. We have the natural isotopes from radium and thorium minerals; ordinary lead is a mixture of these and other isotopes. The reason for the existence of unmixed isotopes of lead is that this lead is newly formed by the breaking up of atoms of radium and thorium. It has not had time or opportunity to become mixed with other isotopes of lead.

ATOMIC WEIGHTS OF ISOTOPES

The atomic weights of some elements are almost exact whole numbers; others are far removed from being whole numbers. Antimony, for example, has an atomic weight of 121.76. We have seen that the mass of an atom depends on the number of protons and neutrons in the nucleus. It might appear therefore that all atomic weights should be whole numbers, since there is no such thing as a fraction of a proton or neutron. The existence of fractional atomic weights which could not be explained away as errors of measurement, was one of the gravest obstacles to the general acceptance of the new theories of matter. The difficulty was completely cleared up by the discovery of isotopes.

The atomic numbers of all isotopes are whole numbers. The fractions arise from the mixture of isotopes. Chlorine, for example, has about three parts of the lighter isotope (35) to one part of the heavier (37), thus giving an atomic weight of 35.46 for the mixture.

NATURE'S LABORATORY

The experiments in splitting the nuclei of atoms conducted with great difficulty in scientific laboratories are paralleled in nature.

The nuclei of the atoms of radium and other radio-active elements are spontaneously breaking up. Any piece of radium is continuously giving out three kinds of rays, which are called alpha-rays, beta-rays, and gamma-rays. (Alpha, beta, gamma are the Greek equivalent of A, B, C.) Alpha- and beta-rays are not rays in the ordinary sense of the word. Alpha-rays are streams of helium nuclei each consisting of two protons; beta-rays are streams of electrons. Gamma-rays are rays of the same kind as light-rays and X-rays.

When a helium nucleus (or alpha-particle) is ejected by a radium atom, the nucleus loses two protons and the radium atom goes down two places in the atomic scale. It becomes an atom of an inert gas called emanation. Thus the breaking up of a radium atom results in the production of an atom of emanation and an atom of helium. Emanation is itself radio-active; it ejects helium nuclei, goes down two places, and becomes a short-lived substance called radium A. After further changes the final result is lead, which is not radio-active.

THE HALF-LIFE PERIOD

The change from radium to emanation goes on at a definite rate which depends on the amount of radium. It has been found that half of any quantity of radium changes to emanation in 1,700 years. At the end of that time there would be only half of the radium left. And so on for further periods of 1,700 years. Thus we have: 1, 1/2, 1/4, 1/8, 1/16, 1/32 and so on, of the original amount. We can go on halving and never reach zero.

The time in which any quantity of radium loses half its mass is called the half-life period. The reason for giving the half-life period is that we can put no limit to the complete change; as we have seen we can never reach zero by halving. Every radio-active element has its distinctive half-life period. In some cases the half-life period is only a few minutes, in others it is many years. Uranium has a half-life period of 6,000,000,000 years.

ARTIFICIAL RADIO-ACTIVE ELEMENTS

When an element is bombarded with neutrons it can happen that a neutron is captured by the nucleus of a bombarded atom without the loss of another particle. We should thus have an atom of an isotope of the element with atomic weight one higher. Such isotopes are often unstable; the nuclei eject the particles gained during bombardment. Thus we have an artificial radio-active isotope with a definite half-life period.

In a recent series of experiments, Professor G. Hevesy used a narrow tube filled with beryllium powder and radium emanation as a source of neutrons. The sealed glass tube was placed in another tube and surrounded with the substance to be bombarded. The larger tube was then placed in the middle of a block of paraffin.

We have already seen that when beryllium is bombarded with alpha-particles it emits fast-moving protons. Emanation supplies the alpha-particles which eject neutrons from the beryllium. The purpose of the block of paraffin is to slow down some of the neutrons. Hydrogen is one of the constituents of paraffin; when a neutron collides with a hydrogen nucleus it is slowed down. Thus the substance in the outer tube was bombarded with fast-moving neutrons and there were also slow neutrons present.

LIKE TO LIKE

The apparatus was left for several days, and then the material in the outer tube was examined. The principle of the method was this : suppose a very minute quantity of potassium has been formed, far too small a quantity to be detected by ordinary chemical means. A potassium salt is added, and then removed by precipitating it. The point is that the minute trace of manufactured potassium comes away with the potassium salt. A sodium salt could equally well be used, if it happened to be more convenient, because sodium is very similar to potassium. The material in the tube was therefore treated with salts of the elements which might be formed, that is those whose atomic numbers were close to that of the element being tested. And then these salts were separated.

Now the merest trace of a radio-active element can be detected; that is what the experimenters were hoping to do. In one series of experiments scandium was bombarded. Two of the salts which were used showed radio-activity; these were sodium chloride (common salt) and scandium oxide. Two unstable isotopes had therefore been formed, one an isotope of potassium and the other an isotope of scandium. Potassium has two stable isotopes, with atomic weights 39 and 41; ordinary potassium is a mixture of these two. The unstable, radio-active isotope, which was formed during the bombardment, probably had an atomic weight of 42—not 38, since we should expect an unstable atom to be more cumbrous than a stable atom. It was found that this isotope of potassium has a half-life period of sixteen hours. Scandium has only one stable isotope, with atomic weight 45. The unstable isotope, therefore, has atomic weight 46; it was found to have a half-life period of several years. Scandium oxide, forecast by Mendeleyev, was discovered in 1879.

CHEMICAL INDICATORS

A whole series of artificial radio-active isotopes have been made by the method described above. These isotopes are useful as chemical "indicators."

In a series of experiments with gold, a thin disk of gold was "activated" by bombarding one side of it with neutrons; this had the effect of creating an extremely thin layer of radio-active gold on one side of the disk. The strength of the radio-activity was measured by means of a delicate electric counter; this instrument counts the number of minute electric charges that fall on it. Radio-activity was at first very unevenly distributed on the disk. As time went on it became more and more evenly dispersed through the disk. This showed that the isotopes of gold exchanged with one another, and tended toward a complete mixture.

Apart from radio-activity there was nothing to distinguish one isotope of gold from another. The disk looked exactly the same after bombardment as before, and by no chemical means could the isotopes be separated. But radio-activity indicated what was happening.

HOW MASS BECOMES ENERGY

UNTIL recently there seemed to be an absolute distinction between mass and energy. The material of a substance was one thing; any power it had of doing work was an utterly different thing. That distinction has been blown sky-high by the electromagnetic theory of matter. At one time an electron may be part of the substance of an atom, at another time it may appear as an electric charge. Part of the mass of an atom may be radiated as energy; or a whole atom may disappear and be replaced by an equivalent amount of energy.

Formerly it was held that matter was indestructible and that energy was indestructible. Matter might be changed in many ways, but its mass did not change. Energy might be changed from the energy of falling water to the energy of rotating coils, and so to electrical energy; but the quantity of energy did not change. Now we have to consider that it is the total of mass and energy that does not change. Mass has an equivalent in energy which can be calculated, and the destruction of an atom of matter results in the release of its equivalent in energy.

BREAKING UP OF THE SUN

The change from matter to energy is going on before our eyes on a stupendous scale. Without the sun this earth would be a dark and dead place, sinking slowly to the temperature of absolute zero, 273°C. below freezing point. The heat and light with which the sun keeps the earth alive are only about the 1/200,000,000th part of the heat and light given out by the sun. The source of the whole stupendous outpouring of energy by the sun has been one of the most difficult problems of science. The mere radiation of the heat of a hot body would have exhausted the sun long ago, and it would now be a mere cinder. The only explanation is that the mass of the sun is being radiated as energy, and the sun is slowly shrinking as its mass changes to energy.

We are receiving heat and light by the disintegration or breaking up of the matter of the sun. The process of atom-splitting that is accomplished with such difficulty in terrestrial laboratories proceeds on a vast scale in the great laboratory of the sun. The extremely high temperature of the sun produces the rapid movement of particles that is necessary for disintegration

SUN LOSING A MILLION TONS A SECOND

It has been calculated that the sun is losing mass at the rate of 1,000,000 tons per second. That may seem an enormous amount, and it is enormous when compared with commercial standards. The total yearly production of coal in Great Britain is over 200,000,000 tons. The sun loses that amount of matter by radiation every three or four minutes. But the sun is a very big body, with approximately 330,000 times the mass of the earth. The earth itself is not inconsiderable, it has a mass of nearly six thousand trillion tons.

Even if the present rate of radiation were to be continued to the end the last of the sun would not be radiated till after sixty billion years. The sun is certainly getting smaller, but the loss of mass in a thousand years is only a sixty thousand-millionth of its immense bulk.

HORSE-POWER OF THE SUN

It has been calculated that every square inch of the sun's surface is throwing out energy at the rate of 13 horse-power. In other words the total energy is more than a hundred thousand trillion horse-power. Even the small fraction that falls on the earth is equivalent to the work of five hundred billion horses. The total number of horses in the world is estimated at 80,000,000. That is only the six-millionth part of what the sun would need for our share of its light and heat.

As already noted, the temperature of an atom, before the nucleus splits up, rises to 40,000,000°C. The surface temperature of the sun is a mere 5,800°C., only 2,000 degrees hotter than the highest temperature that can be obtained by means of an electric furnace. The interior of the sun must be immensely hotter; it must reach at least the 40,000,000°C. necessary for the disintegration of atoms.

ENERGY FROM RADIUM

On a small scale we have the same sort of process going on in the spontaneous breaking up of radium atoms. We have seen that when radium atoms break up, three kinds of rays are emitted—alpha-, beta-, and gamma-rays. The alpha-rays are streams of helium nuclei and result in the presence of the gas helium in rocks which contain radium. The beta-rays are streams of electrons. Gamma-rays are true radiation of very short wavelength.

A radium atom contains more energy than is contained in the products into which it breaks down—the radio-active gas emanation, helium, and the ejected electrons. The excess energy is radiated as gamma-rays, and that is how these rays arise.

The speed of the expelled particles is very great, about 10,000 miles per second; in an absolute vacuum they would travel the distance round the world in two and a half seconds. Actually they are moving in a space crowded with molecules, and are brought to a stop in an inch or so by collision with the molecules.

RADIUM AS A MACHINE-GUN

Moving at such excessive speed, even tiny particles have a great amount of energy, and can do a lot of work, useful or merely destructive, before they come to rest. A tiny fragment of radium, carelessly handled, can produce serious and even fatal wounds. Recently a small quantity of radium was stolen from a New York hospital. The thieves were warned by wireless of the terrible risk to which they were exposing themselves. They were carrying what was in effect a deadly machine-gun pouring out almost incredible numbers of tiny projectiles, thousands of times swifter than any bullet, and capable of piercing through any probable protection.

Radium can only be dealt with safely by keeping it in a container of lead. The tightly compacted molecules of lead stop the deadly little projectiles, and so save the hands and arms of operators.

Radium has been used with considerable success in the treatment of cancer. The most recent method is to direct a beam of rays on to the cancer. Five grammes of radium—less than a quarter of an ounce—is used for this purpose. The beam is directed carefully on to the cancerous growth, so that the malignant tissue only is destroyed.

HEAT FROM RADIUM

The particles expelled from radium quickly lose their great speed by collision with other particles, and so they lose most of their energy. This energy is not destroyed; it reappears in another form, as heat. The heat produced by a piece of radium is sufficient to boil the same weight of water in about three-quarters of an hour, or nearly 12,000 times the weight in a year.

This creation of heat out of the energy stored up within a tiny piece of radium goes on year after year, without any appreciable diminution of the mass of the radium. The process of disintegration of radium is extremely slow, even though the number of particles expelled per second is extremely large. A gramme of radium (about the thirtieth part of an ounce) expels 34,000,000,000 alpha-particles every second. In a year that is about a trillion particles. Yet it takes 1,700 years for half of the quantity of radium (a mere sixtieth of an ounce) to disintegrate. The process goes on spontaneously. There seems to be no means of stopping it, and no means of speeding it up.

WARMING THE EARTH

The quantity of radium produced in the world is very small; the total annual production is only about two and a half ounces. The labour of producing even this small quantity is very great; the radium has to be concentrated by treating tons of the rocks in which it is contained.

In extremely minute quantities, radium occurs almost everywhere. In most rocks there are one or two parts in a billion, or about an ounce of radium in 20,000,000 tons of rock. That may appear to be an insignificant amount, and yet it is an important factor in preserving the heat of the earth. The steady output of heat from radium and other radio-active minerals helps to keep our comparatively comfortable earth from cooling below the level that makes life possible.

ENERGY OF AN ATOM

There is an enormous amount of energy stored up within atoms. The output of energy from radium is only a small fraction of the total energy. The final products of disintegration of radium are lead and helium; the atomic weight is reduced from 226 to 206. There is still a long way to go before an atomic weight of zero is reached by a complete disintegration.

Atomic energy is known, and its amount can be calculated. The destruction of an ounce of matter, or rather its conversion into energy, would supply more than 100,000 horse-power for a year—the equivalent of 100,000 horses working at their best and without rest for twelve months.

All other sources of energy that we are aware of are insignificant when compared with the enormous reservoir of energy in apparently inert and lifeless matter. To keep small patches of Great Britain inefficiently warmed and lighted in winter requires the burning of many millions of tons of coal. England and Wales could have their full share of sunlight and sun heat by the conversion of about 1,000 tons of matter annually into light and heat.

The *Queen Mary* has four propellers, to each of which some 50,000 horse-power is applied. When she was being tested, she took on board 75,000 gallons of fuel oil to carry her through the trials. Compare this with the amount that would be required if the whole atomic energy could be released. An ounce would keep the great vessel running for six months.

WHAT MAN COULD DO IF——

The release of atomic energy, so as to make it available for heating and lighting and running machines, is the dream of scientists, just as transmutation was the dream of the old alchemists. It is a dream far more alluring than the idea of manufacturing unlimited gold. With such forces at his command, it would be difficult to put a limit to what man could do. He could have perpetual daylight if he wanted it. He could keep the surface of the whole globe at a genial temperature. He could control the winds by raising or lowering the temperature over great stretches of the earth's surface. He could explore the crust of the earth far more effectively than now. He might even learn to control himself.

Whether the dream will ever become reality no one can say. There appear to be insuperable difficulties in the way of releasing atomic energy. But so many apparently insuperable difficulties have been overcome by science that no one dare say it is impossible.

MEASURING AN ATOM

An atom is an extremely small particle, so small that it might seem impossible to measure it. Nevertheless, measurements have been made in many different ways, and as the results agree fairly closely we are justified in accepting them as being reasonably accurate.

In the case of hydrogen and some other gases we have to measure molecules and not atoms. The reason is that hydrogen atoms combine in pairs to form molecules of hydrogen. The diameter of a hydrogen molecule is .00000001 inch, that is 100,000,000th part of an inch. In trying to realize what that means, think of an ordinary ruler on which the inches are divided into tenths. It is not difficult to estimate a hundredth, the tenth of a tenth. In that small space, only just measurable, a million molecules of hydrogen could be placed side by side.

MAKING ATOMS VISIBLE

In an account of a new kind of microscope devised by Dr. Vladimir Zworykin, in America, it was stated that an atom was shown on a screen as a bright circle of light an inch across. That would entail a magnification of about 100,000,000, a far greater magnification than any that had previously been obtained. On the same scale of magnification, an inch would become 100,000,000 inches, or about 1,600 miles, a fifth of the diameter of the world. To look at the matter from a rather different angle, the number of hydrogen molecules that stretch an inch when placed side by side, is the same as the number of inches in 1,600 miles, or say the number of quarter-inches in the distance between London and Edinburgh.

Let us see now how many hydrogen molecules can be packed into a small cube with one-inch edges. There are 100,000,000 molecules in the length, 100,000,000 in the width, and 100,000,000 in the height. To find the total number of molecules in the cube we have to multiply 100,000,000 by itself twice. That is a quadrillion, or 1 followed by twenty-four noughts.

MAGNIFYING A CUBIC INCH

The mere setting down of a quadrillion is impressive, but it is possible to get a better idea of what it means. We will imagine the inch cube magnified until it has the same volume as the earth. We begin by shaping the cube into a sphere so that it may have the same shape as the world. We find that the radius of the cube is .62 inch, or a little more than six-tenths of an inch. .62 inch has to be magnified to 4,000 miles, the radius of the earth, so we have to find the number of times .62 inch is contained in 4,000 miles. A little simple arithmetic shows that the magnification is a little more than 400,000,000. With this magnification a little sphere holding a cubic inch is magnified to the size of the world. The diameter of a hydrogen molecule, with this magnification, becomes four inches.

If we can imagine a space as big as the whole earth filled with balls four inches in diameter we shall have some idea of the vast number of hydrogen molecules in a cubic inch.

Actually the molecules of hydrogen are not so tightly packed when the hydrogen is at atmospheric pressure. The number of molecules in a cubic inch, in this condition, is 44 followed by nineteen noughts.

COUNTING MOLECULES

The counting of molecules one by one is, of course, far beyond the bounds of possibility. But suppose the molecules were passed through a fine nozzle at the rate of a million a second, it seems as though we should soon account for the molecules in a cubic inch.

Well, a year is roughly 32,000,000 seconds. In a year, therefore, thirty-two billion molecules pass through. To find the number of years we have to divide the number of molecules by thirty-two billion. It would take about 14,000,000 years for that small mass of molecules to pass through.

EMPTINESS OF AN ATOM

The atom is so small a thing that there hardly seems room in it, as it were, for emptiness. Indeed, the old idea of the atom was that it was an inert thing completely filled with matter, and as solid as a piece of iron seems to be.

When we come to measure an electron there is a different tale to tell. The diameter of an electron is .14 of a billionth of an inch, or about a seven-billionth of an inch. If electrons could be placed side by side it would take seven billion of them to stretch an inch. Set out in full the diameter of an electron is .00000000000014 inch. That distance is many times smaller than the diameter of a hydrogen molecule; it is only 1/70,000th as great. Or we can say that the diameter of a hydrogen molecule is 70,000 times as great as that of an electron.

A hydrogen molecule consists of two hydrogen atoms, each with an electron revolving about a very small nucleus. Thus the distance of an electron from the nucleus is something like 17,000 times the diameter of the electron. The greater part of the molecule is, therefore, empty space. We have a tiny electron at comparatively an enormous distance revolving about a very small nucleus.

If we magnify the atom to get a picture of it, we may make the diameter of the electron a yard; its distance from the nucleus then becomes 17,000 yards, or about ten miles. We have to think of a sphere a yard in diameter, at a distance of ten miles, circling round the nucleus. Apart from this sphere, and the still smaller nucleus, the rest of the atom is empty space. All but one part in five billion is empty space.

MATTER AND MOVEMENT

If that were the whole of the picture there would be no such thing as matter. A bar of iron would collapse into an invisible fragment. The six thousand trillion tons of the earth's mass would collapse into a sphere a mere half-mile or so in diameter.

What has to be added to the picture is movement. We have seen that particles are ejected from atoms at a speed of 10,000 miles a second. Electrons also revolve in their orbits with great speed. We are accustomed to the comparatively slow movement of the earth round the sun, once in a year, at a speed of more than 1,000 miles an hour. The movement of an electron in its orbit is extremely quick, and the orbit is extremely small. An electron revolves not once in a year, but a great number of times in a second.

It is not merely that an electron revolves in a circular or elliptical orbit; the orbit also rolls round. There is the same sort of roll in the orbits of the planets, but it is very small in their case. The orbit of an electron rolls very rapidly, so that the electron actually moves through every point on the shell on which its orbit lies many times per second.

MASS AND SPEED

Einstein explained the movement of precession (the rolling of the orbit) in a very interesting way. The mass of any object increases with its speed. Such an idea did not fit into the old conception of mechanics, in which mass could be changed in form but not in amount. It does fit into modern atomic mechanics, in which mass and energy are two forms of the same thing.

Any body moving round another body in an elliptical orbit moves quickest when it is nearest the body round which it revolves. The planet Mercury varies considerably in its distance from the sun and consequently in the speed at which it revolves round the sun. When nearest the sun its speed is greatest, and therefore its mass is greatest. There is a greater attraction between the sun and this greater mass and the planet is drawn in, so that its orbit is pulled round.

Precession is greatest in the case of Mercury, which has the most elliptical orbit, but it is observable in the orbits of other planets. It is far greater in the case of fast-moving electrons.

ELECTRONIC ARMY OF OCCUPATION

It has been suggested that an electron occupies an atom, a hydrogen atom for example, in the same sense that an army occupies a country. The army does not fill the country it occupies, but it acts in such a way as to exclude any other army that tries to enter the country, by resisting it at the frontier. An electron does not fill the atom, but it moves so quickly that it is almost continuously at every point of the boundary of the atom; it forms an almost impassable boundary. It is only minute high-speed particles that can break through this boundary.

The bulk of matter is almost entirely movement, the movement of extremely small electrons. The solidity of an iron bar is the resistance of whirling electrons to penetration. We can find many large-scale examples of this effect of movement. A rapidly whirled chain behaves as though it were a solid wheel. The chain is in the position of each possible spoke at such short intervals of time that it is just as if it were always in each position. If the whirling chain is released it runs along the ground like a solid wheel. Even a sheet of flimsy paper, if it is spun rapidly enough, acquires a sort of solidity and will resist a heavy blow.

The whirling electron approaches very closely the ideal state of being "everywhere at once." On that fact the universe is based. As science has declared, "all matter is electrical in origin." This is among the outstanding discoveries of modern physics.

ATOMS RESIST COMPRESSION

Molecules can be distorted by pressure or by means of electric or magnetic fields, but atoms put up an enormous resistance to compression.

Molecules of water consist of two hydrogen atoms attached to an oxygen atom. In ordinary water the molecules are so closely packed that water is not easily compressed. It is only when water is subjected to very high pressure that an observable compression is registered. The limit of compression appears to be the point at which there are no gaps between the atoms. No amount of pressure seems to have any effect in reducing the size of the atoms themselves.

The molecules of water are most tightly packed when the water is at 4°C.; at this temperature water is at its densest. There is a very slight swelling out as the temperature sinks to freezing point, and then a sudden swelling out when the water freezes. There is an increase in volume of one-tenth when water freezes; the molecules need this extra room to arrange themselves in the rigid solid form. If we put extra pressure on the ice we can force the molecules together and so compel the water to resume its liquid form, even though its temperature may be considerably below freezing point. If we release the pressure the water suddenly expands once more into ice.

This explains a phenomenon called regelation. If we hang a copper wire across a block of ice, and hang a heavy weight on each end of the wire, the wire slowly cuts its way through the ice. After a time the wire falls out at the bottom, leaving the block of ice intact. The reason is that the wire presses on the ice, the ice below the wire melts and allows the wire to pass through; but instantly, as soon as the pressure is released, the water freezes again above the wire.

EXPANSION BY HEATING

Laboratory methods appear to have no effect in compressing the actual atoms; all that can be accomplished is to reduce the spaces between them. What is, however, impossible to our feeble efforts, is accomplished on a large scale by the very high temperatures of some stars.

We are used to the idea that increase of heat usually forces molecules and atoms further apart. A metal rod expands when it is heated. An allowance of ten inches had to be left on the great Forth Bridge for the expansion and contraction between summer and winter temperatures. In the hot sun the atoms take up more space than in the cool earth; so the density of the sun is only a quarter of that of the earth.

COLLAPSE OF AN ATOM

Expansion by heating is the usual state of affairs, until we reach a temperature so high that the electronic defence of the atom is broken down. At a temperature measured in hundreds of millions of degrees the structure of the atoms collapses. The electrons are forced in on the nuclei and lie side by side with them. There is a sudden and extraordinary increase of density.

This phenomenon has been observed in a number of stars called white dwarfs. These are stars of small size, extremely high temperature, and extraordinary density. Sir James Jeans has described a newly discovered star of this class. It is a very small star, with a diameter only half that of the earth. Its volume, therefore, is only an eighth of that of the earth. The sun is more than a million times as big as the earth; and yet this comparatively tiny star probably contains three times as much matter as the sun.

We usually compare densities with the density of water. When we say that the density of iron is 7.8 we mean that a cubic inch, say, of iron weighs 7.8 times as much as a cubic inch of water. The densest of all the metals is osmium; it is twenty-two and a half times as dense as water, and just about twice as heavy as the same volume of lead.

The density of this white dwarf is so extraordinary that there is nothing remotely like it in our experience. We jump suddenly from a maximum density of twenty-two and a half on earth, to an average density in this white dwarf of 36,000,000.

PENNIES THAT WEIGH TONS

A cubic foot of water weighs about sixty-two and a half pounds. A cubic foot of the white dwarf weighs 36,000,000 times as much—about 1,000,000 tons. A piece the size of a penny would weigh about a ton.

Such a density is surprising, and yet less surprising when we consider that nearly the whole of an ordinary atom is empty space. What the highest temperatures and pressures at our disposal are not within sight of achieving is accomplished by the enormously greater temperatures of the white dwarfs—the empty spaces are filled up by compressing electrons and nuclei into them.

MORE ROOM FOR MOLECULES

When a liquid boils there is a sudden increase in volume. With water as the boiling liquid there is a sudden jump from 1 to 1,700, so that a cubic inch of water becomes a cubic foot of steam. That is an example of one of the essential differences between a liquid and a gas. In a liquid the molecules are closely packed, and slide over one another; in a gas they are much more spread out, indeed they spread out so as to fill all the available space. The expansion of a cubic inch of water into a cubic foot of steam allows each molecule twelve times as much space in which to move to and fro.

If we confine water in a closed vessel, and go on heating it, we can raise it above the normal boiling point, and still it does not boil. This is because there is no room for the molecules to spread out. Water in that condition is said to be superheated. If we release the pressure on superheated water, that is if we allow room for the molecules to spread out, the water boils explosively. The molecules, excited by heating, rush violently into the open space and strike any obstacle that comes in the way. When a boiler explodes it is because the materials of which it is composed break down under the hammering of quadrillions of water molecules.

WHY WATER BOILS

We say the boiling point of water is 100°C., or 212°F., but that is only true in certain conditions; we have just seen that it is not true for water confined in a closed vessel.

If there were no pressure at all on water there would be nothing to prevent molecules jumping out of the liquid into the space above it, and so becoming a gas. Usually there is the air pressing down on the water surface; this checks the molecules from jumping out, but does not altogether prevent them from doing so; we know that water will dry up at any temperature. The hotter the water is the more excitedly the molecules move, and the more readily they jump out of the liquid. At the boiling point there is a balance between the downward pressure of the air and the upward pressure of water molecules leaving the liquid to become gas, so that the air pressure no longer acts as a brake.

If we reduce the air pressure we release the brake slightly, molecules of water escape more readily and so the boiling point is lowered. Actually the boiling point of water varies slightly from day to day; it is slightly higher with a high barometer and slightly lower with a low barometer.

BOILING EGGS ON A MOUNTAIN

There is a story told of two mountaineers who tried to boil eggs at the top of a high mountain. In spite of boiling the eggs for half an hour the eggs resolutely refused to set. Then one of the mountaineers had a brainwave; he placed a large stone on the lid of the saucepan, and in three and a half minutes the eggs were cooked.

At the top of a high mountain, the air pressure is low, so that water boils at a temperature some degrees below the usual boiling point. The stone supplied extra pressure by keeping the lid down and so raised the boiling point.

In some industrial processes it is desirable to have water boiling below the usual boiling point; in making sugar, for example, we want to boil off the water without raising the temperature so high as to injure the sugar. For this purpose vacuum pans are used. The pans are enclosed except for a pipe through which the air and water vapour are sucked out. The pressure on the liquid is thus kept low and the liquid boils at a lower temperature than in an open pan.

NO WATER ON THE MOON

The absence of an atmosphere on the moon tells us definitely that there can be no liquid water there. If there were liquid water for a moment, the absence of air pressure would enable the molecules to spread out instantly and become a gas.

As a rule liquids which are composed of heavy molecules have higher boiling points than similar liquids with lighter molecules. Heavy water, for example, has a higher boiling point than ordinary water. The reason is that it takes more energy to enable a heavy molecule to jump out of the liquid than is necessary in the case of a lighter molecule.

WHAT POLAR MOLECULES ARE

If that were the only thing that counted, we could predict the boiling points of liquids merely by finding the weights of their molecules. But there is another point to be considered. Two or more atoms join together to form a molecule. In many cases they are joined by the outer electrons of the atoms. The link may be not exactly in the middle of the molecule. If it is a little to one side then we get a preponderance of negative charge at that side. We have in effect a tiny magnet, with a negative pole and a positive pole. If the shift from the centre of the molecule is very slight we have a very feeble magnet; if the shift is greater the magnet is stronger. Molecules of this kind are called polar molecules.

We know how magnets attract each other; the north pole of one magnet attracts the south pole of another. This is true also of polar molecules; there is the same sort of attraction between them, and they adhere to each other more strongly than non-polar molecules.

In water molecules there is a considerable shift, and the molecules adhere strongly. This explains why water has a high boiling point in spite of the fact that the molecules are not heavy. The molecules of benzene are much heavier than those of water; water molecules have a weight of 18, whereas those of benzene are 78. And yet water boils at 100°C., and benzene at only 78°C. The difference is due to the fact that the molecules of benzene are non-polar; so that there is no polar attraction between the molecules to be overcome.

WHY WATER AND OIL DO NOT MIX

Water and oil do not mix because the water molecules are polar, and the oil molecules non-polar. If we shake up oil and water together we get a sort of momentary mixture, but as soon as we stop shaking, the polar molecules of water attract one another and so come together. Very soon the whole of the water is in one mass, leaving the oil in another mass.

Alcohol, like water, has polar molecules, and so water and alcohol readily mix. If we stir up the two liquids together, a molecule of water will attract another water molecule or an alcohol molecule indifferently, and so the mixture is maintained.

X-RAYS AND CRYSTALS

The molecules in a liquid can slide about, and sometimes there is a very rapid interchange between one part of a liquid and another. In a solid the molecules are more fixed. They do oscillate, but they have not the same freedom of movement as in a liquid.

In crystals the molecules are not merely fixed in place, but they are regularly arranged. Sir William Bragg was one of the earliest physicists to inquire into the structure of crystals. He used X-rays in his investigations; these are light waves of very short wavelength, shorter even than the ultra-violet rays. X-rays are obtained by allowing cathode-rays (streams of electrons) to strike a target. By examining how X-rays are reflected and refracted by crystal surfaces Bragg was able to deduce the structure of the crystals.

One of the simplest crystal structures is that of sodium chloride (common salt). Each molecule consists of an atom of sodium and an atom of chlorine. When common salt is dissolved in water there is no special arrangement of the atoms. Each sodium atom is loosely attached to a chlorine atom, but there are frequent interchanges.

In a crystal of common salt there is a definite arrangement of the atoms. Each sodium atom has six atoms of chlorine arranged round it symmetrically, and each chlorine atom has a similar arrangement of six sodium atoms round it. If we think of a cube divided into smaller cubes, and then imagine an atom at each corner of each cube, we shall get the arrangement. The atoms are alternately sodium and chlorine in every direction.

This is one example of many possible arrangements of atoms and molecules. It is a general rule that the atoms in a crystal are distributed in such a way as to pack themselves into the least possible space, thus giving what is called a close-packed structure.

HOW GASES SPREAD OUT

Gases are at the other extreme from crystals. So far from the atoms and molecules being fixed in position they are free to move, and do move with great rapidity, so that there are constant collisions. A gas spreads out so as to fill all the available space. This happens even when the space is already filled with another gas. We have a confirmation of this when there is an escape of coal-gas. The room is already full of air, but a small escape of gas at one end of the room quickly spreads through the room and is smelt at the other end. The small amount of coal-gas fills the room just as much as the far larger amount of air does.

The freedom of gas molecules to move, and their property of spreading out, explains why the gases in the air are completely mixed. We do not have a layer of heavy carbon dioxide below, lighter argon above, and still lighter oxygen and nitrogen above these. Each gas spreads out through the atmosphere, and so we have air of very nearly the same composition everywhere.

CREATING A HIGH VACUUM

When a vessel is being exhausted by pumping the vessel remains full of gas at all stages of the pumping. There are fewer molecules of gas per cubic inch than before the pumping, but these molecules spread out and fill the space. Each molecule takes as much space to move about in as the other molecules allow it, and so we have the whole space filled.

A vessel holding a cubic foot will contain 9-100ths of an ounce of hydrogen at atmospheric pressure—a little less than a tenth of an ounce. In this small mass of gas there are about three-quarters of a quadrillion molecules.

To reduce the pressure to a millionth of an atmosphere requires a very good air-pump. Such a pressure would support only 3/100,000ths of an inch of mercury, instead of the usual thirty inches. To get such a vacuum we have to pump out all but a millionth of the gas molecules. There still remain, however, three-quarters of a trillion molecules (75 followed by sixteen noughts). These molecules have 100 times as much space in which to jerk to and fro as before the pumping. The average space between them is only about a millionth of an inch.

To reduce the pressure to a thousand-millionth of an atmosphere we have to pump out all but a thousandth of the very tenuous gas left in the vessel. The traces of gas still left fill the vessel just as much as the dense gas filled it before the pumping began. There are still 750 billion molecules left, and the spaces between them are a 100,000th of an inch.

TENUOUS GIANT OF THE HEAVENS

Some of the stars have their atoms so widely spread out that they are in a state which we should regard as a fairly good vacuum. These stars make up for their tenuity by their vast size; they are consequently known as giant stars.

Betelgeuse is one of the giants; it is the bright star in the top left-hand corner of Orion. Betelgeuse has a density that is only the thousandth part of the density of the sun. Its size has been measured; it has a diameter of about 240,000,000 miles. Compare it with the solar system by imagining its centre at the sun; it would stretch out all round to half-way between the earth and Mars. Its volume is 20,000,000 times as great as that of the sun but it contains only fifteen times as much matter. That is to say, if the tenuous gas of Betelgeuse were condensed to the density of the sun we should have a star fifteen times as big as the sun.

THE EMPTY UNIVERSE

The universe as a whole is as empty of matter as an atom is. It has been calculated that in our comparatively densely populated part of the universe, there is one star in every ten cubic parsecs, and a parsec is about nineteen billion miles. Suppose the solar system were spread out evenly over this space; it would have to be reduced to the state of a very tenuous gas, far more tenuous than anything we have experience of. There would be about seventy atoms per cubic inch. When we compare this with the molecules in a cubic inch of hydrogen at atmospheric pressure we may begin to have some idea of how empty space is. The best high vacuum that it is possible to produce by artificial means is 6,000,000,000 times more dense than the average density of our part of the universe.

Yet we are in a comparatively crowded part of the universe; outside the Milky Way there are vast empty spaces which reduce the average density still lower. A calculation of the average density of the whole universe makes it a thousand quadrillion times less dense than hydrogen at atmospheric pressure; that is, there are about two or three atoms to every cubic foot, which is almost the same as saying that if matter were evenly distributed throughout space there would not be any!

But not quite. It is possible to detect, by their effect on the spectrum, even the faint traces of matter, the few isolated and wandering atoms that are present in the most empty space.

HOW ATOMS ARE LINKED

Atoms do not usually occur singly on the earth; they are combined to form molecules. Even the atoms of the elementary gases usually combine in pairs. Oxygen, nitrogen, hydrogen and chlorine are all composed of molecules, each made up of two atoms of the gas. Molecules are usual; separate atoms are exceptional. There are two distinct ways in which atoms can be linked together to form molecules. Both kinds of link depend on the outer electrons of the atoms.

The electrons of an atom are not arranged haphazard; their orbits are on definite " shells " surrounding the nucleus of the atom. The innermost shell in any atom can contain only two orbits. Hydrogen has only one electron; the inert gas helium has two, so that the shell is complete. Lithium has three electrons; two of them complete the innermost shell; the third starts a new shell further out. The second shell can contain any number of orbits up to eight. When the second shell is filled up we have the inert gas neon, with two electrons in the first shell and eight in the second. The next element, sodium, has eleven electrons; the eleventh begins a third shell of orbits. When there are eight orbits filled in the third shell we have the inert gas argon.

Argon is a sort of half-way house toward completion of the third shell. Additional electrons go either to a fourth shell, or else are added to the number on the third shell. Finally we reach the inert gas krypton with the innermost three shells completely filled, two orbits on the first, eight on the second, and eighteen on the third; beyond these krypton has eight orbits on a fourth shell. The more elaborate elements have still more shells of orbits.

INERT GAS STRUCTURE

In each of the inert gases the inner shells of orbits are completely filled and there are eight orbits in the outermost shell (except, of course, in the case of helium, which has only one shell with both orbits filled). The outermost shell of eight orbits is often called the " outer octet."

When there are eight electrons in the outermost shell the atom appears to be sated (or saturated). Such atoms are chemically inert; they do not form molecules by joining with other atoms; they exist as self-satisfied entities. The structure of the inert gas atoms is referred to as the inert gas structure.

COMPLETING THE OCTET

There seems to be an urge amongst atoms toward saturation, an urge toward completing the outer octet of electrons (or in the case of hydrogen toward the structure of helium with its pair of outer electrons).

Atoms often link up in such a way as to achieve the inert gas structure; the two kinds of link are ways of obtaining it. When this structure is achieved the compound becomes itself inert.

One of the links is called the ionized or electrovalent link. The metal sodium has a single electron on its outermost shell. If it could give up this electron it would become a positive ion with the inert gas structure. Chlorine has seven electrons on the outermost shell. If it could gain an extra electron it would be a negative ion with the inert gas structure.

When an atom of sodium comes in contact with an atom of chlorine, the exchange is made. The sodium atom gives up an electron to the chlorine atom. Instead of two neutral atoms we now have two ions with opposite charges. The ions attract each other, and are held together by the attraction as a molecule of common salt.

THE CHEMICAL LINK

The other kind of link between atoms is called the chemical link. Chlorine has seven electrons on its outermost shell. When two chlorine atoms meet, each contributes an electron toward a link. These electrons become a part of both atoms, so that each atom has eight electrons on its outermost shell, and therefore has the inert gas structure.

The electrons forming the link appear to have orbits round the nuclei of both atoms, possibly in a figure-of-eight form. The rapid intertwined movement of the electrons makes this a very strong link between the atoms.

USED FOR PUTTING OUT FIRES

These are very simple examples of the linking up of atoms to form molecules. To take a slightly more complicated case: the carbon atom has four electrons on its outermost shell, so that it can link up with four atoms of chlorine. One electron of the carbon atom forms a link with an electron of one of the chlorine atoms; the other three chlorine atoms are linked to the carbon atom in the same way. Thus we get a molecule of carbon tetrachloride. Each atom has the inert gas structure; each of the chlorine atoms gains one electron to make up its eight, and the carbon atom gains four to make up its eight, one from each chlorine atom. Thus the compound is sated; that is one of the reasons why it is used for putting out fires.

Oxygen has six electrons on its outermost shell. An atom of oxygen, in suitable conditions, can unite with an atom of carbon to form a molecule of carbon monoxide. Each atom has the inert gas structure; each atom contributes two electrons to form a double link. The oxygen atom is sated $(6 + 2 = 8)$ but the carbon still has two free electrons. It can readily link up with another oxygen atom, and so form a molecule of carbon dioxide.

In some of the more elaborate organic compounds several thousands of atoms are combined in a single molecule.

GIANT MOLECULES

THE biggest molecules are so big that we can see and handle them. They are called giant molecules. The diamond is one of these giant molecules; any diamond is a single molecule. Instead of the few thousand atoms that make up an elaborate organic molecule, we have in a large diamond something like a quadrillion atoms.

WHY A LUMP OF COAL IS NOT A DIAMOND

A diamond is a crystal of almost pure carbon. It is the same element that is found in an impure form in coal and charcoal. The extreme difference between charcoal and diamond is due to the arrangement and linkages of the atoms.

Every atom of carbon has four outer electrons, so that it is capable of joining up with four others. The carbon atom is often described as tetrahedral, because the links are directed toward the corners of a tetrahedron, or triangular pyramid. We have to think of each carbon atom at the centre of a tetrahedron, and linked to four other atoms at the corners of the tetrahedron. Each of these four atoms is in turn linked to four others arranged in the same way. And so on.

THE DIAMOND IS THE HARDEST SUBSTANCE KNOWN

In the scale of hardness the diamond is in a class by itself, far above the next hardest substance. The system of chemical links which tie each atom in a diamond firmly to four other atoms, explains why the diamond is so hard. In most substances the material is held together by attractions between the molecules. In dividing the substance we are merely separating molecule from molecule. In trying to cut a diamond we are trying to cut through the chemical links, which are far more powerful than the attractions between molecules.

To cut through chalk in the same way that we might attempt to cut a diamond we should have to divide the molecules into their constituent atoms—calcium, carbon, and oxygen; actually there is nothing but chalk on each side of a cut.

ARTIFICIAL GIANT MOLECULES

Bakelite, of which many articles are manufactured, is made by mixing together formaldehyde and one of the phenols (the groups of substances to which carbolic acid belongs). The mixture is fused, and it can then be moulded into any shape we wish. The moulded articles are baked. As the baking proceeds the substance gets harder and harder. When the baking is complete it is in the form with which we are familiar, and it can no longer be fused. That is why it is non-inflammable.

The hardness of bakelite, and its resistance to fusion, are due to the fact that it is an artificial giant molecule. A molecule of formaldehyde links up with molecules of phenol, these link up with other molecules of formaldehyde, and so the system of links becomes more and more complete as the baking proceeds. There is not the elegant and exact system of links that we find in a diamond, but even the erratic links of bakelite are sufficiently strong to make it hard and infusible.

HEAT AS A FORM OF MOTION

John Tyndall (1820-93), one of the most famous physicists of last century, wrote a book on heat which he called *Heat a Mode of Motion*. In that phrase he expressed the modern idea of heat—that it is a form of motion. Heat waves are of the same kind as light waves and travel at the same speed; the difference is that they have a longer wavelength.

The eyes can only detect wavelengths within a very narrow range. The ultra-violet rays are too short to be detected by the eyes; heat rays are too long. We now have a great range of photographic plates which are sensitive to light rays on both sides of the visible rays.

Short waves are more easily turned aside than long waves. Long red rays, for example, penetrate through a greater length of air than the shorter blue rays. This explains why we have red sunsets. When the sun is low in the sky, rays from it reach us through a great depth of air. Red and yellow rays get through, but the short blue rays are turned aside to form a blue sky above the people in the west.

The extraordinary effects obtained by infra-red photography are due to the penetrating quality of light of long wavelength. The photographic plate reveals what is not visible to the eye because it is sensitive to light of longer wavelengths than that which affects the eye.

Light of long wavelength can also be used for television. Scenes have been scanned in the dark by means of infra-red rays, and then projected on a screen. This is possible because the photo-electric cell also is sensitive to rays of longer wavelength than those that affect the eyes.

ABSOLUTE ZERO HAS NEVER BEEN REACHED

When heat is absorbed by a substance it becomes another form of motion—the vibration of the molecules of the substance. The temperature of a body is a measure of the rate at which its molecules are vibrating; this is not to be confused with the movements of the electrons within the atoms; it is the molecule as a whole that vibrates.

With falling temperature the molecules vibrate more and more slowly. At absolute zero they do not vibrate at all. This point is 273 C. below ordinary zero, that is, below the freezing point of water. We write absolute zero " −273°C.," or else " 0°abs."

There can be no temperature lower than absolute zero, because at that temperature the molecules have no vibration at all. Temperatures have been reached that are within a fraction of a degree of absolute zero, but zero has not been reached.

HOW SOLIDS MELT

An essential difference between a solid and a liquid is the vibration of the molecules. The molecules are fixed in a solid; they vibrate about a central position. In a liquid the molecules slide about.

When a solid is heated the molecules vibrate more and more quickly. At a definite temperature the vibration is so great that the solid form is broken down; the molecules can no longer retain their fixed positions—they are jerked out of them. The change absorbs a good deal of heat. This heat does not raise the temperature of the substance, but alters the arrangement of the atoms; it is called latent (or hidden) heat, because it does not show itself as rise of temperature. The amount of heat required to melt a pound of ice is four-fifths of the amount required to boil the ice-cold water.

The same sort of thing happens when a liquid boils. The molecules vibrate so rapidly that they jump out of the liquid and spread out into the space above. Still more heat is used up in effecting this change; it requires 5.4 times as much heat to change a pint of boiling water to steam as to raise the water from freezing point to boiling point.

HOW LIQUID AIR IS MADE

If we imagine that the essential difference between a liquid and a gas is the distances between the molecules, then we should be able to liquefy

a gas by compressing it, that is by pressing the molecules closer together.
Many attempts were made to liquefy gases in this way, and pressures of
hundreds of atmospheres were used. The attempts failed, and the
liquefaction of what are called permanent gases seemed to be impossible.
Success came almost by accident. After an unsuccessful attempt, an
experimenter opened a tap to allow the compressed gas to escape. Before
long a liquid was dripping from the tap. He had succeeded in liquefying
the gas.

When a gas expands it cools; the work done in expanding is shown
by a fall of temperature. The compressed gas in this experiment
expanded and cooled as it escaped, and it cooled the remaining gas
sufficiently to liquefy it. That is, it slowed down the vibrations of the
gas molecules to the rate at which they can exist in liquid form.

Liquid air machines are based on the same principle. Air is highly
compressed by means of a pump; the compression heats it. The heated
air is cooled by letting it pass through a coil surrounded by cold water or
brine. The cold compressed air passes down through another coil, and
is allowed to escape through a narrow nozzle at the bottom. The coil
is surrounded by a tube which compels the escaping air to rise round the
coil. The expanding air cools, and cools the air in the coil, and so the
temperature goes on falling until liquid air begins to pour out into a
vacuum flask beneath the nozzle.

VIBRATIONS IN A RED-HOT POKER

The searing effect of a red-hot poker is due to the extremely rapid
vibrations of the molecules. The hand that happens to touch the poker
is instantly hammered by billions of tiny mechanical hammers.

Touching a very cold piece of iron has the same sort of effect as
touching hot iron. There is a sudden rush of heat from the comparatively
hot hand to the cold iron. The molecules of the skin are set vibrating
at a destructive rate, and a wound is caused. Such wounds are more
difficult to heal than wounds caused by ordinary burning. The reason
is that the destruction comes from within, and affects a deeper layer
of flesh.

VIBRATIONS BREAK LINKS

The increased vibration of molecules by heating may have other
effects. The vibrations may be so rapid as to break the chemical links
holding the atoms of the molecules together. At high temperatures the
molecules of many substances break up into simpler molecules or into
atoms. Ammonium chloride, for example, breaks up into ammonia
and hydrochloric acid gas.

The extremely high temperatures of the sun and the stars prevent
the formation of chemical links, and thus of molecules, so that the
elements exist there as atoms. In the hottest stars even the electronic
defence of the atoms is shattered.

THE MYSTERY OF LIFE

OUR race has been asking the question " What is life?" ever since it could be called human. The ancient Egyptians typified it in the egg, the early barbarians saw it in the lightning, the Christians perhaps attempted to express it in the saintly halo. Coming to our own times, Professor Henri Bergson saw it as the *élan vital*, and Mr. George Bernard Shaw, thinking on similar lines, described it as the life force. Both these modern philosophers expatiated on a mysterious " something " which drove all animate nature along an uncertain path, and brought about the moss and the palm tree, the microbe and the mammoth, the savage and the scientist. The great question remains no nearer to an answer than when the cave man heard the voice of the Life Giver in the crashing thunder, or the grinding of the ice floes.

WHAT IS LIFE?

The dictionary can offer little as a definition of " life," though each one of us has his own fairly well-formed convictions as to what the word means. " Life," we say, is movement, at the same time being quite certain that the racing speed boat, or the bubbling kettle are not in the true sense alive.

" Life," we add, is growth; and even as we watch a mass of soda crystals forming—apparently from nowhere—before our eyes, are well aware that this does not represent what we mean by " life." Perhaps the nearest approach to a definition which can be offered is that life is something which can reproduce its own image, and of its own volition.

HOW DID LIFE BEGIN?

Up to within a century ago all unthinking persons, and some thinkers, placidly accepted the whole of living Nature as having been once upon a time set going more or less as we see it today; in a word—created. Parallel with this idea, and apparently quite reconcilable with it, was the notion of spontaneous generation. That is to say, the production of living creatures from slime and decaying matter, or even the birth of eels from horse-hairs and geese from trees. Fossils were explained away as being unborn creatures biding their time to emerge as living organisms, whilst some of the more spectacular finds, such as the bones of mammoths and dinosaurs, founded a general belief in giants and less congenial monsters.

But even as early as the 15th century, a thoughtful few—like Leonardo da Vinci (1452-1519)—were not satisfied with such plausible imaginings. Today our scientists, immeasurably better equipped than in da Vinci's day, are still pondering the meaning of life, though less perhaps its fundamental nature than its first tangible manifestations on this planet. But even if, as is quite possible, life may one day be produced in the laboratory, the scientist is careful to assure us that this may not be at all the way in which it really " happened." The question " How did life begin?" is therefore as unanswerable as " What is life?" since there can be no means of checking the " creations " of the laboratory, assuming they ever come to pass.

Perhaps, as Sir Ray Lankester suggested, there was a time when conditions on this earth were such that vast sheets and blobs of protoplasm-like substance were spread over the waters, and under the action of light, some of it—a millionth-millionth part perhaps, stirred to life, and fed upon the great unresponsive remainder. However it began, it first manifested itself in infinitesimal specks of being to which the yeasts and moulds, and the legions of the germs, beneficent and malignant, are akin.

TINY CREATURES THAT BUILT CLIFFS

Before considering how these crude beginnings led in time to the world we see today, the better in fact to appreciate the vast implications of life, let us pass in rapid review the varied forms of animal life in the order in which we believe the different organisms manifested themselves. To do this we begin with the record of the rocks—a record without certain beginning, and still full of gaps, but invaluable nevertheless.

EARLIEST FORMS OF LIFE

In the first place life of any kind can only be dated from what little evidence it has left behind in the oldest known mineral deposits. It is certain there must have been life before fossils, but it was obviously of so flimsy a nature as to leave no recognizable traces behind it.

The first life therefore of which we can speak with any confidence was similar to that still represented by minute gelatinous creatures that, by extracting lime or silicate from the sea water, build for themselves shells, often of exquisite form and infinite variety. Such shells form our chalk hills, and on the ocean floor vast beds of yet unsolidified ooze. Many of these animals rowed themselves about by means of minute hairs, using the means of propulsion also to sweep food into their interiors. The bulk of this early populace was composed of creatures under 1/100th of an inch in diameter, and these were giants beside the shell-less germs and allied organisms.

At a remote period some of these minute shell-bearers gave rise to great sedentary colonies. The flinty shells were welded to form a kind of skeleton, whilst the thrashing hairs were retained to sweep life-giving sea water and food particles into and through the whole. In some such manner, perhaps, the sponges came into being, and represented the highest and most dominant forms of life many millions of years ago. Some were vast shapeless masses, others graceful tree-like forms securely anchored in the ooze by roots that appeared to be made of spun glass, just as are the living glass rope sponges of the ocean deeps.

WORMS NINETY FEET LONG

Retaining and elaborating the skeletal scheme, there presently arose the corals. Their world-wide distribution at this time points to generally tropic or sub-tropic conditions. Such in fact largely obtained until about 100,000,000 years ago.

Side by side with the corals there began to appear many kinds of worms, some building reefs of stone or gravel tubes that counterfeited coral, and others swimming free. Some of these latter doubtless reached a large size. The bootlace worm, common on many English shores, may span over ninety feet. The worms marked a great advance upon the coral animals, for whereas a coral polyp—which is virtually a sea anemone in a limestone kennel—expels waste matter through its mouth, the worms presented a recognizable digestive tract, and many had quite complex paired limbs. Some, like many anemones, multiplied by division; others, again like some corals, laid eggs.

MOLLUSCS AS MASTERS OF THE WORLD

The next creatures to step upon the stage of life were the spiny-skinned animals; the starfishes and sea-urchins. Some were quite unlike any known today; others, the later comers, were similar to modern forms, but often much larger. There were, for example, vast forests of sea lilies, immense many-armed starfishes, each mounted upon a writhing stem fifteen or twenty feet high.

Life was fast gaining momentum. The branching corals and great reefs of worm tubes offered sanctuary to two more great classes of animals which successively made their appearance. Whereas the sponges, and next the sea lilies must in turn have represented life at its highest, the world's next masters were the molluscs—the oysters, clams, whelks, snails and cuttle fish. Some of these laid strongly shelled eggs, and even showed the beginnings of parental care. For probably about 500,000,000 years the swarming cuttle fish and octopods must have been without any serious rivals.

But whereas the soft-bodied molluscs were only sometimes protected by shells, that must often have been as much hindrance as help, the next comers, the jointed-limb animals, were not merely armoured but in the last degree mobile. This latest life form expressed itself in crabs, lobsters, sea woodlice and a million allied shapes, many persisting, some long vanished. Among the latter were the sea scorpions, lobster-like monsters nine feet in length. It is believed that some members of this great group, together perhaps with some adventurous sea snails, were the first creatures to invade the fast-rising land.

COMING OF INSECTS AND FISHES

With the emergence of the land masses, vegetation came into its own and paved the way for that vast offshoot of the jointed-limb creatures which are now the most numerous form of animal life—the insects. With their appearance there came, and not till then, sounds other than those of wind and waves. Once again the newcomers rose to a zenith. Some of these early insects doubled the dimensions of the magnificent Indian Atlas moth that spans twelve inches across the wings.

Here the records of the rocks present a problem indeed. The gap between the backboned and the backboneless animals is as yet very imperfectly bridged. But perhaps as long as 1,500,000,000 years ago, the seas began to teem with primitive fishes, creatures with jointed armour and suctorial mouths which must have suggested cousins of the sea scorpions far more than anything we understand by the word "fish." Yet there is good evidence that some 500,000,000 years later these gill-breathing creatures were left behind by some few of their number, who, equipped with lungs, crawled ashore and stayed there. In some such manner appeared the monster newts of the coal forests. These in turn gave place to the tough-skinned, shelled, egg-laying reptiles.

REPTILES THIRTY-FIVE FEET TALL

For quite 200,000,000 years the earth, almost from pole to pole, must have abounded with the monstrous forms of reptile life known as dinosaurs. It is questionable whether remains of the biggest of them have yet been discovered.

Whereas the largest complete skeletons indicate quadrupeds 100 feet long, and biped monsters eighteen feet high, both these are dwarfed by footprints found in 1937 in a coal mine at Mesa Verde, Wyoming, U.S.A. They indicate an herbivorous monster which walked erect with a fifteen-feet stride, and towered thirty-five feet above the ground. Not all the dinosaurs were huge; *Compsognathus*, for example, was only about the size of a pigeon, while other species were no larger than hens or ducks.

CONVERTING SCALES INTO FEATHERS

Here at last one might excusably think life could go no further. What new creature could appear and hope to hold its own in such a world? But the sunset of the dinosaurs came about with dramatic suddenness some 60,000,000 years ago. We believe that a general cooling of the temperature cut off food supplies and forced certain small reptiles to develop on quite novel lines in order to survive. Thus must have come about the birds and mammals.

Both developed warm blood and retained heat, the one by converting scales into feathers, the other by transforming them into hair. Both laid eggs, but the mammals, not having conquered the air, were compelled to overcome greater difficulties in colonizing the earth. Under the bludgeonings of chance, an ever changing climate and continuous reshuffling of land and water, they went from strength to strength. Their tale is not yet told, as we, their latest representatives, creatures of but 1,000,000 years' standing—or less—can attest.

WHAT EVOLUTION MEANS

THE average man generally accepts the foregoing summary much as he accepts his breakfast. It is only when at rare intervals he seriously ponders the matter that he asks himself, did life come about in this orderly, progressive way? Assuming that it did, by what right does the scientist so confidently state that certain creatures lived so many million years ago, or that the birds and beasts—including man presumably—are derived from reptile ancestry?

The case for evolution, as this procession of life is called, is founded on the evidence of fossils, and on embryology, the study of the unborn. Evolution does not mean, as some of the Victorians asserted, that " man has come from a monkey." The word simply means " an unrolling " and well describes life, which presents itself as a vast tapestry, ever gaining in complexity as it is unwound for our inspection. It is a pattern in which some features fade out and new ones take their place, though the general theme runs unbroken throughout its length.

ROCK-READING BY RADIO-ACTIVITY

The precise manner in which rock deposits can be dated need not be dealt with in detail. A great advance in the accuracy of rock-reading was made possible by the discovery of radio-activity by Antoine Henri Becquerel, a famous French scientist, towards the close of last century. His pioneer work enabled other scientists to establish that uranium and other radio-active elements were constantly disintegrating and forming other elements. Once it was established how long a period was required for such disintegrating, a relatively accurate calculation of the age of the earth could be made. Meanwhile the geologists had pieced together bit by bit the story of the rocks they found on the earth's surface until they were able to calculate the age of layers hundreds of feet deep. Thus scientists, labouring as individuals and by team work the world over, and pooling their results, have built up bit by bit a very convincing picture of earth's story, though not necessarily a complete one.

Rock layers, with the fossils they contain, can only come to light when upheaved for inspection by earth convulsions, the more gradual exposure by sea, wind and rain, or as the result of arduous mining operations. Moreover, not all plants or animals will fossilize. The skeletons of fish and birds, compared with those of reptiles and mammals, are so weak and friable that the number yet obtained must be hopelessly disproportionate to the number of such creatures that once existed.

WORK OF 150,000,000 YEARS

Accepting the fact that life, starting from the simplest beginnings, has continued with steadily increasing complexity, the question remains by what magic could one form lead to another? One still hears people ask, " Will starfishes in time turn into elephants?" The answer to that is " No." Life has never leapt from one form to another in the facile way in which a conjurer (apparently) converts a bunch of violets into a bowl of goldfish.

It must be remembered that the period of time between the dawn of life and the perfection of the sponges probably covered at the very least 1,000,000,000 years. An animal having once attained to a form well fitted to its environment is likely to remain in that form, unless outside circumstances decide otherwise. Starfishes will remain starfishes—so far as one can say—until the end of time. But the sharp spur of necessity can work wonders, and it is the numerous and dramatic changes of climate and of land and water masses that account for the rapid development of birds and mammals. They are the work of only about 150,000,000 years; little more than half the period popularly spoken of as the Age of Reptiles.

MAN'S MULTITUDE OF CELLS

All life begins as a cell, a minute blob of the stuff called protoplasm. It has a nucleus or centre of life, and a complex fluid content as yet only partly understood. The cell, too, contains the mysterious seeds of heredity. When plant and animal both consist of but a single cell, as many do, they are virtually indistinguishable. Perhaps the best definition of an animal is an organism that can subsist only on other organisms. A plant can, in the main, extract the means of growth direct from soil, air and sunlight.

Life presumably expressed itself first as a single cell. There is that within the cell which causes it to divide and sub-divide, gathering meanwhile from soil, sunlight or other cells the means for continuous expansion. In this manner have been built up all living things. Many millions of cells go to make a man. As in other creatures our cells are grouped. Each group does different work; grows hair, digests food and so on according to its owner's needs.

With this in mind the stupendous pageant of life becomes at least conceivable. The orderly sequence of ascending groups may be regarded as a chain, each group a link joined to its fellows by yet other links, the groups merge gradually one into the other, and though some links in the sequence are still wanting, we can quite often see how creatures have in time given rise to others very unlike themselves. Let us glance at a few links taken at random.

LIVING LINKS WITH THE PAST

On any seashore one can pick up fern-like fronds which under a lens resolve themselves into assemblages of tiny boxes, each housing a gelatinous creature restlessly sweeping the water for food with minute arms or tentacles. Early naturalists were completely baffled by these growths. Some held they were allied to snails and oysters, others to the corals, the sea squirts, or the lamp shells. But the advent of the Marine Research Station some eighty years ago made it possible to keep these

fern-like colonies alive, and presently to hatch out eggs laid by the
animals composing the colony. The eggs released larvæ very like those
of some marine worms, and thus was ascertained the true affinities of
the so-called moss animals.

Another link introduced itself dramatically to the London Zoological
Gardens in 1865, when the first living prongbuck, universally regarded
as an antelope, shed both horns, revealing solid pedicles beneath. These
became again covered by horns, which after an interval were cast. So
today this ruminant is recognized as sole survivor of a race of such links
that once flourished in the prehistoric past. It joins the permanently
horned sheep with the deciduous antlered deer.

FIRST FLYING BIRD HAD FINGERS

Far more links are furnished by fossil deposits, since whereas only
about 500,000 species of living animals have been listed, many times this
number have ceased to exist. A famous fossil link is the so-called lizard
bird—*Archæopteryx*—only two examples of which have been found,
and both in lithographic strata from Bavaria.

This half-way bird was about the size of a fowl, and whilst generally
avian in form and the possessor of feathers, had movable fingers on its
wing, knuckles and a long tail. This, the first flying bird, lived about
150,000,000 years ago. In still earlier deposits are found the skeletons
of reptiles that were developing on quite other lines. Their lower jaws
were becoming less like those of a lizard and more like our own, and
the pelvic region strongly suggested that of two famous living links,
the egg-laying spiny ant-eaters of New Guinea and the Australian
duck-mole. These lizards were, in fact, mammals in the making.

Some solidly built creatures have left such abundant fossil remains
that we can follow every change their races underwent through hundreds
of millions of years. We can trace how the early ammonites or
octopus-like creatures changed their cumbrous church-spire shells for
gracefully coiled ones like that of their only living representative, the
tropic nautilus. We know each step by which the five-toed fox-sized
horse changed to its present form, how the sabre-tooth tiger discarded
its foot-long tusks for more proportionate teeth, and how the elephant
from a hoggish pygmy became the largest land mammal, with a unique
nasal organ.

STANDSTILL ANIMALS

Whilst ever-changing climatic conditions and redistribution of land
and water forced most creatures along an upward path or wiped them
from the scene, an inconspicuous few contrived practically to stand still.

Such so-called living fossils are the little lamp-shells of the North
Sea deeps, and the king crab, teeming in coastal shallows on both sides
of the Atlantic. Retiring by nature and offering little in the way of a
meal to predators, these creatures have survived from long before that
remote period when the first fishes appeared.

ANIMALS THAT LIVE BACKWARDS

Another minority has evaded in another way Nature's edict of progress or perish. Some animals have, so to speak, contrived to live backwards. The little acorn barnacles bespangling every rock begin life as free swimming creatures not unlike the common cyclops of the ponds. But when seemingly on the verge of higher things, the baby barnacle anchors itself by the head, discards most organs save its stomach and a few legs with which to rake food into it, and so remains throughout the rest of its existence.

A near relative degenerates even more, becoming an inert and shapeless mass about as big as one's thumb nail, tucked beneath the tail or apron of the shore crab, and slowly extracting vitality from its unwilling host.

MAKING THE BEST OF CIRCUMSTANCES

THE whole story of animal life has been one of making the best of circumstances: adaptation to environment the scientists call it. This has brought about a vast number of widely differing forms from primitive ancestral stock. For the further we go back in any creature's lineage, the nearer we approach a certain uniformity. Not even the specialist can say of some early mammals, this is a flesh eater, or perhaps a harmless grazer, for both qualities are contained in the same animal. Time and a changing world, however, have bent such indeterminate generalizers into a dozen highly specialized directions.

A homely parallel may be offered by a family of quins. Mary, John, Muriel, George and Henry in the cradle are only to be distinguished one from the other by nurse. Even in six months' time the quins are " much of a muchness." But four years later, what scientists call radiative adaptation has crept in, and becomes more obvious with each succeeding year. Once in their teens we find Mary's dolls have fostered an hereditary gift for nursing, a chance stay at a farm fired John with an urge to the land, Muriel sees herself as a secretary, George's meccano set has turned him into an embryo engineer, and Henry, hearkening to a secret " call," has run away to sea.

GUINEA PIGS THAT DIFFER

Animal analogies to the above are naturally the result of physical rather than psychic influences, and are spread over an immensity of time. In South America, for example, there became established the ancestral guinea pig, which has persisted when many strange monsters sharing the land with it are now known only as fossils. Today this continent fosters guinea pigs so different from each other that only naturalists would suspect their kinship.

What could be more contrasted than the Patagonian cavy and the capybara? A life spent in fleeing from predatory foes has stretched the cavy's legs until the animal suggests a hare or miniature antelope. The capybara, on the other hand, wallowing in marshes, has taken on the semblance of a sort of monstrous rodent hippopotamus.

A classic example of this manufacturing of different creatures from a common stock is provided by the mammals of Australia.

When that continent parted company with Asia, some primitive pouched animals were marooned. Such as remained upon the mainland fell to stronger foes, but the islanders enjoyed an orgy of self-determination. Some, like the kangaroos, developed into big herbivores; others, such as the wombats and koalas, burrowed or climbed and assumed bear-like forms. Others again, preying upon the placid vegetarians, mimicked tiger cats and wolves, whilst some insectivorous species became caricatures of the American and Asiatic ant-eaters. But diverse as all these marsupials are, each betrays its common ancestry in the possession of a pouch.

MAN'S COMMON ANCESTOR

In a similar manner the various races of man are doubtless derived from a common stock: a lemur-like creature related to the tarsius of New Guinea, according to the latest finding of the scientists.

The old Victorian idea of a missing link no longer holds a place in our conception of man's development. During the last few decades remains of "only just" men have been unearthed from many widely separated areas, so that man's development must have been general. Asia is no longer regarded universally as being the cradle of the human race, since tarsius-like animals have been known to live over as wide an expanse as man himself.

EVOLUTION IN THE EGG

The study of the unborn—embryology—is a second route by which to trace the stream of life. Just as the moss animals show kinship with certain worms when very young, so one and all within the egg or womb hurry through phases of animal life, which in the larger issue have come about only in the course of hundreds of millions of years.

Man, dog, pigeon, lizard and fish show an amazing similarity in their earlier stages of development, so that if the embryos at this period were to be mixed up together, an expert might be at a loss to sort them out. Even when hatched or born, the infant animal often shows more in common with its early kinsmen than it does with the race to which it actually belongs. Respectable Mr. X, when first he appeared, had much suggestive of the lemur in his hairy covering and prehensile feet. The chick betrays a reptilian ancestry in its scaly legs and functional wing fingers, and so on down the tree of life we find each form echoing in infancy still earlier forms which preceded it.

In some measure we have speeded up the evolutionary process, and in our domestic animals at least have produced in a few centuries creatures which, left to Nature, would have taken infinitely longer in the making. Only about a century has been needed to squeeze the bulldog's face out of all canine semblance, and not much longer has been required to play even more fantastic tricks with poultry, pigeons, and goldfish.

Such "evolution while you wait" is not of lasting quality. If the freakish fancy variety produced by carefully selected parentage and the perpetuation of some desired feature be left to itself for some generations, reversion to type sets in. The racehorse loses its greyhound-like proportions, the fantastic fowl harks back to the jungle cock, and the goldfish once more dons the drab livery of the wild carp.

MANKIND'S LOSSES AND GAINS

Evolution is not something that was. It is a going concern, in action around us now, a vast continuous movement, started none knows when, and likely to pursue its course until perhaps our cooling planet brings all life to a close. Even in our own persons the processes of change are clearly visible. Our artificial way of life is stamping its mark upon us, as surely as unnatural environment, peculiar food and intensive selection have changed our dogs from the ancestral wolf. It is now generally admitted, for example, that much soft food, not always wisely selected, has reduced the size and strength of our lower jaw, and is even slowly eliminating our back teeth. Cramping footwear also is literally rubbing away our little toes, and in time these features may rank with the appendix as vestigial organs that we could well do without.

On the other hand improved ways of living, with good sanitation, airy bedrooms and the like have set down much upon our credit side. The average height of the individual shows a tendency to increase, and our craniums incline to be larger than those of our medieval ancestors, whilst there is apt to be an extension of the average life-span. The modern "fitness" campaign may result in centenarians being no mere curiosities.

WHERE DOES EVOLUTION LEAD?

However man may weld and alter the animals around him to his needs or fancies, no doubt climate will in the end have the last word in shaping our destinies. Not once but several times in geologic history the Northern Hemisphere has shuddered beneath an ice blanket gliding southwards from the pole. We are in fact living in an interglacial period, and there is no guarantee that the European and North American peoples may not be wiped off the map as were many animals before the dawn of man. The stage may be cleared for the northerly migration, as the ice recedes, of another race of men, with higher ideals and the power to realize them.

THE STORY OF PLANTS

ONCE upon a time—science can be no more exact than that—a microscopically small globule, on the frontier of life, may have swum around in the shoreless primæval sea. Reproducing itself by division, it gave rise eventually to the first life phenomena—the world of the Protozoa. From these the animal world, following a different method of nutrition, finally struck out on its own line of development. The plant stock has since propagated many thousands of species, including more than 250,000 flowering plants alone.

SEAWEEDS ARE AMONG THE OLDEST PLANTS

Seaweeds and other algæ are some of the oldest plants known, some of the earliest fossils being almost identical with those living today. It is possible that land plants gradually developed from these on the shores which appeared when the crust of the earth slowly rose from the waters. Remains of a huge plant with a trunk two feet in diameter have been found in rocks of the Silurian epoch, some 370,000,000 years ago. It has the simple structure of a seaweed but probably grew in swampy ground. Smaller, simple land plants were also living then.

About 20,000,000 years later, in the Carboniferous epoch, there was a rich flora whose remains are preserved in the coal measures. There were many beautiful fern-like plants, though of a type unfamiliar to us. Exceedingly common were giant horse-tails with cones a foot long. The thirty-odd species existing today are of much more modest dimensions, the whole plant being only about the size of the former cone. However, in South America some larger species are still found as much as thirty feet high.

At their zenith in the Carboniferous epoch were the fine scale-trees (*Lepidodendron*) and later the seal-trees (*Sigillaria*). A fossilized trunk of one of the former, found in an English coal mine, measured 114 feet before it forked. The branches were clothed with small narrow leaves which left conspicuous scars when they fell. There were also trees which may have been the ancestors of conifers such as the monkey-puzzles (*Araucaria*). The broken trunk of one of them is in the grounds of the British Museum (Natural History) at South Kensington, London. At its base it is five feet in diameter.

WHEN FLOWERS FIRST BLOSSOMED

In the Triassic epoch, about 180,000,000 years ago, in the earth's middle age, the climate became much drier. There were a great many cycad palms, and conifers allied to such forms as the Australian kauri pine and the monkey-puzzle appeared. Most of the Carboniferous plants had dwindled away, and by the Jurassic epoch, 140,000,000 years ago, had almost disappeared. There were then many ferns of a modern type, cycads and conifers such as the redwoods and cypresses.

It is probable that the flowering plants, nowadays the dominant forms, then began to appear. The record of the rocks is so imperfect that we are not yet able to say which were the first. Some botanists think that trees bearing catkins, such as we see on oak, hazel, birch and so on, were the most primitive forms. Here the pollen dust is carried by the wind from the catkins to the female flowers. Others see as the earliest a handsome, conspicuous flower something of the type of a water-lily or magnolia bloom.

Be this as it may, by the Cretaceous epoch, which marked the end of the earth's middle age about 110,000,000 years ago, there had arrived a wealth of forms with reeds, lilies, true palms and the first deciduous trees. Planes, oaks, walnuts, and willows mingled with the more exotic camphor and bread-fruit trees. At the same time appeared in the animal world the bees, which obtain their food from the pollen and nectar of the flowers and by their visits often transfer pollen from one to another and enable seed to be set.

MIGRATION OF PLANTS

THE plant is a perfect indicator of climate. Before the last Ice Age, Central Europe was, for the last time, a tropical country, with fan-palms growing among pines, and cinnamon trees and bread-fruit with oaks. The annual mean temperature then fell 4°C., and 12,000,000 square miles of the earth's surface was covered with ice that was 6,000 feet deep in Norway. The plant world withdrew southwards, dwarf palms even as far as Sicily, and only the cripples were left. At the end of the Ice Age the moors had thawed and dried, and were colonized by the birch and Scots pine.

INFLUENCED BY CLIMATE

In what is sometimes called the Atlantic period (5500-3500 B.C.), when the climate became moister and warmer under the influence of the Atlantic Ocean, the Scots pine was driven out by the pedunculate oak. Then a period of high rainfall set in, which in its turn gave way to a dry period. Wheat, barley and peas were planted.

The Bronze Age (2000-900 B.C.) was warm, oats and millet spread to Scandinavia, and Central Europe saw a period of advanced human civilization. In the first Iron Age (900-500 B.C.), and until the Christian era the climate became wet again, the surface water rose, and the spruce and beech flourished.

THE VINE MOVES FROM THE CASPIAN

As late as 1000 B.C., the Mediterranean countries possessed virgin forests of oak, birch, beech, pine and larch. A subtropical flora then gradually changed the aspect of the scenery as the cork-oak, Spanish chestnut, stone-pine, fig, and oleander slowly settled down again on the Mediterranean coasts, advancing in sweeping circles. The classical authors inform us that the fruits of these plants would not ripen at first in their new home. Some of them travelled with the Roman expeditionary forces into Northern Italy, Southern France, Tyrol, and even to Britain and Northern Germany.

The vine, whose real home is to be sought on the southern bank of the Caspian Sea, first migrated via Asia Minor to Thrace, in the east of the Balkan peninsula, where, for that reason, a monument to Bacchus, the god of wine, was unveiled in the Maritza valley in 1935. In Homer's time, about 850 B.C., wine was a people's drink, and early in the first century of our era Italy was exporting wine in exchange for corn.

At that period, too, the apricot and the cherry tree found a home on the Mediterranean. In Germany a climate of the Canadian type prevailed, but it soon grew milder; the virgin forests became less dense, the marshes dried up, the vine became domesticated on the Rhine, and wheat growing was introduced. Around the Mediterranean it grew warmer and warmer, even to drought induced by the cutting down of all the forests. Diminution of rainfall compelled the migrations of the Germanic tribes southwards and drove the eastern races to move westwards.

WHEN THE BAMBOO MIGRATED

In the Arab-Carlovingian period, till A.D. 900, oceanic influences prevailed; from then to about the year 1100 the climate was continental; and then came an alternation of wet and dry periods. From the Caspian Sea to Greece the date-palms gradually died out, the bamboo withdrew from North China, and the vine abandoned Northern Germany.

The district from Hanover to the Loire showed a fall of 2°C. in temperature. On the other hand, the mean temperature rose 1°C. in North-East Europe, and in Stockholm, Archangel and Iceland a warmer spell set in.

TRANSPLANTED FROM OTHER LANDS

Artificial transplanting has caused considerable changes in the scenery of Europe since the great period of discovery, about 1450. Even as early as about 1100 the orange was brought to Sicily by the Arabs. Phœnix palms from the Canary Islands extend as far north as Merano, in Italy, and on the Riviera you see dwarf palms from the South Seas, tangerines from China, Australian araucarias, and Palmyra palms from India. The agave, which came from Mexico in 1561, has since flooded all the Mediterranean countries.

The first Tree of Life (*arbor vitæ*) in Europe was planted in 1526 in the park of the Palace of Fontainebleau, the first acacia in Paris in the reign of Louis XIII. About 1770, Landgrave Frederick II of Hesse planted more than 400 species of exotic trees in his park of Wilhelmshöhe near Cassel. Alexander von Humboldt, too, brought back with him from his world tours many foreign plants, which he acclimatized on the Peacock Island near Berlin. The cedar of Lebanon was introduced into

France, England, and the Rhineland in 1822, the plane and the horse chestnut, which are southern trees, still earlier, in the 18th century.

ORIGINAL HOMES OF PLANTS

The original home of the white marguerite is Spain, that of the horse chestnut Greece. Egypt gave the cabbage to the world, the Sudan the mignonette, Central Africa the gladiolus, and South-West Africa the pelargonium (geranium). The mallow originated in Northern Siberia, love-lies-bleeding and the hydrangea in Eastern Siberia, the larkspur, wistaria and pæony in Central China, the peach and jasmine in Burma, the Lombardy poplar in Central Siberia.

The strawberry and the fuchsia came from Chile, the dahlia from Central America, the acacia from Florida, the pumpkin from the Gulf of Mexico. Hudson's Bay in Canada gave us the sunflower, the phlox and the lupin.

FORESTS : THEIR USE AND ABUSE

WHEREAS in the early periods of civilization forests had of necessity to be felled in order to make space for pastures and arable land, since then the gradual tendency has been towards a reckless spoliation and destruction of the forest areas. What was not used for building and heating purposes went to shipbuilding and for export, although certain hardwoods, including the oak and the yew, were also employed for furniture making.

YEW TREES FOR BOWS

The 16th century was a particularly reckless period in respect of tree felling. For instance in the manor of Waidhofen, belonging to the bishopric of Freising in Bavaria, no fewer than 10,000 oaks were felled. Holland and England, comparatively unforested, imported timber for the manufacture of weapons to the extent of 12,000 yew bows in the year 1589 alone.

Stone-pines were felled mercilessly for use in salt mines. Spruce and beech ousted the oaks. Lime trees in large numbers are now only found in Russia. Small-arms factories absorbed six times as much walnut wood as the furniture industry.

MARSHES THAT MENACE LIFE

The Apennine Mountains, the great range that forms the backbone of Italy and is some 800 miles long, was robbed of its forests by the Romans for the sake of shipbuilding, just as Spain was by the Arabs, and the Carso by the Venetians. Many of the mountains of Greece, Guatemala, and China lost their forests. Rain was no longer trapped in them; it washed the good soil down from the heights and deposited it in lakes, which were thus converted into marshy breeding places for infectious diseases. Only within recent years have the Pontine Marshes, in western Italy, been drained and a desolate and pestilential waste turned to use. For over fourteen hundred years they had been a menace.

Forests are also a protection against both cold and hot winds. While around the Mediterranean the climate became hotter owing to the felling of the forests, in the Spessart and Rhön districts of Germany the mean temperature after the clearing of the forests fell 1°C. Since forests no longer act as regulators in China, that unhappy country suffers almost annually from disastrous floods, as in 1936, when hundreds of thousands of people were drowned and 14,000,000 were rendered homeless. If many a great nation had refrained from destroying its forests, it would not have declined so rapidly.

HEALTHY INFLUENCE OF FORESTS

This is what Dr. Frederick Rose, in a British Foreign Office report, has to say on this important subject: " The proximity of forests acts upon those who dwell in or near them in a similar manner as the proximity of the sea exercises a healthy influence upon those who dwell on or near the coasts, and it may be asserted that, to some extent, a country without forests resembles a country without a coast.

" The inhabitants of the forests—the foresters, woodcutters, and other forest workmen and dwellers—are as regards health, strength, and a certain native shrewdness and sagacity, as superior to the peasants of the plain as these again are superior in health, strength and many sturdy virtues to the majority of the inhabitants of towns."

NEW FORESTS FOR GREAT BRITAIN

A determined effort to reafforest Great Britain has been made since the termination of the World War. During the four terrible years of human and material devastation 450,000 acres of woods, representing one-sixth of the country's resources, were felled. The Forestry Commission, which was set up in 1919, is responsible for the task of renewing the sources of supply and also of repairing the neglect of centuries. It owns over 200 forests covering about 620,000 acres, which range from Berkshire to Inverness. Millions of oak, silver birch, mountain ash, laburnum, pines, poplar and sycamore have been planted.

Whereas Germany has twenty-five per cent and France eighteen per cent, only five per cent of Great Britain is woodland. The oak has always been regarded as the representative tree of the country, but the demand is considerably less since metal took the place of timber in the construction of ships. During the reign of William III (1689-1702), 2,000 acres of the New Forest were enclosed and planted with oak solely for the use of the Navy, and 200 acres were added annually for twenty years. Fifty acres of oak had to be felled to provide sufficient timber for a sail-of-the-line.

As an example of what may be done by private enterprise, between 1787 and 1829 some 28,151,000 trees were planted on the Brocklesby and Manby estates of Lord Yarborough. It is said that the extensive

Scotch fir woods in the neighbourhood of Ascot and Farnborough (Hampshire) owe their origin to Robert Elphinstone, page to Prince Henry, son of James I, who casually emptied his pockets of a number of seeds he had brought from Scotland.

One of the loveliest of the many ways of commemorating the fallen in the World War is the planting of Avenues of Remembrance in Italy. They are in the care of school children. Each tree bears the name of a fallen soldier.

FIERY ENEMY OF FORESTS

Appalling loss has been caused by forest fires, which in the United States alone destroy trees to the value of from £2,000,000 to £4,000,000 every year. In Canada, where some 6,000 fires occur every twelve months, observers in aeroplanes carrying wireless sets and portable pumps keep a watchful eye for outbreaks. Elsewhere men or women perched on mountain tops in little houses " spot " for tell-tale smoke, sometimes aided by patrol men on the ground.

A forest fire in the Department of the Var, in the south of France, destroyed timber valued at £100,000. Another in Canada did over £200,000 worth of damage. An area of 14,000 acres has been reduced to no more than blackened stumps in four hours, for the speed of a forest fire is often thirty miles an hour. When the sun bakes the earth and the humidity or water-holding capacity of the air is no more than twenty per cent, the fire fighters hold themselves in readiness.

In the first three months of 1938 trees lost in England and Wales owing to fires totalled 1,000,000. An analysis of 2,650 forest fires in Great Britain from 1929 to 1936 showed that fifty-seven per cent of the outbreaks were due to sparks from locomotives.

VIRGIN FORESTS OF GERMANY

Remains of the virgin forests of Germany are still to be seen in the Bavarian Forest, the Spessart, and the Odenwald, and also in the Gollbachsau near Tegernsee in Upper Bavaria. Unique of its kind is the Neuenburg virgin forest, which is principally distinguished by its picturesque, overgrown condition and its variety of species.

The Hasbruch in Oldenburg, a fragment of an ancient forest surrounded by modern plantations, was a sacred grove of the Teutons and still contains remains of altars and stones of sacrifice. Charlemagne, in A.D. 786, appointed it to be the north-west boundary of the Bremen territory. On account of its venerable aspect, it was preserved throughout the Middle Ages as a hunting ground, and for the same reason it has been spared by modern foresters.

A characteristic of these virgin forests is their mouldering, marshy soil, covered with damp mosses, from which rises a spectral tangle of dead and living branches and roots. Everything is still and dank, and only the woodpecker haunts the eerie wilderness; no sunlit clearings, no flowers, brighten the dark silence.

FORESTS OF STONE

In 1897, in a stone quarry in Pennsylvania, U.S.A., there was found under the earth a tree converted into iron ore. Near the town of Corrizo, in Arizona, U.S.A., there is a forest that is completely petrified and is therefore called Chalcedony Park. One of the tree trunks lies across a fissure in the rocky soil and is known as the Agate Bridge.

Petrified trees of the Carboniferous or coal-forming period have been found in the mines of St. Etienne, in France, and these have been identified as remains of the long-extinct seal-tree (*Sigillaria*). A forest of conifers, likewise petrified, was discovered in the United States, taking the form of innumerable blocks of wood-agate and chalcedony (a semi-precious stone like onyx and cornelian); these were fragments of enormous trees, of a height estimated by Dr. Dandee, the American geologist, at 630 feet.

Near Chemnitz in Saxony a primitive forest was found which was alive and growing millions of years ago, in the Permian period, when Germany's climate was like that of Egypt. On a lawn behind the Chemnitz Museum is a trunk of an araucaria, as tall as a three-storied house, and so thick that three men with hands joined can barely encompass it. An araucaria forest of the same period has survived in a petrified form near Cairo in Egypt, and another was discovered in Patagonia a few years ago.

The lignite deposits in the Senftenberg coalfield in Eastern Germany date from the close of the Tertiary period, and in these strata remains of trees with 2,000 rings of annual growth, swamp-cypresses turned to coal, and relics of antelopes and other tropical animals have been discovered from time to time.

HOW FORESTS BECOME PETRIFIED

Water saturated with silica and other minerals in solution flooded the forests and gradually permeated the trees. After hundreds of thousands of years the water drained off, but the chemical action continued or had done its work.

The structure of the trees was in no way altered; the substance alone was changed, while the form remained exactly the same. A timber forest became a stone one, such as that in Arizona, U.S.A., where sections of trunks, often weighing many tons, are scattered in rich profusion.

GIANTS OF THE PLANT WORLD

IN California lies the fallen Father of the Forest, whose trunk was higher than the spire of Ulm Minster, as it is broken off at a height of 330 feet and is still over fifteen feet in diameter at the fracture. At its roots a tunnel has been burnt through the tree, wide enough for a man to ride through.

TREE WITH THOUSANDS OF TRUNKS

A eucalyptus tree on the bank of the River Latrobe in Australia was measured by Dr. Ferdinand Müller and proved to be 558 feet high. The Botanic Gardens at Calcutta possess a banyan tree with a main trunk thirteen feet in diameter and over 3,000 smaller trunks. The age of the tree is over 100 years.

In the Redwood Park in California there are still living trees believed to be 2,000 years old. The tallest of them is over 320 feet high and has a girth of thirty-five feet. A magnificent specimen of gum tree grew in Victoria, Australia, until it reached a height of 470 feet.

LEAVES USED AS UMBRELLAS

The largest leaves are those of the talipot palm, which grows in Ceylon. They are used as umbrellas and for thatching. The tree flowers only once, and that not till its eightieth year; its flower spike is forty feet high. The giant water-lily known as *Victoria regia* has leaves which measure six feet across; its original home was British Guiana. The year 1935 saw the collapse of the largest known mammoth tree, 333 feet high, near San Francisco.

In the village of Santa Marca del Tule, in South-West Mexico, there is a cypress with a circumference of 175 feet. It is stated to be that under which Cortes pitched his camp 400 years ago. England's tallest tree is a Douglas fir at Powis Castle, Welshpool. Its height is about 178 feet. A silver fir at Kilbride in Argyleshire is Scotland's champion in this direction. It is as tall as its rival and boasts a girth greater by several feet.

The longest plant is a seaweed which is found between Cape Horn and New Zealand; it grows to a length of over 200 feet, and its main stem is as thick as a ship's cable, ending in fronds supported by air bladders. This brown seaweed is probably the source of many a story about sea serpents.

EUROPE'S GIANT PLANTS

The largest vine in the world is at Kinnell House, Killin, Perthshire, the Scottish home of the Marquess of Breadalbane. Planted in 1831, by 1889 it already covered an area of 4,651 square yards with its innumerable stems. The largest bunch of grapes that it has yielded weighed seventy-two ounces. The largest vine in Germany may be seen in Würms. It is eighty-eight feet long and bears 800 bunches of grapes.

In the Botanic Gardens at Dijon, France, there is a black poplar 131 feet high, with a trunk fifty feet in girth. Germany's largest oak tree 124 feet high, is still flourishing near Iveneck in Mecklenburg, while there is a beech nearly as tall on the Dargun Heath, also in Mecklenburg. The tallest Scots pine in Germany (150 feet) is near Pössneck in Thuringia, the tallest elm (164 feet) at Guntersblum in Hesse. The tallest yew (thirty-six feet) grows near Hennersdorf; its age is reckoned as 1,400 years, but the oldest of the yews in the Bode Valley was estimated by Alexander von Humboldt at 2,000 years.

VETERANS AMONG TREES

On the Staffelberg, near Lightenfels on the Rhine, stands Germany's oldest lime tree, 1,200 years old and seventy-eight feet nine inches in girth. Near Neuenstadt on the Kocher, on an ancient Franconian assembly ground, there is a lime tree which was planted in A.D. 743. It has 100 lateral branches, each as big as the trunk of an ordinary tree. A gigantic example of the holly, a tree which has everywhere had to make way for cultivation, is to be seen near Wipperfurth in the Rhineland, a veteran of a thousand winters, which is thirty-three feet high.

Fruit trees are seldom allowed to grow tall and old, but there is a 1,000-year-old pear tree on the island of Rugen which is still flourishing. Horse chestnuts were introduced into Germany only 250 years ago; the largest specimens are to be seen in the park of the palace at Biebrich, on the Rhine.

GIANT BRITISH OAK

One of the most famous British oaks was felled in 1810 some four miles from Newport, Monmouthshire. When cut up, the main trunk provided 450 cubic feet of timber, 1,447 cubic feet came from the six main limbs, and 93 cubic feet each from half a dozen of smaller size, making in all 2,455 cubic feet. The main trunk was nine and a half feet in diameter and the total weight of the bark was estimated at six tons.

It took five months for two sawyers to cut up the oak into the required lengths. A peculiarity was that a large stone was found embedded in the trunk about six feet from the ground.

WHIMS OF NATURE

Although the plant world is much more uniformly organized than the animal world and therefore leaves less room for individuality, nevertheless strange specimens crop up here and there. On the way to Miramar in the Balearic island of Majorca the road is flanked by olive trees of vast age that display the strangest shapes. In the Maloney Gardens at Key West in Florida, U.S.A., is the Giraffe Tree, a date-palm on which a fig tree is growing. Together they look like a giraffe.

In the middle of the road at Tegel near Berlin there stands a 1,000-year-old lime tree, which resembles a bear standing on its hind legs. At Sterling, Massachusetts, U.S.A., there are two oaks that are joined together by a branch three and a quarter feet long and as thick as a man; similarly there are two ashes in Central Park, New York, which are joined together, though their trunks are twenty feet apart. The two Sister Beeches in the Berlin Tiergarten are freaks of the same kind. A double tree, consisting of a maple and a beech, is to be seen on the Gierenkopf in the Algäuer Alps of Bavaria; its girth measures forty feet.

A strange feature of the Platte, a plateau in the Taunus Mountains near Wiesbaden in Germany, is the Weeping Oak, an ancient, gnarled tree with slender branches that hang down like a mourning veil. The trunk of the Australian bottle tree resembles a swollen soda-water bottle, whilst a group of blackboy trees (the Australian grass tree) looks like a band of aboriginals on the war path, for their tangled branches, with the stiff leaves of an aloe, are surmounted by a long, bulrush-like flower that looks like a spear.

The pottery tree of Mexico is so-called because its hard bark contains a large amount of silica. This is burned and the ash mixed with clay, and the ingredients are used in the making of earthenware.

AGE OF TREES

The oldest tree in the world was supposed to be the famous dragon tree, Dracaena, of Teneriffe, which was blown down in 1868. With a trunk forty-five feet in girth, it was said to be 6,000 years old. Professor Bessay counted 1,147 annual rings of growth on a Californian giant in the Mariposa Grove. It was twenty-five feet in diameter, so that its stump made a spacious floor.

Among European trees the maximum age is roughly as follows. The yew can live for 3,000 years, the oak for 1,500, the Scots pine for 1,000, the maple for 600, the larch for 300, the beech for 245, the aspen for 210, the lime for 200-300, the birch for 200, the ash for 170, the elm for 160 and the myrtle for 150.

SACRED TREES

Just as the Bible speaks of the Tree of Knowledge, so the mythology of almost all the nations regards trees as symbols of divinity. In the Gobi Desert of Central Asia, where trees are rare, they are accorded divine honours, as they are also in the pampas of South America. At Palenque in Yucatan, Central America, the sacred world tree of the Mayas was symbolized by sculptured stones in the form of a cross.

The Phœnicians venerated the acacia. Under the Tree of Asoka, in India, it is meritorious to pray to Shiva, the king of the gods. Near Sinsheim in Baden an ancient tree still stretches its bare branches to the sky; it was an object of pilgrimage to the ancient Germans, who had no idols but worshipped their gods in sacred groves. The Teutons venerated the ash Yggdrasil. At Buddh Gaya on the Ganges people still worship a scion of the bo tree under which Buddha sat in a trance until enlightenment came upon him. A cutting of the same tree, said to have been planted in 245 B.C., is at Anuradhapura, Ceylon.

At Souk Ahras in Tunisia the inhabitants venerate the sacred olive tree in whose shadow St. Augustine used to sit 1,500 years ago, and by the sacred waters of Sawid in Arabia there stand some ancient date-palms, which are decorated for religious festivals as in the days when Mohammed walked among them. In the Garden of Gethsemane olive trees, so often mentioned in the Scriptures, raise their pale green branches to heaven. At Mamre, in Palestine, there was 2,000 years ago a famous sacred oak; there is a holy tree there today. Beneath this tree tradition has it that Abraham was buried.

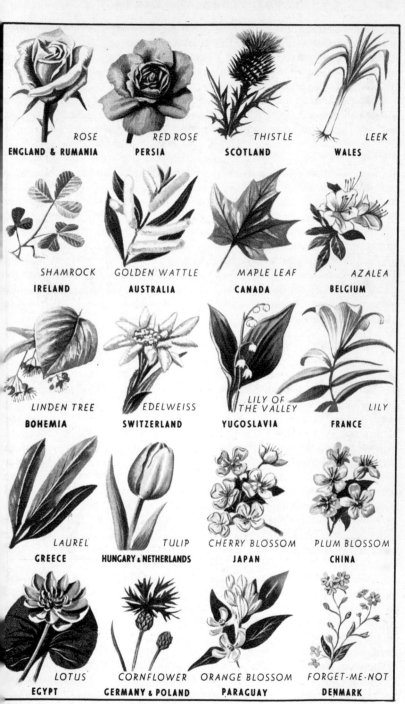

ROSE
ENGLAND & RUMANIA

RED ROSE
PERSIA

THISTLE
SCOTLAND

LEEK
WALES

SHAMROCK
IRELAND

GOLDEN WATTLE
AUSTRALIA

MAPLE LEAF
CANADA

AZALEA
BELGIUM

LINDEN TREE
BOHEMIA

EDELWEISS
SWITZERLAND

LILY OF
THE VALLEY
YUGOSLAVIA

LILY
FRANCE

LAUREL
GREECE

TULIP
HUNGARY & NETHERLANDS

CHERRY BLOSSOM
JAPAN

PLUM BLOSSOM
CHINA

LOTUS
EGYPT

CORNFLOWER
GERMANY & POLAND

ORANGE BLOSSOM
PARAGUAY

FORGET-ME-NOT
DENMARK

National Flowers and Plants

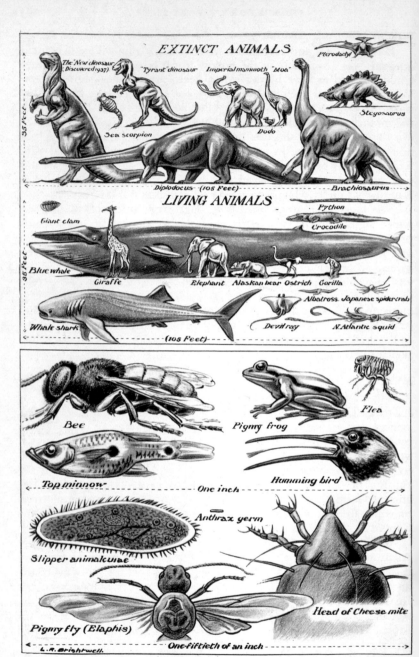

Giants and Dwarfs of the Animal World

WISEST OF ALL TREES

Between Cairo and Helouan a scion of the Virgin's Tree is pointed out; this was a sycamore in the hollow trunk of which the Virgin and Child are said to have hidden when fleeing from Herod into Egypt. When the original tree perished in 1665, one of its seedlings was planted in its place. Not far from Peiping (Peking) is the hill of Ni, to which the mother of Confucius is said to have made a pilgrimage in 551 B.C. On the way thither, she was ordered by a god to betake herself to a hollow mulberry tree, in which she was to give birth to a child who would one day overshadow all China. This tree, or a successor, is still venerated. A cypress, believed to have been planted by Confucius at Kuhfu, and under which he was buried, continues to flourish.

The Japanese are fond of making pilgrimage to fruitful plum trees, which signify goodness of heart, and also to gnarled fir trees, which promise them a long and vigorous life. When the world was younger, and knowledge less, wine was poured on the roots of the beech by lovers, who then embraced the tree in the belief that their fondest wishes would be realized. The mulberry was dedicated by the Greeks to Minerva, the goddess of wisdom, and was regarded as the wisest cultivated tree because it had the good sense to open its buds last of all in the spring. The fir, yew, fig, ivy, and vine were all regarded as sacred to Bacchus, god of wine; the olive, laurel, and palm to Apollo; the white poplar to Hercules.

MYSTIC TREES

The most famous of mystic trees is the " Tree of Knowledge " or " Tree of Life " that figures in the Biblical account of Paradise. It is a symbol derived from the Persian and Egyptian religions and adopted by the Jews. In the Persian religion it is known as Hom. In the underworld of the ancient Egyptians the winged souls of the departed used to perch on the branches of a sycamore. Among the Aryans the rustling of the oak leaves was considered as a divine oracle. The ancient Germans and Slavs sacrificed their prisoners under lime trees, on which they hung their booty. The Romans used Jupiter's oak on the Capitol for the same purpose.

In Islamic art there is the mystic giant tree Tuba, over which only Allah and Mohammed can look. On the Japanese island of Formosa each village has in front of it a " spirit tree," in which the souls of the ancestors dwell; the villagers offer wine to them at the vintage festival. In Greek mythology there is the tree of the Hesperides in Paradise, watched over by dragons, and in Germanic legend the apple tree of Iduna, by eating the fruit of which the gods retained their eternal youth.

That lights are visible in certain ash trees is a venerable belief in the Highlands of Scotland. A similar phenomenon is legendary in Iceland, where it is said that a mountain ash grew on the spot where two innocent victims were executed.

GARDENS AND GARDENING

THE art of gardening is the product of a highly developed civilization. It flourishes most in the sunshine of peace, and in stormy times soon perishes. The oldest known representation of a garden, with decorative hedges and lakes, is seen in an Egyptian relief from Tel-el-Amarna and dates from 1500 B.C. The so-called " hanging gardens " of Babylon, one of the seven wonders of the ancient world, were terraces of masonry on which grew gorgeous flowers, shrubs and trees. They are believed to have been built about 660 B.C.

Homer describes the splendid gardens of Corfu. Where once grew the " golden apples of the Hesperides " (probably oranges) are now the gardens of the Sultan of Morocco. Near Jericho are still to be seen the relics of Herod's palm garden, where the Egyptian queen, Cleopatra, was received. Herodotus, the Greek historian, mentions the gardens of King Midas in Asia Minor, and the *Nibelungenlied*, the German epic of the 13th century, the rose garden of Krimhilde.

" DIGESTION WALKS " AND HERB GARDENS

The art of gardening is said to have been introduced into Athens by the pleasure-loving philosopher Epicurus (342-270 B.C.) who used to instruct his pupils in the arbour of his little garden.

The Romans were famous for their garden architecture, which was under the protection of Venus, the goddess of love. Their gardens were adorned with topiary hedges, dwarf trees, fountains, and the so-called " digestion walks." Julius Cæsar bequeathed public gardens to the people, and Pliny refers to the window gardens kept by the poorer citizens.

In the Middle Ages, the growing rigidity of Chinese art was shown in their over-elaborate landscape gardening; they principally concerned themselves with plants that were becoming extinct. The Arabs, with their systems of artificial irrigation, perfected the ancient Oriental art of gardening, and brought it to the highest pitch in their fairylike gardens, from Agra in India to Granada in Spain.

In Europe this branch of culture was entirely neglected. In the former Roman provinces, instead of villas and pleasure gardens, there arose dark and gloomy castles, where a scanty space was reserved for a purely utilitarian kitchen garden. On the other hand, the monks, who rescued so many of the cultural elements of antiquity, busied themselves with horticulture, but only in the interests of medicine. Their herb gardens afterwards developed into botanic gardens, where plants were scientifically studied.

EARLIEST FORMAL GARDEN IN EUROPE

The Renaissance of antique civilization and the revival of learning gradually changed Europe into a flowery garden. The earliest formal garden is considered to be the Prati di Castello around the palace of the

Dukes of Milan, which was laid out in 1450. Box trees were trimmed to resemble all manner of strange fancies in the 15th century. Thus an Italian living near Florence boasted of the ships, spheres, porticos, temples, vases, urns, giants, men, women, donkeys, oxen, "Pope, Cardinals and other similar fancies" that decorated his garden.

It was the great architect Bramante of Urbino who created the gardens of the Vatican, with their flights of steps, their grottoes, and the Belvedere summer palace. Straight lines, that had been customary in classical times, again began to prevail. The garden lay-out had to conform to the lines of the building of which it was an annexe. The formal sunk garden, with geometrical flower beds and stately fountains, was enclosed by a terrace, with slopes covered with evergreen vegetation. The oldest examples of this type are the Doria Garden at Genoa (1529) and the Boboli Gardens at Florence.

ARCHITECTURAL GARDENS

At a later period absolutism fettered nature, just as it enslaved the people. The site was subjected to a strictly uniform layout; details disappeared or were treated in the mass. Playthings like water organs, mechanical theatres, gusts of wind, surprise jets, had their place. The parks of the Villa d'Este, of Mondragone near Rome, and on the Isola Bella on Lake Maggiore, served as models for Versailles, the stately palace of Louis XIV, the gardens of which were designed by André Le Nôtre, who also brought into being those of Fontainebleau, Saint-Cloud, Saint-Germain, Meudon and St. James's Park, London.

The so-called French style of landscape gardening, a misnomer, gradually conquered all the countries of Europe in the course of the 17th and 18th centuries. Gardens such as those of Schönbrunn, Würzburg, Peterhof and Dresden were really subject to the laws of architecture. Parterres are merely rooms and galleries of palaces prolonged into the open air, and everything is made to correspond with them exactly. The grandest example of this style is the Fürstenberg Garden at Prague, Czechoslovakia.

KEW GARDENS SET A NEW FASHION

Towards the close of the 18th century these gardens were ousted by the so-called English style, which, though inspired by the Frenchman Dufresnoy, was adopted in England from the year 1710, Kew Gardens being the first specimen of the type. Dead-straight walks were replaced by winding paths with picturesque vistas, clipped hedges by informal groups of trees, basins by streams and ponds, cascades by little waterfalls, while scattered everywhere were imitation ruins, pavilions and temples.

Finally in the Trianon Garden at Versailles, an attempt was made to represent in miniature the whole of nature. A garden must contain something of everything, all styles must merge into one—Indian, African and French trees, Dutch tulips, American magnolias, a pond, a streamlet, an artificial mountain, a love grotto, romantic ruins, hermitages, windmills, Turkish kiosks, Chinese pagodas, dairies, pyramids and obelisks.

Famous examples of this style are the Wörlitzer Park near Dessau, the gardens of Wilhelmshöne near Cassel, the Jardin del Principe at Aranjuez, south of Madrid, and the New Gardens at Potsdam.

MOST NORTHERLY GARDEN IN THE WORLD

The last derivative of this style was the romantic garden, as portrayed by Lenné, the landscape gardener, at Glienicke near Potsdam, and by Prince Pückler at Muskau in Lusatia. The Nordic garden at Sans-souci, Potsdam, may be included under the same head. Repetitions and combinations of all previous styles then set in. The modern tendency is to eschew formality of any kind.

The northernmost garden in the world was laid out at Tromsö, Norway, in 70° N. latitude. Many varieties of plants, including roses, have been planted in it, although they have to endure snow in June.

BOTANIC GARDENS

Botanic gardens were not unknown even in ancient times. Charlemagne had gardens of the kind laid out in the Frankish Empire. The monks used to plant herb gardens for medicinal purposes next to their kitchen gardens. The first botanic garden proper was perhaps that created by Silvaticus at Palermo, Sicily, in 1320, and in the 16th century, in the period of the voyages of discovery, similar gardens were planted at Ferrara, Padua, Pisa, and Bologna.

The oldest botanic garden in France is that laid out by Henry IV at Montpellier in 1593. The Jardin des Plantes in Paris was founded in 1635, and needlewomen used to go there to find flower patterns for court dresses. The world-famous gardens at Kew, near London, were founded about the year 1760 by Princess Augusta of Saxe-Gotha, widow of Frederick, Prince of Wales. The botanic gardens at Amsterdam, founded in 1646, became one of the largest collections in Europe. Germany's oldest garden of the kind is the one at Leipzig dating from 1580. Berlin had none till 1801.

The most beautiful gardens in the East are those of Calcutta (1786), the Peradenya in Ceylon, known also as the Garden of the Four Seasons, and the arboretum planted in 1817 at Buitenzorg in Java, which has served as a model for many later gardens.

GARDENS THAT FLOAT

Lake Xochimilco, near Mexico City, the capital of Mexico, is famous for its floating gardens. Here, in the time of the Aztecs, rafts of wood and wickerwork, sometimes 300 feet long, were built and covered with soil, on which all kinds of plants were grown. Some were entirely devoted to vegetables, others to flowers for the decoration of the temples of the sun. A similar plan is used in Kashmir, which is much subject to floods.

FASHIONS IN FLOWERS

In the Middle Ages, lilies and roses, emblems of the Virgin Mary, were grown and worn everywhere. In the 15th century the pink, recently introduced, was the fashionable flower, and in the following century the sunflower from North America and the Mexican aloe, while the flower of the Baroque period was the tulip from Turkey.

The 18th century was particularly fond of the hyacinth, which was afterwards displaced by the aster and the Chinese camellia. In the early 19th century the narcissus, wallflower and stock were very popular. After the World War orchids and cacti were favoured in Germany.

Carnations are among the most popular blooms in the United Kingdom; over 2,000,000 dozen are bought annually. Nearly £15,000,000 a year is spent in Great Britain on cut flowers, and over 100,000 people are employed in the industry.

FLOWERS AS NATIONAL EMBLEMS

Certain plants or flowers are definitely associated with countries. They include the following: England and Rumania, rose; Persia, red rose; Scotland, thistle; Wales, leek; Ireland, shamrock; Australia, golden wattle; Canada, maple leaf; Belgium, azalea; Czechoslovakia, lime tree; Switzerland, edelweiss; Yugoslavia, lily of the valley; France, lily; Greece, laurel; Hungary, tulip; Netherlands, tulip; Japan, cherry blossom; China, plum blossom; Egypt, lotus; Germany and Poland, cornflower; Paraguay, orange blossom; Denmark, forget-me-not

WILD FLOWER SANCTUARIES

Wild flowers have their sanctuaries as well as animals and birds. Probably the pioneer attempt in this connection was made by G. A. Hay, a teacher of botany, who lived in the closing days of last century near St. John, New Brunswick, Canada. Forty acres of Glenwood, a beautiful park in Minneapolis, U.S.A., are devoted to the same purpose, and most species of wild flowers in the State of Minnesota are represented.

The uprooting of plants in the Home Counties of England has led to the extinction of a number of once familiar flowers, and in many places cowslips and primroses have disappeared from their favourite haunts. In Switzerland it is a punishable offence to remove Alpine plants.

MOST FRUITFUL TREES

The greatest profusion of plants is to be found on the equatorial belt in Africa, where 30,000 species have been enumerated, while the Sahara has only 300. Spain has 5,000, Germany 2,609 and Poland 2,396 species.

Among the trees that bear fruit the longest-lived are pear trees, some of which bear for 300 years, while the apple tree rarely exceeds 150 years. The fig tree is also long-lived, and the orange tree carries a good crop at eighty years. The nutmeg tree, even after sixty years, yields three crops

annually.   The most productive individual walnut tree is one that stands
in the valley of Baidar near Balaclava in the Crimea; it yields 100,000
walnuts a year, and five Tartar families share the crop.

The most fruitful vine in the world grows near Graz in Austria;
recently it produced 200 litres of wine.   The skunk of the plant world
is the durian of Malaya, a fruit with a delicious flavour but with a
horrible and lasting smell of rotten onions.

PLANTS STRANGE AND RARE

The Californian rose produces the largest number of blooms, as many
as 21,000 in a summer.   The largest single flower in the world is that
of the rafflesia of Malaya, which measures a yard across, but the largest
flower-spike is that of *Amorphophallus titanum,* a giant arum with a
flower about six feet high.   The largest bean plant is the Chilean guama,
the pods of which are as long as the arm of an adult man, while the
beans are as large as a child's hand.

The most expensive flower is the nun's head orchid, which was
discovered by George Taylor and purchased by a collector for £30,000.
In 1930 an expedition searched the primeval forests of South America
without success for the still more valuable tiger's head orchid.   Some of
the orchids are high-priced because they take forty years to flower.

The rarest flower that ever bloomed appeared at Kizablek in
Bulgaria; it was a turquoise-blue rose and bloomed on a yellow rose tree.

CHRISTMAS TREES PAST AND PRESENT

The Christmas tree incorporates ancient traditions from early
Teutonic times.   The Germanic priests used to make sacrifice under the
tree near the sacred springs, lights and offerings being hung on the
branches in honour of the god to whom it was consecrated.   Candles,
ornaments representing the sun's disk, and presents are still hung on the
Christmas tree.

The French poets of the 12th century refer to it as the shining tree.
The Christmas tree then vanished completely, perhaps owing to the
Church's hostility to old customs, only to reappear in Alsace hundreds of
years later.   It was in 1605 that the first fir tree was decorated in a
parson's house at Strasbourg.   The custom spread at first through the
Protestant districts of Nassau, whence the wife of the Grand Duke
Charles introduced it to Austria in 1816.

At that time the tree was not lit up till Christmas morning, as is still
the custom in Holland.   The Christmas tree then was the thuya, with its
drooping pyramidal branches.   It was not till the middle of the 19th
century that the Christmas tree invaded Catholic South Germany.

Queen Charlotte, consort of King George III, introduced the
Christmas tree into England, though it is commonly believed that the
Prince Consort did so.   The future Queen Victoria notes in her diary
that in 1832 two tables at Kensington Palace were decorated with trees
on which hung lights and sugar ornaments.   Following the revolution

in Russia in 1917, Christmas trees were banned, but made their re-appearance, with official approval, in 1935, when they were banned in Italy and forbidden in Greece in order to conserve the forests.

The previous year " any living plants of the various genera of pines " were debarred from entering Great Britain owing to the prevalence abroad of diseases that infect elms and conifers. All Christmas trees were therefore home grown. The main sources of supply in the United Kingdom are the Forest of Dean, Wales, Devon, Surrey, Norfolk, Suffolk and Scotland.

CHRISTMAS TREE DECORATED WITH NUGGETS OF GOLD

An expensive Christmas tree was set up by an American millionaire some years ago in an hotel in New York. Each branch was hung with nuggets of crude gold from the Klondike mines of Alaska, while the trunk was supported on a pedestal formed of twenty-dollar gold pieces. The largest Christmas tree ever seen at a family gathering was set up at Arundel Castle, the residence of the Duke of Norfolk. Grown on the estate, it was seventy feet high and weighed some four tons.

The tallest Christmas tree is set up every year in a square at Boston, U.S.A. It is composed of several trees and adorned with coloured electric lights. It is estimated that in the United States alone, 5,000,000 young trees are cut down every year for Yuletide celebrations. Balsam fir, spruce, red cedar, and scrub pine are mainly used.

LARGEST PLANTATION IN THE WORLD

This is being created in the United States and extends from the Canadian frontier to Texas. Its purpose is to protect the eastern states from the dust storms of the west. The total number of trees of different varieties will be 30,000,000.

CHEMISTRY OF PLANT LIFE

Plants are living things which breathe, take in food, grow and produce other plants like themselves, and certain conditions are essential before these processes can be carried out. Even a seed must have air and moisture before it will show life by sprouting.

THREE ESSENTIAL NEEDS

All seeds must have a rest after they are scattered by the parent plant or taken from it; but sooner or later they are ready to sprout, and then the first thing they require is air. This can easily be shown by placing some seeds in a tightly stoppered bottle and others in a jar open to moist air. Those in the airtight bottle will not sprout; if the temperature is suitable, the others will. Seeds planted in the garden are not buried deeply, but scattered in loose, well-dug soil. Indoors, they are put in porous pots or shallow seed-pans. The need for air is always kept in mind.

The second thing that the seed requires is warmth. The temperature needed to make a seed germinate varies according to the kind of seed. Wheat, for instance, will sprout at a little above freezing point, and so blades of green may be seen in the fields in winter time. The seeds of plants, such as dates, belonging to warm countries need higher temperatures than those of Britain, where the temperature of a comfortable sitting-room is suitable for encouraging seedlings to grow earlier than they normally do out of doors.

Seeds must have water, but not too much of it. In waterlogged soil seeds will rot; but they must have enough moisture to soften the food store packed inside the seed and prepare it for passing to the growing parts of the young seedling. As soon as growth begins, the plant needs food. When the store within the seed is used up the plant must be able to draw food materials from the soil by means of its roots. Seedlings grown in sawdust die before long, while those in flower-pots filled with good soil have a fair chance of growing into healthy plants. It is not the soil which is necessary to the plant, but the " soil-water," which contains certain salts in solution. The water sprinkled on seedlings grown in sawdust is likely to be too pure to supply the necessary mineral salts, whereas the water in contact with soil-particles acquires the ingredients needed by the plant.

SPARTAN PLANTS

Certain plants in north-east Siberia have been observed to put forth buds in temperatures as low as $-50°$ C. The Christmas rose blooms in frosty weather, and some plant seeds will only germinate when they have had the right amount of frost.

FEVERISH PLANTS

Whereas in the human organism and in warm-blooded animals a body temperature far above the outside temperature is produced by food combustion, plants lack an internal system for producing heat. Their temperature, induced by breathing, is only a few tenths of a degree above the outside temperature.

A " feverish " temperature can be caused by injury, stimulation, or infection, though as a matter of fact the rise is usually less than $1°$ C. In the case of several flowers, including Aaron's rod, a particularly rapid digestive process may cause a rise of temperature of as much as $2°$C.

ELECTRICITY HELPS PLANT-GROWTH

Interesting experiments have been made in electro-culture to show the effects of electric heating, lighting and voltage-stress on plant-life. In Arctic regions, where a great amount of natural electricity is present in the atmosphere, the growth of vegetation during the short summer is amazingly vigorous. Extra growth has also been observed during thundery weather. These hints led to successful endeavours to stimulate growth by producing high-voltage discharges close to various plants, and this was subsequently carried out on a larger scale in various ways. Electricity in the form of light was next brought to the aid of horticulture; and, more recently, soil-heating has been introduced.

LETTUCES BY ELECTRICITY

In 1922 a Norwegian electrical engineer noticed that vegetation was more profuse near certain underground transmission cables and decided to make experiments, which ultimately resulted in the introduction of the soil-heating cable. This discovery was turned to commercial use, principally for the production of table vegetables. In 1926 it was estimated that 50,000 lettuces alone were raised in electrically heated beds in Sweden. In 1933, in France, tests were made with cuttings planted in electrically heated frames, and in due course the plants were found to be a fortnight in advance of cuttings grown in similar frames on hot-beds of manure. By catching earlier markets the growers more than made up for the expense involved in electrical soil-heating.

Thousands of gladioli bulbs forced by electrical cables in an open field in America in the following year led to a handsome profit, when the unusually early blooms came on the market and commanded high prices; and in succeeding years this method of soil-heating has grown in importance. Sterilizing of the soil to destroy harmful organisms can also be done by electric currents.

COLOURS AND PLANT GROWTH

Yellow and red light are favourable to plant growth. The best promoter of chlorophyll, the colouring matter of green plants, is light waves between 0.00035 mm. and 0.00073 mm. in length. Dutch horticultural experts encourage the production of the hydrocarbon necessary for the formation of leaves, flowers and fruits by flooding the plants with neon light, which contains yellow and red rays, but is devoid of heat.

The plant with the most rapid growth is the casuarina, a native of Australia and Polynesia, which grows about 100 ft. in ten years. The slowest-growing plant is the lichen, which has survived from primeval times. It grows hardly more than a hand's breadth in fifty years and can attain the age of 200 years.

AMAZING FERTILITY OF PLANTS

A striking example of the number of seeds produced by some plants is the poppy, one head of which contains 3,000 seeds. If each seed had as many descendants then in six years there would be approximately two billion billion poppy seeds. These would measure 42,720 billion cubic inches, enough to cover 7,000 continents the size of Europe with a layer of seeds two feet three inches high.

Orchids produce thousands of seeds as fine as dust; a single plant of the genus *Acropera* may produce 74,000,000 in one season. The humble willow herb, seen on the banks of so many streams, may have as many as half a million seeds.

HOW PLANTS BALANCE THEMSELVES

By the sensitivity to pressure of their protoplasm (cell-content), plants such as the mimosa and the sundew can feel pressure stimuli much smaller than those perceptible to the human organism. Man cannot feel anything less than 2/1,oooths of a milligramme.

Tiny starch grains embedded in the protoplasm of plant cells often perform the same function as the otocysts or balancing sense-organ of many lower animals. These granules normally lie on the base of the cell, but under the action of gravitational force they shift their position when the animal ceases to be upright. Pressure of the granules on an unfamiliar spot stimulates the animal to regain its normal posture.

Normally the main roots of a plant grow down towards the centre of the earth. At the tips are concentrated many starch grains. If the root is placed horizontally the grains will fall on to the side instead of the bottom of the cells. The root perceives the change and the tip turns through a right angle to bring itself into the normal position, pointing downwards. But if the root-tip is cut off and the starch grains therefore removed the root loses its sense of direction.

THE PARTS OF A PLANT

THE root is the first part of the plant to appear when a seed sprouts. The root has two main uses—to fix the plant firmly (a gardener always presses the soil well down about the roots when he puts a plant in a new place) and to draw in soil-water, containing dissolved salts. In addition, roots frequently act as storehouses of food, the carrot for example. Other pieces of work may be done by roots, and when this is so they become modified and look unlike the usual plant roots. In many orchids tufts of " air-roots " grow out from the stem and hang in the air and absorb water from it. Some palms have " stilt-roots," which grow out from the base of the trunk, and make tripod-like supports between it and the ground, or even from high branches, in which case these extra roots look like pillars and help to prop up the trees.

UNDERGROUND STEMS

The stem of a plant lifts the leaves so that they get the air and light they need, and holds the flowers up within reach of their insect-visitors. Its other chief function is to carry food materials and water between the roots and leaves. As in the case of roots, extra duties may be taken on by plant-stems. Sometimes, as in the iris, the stem looks like a thick root running along horizontally just below the surface of the ground and is a food-store. It is then called a rhizome. If it is still more modified it becomes a tuber, a potato for example. A potato is a swollen stem packed with food. That it is not a root, like a dahlia, can be proved by a close examination of the " eyes," which are very much reduced buds with scale-leaves round them.

Certain stems take on the work of leaves. In some kinds of cactus, for example, the whole plant consists of a mass of green tissue, the modified stem, and the leaves are only represented by tufts of hairs or prickles. In this case the green stem does the food-building work usually carried out by the leaves of a plant. Among the other pieces of work a stem may do is the starting of a new plant by means of runners. The stem bends over into the earth again and gives rise to what are known as adventitious roots, which grip the soil. This rooted stem-tip may then become separated from the main plant and begin to build up a completely new individual.

LEAVES ACT AS LUNGS

The leaves of all ordinary green plants are the chief breathing parts and also the food factories, in which starchy food is built up. Instead of doing this work, some leaves may become sharp spines, which protect the plant from browsing animals, or fine tendrils, which twine round supports and help the plant to climb.

The work of flowers is to make seed, so that there may be new plants by and by. Their structure is adapted in various ways to help in the formation of fruit, containing living seed. The different parts have special work to do, but all to this end. The outer green parts, the sepals, which make up the calyx or cup, are protective. In the bud they are folded over the inner portions of the flower. Within the calyx is the corolla, made up of petals, usually coloured and shaped in a way that makes them attractive to passing insects. In the centre are the stamens, dusty with pollen, and, most important of all, the stigma, the sticky tip above the seed box, which receives the pollen.

PLANTS AS FOOD MANUFACTURERS

When their prepared food supply—the contents of the seed—is used up, plants must draw on other sources. Some of the materials they use for food manufacture are contained in the water absorbed by their fine root-hairs from the soil. These are mineral salts, such as potassium nitrate.

Seedlings with their roots in distilled water die before long; those supplied with a few salts in solution may do better; but only those whose roots have access to a complete food solution compare favourably with a similar plant grown in good garden soil. The following solution gives the plant what it needs:—

Potassium nitrate	1	gramme
Calcium sulphate	$\frac{1}{2}$	,,
Sodium chloride	$\frac{1}{2}$	,,
Magnesium sulphate	$\frac{1}{2}$	,,
Calcium phosphate	$\frac{1}{2}$	,,
Iron chloride (dilute solution)	a few drops	
Water	1	litre

These salts form an important part of the plant's food materials; but an extra substance is required, namely carbon. This the plant gets from the carbon dioxide or carbonic acid gas in the air. In splitting up the gas to get the carbon, the plants set free the oxygen in it. A sign that carbon is an important ingredient of sugar, starch and other compounds is that they char when overheated, the blackening being due to the loss of water and other constituents leaving a residue of carbon.

MIRACLES PERFORMED BY LEAVES

In order to build up its food the plant requires the minerals absorbed in solution by its roots, the carbon dioxide absorbed by its leaves, and energy for its food-manufacturing processes. The power of sunlight, shining through a screen of green pigment called chlorophyll in the leaves, is the energy utilized. Carbon assimilation only takes place when chlorophyll is present and under the influence of light. The particular virtue of the green pigment is that it absorbs both blue light from the sky and red light from the sun, yet shuts out strong yellow rays, which would overheat and harm the tissues of the plant.

Animals need to get their starchy foods ready-made; but the hard-working leaves of green plants raise simple things like air, water and mineral salts into complex foodstuffs. Indirectly all life depends on the work of leaves. They make the starch of the potato, the sugar of the beetroot, and the proteins for the sake of which man eats bread. A single leaf may not build up as much as half an ounce of sugar in a month; but an acre of wheat has been estimated to make the impressive amount of a hundredweight of foodstuff a day or five tons in the whole growing season.

CURIOSITIES OF PLANT LIFE

A CERTAIN number of flowering plants have adopted special modes of nutrition. This group of odd feeders includes the saprophytes, plants which live on decaying vegetable matter; the parasites, which draw nourishment from other plants; and the insectivorous plants, the most curious of all.

Partial saprophytes have green leaves and manufacture some of their food in the normal plant way, but in addition obtain food by the method used by total saprophytes, by assimilating organic food with the assistance of a fungus. Total saprophytes have lost practically all their green pigment and are dirty brown in colour. A British example of this group is the bird's-nest orchid, which has the lower part of its stem covered with short, thick roots and the upper part with yellowish-brown scales instead of leaves.

The bird's-nest orchid can only grow in leaf mould, rich in organic substances. Instead of absorbing this food by root hairs, this strange orchid has a fungus servant, whose threads penetrate its roots and pass the dissolved food to it.

PLANTS THAT BORROW FROM OTHERS

As in the case of the saprophytes, parasites may be partial or total. Some have green leaves and make at least a little of their own food, but draw water and dissolved salts from another plant, instead of from the soil. Among these are the mistletoe and also some less obvious robbers, whose roots fix themselves by suckers to the roots of other plants. Eyebright, cow wheat and yellow rattle can all live independently, but are frequently partial parasites, stealing from the roots of their neighbours, especially grass plants.

Total parasites include the dodder, whose reddish stems are seen twining on the plants it robs, for example heather, gorse, hop, clover and thyme; the broomrapes, which attach themselves to the roots of gorse and broom bushes; and the toothworts, also root parasites, chiefly attacking hazel trees.

LEGEND OF THE MISTLETOE

Mistletoe is a parasite. It grows principally on the boughs of apple trees, rarely on oaks, the seeds being sown by birds. While it draws on the sap of its foster parent, it also manufactures food for itself by means of its leaves. In Norse mythology the plant is associated with Balder, son of Odin, whose mother Freya loved her son so much that she persuaded all things living to protect him. Unfortunately she neglected the mistletoe, with the result that Loki, the god of evil, slew him with a spear of its wood. When Balder had been restored to life by the other gods, the mistletoe promised that it would do no harm to their favourite provided it was kept from touching the earth. It was placed in the keeping of Freya, the goddess of love, hence its association with kissing.

SOME PLANTS EAT MEAT

A few plants have departed a long way from the normal mode of food-getting. They catch insects by means of modified leaves, and kill and digest their prey.

The common sundew has round leaves fringed with rosy hairs glistening with a sticky fluid. The hairs are extremely sensitive, and when a fly or gnat alights on the leaf—or a piece of meat or white of egg is experimentally placed there—they bend over it and pour out a fluid which has the power of dissolving and digesting such food. When it has been absorbed, the hairs or tentacles resume their former position, ready to capture another victim.

Another British insect-catching plant is the butterwort, whose rosettes of pale green leaves sprawl like starfish on the bogs. In this case it is the edge of the sticky leaf which rolls inwards to hold the insect while a digestive fluid is poured over it. The bladderwort is a rootless water plant which traps water mites and minute aquatic insects in little bladders, closed with hinged lids. In other countries grow various pitcher plants and Venus' fly-trap, sometimes seen in hothouses.

PLANTS THAT GO INTO PARTNERSHIP

Owing to the fact that it is a double plant, made up of two different kinds of lowly plant in partnership, a lichen can flourish in places where no other plant could grow. Most of the simple little green plants called algæ grow in water or in moist places and cannot stand drought, while most fungi (plants of the mushroom and toadstool group) are sensitive to cold and scarcity of water; but the lichen, which is composed of a number of algæ and a fungus closely united, can thrive in practically all weathers and at all seasons. It often grows where neither a fungus nor an alga could survive alone, and is, therefore, an example of a successful partnership.

The green algæ make the food for the lichen in the usual plant way, while the fungus fixes the plant in position, and secures food materials from its surroundings and passes them on to the algæ to build up. The green cells are enmeshed in the fungus threads and thus saved from the danger of drying up; they are also spread out so that they catch the sunlight necessary for food manufacture. Lichens are extremely hardy plants, slow growing but long-lived, but though they are not sensitive to changes of temperature, they do suffer from impurities in the air and for that reason grow better in the open country than near large towns. Many thousands of species of lichen are known, and many of these species can grow in almost any climate.

SECRET OF MANNA REVEALED

The so-called reindeer moss is really a lichen. It is of great importance to the Laplanders of the far north, for it provides food for their herds of reindeer. Another lichen, the Iceland moss, is eaten by human beings in northern countries. In a very different region, the south-west of Asia, lichens are still eaten by certain tribes instead of grain, and one kind of " manna," used long ago to feed the children of Israel in the wilderness, was a lichen.

SMALL BUT IMPORTANT PLANTS

Among the smallest but most important plants are the diatoms, single-celled algæ with delicate coats of silica, shaped like a box and its lid in varied forms with a thousand beautiful patterns. They exist in myriads in cultivated soil, in the water of rivers and lakes, and in the upper layers of the ocean. They live on the simplest fare. With the aid of the green pigment they contain they are able in the presence of sunlight to produce in their bodies a fatty oil from the carbon dioxide dissolved in the water. With the addition of mineral nitrates and phosphates absorbed from the water more complicated proteid substances are built up. The tiny forms of animal life in the sea devour millions of diatoms, while they themselves in their turn serve as food for larger marine animals, such as the fishes which we eat. The vitamin A which makes cod and halibut liver oil so valuable to us was originally manufactured by the tiny diatoms.

PLANTS IN A SICK-ROOM

Plants are usually removed from a sick-room at night, and the reason given for this is often that " plants breathe out oxygen in the daytime and carbonic acid gas at night." This statement is incorrect. Like animals, plants always take in oxygen and give out carbon dioxide during respiration. This goes on day and night. But in the daytime the breathing process of the plant, which takes place over its whole surface, is masked by that other process, carbon assimilation. This, as has been shown, involves the taking in of carbon dioxide and the giving out of oxygen—the exact opposite of the exchange of gases made in respiration —and counteracts the pollution of the air by breathing.

At night, however, carbon assimilation ceases, owing to the absence of sunlight, and the breathing plant continues to use up oxygen and give off carbon dioxide. Actually the amount of " impure " gas given off by a plant is unlikely to be harmful; and, although strongly scented flowers are undesirable, it is much more important to keep a sick-room properly ventilated at all times than to remove the plants at night.

PLANTS AS FACTORIES

THE greatest chemical factories are the forests, which are continually circulating the materials of the air. They literally breathe by means of pores or stomata, of which there are several millions on the under surface of an oak leaf and about 200,000 per square inch in the leaf of a sunflower. The oxygen from the air is consumed and carbon dioxide passed out. At the same time green leaves, in the presence of sunlight, take in the carbon dioxide of the air and combine it with water to build up sugars and starches. In this process oxygen is released and diffuses back into the air, thus compensating for that which is used up by animals in their breathing.

If the beneficent action of trees and other green plants were diminished all animal life would be endangered. Much water is given off too from the leaves of forest trees. It has been calculated, for instance, that a plantation of beech loses 40,000 gallons of water daily.

APPLES STILL BREATHE WHEN PICKED

Remarkable developments have taken place in the storage and preservation of foodstuffs. One of these is the discovery that an atmosphere of carbon dioxide retards the ripening of fruit and prevents the growth of minute but important members of the plant world— moulds and bacteria.

A fruit, such as an apple, is a living thing which goes on breathing after it is picked. It houses and protects the seeds until they mature, and when the apple is severed from the tree the seed feeds on the fruit. Ripening can be retarded and the life of the picked apple prolonged either by storing at a low temperature or in an atmosphere poor in oxygen and rich in carbon dioxide. The latter method has made it possible to keep for long periods—say, a voyage on a fruit-ship from New Zealand—varieties of apple which are unsuited to ordinary cold storage, because they collapse shortly after removal from the refrigerator.

In sealed chambers or gas stores the apples are allowed to consume some of the oxygen and give off carbon dioxide, until they become saturated and preserved by the latter. Delicate adjustments are required, and modern electrical science has provided instruments for the purpose, for though the breathing of the fruit has to be retarded, to delay ripening, it must not stop or the apple will die and decay or form " brown heart " and become worthless.

VALUABLE PRODUCTS OF PLANTS

A green plant has been likened to a factory. Owing to its power of capturing and utilizing the energy of sunlight, it is able to build up complex substances. The formation of sugar is the first step. This is brought about through the conversion of water and carbonic acid. After that, more raw materials—phosphates, nitrates, sulphates, and so on, drawn in by the roots from the soil—are combined with the water and sugar to form proteins. Thus food is manufactured for the plant, giving it energy for growth and movement.

During the expenditure of energy, as in animals, respiration goes on. Breaking-down processes replace the building-up process of food manufacture. Ultimately the breaking-down of the proteins and other substances, that occurs through the plant's activities, leads to the release of carbon dioxide, but during the process various other products emerge. Different families of plants have different ways of carrying out their work, involving different chemical combinations, and the substances they make include waste products and reserve food products.

The waste products are of no further direct use to the plant and are often isolated as crystals in the plant tissue. (They may be indirectly helpful by forming a protection against the attacks of snails and slugs.) Some of them are alkaloids, such as morphine, strychnine and quinine, which are extracted for use as drugs. These alkaloids are poisons, but small quantities of them are valuable ingredients of medicines, and so it may be that " poisonous plant " and " medicinal herb " are two names for the same thing.

OILS THAT GIVE FLOWERS THEIR PERFUME

Other waste products of the life processes of plants are aromatic acids, for example prussic acid and salicylic acid (an ingredient of aspirin); and resins and balsams, which are semi-solid plant secretions.

In some cases the substances sought by man are not waste products but by-products which still have a useful part to play in the plant's life, namely ethereal oils, such as oil of cloves, camphor, and the oils of cinnamon, lavender and mint. Volatile oils of this sort give the flower its perfume and attract the insects that benefit the plant by acting as pollen carriers. The oils are secured by distillation of the flowers.

Reserve products is the name given to substances which plants make and store in their fruits and seeds to supply food for the embryo plants of the next generation. These substances include oils and fats, many of them used in commerce : linseed oil, rape oil, cotton seed oil. Numerous flavouring substances are taken from seeds and fruits : vanilla from the seed pods of an orchid, which in the wild state grows on trees in tropical forests, but which is now cultivated; black pepper from red berries, which turn black when dried and can then be used as peppercorns or ground to powder; allspice or pimento, made by drying and grinding the unripe fruits of a tree allied to the myrtle; nutmeg, the seed of a tree cultivated in the East and West Indies; mace from the covering of the nutmeg seed; and mustard from the ground seed of the mustard plant.

FLOWERS WHICH ARE EATEN

The seeds of sunflowers are used by American Indians in making bread. They also furnish food for poultry and cattle, and the oil they contain is valuable for soap and oilcake. Rose leaves boiled in sugar and made into a preserve are enjoyed in Turkey. Dried rosebuds, violets and jasmine are candied by Chinese cooks, who use a species of lily as a vegetable and for seasoning.

Blossoms of the butter tree, prepared in various ways, are eaten by some of the hill tribes of India. The flowers of the banana are appreciated in Japan as a preserve. Oil is extracted from peppermint leaves and used in the manufacture of sweets and medicines. Surrey, England, once had extensive farms entirely devoted to the cultivation of this plant.

BITTERSWEET POTATO FAMILY

One very important family includes some of the deadliest of poisonous plants, yet it is the source of valuable medicinal products and also of wholesome and nutritious food. This is the potato family. Other members are tomato, tobacco, henbane and various nightshades.

The woody nightshade or bittersweet, which scrambles about the hedgerows, has clusters of purple flowers with projecting yellow centres, followed by tempting scarlet berries that are very poisonous. Its relative, the deadly nightshade or belladonna, has purple, bell-shaped flowers and shining black berries, sweet to the taste but extremely poisonous. Even more poison is concentrated in the roots, and it is from them that atropine is extracted for the preparation of eye drops. Belladonna is used for dilating the pupils in certain eye treatments and also for plasters for external application. It is a useful drug in the right hands, but, like all poisons, must be used with caution. Henbane is also of medicinal importance as an opiate, but all parts of the plant are poisonous and accidents sometimes happen through its root being mistaken for a parsnip. It has a cream-coloured flower, heavily veined with purple, and large, hairy leaves. Its disagreeable odour should keep most people from touching it.

Tobacco is closely related to the nightshades and is a narcotic, which may become dangerous if misused. The tomato is a wholesome member of the family; and so, up to a point, is the potato itself. When the potato was first brought to England, botanists of the day looked at it askance, recognizing it as one of the same family as the deadly nightshade, and hesitated to eat it.

It is not widely known that the potato plant does contain poison. Its leaves and berries are narcotic, and even the edible tuber sometimes has some poison in it. This is most abundant in potatoes which have lain near the surface of the soil and become green. Peeling usually removes the unwholesome layer, and, in any case, cooking destroys this poison —this is not the case with henbane—and most of the potato poisonings recorded have been of animals fed on raw greenish potato peelings.

PLANTS THAT GIVE LIGHT

Plants are sometimes seen to be giving off light, but the source of the radiance is not always the plant itself. Just as meat or fish may shine in the dark, owing to the presence of certain bacteria, large plants may be ornamented with minute forms of plant life, either bacteria or fungi, which shed light.

When logs or tree stumps appear luminous, it is not from the wood itself that the light comes, but from fungus threads which have penetrated it. Under particular conditions of atmosphere or temperature, many fungi are luminous, either in their fully developed toadstool form or while they still consist of the simple threads or *mycelia* that grow from scattered fungus spores. The olive tree agaric is a brilliantly luminous toadstool, and there are coal mines in Germany where festoons of fungus threads shed a remarkable white radiance and transform the gloomy places into fairy palaces.

CELLS FOR CATCHING RAYS

The daughter of Carl von Linné, the great Swedish naturalist, long ago asserted that she had seen light flashing from the garden nasturtium, and other observers have maintained that poppies and marigolds have light-giving properties. It is, however, generally believed by scientists that though actual light may occasionally be flashed from the petals of flowers, when the air is highly charged with electricity, there is more often a mere illusion of light-production. This is probably due to the fact that the colours of flowers appear more intense for a short time at dusk.

Nor does the so-called luminous moss really produce light. The gleaming of this plant in the dark caves where it grows is simply a reflection of the daylight that filters through the darkness. Since it is a green plant, the moss cannot live without some sunlight, and it has tiny lens-like cells which enable it to make the most of the poor supply in the cave. These special cells gather up and flash back the rays, and so gleam like miniature cats' eyes in the dim surroundings.

PLANTS AS BAROMETERS

Many flowers are exceedingly sensitive to light, heat and humidity, and behave in such a way that they may be said to act as barometers. The scarlet pimpernel is in fact called "the poor man's weather glass." This pretty little flower of the cornfields and the wayside remains closed altogether on dull days; on sunny days it opens in the morning and closes early in the afternoon. If rain threatens while the flower is open, the petals close over the stamens to prevent the wetting and spoiling of the pollen.

A low-growing yellow flower, the rock rose, common on downs and dry commons, has a scientific name which means "flower of the sun." On bright days the petals open widely; in damp weather they appear crumpled and depressed. The wood anemone also has its place among plant barometers. Its name of windflower refers to the pretty movements of the white heads in the spring breezes. Hung on delicate stalks, the dainty flowers turn the backs of their mauve-tinged petals to the slightest puff of wind. They also follow the movements of the sun, and are sensitive to changing temperature, curling in their petals before nightfall and when rain approaches. One of the best-known plant barometers is the common chickweed, and when its tiny white stars are fully expanded fine weather may be expected, while their closing gives warning of coming dampness.

In several ways the wood sorrel shows a sensitive nature. Its clover-like leaflets droop close to the stalk at night or when rain is coming; they respond quickly to light and darkness and also close when touched. The seed of the stork's bill, one of the wild geraniums, has a corkscrew-like beak attached to it, which is markedly responsive to moisture in the atmosphere. Its real purpose, like that of the feathery awn of the stipa grass seed, which uncurls when it is damp, is to anchor the seed and drive it into the soil; but it serves as a novel weather indicator.

FLORAL CLOCKS

The opening and closing habits of some flowers are so regular that flower beds have sometimes been constructed, notably in the Princes Street Gardens in Edinburgh, in the form of floral clocks, the approximate time being indicated by the open blossoms in particular sections of the circle. Goat's beard, or John-go-to-bed-at-noon, or the noonday flower, as it is variously called, is said to shut at noon; but it closes even earlier if pollination has been brought about by an insect visitor.

The dandelion is supposed to have served the shepherds of olden days as a clock. Children today " tell the time " by counting the breaths needed to blow off all the seeds; but it was the golden flower that was the shepherd's clock, and it was said to open at five o'clock in the morning and close at eight in the evening. Similarly, the wild chicory or succory, a plant of the dry roadsides and chalk downs, flowering from

July to October, is said to open its pale blue many-rayed flowers at eight o'clock in the morning and close them at four o'clock in the afternoon; but this is claiming too great a degree of accuracy.

SOME FLOWERS DISLIKE MUSIC

Sound has a marked influence on certain flowers, some of which are more sensitive to the vibrations which are set going than others. It was found that after some hours of dance music in which there were practically no intervals all the carnations and cyclamen that decorated the hall inclined away from the players. Another experiment was then tried. The blooms were adjusted and placed immediately in front of the orchestra and facing it. The flowers without exception again showed their " disapproval." There was not one which continued to face the orchestra.

MUSHROOMS AND TOADSTOOLS

THE number of really poisonous fungi is relatively small, and the edible fungi are more varied and numerous than is generally supposed; yet there are toadstools so virulent that caution in handling fungi of all sorts is extremely important. It is frequently stated that poisonous fungi, while being cooked, will blacken a silver spoon and so reveal their true nature, and also that mushrooms which are easily peeled are edible. Such rule of thumb methods are unreliable, and fungi should never be tasted unless they have been identified beyond all doubt by someone who knows their botanical characters. It is safer to keep to the varieties of cultivated mushrooms usually sold nowadays, than to experiment with wild fungi, other than a few easily recognized types.

MANY DEADLY SPECIES

Only the common mushroom and the horse mushroom are freely used in Britain, but in France and Germany other fungi are much sought for food. All must be perfectly fresh and free from traces of attack by insects or bacteria which cause decomposition. A common but mistaken belief is that all highly coloured forms of fungi are poisonous, while the duller ones are harmless. Many pale species are deadly, whereas one of those freely eaten on the Continent is of a brilliant orange colour.

A toadstool or a mushroom is a fruit body of a fungus. It is shaped like an umbrella, a form not seen in other types of plants, and consists of a cap (the *pileus*) and a stalk, rising from an underground mass of whitish threads, known as *mycelia*. Mushroom spawn as sold to gardeners consists of *mycelia* moulded into bricks along with suitable manure. If these fibrous blocks are broken up and placed in damp soil, preferably in a warm place, they give rise to the edible fruit bodies. But mushroom cultivation is for the amateur a chancy business.

MEALS FOR MUSHROOMS

Mushrooms and toadstools grow chiefly in woods and fields, where they obtain the moisture and the dead vegetable matter necessary for their growth. They do not contain any of the green colouring matter called chlorophyll which in other plants plays an essential part in food manufacture. By means of this pigment and sunlight, ordinary plants use the carbon dioxide in the atmosphere in making their foodstuffs; but toadstools and mushrooms can do without sunlight. They draw their carbon from the dead plants in the soil. Since the food is obtained in this way, the tangle of threads remains out of sight; but the fruiting parts must appear at the surface, so that the spores may be scattered.

The cap of the mushroom is covered with smooth skin on the upper side and is well padded with a firm, fleshy substance. On the under side of the cap the gills are seen, a great many thin strips hanging down from under the sheltering " umbrella." They get their name from their resemblance to the breathing gills of certain animals, but they are not breathing organs; they are the parts of the fungus which bear the spores.

The stalks of mushrooms are thick and fleshy, sometimes swollen near the base and often showing a ring near the cap. This ring or frill (the *velum*) remains after the cap of a growing mushroom has been torn to expose the spores. In young mushrooms the gills are not seen, and the cap appears as a knob.

Fungus threads sometimes penetrate very deeply into the timber of old trees. In one case a block of wood sawn across revealed a number of egg-shaped bodies embedded in a compact felt-like substance. What looked like a mass of fossil eggs in the core of the timber turned out to be the remains of a squirrel's hoard of acorns, stored in a hollow in the tree and invaded by a fungus, which had destroyed the contents of the acorns and filled and surrounded the hard shells with its tangled threads.

RECOGNIZING THE COMMON MUSHROOM

The common edible mushroom, which is cultivated for the market, appears as a wild fungus in grasslands in summer and autumn. In the young stage it is a round white knob, a " button." The flatter, larger cap of the mature mushroom is white fading to a brownish shade, with a thin, dry skin, easy to remove, and thin, pink gills which later become purplish-brown.

The flesh is thick and soft, and when broken changes from white to reddish brown. The thick white stalk carries a noticeable ring. The somewhat similar " death cap," which is common and extremely poisonous, may be distinguished by its white or greenish gills.

FAIRY RINGS PUZZLED OUR GRANDFATHERS

Circular patches of dark green grass are sometimes observed in the midst of poor pasture. These " fairy rings " are the sign of the presence of a fungus. As the fairy-ring mushrooms feed they exhaust the soil in a central patch, but from their scattered spores new mushrooms spring up in a ring farther out. Gradually the circle is widened and the central patch, after a period when it may be quite bare, now becomes rich again, as the result of the decay of the earlier mushrooms, and is soon covered with healthy grass.

Such circles are of a different shade of green from the half-starved grass around them, and they were a puzzle to our ancestors, who first believed them to be caused by fairies and later advanced the equally fantastic theory that the effect was produced by thunderbolts.

ONCE USED FOR FLY-PAPERS

The fly agaric toadstool, a beautiful fungus common in birch woods and among fir trees, is very poisonous. The expanded cap of the mature toadstool may measure as much as seven inches across and it is of a brilliant red colour, spotted with white " warts." The long stem, white or yellowish, often has a scaly appearance and the white gills have minutely toothed margins.

At one time a poison for use in making fly-papers was prepared from this fungus and this gave rise to the name fly agaric.

SEEDS AS TRAVELLERS

ONE of the differences often pointed out between animals and plants is that an animal moves about, while a plant remains rooted to one spot. This is not a hard-and-fast distinction, for some creatures lead extremely sedentary lives. A sea anemone, for instance, spends all its adult life on one piece of rock, unless it is carried about on a hermit crab's back. On the other hand, plants are by no means all stay-at-homes. A seed contains an embryo plant, and seeds often travel long distances. Water plants, such as duckweed and the still smaller diatoms, which are not anchored by roots, naturally float about; and there is an instance of a complete land plant that goes on a journey.

DESERT PLANTS THAT FIGHT DROUGHT

Street vendors sell packets containing multi-coloured material which opens out in a tumbler of water into a spray of tiny artificial flowers. Even more surprising is a dry, brown object, like a ball of wicker work, which after a similar soaking unfolds green fronds, not unlike the foliage of a cypress tree. This is a living plant, which is able to resume growth after spending long periods in a dry state. There are two well-known plants of this type, the resurrection plant, a kind of club moss, which reproduces itself by means of spores, and the rose of Jericho, a seed-bearing plant of a higher order. Both are desert plants with an extraordinary power of resisting drought and " coming to life " after being dried up and dormant for many months or even years.

The rose of Jericho is a wanderer. In the dry season, when its seeds are ripening, its leaves fall off and the branches curl inwards to protect the fruits; the roots wither and the detached plant rolls about the desert till it is blown by the wind to a moist spot or the rainy season begins. Then and only then this dry ball of a plant revives and sheds its seeds where they will have a chance to sprout.

SEEDS THAT LIVE FOR A CENTURY

There are many authentic records of seeds which have sprouted after resting in a dormant state for a great many years. A distinguished French scientist, A. Becquerel, proved that some seeds could give rise to plants after being kept in a herbarium for eighty-seven years, and it is accepted that Indian lotus seeds can survive desiccation lasting a century or more.

Stories of the sprouting of "mummy wheat," however, must be regarded as fairy tales. There is a small but profitable trade in seeds said to have been found inside mummy cases, and such seeds frequently do sprout—and sometimes give themselves away by producing crops of a modern variety of wheat not known at the time of the Pharaohs. Scientists who have made careful experiments with seeds really taken from mummy cases have invariably found that the ancient seeds refused to awaken from their long sleep.

SEEDS FIRED FROM "POPGUNS"

Some plants drop their seeds close beside them. The poppy, for instance, has a large seed box, like a covered cup with holes under the cover, and it hangs its head to let the ripe seeds fall out. Even so, the poppy seeds may travel a good way, for the wind shakes the poppy "pepper pots" and blows the light seeds around.

If all the seeds of all the different plants remained close to the parent plant, the growing seedlings would smother one another; so plants have all sorts of ways of sending their offspring farther afield. Sometimes the seeds travel alone, leaving the seed box behind on the plant to wither and fall off later; sometimes the whole fruit goes on the journey and continues the work of protecting the seeds for a little while longer.

One of the ways in which seeds are sent on their travels is by the fruits exploding or opening with a jerk. A favourite plant in cottage gardens, the American balsam, is called touch-me-not, because if the ripe fruits are lightly pinched the seeds come popping out. Crossing a common on a hot day, people hear the sound of tiny "popguns," as the ripe seed pods of the broom bushes crack in the sun. The two sides of the pod curl up and the seeds are shot out so violently that they often fall quite a distance away from the bush. Gorse, lupin, vetch and sweet-pea pods all behave in much the same manner. Other fruits which explode are the geranium, pansy, dog violet and wood sorrel.

The herb robert is a wild geranium of the wayside. After the pretty pink flower has faded, a spike remains above the little seed box. When the seeds are ripe, the seed box opens outwards and the seeds are slung out from the threads at the foot of the spike, as if they were tiny missiles held in a noose of string. It has been shown by experiment that the herb robert can catapult its seeds a distance of twenty feet, so obviously there is a good chance of some of them reaching suitable spots where new herb robert plants will be able to grow. The pansy and violet have smooth, slippery seeds, which are flicked out when the seed boxes dry and split. They often travel several feet. Attached to the wood sorrel seeds are little fleshy outgrowths, which are very elastic. When the seed box opens, these suddenly turn inside out and jerk the seeds away.

SEEDS THAT USE A PARACHUTE

Many seeds travel by flying through the air, blown about by the wind. They may simply be very small and light, or they may be flattened to fly more easily. In many cases, however, there are more elaborate preparations for flight. Winged seeds are found in the yellow rattle, while common winged fruits are those of ash, elm, birch, maple, sycamore, lime and dock. Plumed or feathery seeds are seen in willow, poplar and willow herb; and feathery fruits include the dandelion and the wild clematis.

The dandelion head is made up of a great many tiny florets, which are followed by fruits. Actually each part that flies away is a fruit, but the seed and fruit or seed box are indistinguishable to the eye. What is seen is a tiny fruit, enclosing a seed, and topped by a silken tuft. The tuft acts as a parachute. The seed floats away and may be carried a long distance by the wind. When it drops at last the silky hairs help to fix it to damp earth.

SEEDS SCATTERED BY ANIMALS

Animals help many seeds to travel. Seeds may be carried from place to place in a piece of mud sticking to a bird's foot. Berries and other tempting fruits are eagerly sought by many birds; some which are poisonous to human beings do the birds no harm. Sometimes the bird eats the soft part of the fruit and wipes the hard seeds off its beak—mistle thrushes have been seen " planting " mistletoe on the bark of trees in this way—but more often the bird swallows the whole fruit and the seeds pass through its body unharmed.

Hips and haws, which are like apples on a small scale, are brightly coloured to attract the birds. Many other fruits are noticeable for their gay tints and sweet smell. The colour and scent of fruits are as important in the plant world as the attractive colour and perfume of flowers. People also scatter seeds when they eat cherries and other soft fruits and throw away the stones or pips; but not, of course, when they eat the kernels of nuts.

FRUITS WITH HOOKS

Another seed-scattering arrangement is for the seed boxes to have hooks, so that they may be carried about by animals, whether the animals know it or not. The goose grass or cleavers which grows in the lanes is covered with hooks. Its stem and leaves have hooks, which help the plant to climb, and the fruits have hooks, which stick closely to cloth, hair or fur. They may be carried a long way before the seed boxes set free the seeds within them.

A bigger "burr" is the fruit of the common burdock, a tall plant with heart-shaped leaves and pink, thistle-like flowers. Each prickly ball is a whole flower head, containing seeds. These burrs are carried by sheep, dogs and human beings. Other prickly fruits are those of the wood forget-me-not and the wood avens or geum.

PRAYING PALM OF FARIDPUR

At one time thousands of pilgrims in India every year visited the famous praying palm of Faridpur, which was said to bow its head every evening when the temple bells were calling the faithful to prayer. This was a fanciful interpretation of the perfectly normal behaviour of a plant responding to an outside influence, in this case temperature.

The tree was an ordinary date-palm, but it had been displaced by a storm and had grown in a markedly slanting position. Every day, in response to the waxing and waning temperature, the highest part of the trunk moved up and down through more than a yard, while the large leaves which pointed high up in the morning were swung round through a vertical distance of about six yards in the afternoon. To the popular imagination the tree appeared as a giant bending its mighty neck every evening in an attitude of devotion.

The bending and bowing of the tree was due to expansion and contraction according to the changes of temperature in the evening and in the morning, coupled with the natural tendency of a growing stem to grow upwards. Every common tree in Britain exhibits a slight rise and fall of its leaves for the same reason. The explanation of the praying palm is simply that the tree's unusual sloping position greatly exaggerated this normal answer-back to the chill of the evening.

ENEMIES OF PLANTS

ABNORMAL growths—some beautiful, others disfiguring—are noticeable on many trees and smaller plants. These are galls, and are the result of some intruder's attack upon the plant. Galls may be produced in response to the irritation set up by thread-worms, mites or insects, the greater number being due to the attacks of gall wasps or gall flies. They are also caused by other plants, the crown galls of fruit trees and the warts on potatoes being induced by fungus attacks.

HOW PLANTS "ANSWER BACK"

There are two main groups of galls: an abnormal growth of a part, such as a leaf or flower, resulting in a "bunch," for example, "witches' brooms," and, secondly, a swollen growth of the plant's tissue, such as the compact marble gall on the oak. Galls illustrate one of the ways in which plants "answer back" to some outside stimulus; and where they are due to the intrusion of an insect they show how closely linked are the plant and animal worlds.

This particular linkage is of advantage to the insect, for inside the gall it receives the shelter and food it requires during its development; and in most cases the plant as a whole does not suffer. It protects itself by enclosing the intruder in an extra growth of tissue—a gall.

OAK-APPLES ARE CAUSED BY FLIES

One of the most familiar galls in Britain is the oak-apple, not to be confused with the acorn, the fruit of the tree. It is a large, round gall caused by a small fly which pierces a bud of the oak with her sharp ovipositor, lays her egg there and then closes the tiny hole with a drop of gummy fluid. For a time the plant shows no response, but when the maggot-like larva hatches and begins to move, the plant cells around it multiply with great rapidity, until a mass of tissue surrounds the intruder. This isolates the grub from the rest of the tree, yet provides it with a safe nest.

Inside the ball of tissue, the oak-apple is out of reach of birds and other enemies and is able to get all the food it requires from the gall surrounding it. The oak-apple is no prison. In due course the grub gnaws a passage through to the exterior and leaves the gall just when it is due to pass into the next phase of its life history. It becomes a chrysalis and falls to the ground, and later takes to the air as a fully developed fly.

KNOWN AS "ROBIN'S PIN-CUSHION"

One of the prettiest galls of the countryside is the robin's pin-cushion or bedeguar gall, a crimson and pale green mossy outgrowth found on wild roses.

This gall may be seen on cultivated roses, if the rose-gall fly happens to visit them. It consists of many tiny compartments, covered with a tangle of bright fibres, and is the result of an abnormal development of one of the rose bush's leaf-buds, due to the presence of a gall-fly larva.

WITCHES' BROOMS ON BIRCHES

A different type of gall, consisting of a big bunch of twigs, gets the name of witches' broom. A birch tree may carry on its boughs as many as two dozen such tangled masses, and they look so like old birds' nests that anyone might be excused for mistaking a gall-laden birch for the site of a rookery. The great bunch of twigs is an abnormal growth, provoked by fungus attacks. The fungus spores may gain access through wounds in the birch made by mites. The fungus pushes its threads into the plant and the effect on a bud of the birch is to make it send out numerous weak twigs. In course of time there is a whole "broom" of twigs, many of them dead. The tree has been stimulated to behave in an unusual way; the effect of irritation upon its tissues recalls the abnormal growths or tumours which occur in man. Witches' brooms have been artificially produced on alder trees by infection with fungus spores.

PLANT WEAPONS AND ARMOUR

Although the little creature shut up inside a gall does not kill or even greatly weaken the tree that harbours it, many plants are on the defensive against intruders. Innumerable animals live upon plants; but the plants are not all devoured and many of them have safeguards. The defences against large animals are obvious, though not always effective. The donkey loves a mouthful of prickly thistles. Spines, thorns and prickles of such plants as gorse, rose, holly and bramble do ward off some attacking animals, and are the most noticeable defences.

Some plants, such as the arum, have armour inside them, that is, sharp crystals which resist the rasping tongues of snails and the jaws of caterpillars. Others, including poison ivy, hemlock and deadly nightshade, are poisonous to certain animals. The nettle has an irritant sting; it has poison at the bases of the fine, sharp hairs that cover its leaves.

Some plants have mechanical devices for blocking the paths of small, creeping visitors; the teasel, for example, has joined leaf bases which, filled with rainwater, form little moats, and some campions have ramparts of sticky hairs, which help to keep out unbidden guests.

THE PLANT'S STRUGGLE FOR LIFE

ONE of the most attractive wayside flowers to be found in the United Kingdom is the white clematis or traveller's joy, which covers the hedges with foamy masses of blossom. Later in the season the starry flowers are replaced by equally noticeable fruits, feathery seed vessels known as old man's beard. At first grey, this "beard" turns white after severe frosts and decorates the wintry hedges. This plant, common all over the southern part of England, especially in chalky districts, is also known as the white vine and the virgin's bower. Cultivated varieties of clematis are common in parks and gardens.

USING TREES AS LADDERS

The sight of the clematis scrambling over neighbouring shrubs recalls the fact that one of the chief needs of every green plant is light. Very few plants grow well in deep shadow. In a pinewood there is hardly any undergrowth at all. When a great many plants grow close together, as in a thicket or a hedgerow, the tallest plants naturally get most light; but some plants have found a good way of getting into a favourable position. Instead of slowly building up strong stems or trunks, as trees do, they climb up, using other plants as their support. There are a number of ways in which plants do this.

The stems of the clematis, the ivy and the honeysuckle are often fairly woody, yet they are not strong enough to hold up the leaves and flowers without some extra support. A trail of clematis or of honeysuckle pulled down seems quite limp, and if it is cut through it will be seen to be loosely built, because it has grown very quickly and is not a supporting stem but simply a supply-pipe carrying water up from the soil to the leaves. The simplest way in which plants climb is by twining their stems round other plants. The hop, the convolvulus or bindweed and the honeysuckle or woodbine climb in this way. They are twiners, and most climbers growing among other plants are, to a certain extent, similarly supported; but there are several additional ways in which a climber may attach itself to its support. The clematis is partly held up by its long stem lying across other plants, but it also clings more closely by twisting its leaf-stalks round twigs or other supports. These leaf-stalks often become as hard as wires.

IVY SUPPORTS RUINS

The ivy has its own special way of climbing by means of the hairy rootlets—" adventitious roots "—seen in clusters along its stems. These extra roots may be seen gripping stonework as well as tree-trunks, and many an old building would become still more of a ruin if the ivy were torn down from its walls. Nasturtiums climb by twining their leaf-stalks round any convenient prop. A number of other plants, including the pea, the vine and the passion flower, have special climbing parts, called tendrils, which are very sensitive. As soon as one of these delicate green threads touches a twig or a string, it curls round the support till it looks like a little spring.

In the Virginia creeper the tendrils do not twine, but have at their tips small, sucker-like pads, which fix themselves firmly to the walls on which the creeper grows. Still another way of climbing is shown by the blackberry and goose-grass or cleavers, which grip other plants with their hook-like prickles and so raise themselves up into the light.

WATER AND WIND AS FOSTER-FATHERS

In some cases flowers are invariably self-pollinated; that is to say, pollen from their own stamens falls upon the stigma, and some reaches the " possible seeds," the ovules, in the seed-box and fertilizes them, so that they develop into " real seeds " capable of giving rise to new plants. In many more cases self-pollination only occurs if cross-pollination fails; that is, if the flower in question does not receive pollen from some other flower of the same kind. The seed produced by self-pollination tends to be scantier and weaker, so most flowers have some device for securing cross-pollination.

The transference of pollen from one flower to another may be achieved by several different agents; insects and the wind are the most important. The pollen may be carried by water, not a common method, since most of the aquatic plants flowering at the surface are pollinated by the wind or by visiting insects; or it may be blown from one flower to another by the wind, the usual method for early flowering trees and a number of other plants. In many cases the agents are animals: birds and bats (in the tropics); snails and slugs; and, above all, insects of various kinds.

COLOURS AND SCENTS ATTRACT INSECTS

The gay gardens and flowery meadows of summer are visited by a great company of insects. One can hardly think of purple clover-heads, or recall their fragrance, without hearing in fancy the hum of bees. Naturally the bees do not visit the flowers with any intention of doing a good deed by carrying pollen from one to another. They are going about their own affairs, seeking nectar and pollen for food for themselves and the rest of the community to which they belong.

The visits of insects are not always beneficial to the flowers. Some bees discover a way of robbing the flowers of their sweets, by biting through the nectar-tubes, without coming in contact with the pollen. If the bees become dusted with pollen while they are seeking food, however, they are likely to act as pollinating agents. It is therefore to the plant's advantage to attract insect-visitors, and many flowers have two powerful lures—colour and scent—which help them to secure cross-pollination.

It has been proved by experiment that bees have a colour-sense and also that they can perceive odours. The colours and scents of flowers undoubtedly attract insects and no doubt come to be associated with the rewards that flowers offer.

COLOUR SIGNALS OF FLOWERS

Colours are displayed in a variety of ways. Bright flowers are noticeable in the sunshine and pale flowers glimmer in the dusk. In many flowers the petals are gaily coloured, particularly on the surface most readily seen by flying insects; but other parts frequently give the signal. It may be the sepals which are bright, as in winter aconite, or the surrounding bracts or leaves, as in sea-holly and sun-spurge. The pollen-covered stamens themselves sometimes add to the conspicuousness of the flowers. Often the insects are attracted by flowers which are small individually, but which are so grouped that they form a cluster or spike, as in lilac, guelder-rose, horse-chestnut and many others.

LURED BY SCENT

Many brilliant flowers seem to have little or no scent, though possibly insects detect an odour even in these; and many fragrant flowers, for instance thyme and mignonette, are far from showy. In many cases, however, flowers have a double lure.

Insects have a well developed sense of smell. Strongly scented blossoms attract them from distances at which the colours could not be perceived and after dark when even white flower candles have ceased to shine. How sweetly the lime trees perfume the evening air! Many scents are intensified by sunshine, by rain, or by the coming of night.

WHERE THE BEE SUCKS

It is said that 37,000 loads of nectar are needed to make one pound of honey. No wonder people talk of the busy bee! The worker-bees, which collect nectar for honey-making and pollen for bee-bread, do not fly from flower to flower in haphazard fashion; they fly from one flower to another of the same kind. The advantage of this to the flowers is obvious; a clover flower does not want pollen from a poppy but from another clover flower.

On the bee's side there is also much to be gained by systematic exploration. Nectar-finding has to be learnt. Once a bee has found out where a foxglove keeps its sweet store, time and trouble are saved if other foxgloves are visited rather than flowers with fresh secrets.

THE FLOWER AND ITS VISITOR

The bee has a long " tongue " used for lapping up small drops of nectar. It also has other long mouth-parts which, closing about the " tongue," form a sucking-tube. The nectar is sucked into the mouth and thence into a honey-bag, and an acid secretion in the insect's mouth begins the transformation from nectar into honey. The change is completed after the sweet stuff has been stored in the cells of the honey-comb in the hive, and the heat of the hive has a good deal to do with the process.

There are honey-bee flowers, humble-bee flowers, wasp flowers, butterfly flowers, moth flowers and fly flowers; that is to say, flowers with parts so arranged that one particular kind of insect-visitor brings about the desirable cross-pollination. These different insects have different types of mouth-parts, different lengths of " tongues," and it follows that one will be more likely than another to brush the pollen-covered stamens and the pollen-catchers (stigmas) while it is sucking up the nectar. For example, the honeysuckle is a moth flower, the red clover a humble-bee flower, the cuckoo-pint (arum) a fly flower, and the figwort a wasp flower.

" SHOWERS OF SULPHUR "

In many districts there are what are known as " showers of sulphur " every year. The ground and the herbage may be thickly dusted with a fine powder, which is not sulphur, although sulphur-coloured. It is pollen from pine trees and other conifers.

This golden dust is set free in great quantities at the flowering season of these evergreen trees, and since each grain has two little bladder-like floats, it may be carried a long distance from the forests. It rises like a cloud and may travel miles before it sinks, so it is not surprising that many people mistake " sulphur showers " or " golden rain " for something supernatural.

Grasses of many kinds, including the cereals, rye and wheat, and so on, produce large quantities of pollen about midsummer. It is very fine and light, suitable for being borne by the wind rather than by insects, and it has irritating properties, which, in susceptible people, contribute to the affliction known as hay-fever.

POLLEN AT A HEIGHT OF 16,000 FEET

Flower-pollen has been found at a height of over 16,000 feet, whence it is carried over enormous distances by the strong winds that always prevail at these high altitudes. This is why volcanic islands that occasionally make a sudden appearance in the sea are rapidly covered with vegetation.

UNBORN PLANTS

Unborn plants are those that are produced by means of cuttings, and not from seed. Among them are the La France roses, which are increased by grafts and wildings. All La France roses are really nothing else than one great bunch which was at some time or other born out of a single seed. The Bengal rose came to Europe in 1789, the tea rose in 1809, the noisette in 1814. By crossing these with native roses, some 300 varieties were produced by 1863, and as many as 10,000 up to the present time. The Maréchal Niel rose, which came from Avignon in 1863, is becoming extinct. Varieties of potato also die out from time to time as they are multiplied asexually by means of sets. The potato-grower, therefore, has to go in for seed-crossing.

All malmsey grapes and pyramid poplars in Europe come from ancestors introduced from the Orient, which were planted 120 years ago in the park at Wörlitz near Dessau. All the acacias in Germany are descended from a single ancestor, which is still standing on the Gute Brietz near Berlin. King Frederick William I of Prussia had it sent from North America as a pot plant in 1710.

WHY LEAVES CHANGE COLOUR

The colours usually seen upon autumn leaves are yellow, orange, red and brown. Leaves of different trees show different colour sequences. Sycamore leaves habitually fall while still green; but when there is no marked change of colour it often means that the leaves have been snapped off by high winds before the processes leading to the normal fall have been completed. In some cases, such as young oaks and beeches, the leaves do not fall even when they have become dry and withered, but cling to the twigs till the following year. Speaking generally, however, the leaves of trees in Great Britain, apart from evergreens, change colour in autumn and then fall.

The autumn tints are the external sign of important internal changes taking place in the leaves. The green matter, chlorophyll, in the leaves plays an important part so long as each leaf is a food-factory for the plant; but in autumn the trees prepare to give up active life for a season and the food-making activities of the leaves are over. Before the leaves fall they return much useful material to the plant that bore them. Green pigment, sugar and other substances retreat to the stem and roots.

With the breaking up of the chlorophyll at this time other pigments become visible, a yellow pigment, called carotin, similar to that found in shrimps and prawns and, of course, in carrots, and also a blue pigment, anthocyanin or "flower-blue," to which the vivid purple tints are due. "Flower-blue" is a combination of glucose and an aromatic substance and is found in leaves where there is an accumulation of sugar, a common occurrence when the temperature is low.

EXCHANGING BEAUTY FOR ASHES

Autumn colouring tends to be bright when a low temperature is accompanied by plenty of water and sunshine, for under such circumstances the leaves die slowly and there is time for a gradual breaking up of the green and yellow pigments and an abundant formation of "flower-blue."

It is possible that the bright colours are of use to the leaf, perhaps screening it from harmful rays or else absorbing rays which prolong its life, but this is by no means certain. Leaves are often most beautiful just before they wither, and by that time they contain nothing but waste-products, a state of things which has been well described as "beauty for ashes."

NATURE'S MARVELLOUS SURGERY

The leaf that is ready to fall is almost empty, having sent its last load of sugary sap to the heart of the tree; but the branch still holds sap and might lose it, might bleed, as it were, if an open wound were left by the severing of the leaf-stalk. No wound is left. A wonderful piece of natural surgery prevents this. The leaf-stalk and the parent stem are separated before the fall of the leaf by the formation of a tiny cushion of cells. When the gentle breakage occurs, by the cushion pushing off the delicate leaf-stalk, helped perhaps by the wind, the leaf drifts away and the cushion is exposed to view. Soon the cushion becomes a corky scar.

The loss of its leaves is a benefit to the tree, enabling it to pass the winter without a dangerous loss of water. The tree, whose roots cannot make use of the water in cold, sodden soil, cannot afford to have working leaves giving off water-vapour during the winter. Safety lies in a season of rest.

TRUTH AND LEGEND IN PLANT NAMES

MANY plants have popular names referring to some association with animals. Sometimes the shape of some part of the plant suggests the name; in other cases there is a legend to explain it; or, again, the name may indicate that a particular animal likes or dislikes it. The last group includes such plants as fleabane, leopard's bane, and henbane, and the idea behind the name is often far-fetched. Chickweed and duckweed suggest that these plants are favourite foods, but a complication

QUEENSLAND
NATIVE

JAPANESE

CHINESE

ESKIMO

ENGLISH

KOREAN
COOLIE

BELGIAN
PEASANT

ALGONQUIN
INDIAN

ARAB
IRAQ

Some of the Groups into which Mankind is divided

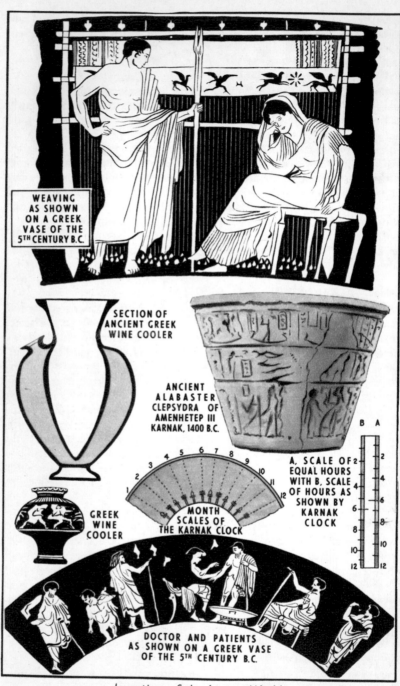

WEAVING AS SHOWN ON A GREEK VASE OF THE 5TH CENTURY B.C.

SECTION OF ANCIENT GREEK WINE COOLER

ANCIENT ALABASTER CLEPSYDRA OF AMENHETEP III KARNAK, 1400 B.C.

GREEK WINE COOLER

MONTH SCALES OF THE KARNAK CLOCK

A, SCALE OF EQUAL HOURS WITH B, SCALE OF HOURS AS SHOWN BY KARNAK CLOCK

DOCTOR AND PATIENTS AS SHOWN ON A GREEK VASE OF THE 5TH CENTURY B.C.

Inventions of the Ancient World

added when a plant is given the name " mouse-ear chickweed "—
vidently a plant which chickens like to eat and which has leaves shaped
ke the ear of a mouse.

NIMAL LIKES AND DISLIKES

Some of the descriptive names are very apt: hound's-tongue, which
as flabby leaves; hart's-tongue fern; goat's-beard, with its hairy
eeding-heads; ox-eye, the great staring daisy; and cat's-tail, dog's-tail,
nouse-tail and fox-tail grasses. Many more belong to the group of
likes and dislikes ": catmint; cow-quake (quaking grass); bearberry;
og's mercury and so on. Among the well-known plants to which some
nimal superstition is attached is the dog-rose, once thought to be a cure
or the bite of mad dogs; and there are many others with legends no
nore credible. These superstitions die hard and often obscure the fact
nat many plants are genuinely useful for medicinal purposes.

Other names which appear to refer to animals may not really do so;
ne name foxglove, for instance, is generally supposed to mean folks'
loves, that is, fairy-folks' gloves, rather than to refer to the fox.

NAMED AFTER BIRDS AND REPTILES

Some of the flower names connected with birds have no apparent
neaning beyond the fact that the flowers are in bloom about the time
vhen the bird is most often heard. For instance, the mauve lady's-
mock, a flower of spring, is also called the cuckoo-flower; and crowfoot,
vhich gets one name from its likeness to a bird's claw, is supposed to be
hakespeare's " cuckoo-buds of yellow hue." Other springtime flowers
re cuckoo's sorrel and cuckoo-grass.

Truly descriptive names are, however, abundant: crane's-bill, which
ets its name from the shape of its seed-vessels; pheasant's-eye, a bright
ower with a dark centre; sparrow-tongue (knot-grass), which has small,
harp leaves; and cock's-head (sainfoin). The snake's-head fritillary
as scale-like markings on its petals, and its unopened bud is thought
y some to resemble a snake's head; while viper's bugloss refers to a
 cure " for snake bite that few would care to trust.

DOVE'S NECK AND EAGLE'S CLAWS

The beautiful garden flower, the columbine, is associated with two
irds. A knowledge of Latin is required to understand its two names,
olumbine and aquilegia—*columba,* a pigeon, and *aquila,* an eagle—but
he flower itself shows clearly what is meant. The long honey-tubes
nectaries) curling in towards each other appear, according to the eye
f the beholder, as the heads and necks of a circle of doves or as the
ripping talons of an eagle. Columbine is perhaps the better name,
or the tiny doves in the flower are distinct and charming, and the
rowfoot is more like a bird's claws.

No flower names are more allusive than those of the common larkspur
Delphinium ajacis). The projecting nectary gives the flower its popular

name, for it suggests the long fourth toe of the skylark directed back
wards. *Delphinion,* Greek for a dolphin, supplies the next name
delphinium, and the unopened flower-buds are undoubtedly dolphin
shaped; while *ajacis,* the specific name, refers to the hero Ajax. In the
centre of the common blue larkspur the letters A I A are plainly seen
The legend has it that this is an exclamation of woe for Ajax, after
whose death, it was said, the flower first sprang from the ground.

SWALLOWS DISCOVER PLANT'S VIRTUE

Many other interesting stories could be told of how wild plants got
their names. *Clematis vitalba,* for instance, became known as traveller'
joy, so we are told, by reason of its "decking and adorning waies an
hedges where people travel." The reason for the name of "old man
beard" given to the tufts of feathered seed vessels it produces i
autumn is obvious.

The botanical name of the celandine is *chelidonium,* which is derived
from *chelidon,* a swallow. The orange-coloured juice of the greate
celandine is a remedy for warts, and has been used to remove films from
the cornea of the eye. This medicinal property, so Pliny the Roma
naturalist says, was discovered by the swallows. He also asserts that th
celandine comes into flower on the arrival of these birds, and fades on
their departure.

The name holly is a corruption of "holy," given because of the us
of this evergreen to decorate churches at Christmas; nasturtium o
nasus tortus, distorted nose, because the pungent properties of the plan
cause one to wrinkle the nose.

ANIMAL WAYS AND MEANS

ALL life begins as an egg. We call the egg of a mushroom a spore, that of a geranium a seed, of a frog, dog or man an ovum, but they are all eggs, though the term is usually applied only to the first beginnings of an animal. Animals' eggs vary greatly in number, size and shape, and some primitive animals rely on supplementary ways of propagating their kind. Anemones, starfish and some worms, for example, can multiply by mutilation. Dismembered, the fragments become new individuals. The species prospers by seeming extermination. But an egg of some sort is the animal's usual entry into the world.

IN THE BEGINNING

THE human egg measures less than a hundredth of an inch across. The making of a city's populace could be packed into a hen s egg. But we must remember that the hen's egg is well advanced by the time it is laid. A dead hen will often be found to contain scores of eggs ranging from the size of a marble to mere specks, and these are giants to others the microscope will reveal.

EGGS BY THE MILLIONS

The further we go backwards in the scale of life, the more we find a tendency to broadcast eggs with prodigal liberality. Few invertebrate animals produce families less than some scores strong, many launch their eggs upon the world by millions.

There are, however, exceptions. In every class of animals not lower than the worms, we find some crude foreshadowings of parental care, and where this exists the family is invariably of modest dimensions. The most prolific of backboned animals is the ling. It broadcasts 160,000,000 eggs. The featherweight stickleback lays only a few score eggs, and these are guarded by the male, who practically wears himself to death on their behalf.

SOFT AND HARD EGGS

To within 1,000 million years ago all life was confined to the water. Eggs laid within that relatively even-temperatured medium could afford to be of a soft, gelatinous nature, and even when hatched the result was, by our standards, premature. Nearly all invertebrates, and such advanced creatures as fish and frogs, tend to come into the world far less like their parents than a chick is like a hen. Even the insects, though early pioneers ashore, have not evaded so-called larval stages. They must pass through complex changes over a period of years perhaps, and when at last mature, their exhausted energies suffice for little more than a brief courtship and the ensurance of the rising generation.

When the reptiles stepped ashore, the hard-shelled egg came into

being, just as the advent of terrestrial plants led to the formation of the
hard-shelled seed. In both cases the germ of life could survive where a
gelatinous envelope, like that of a frog's egg, would have been no
protection. Mostly the reptiles buried their eggs in sand or decaying
matter, where the sun warmed them and served as foster-mother.

Here again, as in all other animal activities, some few seemed to have
moved, as we say, "ahead of their time." Some tropic snails have, like
the reptiles, met the exigencies of climatic changes by laying hard
shelled eggs, indistinguishable from those of birds. A few reptiles
similarly, instead of laying eggs and leaving them to chance, hatch them
within their own bodies—so mimicking the higher mammals. The
viper does this, and has earned a rustic reputation for swallowing its
young by way of protecting them in emergency.

NATURE'S WAR OF WITS

As life progressed, it became more and more a war of wits—and as
an offshoot of intellectual development, "child welfare." The birds
improved upon the reptiles' eggs by giving theirs a still harder shell and
hiding it within cunningly contrived nests, or laying eggs that wonder
fully copied their surroundings. Yet the most carefully tended egg is
more exposed to sudden extinction than any baby in a cot.

The mammals made, what was a rare occurrence amongst fish and
reptiles, a generality. Having hatched the egg within themselves, they
enclosed the embryo in a sac of blood vessels (the placenta) which
connecting with the maternal circulation, transferred nourishment
directly to the growing babe. As a result the infant when at last born
showed a very high state of perfection, though again the word can only
be used in a comparative sense. A man is still quite helpless at the age
of ten weeks, whereas a deer can make shift to walk within as many
hours, and such snakes as are born alive present a perfect picture of
self-helpfulness within the same number of minutes.

ANIMALS THAT CARRY POCKETS

Just as the various animal groups are joined by links, so the change
from broadcast floating egg to helpless breast-baby can be traced step by
step. The earliest mammals had no means of nourishing the young—
after hatching—within their own bodies. They laid eggs as did most
reptiles. The Australian duckmole, a living link, still does so, but it is
a true if crude mammal, for it feeds its young with milk. The milk is
not "fed" through nipples, but oozes vaguely through the walls of the
maternal abdomen.

The pouched mammals, now chiefly settled in Australia, carried this
a stage further. They hatched their eggs within themselves, and then
transferred them to the brood pouch, where they fed on milk, sucked
through nipples. The kangaroo thus carries its baby perhaps for nine
months, and for a year later the infant regards the pram-pocket as a
convenient shelter in a crisis.

NIMALS IN THE MAKING

The length of time which the higher animals take in the making eems largely to depend upon the size and number in relation to the arent. A hen's egg will hatch in twenty-one days, a swan's egg equires twice as many. A man spends nine months between conception nd birth, a long time in consideration of his size, for only about twice his period suffices to bring forth the largest land mammals like the lephant and the giraffe. The Kodiak Island bear, almost as large as he biggest ox, produces twins, each no bigger than a rat.

As a general rule small mammals, like the mouse and hedgehog hrew of Madagascar, bring forth big families at an early age. Their progeny similarly mature early, but their lives are very short. The higher a mammal's ultimate development, and the longer its life, the more extended must be the time spent in Nature's factory.

FOOD AND FEEDING

WHATEVER the nature of an animal, its food is derived directly or indirectly from plants. Even such creatures as the lion and tiger, which one seldom sees eating anything but meat, derive such vital matters as carbon, oxygen and hydrogen at second-hand from their herbivorous prey. The lion, like the domestic cat, is not above eating grass for its stomach's sake, and in the wild frequently eats the ready peptonized grass contained in the paunches of grazing animals. Protein, which figures in the first necessities, is derived more from flesh than vegetables, which largely accounts for the greater bulk of food most rigid vegetarians must eat in order to keep the body machine running.

MANY MODES OF EATING

Eating, like life itself, began as a comparatively simple matter. A one-celled animal, like the amoeba, found both in soil and water, literally " surrounds " its food. Assuming the most grotesque shapes, it flows round some food particle until the foreign body appears as an integral part of itself. Such primitive creatures as the chalk-forming animals and the sponges feed by wafting food atoms into themselves by restlessly waving hairs, and this method of feeding has been generally adopted far up the animal scale.

It is the accepted mode of feeding with innumerable larval animals, advanced organisms like various aquatic worms, oysters and clams, and the mysterious lancelet, a glassy marine animal about an inch long with the first foreshadowings of the central nerve cord seen in vertebrates.

GARDEN SNAIL WITH 14,175 TEETH

Teeth, as we understand them, were a late development in the march of animal life. Their work was, and still is, done amongst invertebrates by many other means. A beetle's, ant's or lobster's teeth and jaws are really legs modified to seize, tear and mince up food instead of carrying their owner about in search of it. Crabs and lobsters have supplemented this by growing hard, knobbly processes on the inner walls of their stomachs (easily seen in a boiled " table " specimen) which grind one upon the other like mill stones.

Some of our common sea snails that swallow other molluscs, shells and all, are provided with a similar contrivance. Most snails, however, bite their food by means of a kind of band saw. This is a long, tough ribbon with horny teeth set on it in rows. The garden snail has 14,175 such teeth, arranged in 135 rows. In the octopus and squid the teeth are condensed to form a horny beak in two parts, perfectly imitating a parrot's.

BIRDS ONCE HAD TEETH

Jaws came into fashion before true teeth. They were at first mere modifications of the gristly arches which supported the gills of the early fishes. Later the skin covering them became wrinkled to form a corrugated surface, and so came about such close-set, pavement-like teeth as we see in sharks and skates. Not until the first gristly skeletons became heavily reinforced with lime did jaws acquire enamelled teeth, set in sockets and drawing their nourishment from their owner's general circulatory system.

This complicated chewing apparatus was only arrived at by very gradual stages. Reptile teeth are arranged simply in one long groove, or merely lean up against a ridge running the length of the jaw bone. Teeth not unlike these were once owned by the pioneer birds.

TEETH THAT WEIGH NEARLY HALF A TON

Amongst mammals, the tooth has become the key to the entire creature. A reptile's teeth are all much alike, but those of every mammal resolve themselves into three kinds—chisels, tearing tools, and grinders. Each kind has lent itself to extraordinary variation. The chisel teeth or incisors, for example, provide the elephant's tusks, perhaps ten feet long and weighing nearly half a ton each. In the beaver the incisors are powerful wood-cutters, in the kangaroo a pair of shears, and in ourselves very feeble nibbling tools, effective only with comparatively soft substances.

Ant-eaters have discarded their teeth altogether, but when very young have a few teeth, proving that the living ant-eaters are descendants of more generalized ancestors. Strangest of all dental modifications are the fangs of some snakes. They have been turned into hypodermic syringes, injecting poisons of varying virility but all evolved, it is believed, from saliva.

We have come to regard teeth as essentially masticatory organs, but the more primitive teeth are quite incapable of chewing. Their first function is to seize and prevent the escape of living food. Such teeth are typical of fishes and reptiles. Some fish have grinding teeth strong

enough to grind hard shells, but chiefly the prey is swallowed whole
Fish like the cod are simply living trawl nets, taking in worms, shells
and big stones as they come.

Teeth of fish and reptiles incline to point throatwards. This accounts
for the often amazing swallowing feats of snakes. A snake seizing a
companion who is attempting to engulf the same dead rat is obliged
to go on swallowing to the end. The same happens if it once grasps a
blanket placed in the cage to keep it warm. Snakes are incapable of
" spitting out " a mouthful, whatever its nature.

A deep-sea fish known as the black swallower has so distensible an
interior that it can engulf five or six times its own bulk. Such a mouthful
not unnaturally protesting, its struggles carry dinner and diner to the
surface, where a sea bird usually disposes of both.

TONGUE AS FLY-PAPER

Some highly constituted animals are independent of teeth. All
living birds are toothless. Grit swallowed with their food does for them
what the three-toothed gastric mill does for the lobster. Some few
animals, like the ant-eater and woodpecker, rely solely upon their
tongues for gathering food. Such long and powerful tongues have very
unusual roots.

Whilst most tongues are attached to the back of the owner's palate,
that of the ant-eater is anchored to its breast bone, and that of the
woodpecker passes behind the ears, over the top of the head, and is
finally fixed between the bird's eyes. The last word in vertebrate
tongues perhaps is that of the chameleon. It is used as a fly-paper, and
can be shot out at an insect for a distance exceeding that of the
chameleon's body-length.

BOA CONSTRICTOR THAT FASTED FOR FOUR YEARS

The converse of feeding is starvation, and though no creature can
survive this indefinitely, powers of endurance vary much. The record
is held by a boa constrictor in the Paris Zoological Gardens, which
fasted for four years and a day.

Usually animals tide over periods of dearth by living on their own
fat. The camel is a classic example. Some other creatures, like the
Egyptian desert mice and Arizona poisonous lizard, carry huge reserves
of fat in their tails. These, like the camel, keep quite active throughout
a long fast. The popular plan is to consume fat, gathered in times
of plenty, whilst wrapped in sleep. A homely instance is the hedgehog,
which retires in autumn and emerges lean but fit the following spring.

The common toad, despite legends, can survive total starvation for
not more than a year. Its powers of endurance are far below those of a
desert snail which spent two and a half years gummed to a label in the
British Museum. At the end of that time, the " dead shell " awoke to
unmistakable life, and showed the keenest interest when a warm bath
and a meal were provided for it.

MOVEMENT BY MANY MEANS

THE first vigorous motive power perhaps was derived from the lashing hairs fringing the animalculæ and numerous aquatic larvæ. The baby oyster thus rows itself about at a great rate, but though it is attracted to a light, it is doubtful if it knows where it is going.

Innumerable ways of " getting about " were developed and perfected long before the first vertebrates appeared. The jellyfishes travel by a laborious pulsating of their umbrella-shaped bodies, but with no more sense of purpose, other than to keep afloat, than the infant oyster. The worms carry movement much further, mimicking snakes and fish with their sinuous undulations. The spiny-skinned animals and molluscs, which appeared later, cover almost all the known means of travel, save flight.

The first group—starfishes and sea urchins—employ a wonderful system of tube feet and hollow legs distended and animated by a complex hydraulic device. With these tube feet a starfish rights itself when turned over, forces apart the shells of an oyster, and travels easily in any direction. The more or less spherical sea urchins can push out tube feet through all parts of their globe-shaped skins, and are for all practical purposes " right side up " whatever befalls them.

ANIMALS THAT GO BACKWARDS

The molluscs are even less restricted. A snail glides upon its one big foot, and the clams employ similar organs to burrow deep in sand, or even tunnel wood and limestone. Some molluscs, such as the sea hare, flap their way through water like birds through air. The octopus, highest of all molluscs, has split its foot into eight sucker-studded arms, by which it walks spider fashion. When pressed, it brings the arms into compact formation, and by blowing water through its siphon pipe, darts along backwards at high speed.

For millions of years after the dry land became populous, the water was, as it still is, the home of the largest animals. A fluid environment is a harder medium in which to move than air, but it reduces weight. The whale and the gigantic elephant seal, so helpless ashore, become things of beauty when afloat.

When the first fishes enjoyed brief shore excursions, as do the tropical mud skippers and climbing perch today, they dragged themselves about laboriously on their bellies.

WHY THE REPTILES LEFT THE AMPHIBIANS BEHIND

Lungs were an essential to easy progress upon land, and possessed of these the reptiles soon left the sprawling amphibians far behind them. A crocodile can lift its body clear of the ground, but its limbs are set akimbo, retarding quick movement. The mammals, by bringing knees and elbows in line with the body, distributed their weight so that its carriage was no longer an effort.

Relatively speaking, mammalian progress was almost as spectacular as man's mechanical advancements during the last forty years. Well over 1,000,000,000 years elapsed between the first efforts of the walking fish and the appearance of a vertebrate which so poised its centre of gravity as to walk erect.

TAILS AS BALANCING POLES

No other creatures besides man can do this. The man-like apes contrive a hunchbacked stagger only. Some use their arms as balancing poles, but all are most at ease upon all fours. All other creatures imitating man must use their tails as counterpoises. Without such aid the kangaroo and Australian frilled lizard would topple forward on to their noses. Even with their tails to help them, they must keep moving quickly to remain tolerably upright. Birds are less handicapped owing to their lightness, and the wide spread of their toes gives a firmer stance.

All quadrupeds are rotatory or diagonal walkers. We walk erect but automatically move our arms, an echo of less upright days, and in walking we swing our limbs from opposite corners. A dog, however, uses one limb at a time, beginning with one hind leg, and so moving each in turn—round its body—clockwise or anti-clockwise.

ANIMALS THAT HAVE RETURNED TO THE SEA

A feature of animal progress is what may be termed the back-to-the-water movement. Life started in the water but much eventually left it for the land. A little has returned. Examples are the sea lion and the whale. Both are carnivorous mammals. The sea lion is built on closely similar lines to such familiar carnivores as the wolf and the bear.

The whale also, judging by fossil remains, is the descendant of much less whale-like animals, big flesh-eaters, with well formed hind limbs. Either in the search for food, or to evade larger foes ashore, the whale's forbears are believed to have reverted to the water, there to find a freedom denied them on land. Whatever their motive, it was a tragic instance of " out of the frying-pan and into the fire." Man, with his explosive darts and floating factories, is fast exterminating all save a few small and worthless remnants of this once mighty race.

SPEED OF ANIMALS

The motor car, the aeroplane, the stop-watch and a dozen other devices have made it possible to check the speeds of animals with tolerable accuracy. Only a few insects are believed to achieve the speed of an aeroplane, but various birds, such as hawks and eagles can make between 170 and 180 m.p.h.

On land no animal has yet exceeded the cheetah or hunting-leopard's 60 m.p.h., and all high speeds on land can only be maintained for short distances. No man has yet sprinted beyond 30 or cycled more than 70 m.p.h. In water, travel is still more restricted. The record speed is possibly held by the tunny with an alleged 40 m.p.h.

MIGRATION OF FISHES

A much more important aspect of animals' travels from an economic viewpoint is that concerning the yearly or twice-yearly movements spoken of as migrations. On them our fisheries and many other food supplies largely depend. Much sentiment and superstition has from early times been centred round migration. The ancient augurs foretold political and other events from the flight of birds, and even today some attribute a sentimental urge to the mass movements not only of birds but of fishes and insects.

The great migrations inshore of such fishes as the herring and tunny are made largely at the will of ocean currents, or certain physiological changes which find a response in similar temporary conditions of the fishes themselves. A century or less ago it was believed the herring moved each autumn in packed formation from the North Sea down the eastern seaboard of Great Britain and so via the English Channel to an unknown destination, shedding eggs as they went. Now it has been ascertained that the shoals are permanently off shore opposite those coastal waters to which each shoal makes for its spawning, such spawnings happening in rotation, beginning far north in mid-summer and working southwards during autumn.

DO BIRDS FOLLOW PLANNED ROUTES?

The practice of fixing numbered rings to the legs of birds and so keeping track of their movements is now casting quite a new light upon the subject of their migrations. The birds, it would seem, often " wing their trackless flight " very much at the mercy of seasonal winds, and quite irrespective of any planned route.

Another recent suggestion is that in some cases the flocks follow the courses of vanished coastlines, long since buried beneath the waves or left far inland by the receding tides.

It is believed by some authorities that bird migration began as a result of the glacial epochs of the earth's history, when it was a case of fleeing from the cold or perishing. When the ice receded, the birds returned to their native haunts.

CROSSING THE ATLANTIC TO BREED

Some animals, like the house spider, migrate only a matter of yards, others, like the swallows, traverse continents. Whatever the distance, food or courtship are the main incentives. Food brings the young eels in their countless myriads 3,000 miles across the Atlantic, from the Sargasso Sea to Europe. The reproductive urge drives them back again many years later.

A bare living forces the woodland reindeer in one vast, unbroken stream of hoofs and horns across Canada for days on end; and " sentiment," it is believed, inspires that strange convergence of the sloths to some as yet undiscovered Mecca of their species 100 feet above ground in the Brazilian tree tops.

ANIMALS AND SOCIETY

Many kinds of small crustacea and molluscs are so plentiful as to discolour the open sea for acres—even miles—in extent. The locust swarm can shut out the sun, and cover vast areas of the earth as with a blanket. Fishes and even jellyfish have held up big ships, so vast their numbers and so closely congregated; caterpillars have been known to stop trains and road traffic. Yet none of these great gatherings of animals that are alike can be called a society, as we understand the term. Society implies more than mere numbers.

Society of a sort is certainly provided by such insects as bees, wasps and ants. Yet such co-operative bodies do not present the slightest parallel to human society, at least on a democratic basis. The frequent analogies one still hears drawn between insect and human society reveal an imperfect acquaintance with the one and a complete misunderstanding of the other. The ailing ant is left to its fate, and the young, tended with bloodless solicitude, may be left to bandits, provided the bandits leave some sweetmeats in exchange. A worker bee, fresh from the cocoon, "knows its job" from the beginning and without a hint at instruction. It does its work—and can do nothing else. Crippled or even decapitated, it still struggles at its task, with the intelligence and resource of a clockwork toy. Insect society, despite its admitted superficial resemblances to certain features of our own, has been as we see it for countless ages, and is likely to continue to the end without hope of reform or betterment.

Society is a matter, not of crowding bodies—even hard-working bodies—but pooling brains, the only form of unity with strength. There is no real strength in the vast unions of fish or water fleas. These come about merely as mechanical results of mass breeding in a circumscribed area. Often such mass formation exposes the whole as an easy prey to foes from without and disease from within.

ANIMALS HAVE LEADERS

Society has its foundations in the family. It is in fact a league of families held together by some sort of mutual toleration and agreement to combine for the common weal. This implies intelligence, and so society is found only in the more advanced animals. We find hints of it amongst birds, but see its fullest realization in the highest mammals. No social insect gives warning of danger as does a goose on the outskirts of a flock when a fox is near. But despite all their parental care, elaborate home-making, and often æsthetic courtships, the birds are far from realizing the benefits of co-operation, as seen amongst such animals as sheep, wolves and monkeys.

Cattle of all kinds form themselves into well planned battle array when attacked. Often they form a hollow square, with all males, their horns presented to the enemy, on the outside. Unlike birds, mammals show a general appreciation of leadership, and some even seem to have a crude regard for parliamentary rule. The wolf pack recognizes one leader, whose orders are repeated and enforced by elderly subordinates.

Still more human is the society of apes and monkeys. Large troupes are always composed of families governed by a system of overlords. The law, not less stringent because unwritten, controls the apportioning of wives, the correction of offspring, and the disciplining of the adolescent. The retreat from danger of some old or less able member is covered by the elders with courage, and some show of tactics quite unlike the panic scuffling and sporadic defiance of a disturbed ant hill.

PARLIAMENT OF THE APES

An epic of ape society is preserved in the records of the Gibraltar garrison. The rock was once the home of a considerable troupe of Barbary apes, and in 1856, to preserve the peace, a redoubtable Sergeant Brown of the Signal Service was appointed to look after their interests. He tended the ailing and enforced justice. Once when a young subaltern shot two apes for rifling his rooms, he was ordered to provide substitutes. The apes, however, after holding a species of parliament, decided that the newcomers were below standard, and hurled them into the sea.

In 1873, when a fire broke out, the tribal elders marshalled the clan, and all tobogganed to safety down the famous catchments on the western rock face. At one time the troupe was split by civil war, and until a truce was called the affair was carried out in a manner that won the professional admiration of every soldier on the rock. By the close of the century this ape society was so perfectly organized for the embarrassment of the human populace that it had to be disbanded. A few survivors only, in private ownership, are now sad witnesses to a society that failed in tolerance for the rights of others.

ANIMAL PARTNERSHIPS

A curious feature of animal society is the co-operation shown by totally unlike creatures for mutual profit. The gate crashers which infest ants' and bees' nests, though sometimes offering goods in exchange for what they take, are outside this class of partnership. A common example is the hermit crab, to whose borrowed whelk shell home are often affixed several large sea anemones. When the crab is feeding, the anemones snatch at all discarded scraps. Should a fish seek to engulf the crab, shell and all, the anemones throw out stinging threads, and so the crab is saved. Hence there is a very real exchange of benefits, though they are not always evenly balanced, for in time the anemones wax so fat and numerous as to take more than a fair share, and the crab is obliged to seek another shell less hampered by lodgers.

A parallel to this is offered by the prairie marmot, a little burrowing rodent of America. Its holes are invaded by rattlesnakes and owls. At one time these three were regarded as a Utopian commonwealth, but this has since been proved no more than a pleasing fancy. The owls and snakes feed on the marmot's and each other's young. They seek, not society, but free meals and shelter, so that the vegetarian marmot's only resource is to effect a moonlight flit, and live at peace elsewhere until once more the uninvited guests appear, when its troubles begin anew.

FOR SERVICES RENDERED

In many parts of Africa and India, small white egrets and monkeys are commonly seen riding upon the largest and most dangerous game animals other than carnivorous kinds. Similarly plover-like birds are often witnessed fearlessly running in and out of the wide-open jaws of giant crocodiles. In all such cases the smaller creatures are tolerated for the services they render in removing irritating parasites.

A homely example is that of the rook, which frequently rides upon the backs of sheep. The bird purges the sheep's fleece of ticks, and in winter when other food is scarce, thus enjoys not only an easily obtained meal but the additional advantage of a warm bed.

NEW BODIES FOR OLD

Our bodies are continually wearing away and being renewed. Even if a portion of our bodies is lost by accident, it can to a limited extent be made good. Modern surgery can even make presentable ears and noses out of flesh taken from the arms or thighs.

The higher the animal in the scale of development the less is it able to renew lost portions. Such comparatively simple animals as worms can renew themselves if cut in half, and such lowly creatures as sea anemones are even more adaptable. When chopped into many pieces, each portion becomes in time a whole animal. When this was first noticed, there arose the ancient legends of such creatures as the hydra, which grew two heads for every one cut off. Some creatures, like the amœba, habitually multiply by deliberately breaking themselves in half.

Starfishes can renew lost portions. Many years ago, oyster fishermen, knowing the starfish ate oysters, tore all starfish in half as soon as dredged from the oyster beds. It took several years of propaganda on the part of the Board of Fisheries to make the oyster farmers of Great Britain realize that each starfish so " killed " renewed the missing arms of its two halves, and so doubled the work of destroying oysters. Today starfish are brought ashore and used as manure. Sea cucumbers, which are really long-bodied starfish, when suffering from indigestion, vomit all their internal organs and grow a new set.

RENEWING LOST LIMBS

Crustaceans—crabs and lobsters—renew lost limbs, but it is a slow process. When a crab's claw or leg is injured it casts off the limb at a special joint, and for a time lives with some difficulty. But when next

it changes its shell, a new limb appears in the place of the old one. This
is a mere miniature model, however, and of little use. Several changes
of shell are required before the new limb reaches normal size.

Many fishes lose their tail portions when fleeing from predaceous
foes. They cannot grow new tails, but the back and under fins
eventually meet behind, and to some extent do the work of a tail.
Lizards habitually throw off their tails when pursued. Nervous energy
causes the discarded tail to lash and wriggle in a very lifelike manner
which holds the pursuer's attention, and so allows the lizard to escape.
In time a new tail sprouts from the stump, the site of the accident always
being marked by a scar. If the tail is merely injured, a new tail
automatically sprouts from the wound.

The same sometimes happens with limbs, but the extra limb proves,
like the forked tail, of more hindrance than help, and is incapable of
much movement. Chameleons, though classed as lizards, cannot renew
lost tails, and once shorn of its tail a chameleon soon falls an easy prey
to foes.

TOOTH GRAFTED TO A COCK'S COMB

Mammals and birds cannot renew lost limbs, though a piece of lost
flesh is made good, and even a broken tooth will continue to grow.

The plastic nature of flesh was first realized by John Hunter
(1728-1793), founder of the museum of the College of Surgeons, London.
Amongst other experiments, he grafted a human tooth to a cock's comb.
His work laid the foundations of plastic surgery, which can make good
all manner of terrible injuries and has been perverted by fashion for
the purpose of " face lifting."

ANIMALS AS FOOD

THE annual output of beef of the United States amounts to about
65,000,000 carcases. This figure represents only a fraction of the
animals of different kinds that are eaten by human beings, and though
some popular dishes in foreign lands may not appeal to the Westerner, it
is well to remember that people who enjoy rhinoceros or flying-fox
might possibly recoil from eating beef or jellied eels. Most animals are
eaten and few are uneatable. Exceptions are the tropical file fishes.
The flesh of these contain poisonous alkalis, the poison increasing in
virulence with the temperature of the sea in which the fish live.

Most vegetarian, mixed feeding, and fish-eating animals are eaten in
different parts of the world. Men and monkeys are mixed feeders, and
wherever cannibalism has been stamped out natives have shown a
tendency to fall back on such substitutes as the gorilla and various
monkeys, making it necessary to protect these animals by legislation.
Only carnivorous animals are generally unpopular as food, but there
are exceptions. In the Sudan natives commonly eat lion, even carrying
supplies of dried lion meat with them when on a long trek. They eat

lion meat chiefly in the belief that the lion's strength and courage may
be so acquired.

Apart from the file fishes, most fishes are good eating; but though
about 200 kinds of fishes are found in the waters that surround the
United Kingdom, only about twenty come to table. Often these can
only be sold under fancy names. In 1911 the British Government made
a special campaign to put dogfish on the market, and now it is the
mainstay of the fried-fish shops.

ALLIGATOR TASTES LIKE VEAL

Most people recoil from the idea of eating reptiles, forgetting that
turtle soup is one of our most highly prized and priced dishes. In the
United States freshwater tortoises and iguana lizards are just as popular.
Alligator, which tastes like veal, is now also largely sold, and in France
and America frogs are widely farmed for table. Snake flesh is eaten in
many lands. In France grass snakes are commonly sold as " hedge
eels." In Mexico a big newt known as the axolotl is farmed for food.
This curious creature in many instances never metamorphoses.

All molluscs and crustaceans are good to eat. Oysters, mussels,
scallops, whelks, winkles and cuttlefish are the chief molluscs eaten in
Great Britain. Crab when tinned is indistinguishable from " fresh "
crab, and is just as wholesome.

Insects, like reptiles, are unpopular as food with most of the white
race, but we all eat cochineal, an insect dye, with cakes and other
delicacies. Cochineal is obtained from the dried bodies of small plant-
bugs related to greenfly and extensively farmed in Mexico, the insects
being fed on cacti. Locusts, fried in oil, are a favourite dish with both
natives and Europeans in the East. A giant water bug, similar to the
water scorpion, is farmed for food in Mexico.

DINING ON WORMS

The most daring diner in Great Britain or the United States might
hesitate to eat any kind of worm, but in Samoa the Palolo worm harvest
is the great event of the year.

Just before dawn, for two days only in the months of October and
November, the sea surface swarms with rainbow-coloured worms,
wriggling in all directions. These are not whole worms but the
spawning portions, which break off, the worms themselves remaining
on the sea floor. The writhing eggs and milt are scooped up by every
available means, hundreds of boats putting out from shore to engage
in this strange harvest. The catch is then rushed ashore and eaten by
all and sundry, either raw or cooked. It smells like fresh fish and tastes
much like spinach.

Almost any kind of egg is good eating. A recent delicacy to be
put on the British market is sea-urchin spawn. This looks like a mass
of coral beads. It is eaten with a spoon, and has a pleasant shrimpy
flavour.

NURSING FATHERS

NURSING and rearing a family are universally regarded as the chief duties of motherhood. Many male animals not only help to rear a family, but may even be saddled with its sole care. Some of the common sea worms, whose stony tubes encrust shells and stones, are nursing fathers. One species commonly used for fishing bait not only nurses the eggs but eats the mother after she has laid them—to prevent her indulging in cannibalism.

BRINGS UP THE STICKLEBACK FAMILY

A great many common fishes are nursing fathers. The most familiar is the little stickleback, found in both fresh and salt water. In spring the male develops a bright red breast, whereby to attract the females. These he leads to a globular nest of weeds, leaves and so on built by himself, and as soon as the eggs have been placed within it, mounts guard.

The eggs he incubates by fanning them with his fins, so ensuring a current of fresh water passing over them continuously. He drives off all intruders, particularly the cannibalistic mothers, and guards the fry for some weeks after they have hatched, until he finally dies, quite worn out by his labours.

GUARDING 140,000 EGGS

On the seashore one can meet the little bull heads, blennies and other fish similarly guarding eggs. The male butterfly blenny tucks the eggs inside a whelk shell, and then shuffles in backwards, with his large head and formidable teeth blocking the entrance. The male of the lumpfish guards about 140,000 eggs, attached to the underside of a rock. So many foes—fish, crabs and gulls—have to be warded off, that the male seldom lives to survive his ordeal for long.

The male sea horse and pipefish both " nurse " the eggs in special brood pouches on their undersurfaces. These pouches are supplied with blood vessels, thus imitating the network of blood vessels, or placenta, which nourishes the embryo, be it of calf, dog or man.

MALE FROGS ARE EXPERT NURSES

Many male frogs and toads are expert nurses. Some tropical species swallow the eggs and carry them in pouches covering the greater part of the body. The male of the midwife toad, common all over the European continent, wraps the eggs, which are laid in strings, round his hind legs and carries them thus for weeks. Hiding by day, he steals forth at night to moisten the eggs in dew, and when the tadpoles are ready to hatch launches them in the nearest pond.

The nursing father is a feature with every member of the ostrich family, making the rude nest and sitting on the eggs for a month or more. Amongst penguins the male's duties are less arduous, though he takes a full share. When the hen needs food or rest, she loudly calls her mate and hands over the family to his care.

The only known nursing father amongst mammals is the male marmoset. This little monkey from tropical America enjoys sole custody of the child, save when it is being fed by the mother. He carries it, first on one hip and later on his back, his care never relaxing until the weight of the infant makes it impossible for him to hold the baby any longer.

LONGEST SNAKES AND WORMS

THE size to which snakes may grow lends itself to exaggeration, but the truth is stranger than the tallest stories. The largest snake known is a species of water boa or anaconda that lived many millions of years ago. It measured fifty-eight feet.

GIANT AFRICAN PYTHONS

The longest living snakes are the African pythons and the anacondas of Brazil, which both reach a length of thirty feet. Such examples are rare, and all tales of still larger specimens should be taken with reserve. So, too, should stories of these giant snakes killing and devouring horses and cattle. They are strong enough to kill even large mammals, but their mouths are not large enough to swallow them.

The largest sea-snakes, found in tropic seas, seldom grow beyond six or eight feet.

LIVING FISHING LINE

Such figures are made to seem negligible when compared with the lengths commonly reached by many living worms. The longest tape worm ever taken from a human being measured over eighty feet in length. Even longer is the bootlace worm often found under rocks at low tide round England's shores. At first the worm looks like a mass of calves' liver, but when touched with a stick, soon reveals itself as a sluggishly moving worm, seemingly limitless in extent.

At one end is a bell-shaped mouth which attaches itself to some passing fish. The living fishing line, as this worm has been called, then " plays " the fish until it is exhausted and can be swallowed whole. The bootlace worm may grow to a length of ninety feet.

FOUND ONLY IN AUSTRALIA

The world's longest earthworm measures twelve feet from end to end and is found only in the fertile agricultural province of South Gippsland, Australia. This worm is only about an inch thick and is easily broken. It burrows to a great depth and lays tough, horny eggs about three inches long.

This worm is often the victim of the laughing jackass, which, however, only enjoys eight or ten feet for dinner, after a long and tiring tug-of-war.

CHANGES OF SEX

STRANGE changes of sex in human beings are occasionally recorded in the Press. But what rightly appears to us as a somewhat strange process is quite normal in many of the lower animals.

CHANGES SEX ANNUALLY

The oyster begins life as a male, changes to female, and so continues to change sex annually throughout its life. One of the commonest shells to be found on the shores of Great Britain is the slipper limpet, a shell like half a Brazil nut, with a shallow shelf on its underside. This mollusc changes from male to hermaphrodite, and hermaphrodite to female. In this way it multiplies at a great pace, smothering the shellfish and constituting a serious scourge for which there is at present no remedy.

One of the most popular aquarium fish is the little sword-tail fish from Mexico. There is normally a great female surplus population of these fishes, and as though to counterbalance it, females, after producing several batches of eggs, often change into functional males.

BIRD FOUND GUILTY OF WITCHCRAFT

In older times these changes of sex gave rise to many strange beliefs. At Basle, in Switzerland, during the 14th century, a barnyard cock laid an egg. The bird was tried, found guilty of witchcraft, and with its egg burned publicly by the town executioner. Such freak birds were known generally, for an old rhyme declares:—

> A whistling maid, and a crowing hen
> Are neither fit for God nor men.

Of late years there have been several instances of hens growing spurs and learning to crow. Conversely several cocks have laid eggs, and hatched them. A disease of the reproductive organs was responsible.

ANIMALS IN MEDICINE

OVER the doorway of Apothecaries' Hall, London, stands the figure of a rhinoceros, a reminder that animals now, as in the past, play an important part in medicine. In medieval times all kinds of preparations from shrews, moles, toads, snails and many other creatures were habitually used by the best doctors of the period. Only sixty years ago, adders' fat as a cure for various ailments was sold in London, and in a few remote districts the slime of snails is still recommended as a cure for warts.

SNAKE POISON FOR CURING EPILEPSY

Animals are still indispensable to medicine. Thousands of animals of all kinds are employed, without hurt to themselves, in preparing the anti-toxins used to prevent us catching such diseases as smallpox.

Snake poisons are now used so much in the cure of hæmophilia or bleeding, epilepsy, and other disorders, that special snake farms have sprung up all over the world, the largest being at Santo Paulo, Brazil, and Port Elizabeth, South Africa. The snakes are made to strike at a sheet of rubber covering a glass vessel; the poison drips through, and is converted into a powerful extract. So strong is the poison of the puff adder that a minute quantity liberally diluted is sufficient to cause clotting of the human blood.

ANIMAL OILS ARE VALUABLE

All kinds of animal oils have their use. Cod and halibut liver oil are rich in vitamins and famous body-builders. Castoreum, an oil obtained from the beaver, is used in medicine and perfumery, whilst a thick, heavy oil exuded by some of Great Britain's native beetles is an effective blistering agent. Ambergris, essential to " fixing " perfumes and valued at £3 per ounce, is a hard concretion, formed largely of the horny beaks of cuttlefish, and is found in the intestine of the sperm whale, which feeds upon these molluscs.

The medicinal leech is still widely farmed on the European continent, and is invaluable for releasing small quantities of blood from the region of the eye or ear. About fifty years ago one London firm alone dispensed about 40,000 leeches a week. These were obtained partly from leech farms in Norfolk and Essex, and partly from abroad.

GROUND RHINOCEROS HORN AS REJUVENATOR

The rhinoceros at Apothecaries' Hall refers to the time when monarchs and others fearing assassination by poisoning kept a drinking cup made of rhinoceros horn wherewith to test their wine. Poured into such a vessel it was supposed to change colour if containing poison.

Rhinoceros horn is composed of compressed hair, and there is no truth in the notion, any more than in the notion that the horn ground up and made into a drink serves as a marvellous elixir and rejuvenator. So universal is this belief throughout the East that today rhinoceros horn still commands £14 per lb. in the Chinese markets.

POISONOUS ANIMALS

POISONING is a matter of degree. The saliva of a baby has been found to cause death when injected into the blood streams of various small animals. The number of creatures actually carrying poisons for use is not large, and such as exist vary greatly in the quality of the poisons they carry.

THOUSANDS DIE FROM SNAKE BITE ANNUALLY

The only known poisonous mammal is the duckmole of Australia. The male carries a sharp, curved spur on the inside of each hind leg, the spurs being hollow and connecting with poison glands. They cause severe and painful symptoms in human beings, though no deaths have been recorded.

Of the living species of snakes, about one-third are poisonous, virulence varying from that of a severe wasp sting to death within a few minutes when applied to a human subject. In India about 40,000 deaths occur from snake bite annually, in Africa only a few score, and in America scarcely any. Snake poison is a development of the saliva, is contained in two large glands, one on either side of the head, and conveyed through hollow teeth into any puncture made by the bite.

MOST DEADLY SNAKES

The most deadly snakes are the mamba and puff adder of Africa, the Indian cobra, Malayan king cobra, and the coral snakes of the New World. The South African spitting cobra is unique in squirting two streams of poison at its victims. Directed at the eyes it causes temporary blindness, and if it enters a scratch or other slight wound, death.

The common toad, called " deadly " in Shakespeare's time, exudes a poisonous fluid from the warts covering its skin. Its effect on a human being is similar to the early stages of a severe cold. A tree frog from Columbia exudes a poison so deadly that it is used by the natives to tip their arrows.

Many fishes, such as the trigger fish and sting rays, carry poisonous spines. The two native species of weever fish found in English waters have spines on gill covers and back fins which are hollow and connect with poison glands like the fangs of a snake. Permanganate of potash is the best first-aid antidote.

The only known poisonous molluscs are the beautiful tropic sea snails termed cones. The animals inhabiting cone shells have poison glands and fangs, inflicting severe wounds.

All centipedes, scorpions and spiders are provided with poison glands and fangs, those of the scorpion being situated at the end of the tail. The most deadly spider is the black widow of America, so called from its colour and the habit of the female—common to many spiders—of devouring her spouse after the eggs have been fertilized. Deaths are not frequent from black widow bite.

TAILS—HUMAN AND OTHERWISE

ONE often hears it said that man has rubbed his tail away by sitting on it. This is not true. Many monkeys and other creatures—marmots and beavers, for instance—spend as much time sitting down as any overworked clerk, but still retain very active tails.

REDUCED TO A FEW SMALL BONES

Man's tail has been reduced to a few small bones as the result of persistently walking upright on the ground. A tail is no longer of service to him when so engaged. But if he returns to the trees and spends much time running along horizontal branches, he must take the counterpart of a tail with him.

In the Andaman, Philippine and other tropic islands are races of savages who habitually spend half their time tight-rope walking slender branches, and this they only achieve by carrying a long balancing pole, just as does the circus artist. A rat, squirrel, or other arboreal animal similarly uses its tail, turning it to right or left the moment a counterpoise is wanted on one side or the other.

TAILS AS HANDS AND ANCHORS

The vertebrate's tail is a bit of the backbone left over from the dim past, when the first fish scrambled ashore and developed serviceable walking limbs. The tail has been put to endless purposes, and often to the same uses by very different animals which happen to lead similar ways of life. In the spider monkey, tree porcupine, binturong or Himalayan bear-cat, the Brazilian honey bear, the chameleon lizard, and the little fish known as the sea horse, the tail is used as a hand for grasping any object the animal wishes to use as an anchor.

The chameleon can throw out its tongue to a distance exceeding its body length. Unless the animal anchored itself to a branch by its tail, the force of this effort would throw it headlong. The tail acts like the shoe of a field gun—it takes the recoil.

Lions are cats that have given up climbing, but they retain the tail as a fly whisk, and this function it serves in the elephant, horse, ox and similar hoofed animals. A few creatures use the tail as a seat. The kangaroo and woolly monkey employ their tails as shooting stools, while the woodpecker and scaly ant-eater, taking a firm hold of some vertical tree trunk, sit back on their stiff tails, much as a man repairing a telegraph wire leans back against his protective belt.

A few fishes, such as the Malayan mud skipper and Indian climbing perch, use the tail to propel themselves over the ground, employing it as a punt pole; it can even help them up vertical surfaces. A big, bushy tail, such as that of the ant-eater and squirrel, serves as a coverlet at night, and when a tail is as stout as the African ant bear's, or armed with knobs and spines as in many lizards, it becomes a very effective weapon.

BEAVER'S ALARM GUN TAIL

There are two ways in which the tail can even be used as a danger signal. A familiar example is the rabbit's " bob." This, like the deer's short tail, with conspicuous marks on either side, serves as a guide to others in the rear, and points out the selected route for retreat.

The beaver's tail, which is shaped like a big laurel leaf, eight inches long and half an inch thick, is not, as old writers declared, used as a trowel for beating mud into position when dam building. It is a very effective swimming organ, and when danger threatens can strike the surface of the water so as to give a loud report. It is the only tail used as an alarm gun.

The tail, which as originally used by fish was only an organ of propulsion, usually contains a good deal of fat. A few desert mice and lizards have even used it as a fat storehouse. In lean times they literally live upon their tails, just as the camel can live upon its hump.

FREAKS AND MONSTERS

Freaks and monsters, which scientists call biological absurdities, are of fairly frequent occurrence, though as the result of slowly improving standards of entertainment they are less frequently exhibited to excite the idle pleasure seeker than formerly.

MAKING A TWO-TAILED FISH

Abnormalities have their beginnings in the egg, whether of human being or insect, at its earliest stage of development. When the egg is first formed it behaves for a while as a single whole. The distribution of the substances of which it is composed is general. Long before it begins to form itself into head, limbs, heart and so on it embarks upon a course of cell division, dividing and sub-dividing into smaller and ever smaller cells, until at last these cells reveal themselves as groups, each group doing special work. But if some accident occurs in the early stages, a monster is the result.

The lower the organism, the more likely are such monsters to survive. It is possible to make in the laboratory two-headed frogs, one-eyed and two-tailed fish, and so forth by " doctoring " the egg during its early stages of cell division. The higher the animal, the less likelihood there is of a freak surviving the throwing out of gear which has overtaken its machinery. The two-headed giant of fairy lore is never likely to be seen in life.

SNAKE WITH TWO HEADS

A few years ago a two-headed milk snake was found in the Bronx Zoo, New York. Each head had a separate neck, several inches long. The snake was fully grown, about two feet long, and its survival was surprising because it threatened unintentional suicide.

At meals, the heads had to be fed separately, or they would have choked the main food pipe, where the two separate food pipes met. A card was placed between them to prevent quarrelling, yet, in spite of all precautions, one head eventually attacked and devoured the other.

LEFT-HANDED WINKLES

A strange freakishness is sometimes seen in snails. Some factor, not yet fully understood, affects the eggs so that instead of the shell twisting to the right, it turns left. Such sinistral shells, as they are called, are much sought by collectors. About one whelk in 10,000 turns left instead of right. The left-handed winkle is much less frequent, and is probably one of the most valuable shells in the world.

In moths and butterflies, accident may cause the strange freak known as a gynander. This is a sex mosaic, and is brought about by jarring the chrysalis—usually by dropping a box or other receptacle in which it is being carried. Only certain species respond to such treatment. When the perfect insect emerges, the wings show a strange blend of male and female patterns, the two being mixed together in patches, like an old-fashioned crazy quilt.

Another specialized freak is that born only to cows of the Dexter breed. From time to time calves are born exactly resembling bulldog pups; such monsters never survive birth.

MARKET VALUE OF ANIMALS

THE price of a wild animal depends chiefly upon its value as a show beast and its hardiness in captivity. So far as Great Britain is concerned, until it has spent six months in the somewhat treacherous climate its market value is uncertain, and often a rare creature commands only a small sum because it is of interest only to a few scientists.

The most valuable animals at the London Zoo are the giant pandas, gorilla, okapi, and the Indian rhinoceros. These are reckoned to be worth about £1,000. All are valuable since they are big and attractive, and because specimens are difficult to obtain, either on account of rarity or comparative inaccessibility.

COSTLY ELEPHANTS AND CHEAP LIONS

An Indian elephant is worth £600. This price has not varied for a century, but the elephant must be a female and of good character to be safely shown in a zoo or circus. The big Nile hippopotamus commands £800, but the pygmy hippopotamus of Liberia only £300, or even less. Since first discovered, about ninety years ago, this animal has been bred so easily in captivity that, like the lion, it promises to become a drug on the market.

A century ago lions might fetch £200 each, now £40 is a top price, and cubs can even be bought for 7s. 6d. Lions breed in captivity as freely as dogs, but they are dangerous when adult, and need quite 60 lb. of meat a week—two more reasons for their reduced market value.

Tigers are still worth £100, but now that they are being reared easily in a few zoos, the price may soon fall. Chimpanzees can always command £80, and a sea lion £50. Despite its value as a show beast, the sea lion's menu of nearly 300 lb. of fresh fish per week precludes it from being everybody's pet. Still more expensive is the Californian elephant seal, which may require 100 lb. of fish per day.

BUDGERIGARS FOR JAPANESE BRIDES AND BRIDEGROOMS

The African wattled crane and the king penguin head the list of valuable birds—£75 each. Birds of paradise come next, £40, and the king vulture, because it is handsome, rare and hardy, £25. Some forty years ago a pair of blue budgerigars commanded just eight times as much as a king vulture. Such a pair used to be the prerogative of Japanese nobility, and was a favourite wedding present amongst the Sumurai.

Hardiness and readiness to breed in captivity have caused these little birds to slump as dramatically as the lion; 15s. is a fair price for a budgerigar. Accident may enhance an animal's price. The parrot disease scare and subsequent embargo on parrots has sent up the prices of these birds, but a good talking parrot always commands a high figure.

SOLD ACCORDING TO LENGTH

Crocodiles and snakes are generally sold according to length. A boa constrictor is of no great value until twelve feet long, when it may command £40; 30s. being charged for every additional foot. This price is not likely to change owing to restricted demand. Fan-tail goldfish, on the other hand, cost a few shillings each, and the price tends to fall owing to the ease with which they are bred, yet the first brought to Europe realized £50 a pair.

Transport is another factor controlling an animal's value. Giraffes over twelve feet in height are almost unsaleable. The long but inflexible neck makes it impossible to take a big giraffe under most bridges. Aquatic animals also are valued largely according to the ease or otherwise with which they can be accommodated en route from dealer to purchaser. A dozen boiled whelks are worth only a penny, but a live one, packed in damp weed and guaranteed to arrive in good condition, cannot be obtained under a shilling.

DWARFS OF THE ANIMAL WORLD

THE smallest living mammal is the Asiatic pygmy shrew. Without its tail, it measures only 1/144th the height of an adult African elephant. Small size has advantages. A shrew has more foes than an elephant, and since its surface is greater in relation to its size than that of an elephant, it must eat proportionately more food to compensate for the loss of heat (which means energy) given off from its body. On the other hand, a shrew can fall 50 feet or 100 feet and suffer nothing worse than a shaking, whereas the elephant would be killed outright.

BIRD NO BIGGER THAN A QUEEN BEE

The smallest living bird is a species of humming bird from Ecuador. Stripped of its feathers it would be no bigger than a queen bee and weigh very little more, which largely accounts for its being so powerful on the wing.

The smallest frog, also from Ecuador, when sitting with its limbs drawn close to its sides, is even smaller than the queen bee. It is a dwarf even beside the world's smallest fish, a minute goby from the lakes of Luzon in the Philippine Islands, which measures only half an inch from nose to tail fin.

WORLD'S TINIEST INSECT

Insects tend to be small, and whilst this has aided them in colonizing the whole earth by reason of their extreme mobility, it has hampered them in other directions. An insect cannot drink in a normal manner. An attempt to do so results in its being caught by the surface film of the water and there held prisoner. As Professor J. B. S. Haldane has said, " an insect going for a drink is in as great danger as a man leaning out over a precipice in search of food."

The world's smallest insect is a fly called elaphis. Across the outspread wings it measures less than the body length of a cheese mite. A flea is an enormous animal compared with a cheese mite, almost as large in proportion as an elephant is to a shrew, yet 80,000 fleas weigh only one ounce.

INVISIBLE UNDER THE MICROSCOPE

The great majority of animals are small, and ninety-nine per cent of the entire population of the seas consists of pygmies. The rotifers, or wheel animalculæ, swarm in all salt and fresh waters. The largest weigh less than ten milligrammes, and the smallest less than $1/1,000,000$th of a gramme. One such rotifer is about ten times as large as the amœba which causes dysentery.

Below this standard are innumerable other living organisms, the precise identity of which is often doubtful; scientists hesitate to class them as definitely animal or vegetable. Such living things are the germs and bacilli. Many, like the germ which causes foot-and-mouth disease, are so minute that they are at present invisible under even the most powerful miscroscope and escape through the finest porcelain filters. That they exist is all too obvious.

LUNGS AND NO LUNGS

LORD NUFFIELD's gift to every hospital in the British Empire of an iron lung, which keeps alive persons whose lungs can no longer work by themselves, made many people realize that breathing is not such a simple matter as it appears. Breathing is really burning—burning oxygen, food being only the fuel which makes this burning possible.

We draw air into the lungs, it is taken up by the blood vessels, of which lungs are largely composed, sent round the body by means of the heart, and the " slack "—poisonous gases and moisture brought back to the lungs—is shovelled out into the air via the nose, which immediately afterwards lets in a fresh supply. This roughly is the way we and all other mammals breathe.

MOUTH AND THROAT AS BELLOWS

Birds have air sacs; bags attached to the lungs. These take in oxygen and send it not only round the body, but even into the bones. This gives the bird greater lightness than a mammal. It also enables it to put forth enormous energy, for a bird unless asleep is scarcely ever at rest. As in ourselves, the lungs are bellows worked by the ribs and diaphragm, the dome-shaped muscle dividing chest and abdomen.

A frog has no ribs and no diaphragm. Its mouth and throat act as bellows. The frog has literally to swallow via its nostrils all the air it wants, keeping the mouth shut, or pumping would be impossible. This accounts for the panting appearance of a frog or toad, which people mistake for fright or palpitations.

Beasts, birds and amphibians therefore breathe in three different ways, but all have this in common : the breathing apparatus must be kept moist, or the tiny blood vessels cannot absorb oxygen. This is why breathing in very dry air is so difficult, and explains why asthmatic people are happiest in a muggy atmosphere. Bad cases need their rooms to be kept steamy by means of a kettle.

BREATHING THROUGH THE TAIL

Fishes living in water take in air quite easily by means of their gills, which owe their red colour to being literally a mass of blood vessels. Many fishes also have very thin skins, particularly in the tail region, and this also helps to take in oxygen. Those that are so fashioned have an advantage over others; they are not so " out of water " after all when high and dry.

Frogs and earthworms similarly take in much oxygen through the skin, and like the thin-skinned fishes, such as the little blenny and tropical mud skipper, are quite happy ashore, if only they can keep moist. A few fishes have the swim bladder, chiefly intended to keep them afloat, so made that it can do the work of a lung. Famous examples are the Australian, African and American lung fishes, which though at their best in water, can live for several months out of it.

The land snails have a remarkable breathing apparatus. When a garden snail is walking two-thirds of its shell space is taken up by a big inflated sac—the lung. The opening to this can be easily seen as a small round hole on the snail's right-hand side near the mouth of the shell

CATERPILLARS HAVE PORT-HOLES

Insects breathe on yet another principle. Everyone has noticed the little openings like port-holes on each side of a caterpillar. These lead to a most bewildering maze of tubes inside the animal, all filled with air in circulation. Insects, like birds, are feverishly active.

Many creatures breathe air whilst under water, though having no gills like fishes. They do this by having the nostrils poised on the top of little hillocks, or they breathe through their tail-ends. Water beetles may be seen doing this on any pond surface in summer. Often in tubs of manure water one finds a fat grub, about an inch long, with a " tail " drawn out to a hair's breadth six times its own length. This is the rat-tailed maggot which turns into a drone fly. It contrives to live in the filth on which it feeds by breathing clean air through its hollow tail. Some people believe this grub inspired the first crude diving dress—a helmet and air tube, but with no pump or complex poison absorbers as used in the latest models.

MARVELS OF THE SEEING EYE

Eyes do two things. They receive light and pictures. The first eyes of any sort were merely sensitive to light: scattered light-catching cells such as we find in the amœba and various worms. As animals became more complicated these cells were gathered up into groups, and at last pictures of a sort became possible.

It is likely that a snail can get blurred pictures of objects, but only when they are very close. Insect grubs such as caterpillars have seven or more eyes on each side of the head, and here again only blurred pictures may be possible. A perfect insect such as a butterfly often has several thousand eyes, arranged in two big groups. The pictures such eyes receive are probably much as though seen through very finely latticed windows.

BIRDS HAVE BETTER SIGHT THAN MAN

Even the eyes of backboned animals vary greatly. Everything depends on the eyes' powers of focus. The lens must be pushed back and forth by muscles, as that of a camera is moved by a screw. A cod can focus its eyes, but a dogfish only enjoys a close-up by nearly touching the object.

Man has the best brains of any animal, but not the best eyes. We can enjoy colours, while a dog, it is believed, lives in a black and white world, but we have much less keen sight than that of a bird. A bird enjoys marvellous powers of focus by means of a ring of bony plates in each eye. These work precisely like a diaphragm of a camera, letting in more or less light as required. In an eagle owl each such bony ring is about as big as an average pill box. The extinct fish lizard *Ichthyosaurus* had eye-rings as big as soup plates.

EYES ON TOP OF THE HEAD

Much depends on the position of the eye in the head. Men, monkeys and cats probably see much better than pigs or horses. When both eyes point straight forward they enjoy a stereoscopic picture; they see things " in the round." Put one on each side, and only a blurred, or part-picture can be had. At the same time such eyes can glimpse danger approaching from the rear or side, an important matter to creatures like the horse or deer.

Aquatic animals often have the eyes placed on top of the head. A crocodile, hippopotamus, or frog can stay submerged, leaving only its eyes above water, and so decide whether it is safe to land or better to stay below.

EYES THAT WORK INDEPENDENTLY

In fishes and some reptiles, like the chameleon, the eyes work independently.

The eyes of a few deep-sea fish, and all such creatures as snails, shrimps, lobsters and crabs are not only made to work independently, but are placed at the end of a long stalk, which when not in use can be folded back into grooves or telescoped and tucked out of the way.

ANIMALS WITH THREE EYES

All eyes need care. Our own have two eyelids, those of many mammals and all birds three, the third moving across the eye from the inner corner outwards. These, together with tear glands, when present, serve to keep the eye washed clean of dust and grit.

In a few invertebrate animals, like the king crab, there is a third eye, placed on top of the head. One reptile, the rare Tuatera lizard of New Zealand, even has the remains of such a third eye, handed down from prehistoric ancestors, but it has now ceased to be of actual service. A very few animals, like the cave fish of Kentucky, by living in almost total darkness, have forfeited their eyes, and lost the power of sight.

HOW ANIMALS BECOME EXTINCT

For every kind of animal now living, a hundred or more have become extinct. Animals, however, do not just die out; there is always a reason for their disappearance. In the remote past slow changes of climate killed off whole races of animals, as is happening today, though such things occur so gradually we do not notice them.

TRAPPED BY ASPHALT

The records of the rocks prove that sometimes whole herds and flocks must have been wiped out quite suddenly. Only one or two million years ago elephants, giant sloths, bears, bison, wolves, lions, vultures and scores of other creatures came to an end in South America, where now are vast sheets of cold, hard asphalt. This stuff is full of the bones of the vanished animals.

Ages ago the asphalt was soft lava, poured out by a volcano. From time to time rain and dew collected in dimples on its surface, and in a drought this tempted the creatures to their destruction. They ventured out on to the solid-looking but treacherous asphalt to reach the water, and were engulfed.

KILLED OFF BY NATURE

In Mongolia scores of skeletons of a vanished species of elephant have lately been found. It had an enormous lower jaw shaped like a shovel, which was evidently used for digging up soft vegetation from swamps. All the evidence points to these monsters browsing on the edges of a lake that was slowly shrinking. The animals ventured further and further out on to the soft mud, and met a fate similar to that of the creatures caught in the molten asphalt.

Volcanic upheavals on the sea floor sometimes kill fishes by myriads, as when some years ago the surface waters off parts of the coast of America were covered with dead and dying fish. Severe cold killed off nearly all the manatees in the rivers of Florida during 1894-95, and in 1920 frost similarly exterminated all the blue birds in the New York area, and the fish-crows of Washington.

MURDERED BY MAN

The extinction of all kinds of animals has been dramatically speeded up by man. He probably killed off the sabre-toothed tiger and mammoth, and within historic times has definitely been known to wipe out all sorts of animals on the grand scale.

Amongst his victims may be mentioned the New Zealand moa, the dodo of Mauritius, the Arctic sea cow, the African quagga, and the great auk. The American bison has only been rescued from extinction in the nick of time, but the thousands of giant tortoises that once peopled the Galapagos and Seychelles Islands have gone beyond recall. The early explorers used them to victual their ships, and as a result the few giant reptiles surviving are now beyond price.

Legislation is being enforced to save the last of the whales and other animals, but many seem beyond aid. For example, fruit farming renders it necessary to kill noxious insects wholesale. This can only be done by spraying the orchards with poison. The insect pests are killed, but so also are useful insects like the ladybird and lacewing fly, and many harmless and beautiful species. There are far fewer butterflies about the countryside today than there were forty years ago.

The extermination of animals is as easy as tree-felling—their reinstatement more difficult even than the creation of new oak and fir forests.

EARS AND HEARING

An ear, reduced to its simplest form, consists of a tightly stretched membrane in a box which serves as a resonator. Vibrations of the air around cause the drum to quiver in response, and this being received through nerves by the brain is called hearing. Hearing and a sense of touch are therefore practically the same thing.

HEARING THROUGH THE LEGS

By means of a machine called the osiphone, persons whose ear drums have been destroyed can hear via their neck bones, or even elbows. Vibrations made by sound are carried up to the brain, and so hearing of a kind results. Snakes, fishes, crabs and many insects, though quite without true ears, largely " hear " in this manner.

Most animals that are capable of making vocal sounds or instrumental music can hear. A bee or mosquito cannot perhaps hear its own buzzing, this being merely a result of its progress through the air, and as meaningless as the note of an aeroplane. But the cricket's chirp is an important factor in its life; it is a love song. The cricket hears its fellow by means of a simple ear drum carried on its thighs or forelegs instead of in its head. Some crustaceans, like the crawfish and pistol prawn, can make loud noises, and it is believed these can be heard through hearing hairs that fringe the legs, and connecting with the central nervous system convey a message to the brain.

Frogs and lizards have ears, since they are often highly vocal animals, but snakes are deaf by our standards. The music that invariably accompanies a snake charmer's performance is simply a piece of professional bluff. The so-called ear bones of fish serve principally to maintain the creature's balance, much as the semi-circular canals adjacent to the Eustachian tubes of our ears help to maintain our equilibrium. Defects in these canals make it difficult to walk straight, and harder still to ride a bicycle.

EARS A YARD ACROSS

Ears are well developed in birds, particularly in the night-flying owls, but reach their highest development in mammals. Despite our intelligence, far transcending that of any other animal, our hearing is poor compared with many mammals. A dog can detect sounds both above and below our range of hearing, which seldom covers more than eight octaves.

The outer ear, which serves as a sounding board, is a good index to an animal's hearing. It reaches its maximum—sometimes a yard across—in the African elephant, and is also at a high standard in deer and rabbits. Strangely enough it is also well developed in the giraffe, though this animal is without vocal cords, and as a result silent. In seals and whales it has been reduced almost to vanishing point.

The ear can be merely an organ of balance, as in the jellyfish. A jellyfish has eight little bags arranged round its margin. These contain fluid in which float lime particles. When the lime grains knock against the sides of the bag, it is a warning to the jellyfish that it is swimming lop-sided, and the creature automatically rights itself.

BRAINS AND FEELING

THE brain is very literally the head office. Nerves from every part of the body take messages to it, and if a nerve is cut no message can come through. This is the basis of anæsthesia. A local anæsthetic merely puts the nerves, the body's telegraph system, out of action, but a general anæsthetic closes down the brain, the receiving station.

A brain is made up of the same stuff as nerves, but the grey matter, which is supposed to be responsible for most of the thinking, is spread over the whole in a layer of varying depth according to the brain. It is not possible to make a detailed map of a brain. Reasoning, however, it is agreed, is centred largely in the forehead or cerebrum, sight at the back, and the hind brain or cerebellum controls the body balance.

SECONDARY BRAIN CENTRED IN THE HIPS

No other organ in the world compares in complexity with the human brain. An average man's brain weighs two and a half pounds, roughly one-sixtieth of his entire weight. An elephant's brain may weigh fifteen pounds, but this is only 1/600th of the animal's total heaviness.

Even such a poor brain as this is a great advance on the brains of reptiles. The limited minds of the huge dinosaurs largely hastened their extinction. The stegosaur, for instance, had a brain infinitely smaller in proportion to that of the elephant. It was so small that a sort of secondary brain many times the size of the true brain was centred in the hips to direct the movements of the hind legs and swing the huge tail.

A similar state of affairs obtains with invertebrates. Crabs and flies, for example, have minute true brains, but " belly brains " centred at the junction of their legs. In a jellyfish or sea anemone there is nothing that can be called a brain—merely a tangle of nerves, with no central receiving station.

It will be realized from this how misleading is the humanizing of insects and similar creatures, as one often finds them humanized in popular nature stories. An insect is more comparable to a machine than a mammal. Even if dismembered, the parts mechanically attempt to carry on, as under normal conditions. Pain is an unmeaning term when applied to the invertebrates, and possibly many of the lowest backboned animals.

GIANTS AMONG ANIMALS

NATURAL giants, as distinguished from mere freaks, caused by over-activity of the pre-pituitary gland, occur in every branch of the animal kingdom. In the history of life on this planet each main group of animals has risen to one or more peaks, during which some members have reached a maximum development. Today the warm-blooded mammals that bring forth their young alive and feed them with milk hold the stage.

WORLD'S BIGGEST MAMMALS

The biggest mammals that ever lived were the hornless rhinoceroses that flourished for a short while in Baluchistan about 1,000,000 years ago. Males sometimes stood seventeen feet at the shoulder. The biggest living land mammals are elephants, some standing about two-thirds this height. It is doubtful if they will grow any larger, for size is a matter of mechanics. An elephant weighing over six tons would need legs so massive that they would be almost immovable. The giant rhinoceros was very slender, and an eighteen-feet giraffe is still more lightly built.

In water size does not count for so much. A fluid medium renders weight relatively negligible, and so the sulphur bottom whale, though growing to over 100 feet long, and weighing nearly as much as thirty elephants, can still move with ease. During the Age of Reptiles some of the quadrupedal dinosaurs measured 100 feet long, and the biped species often towered twenty or more feet high, but the body bulk seldom exceeded that of an elephant. Many also were probably aquatic.

FLYING DRAGONS OF YESTERDAY

Like the whales, some other swimming animals reach a great size. The whale shark measures fifty feet long, ten feet more than the elephant seal, twenty feet longer than the largest crocodile, and forty feet longer than the giant cuttle fish. All these creatures breathe by means of lungs or gills, which are essential to extensive growth.

Some flying animals reach an impressive size, but the fact that they fly sets a limit to their dimensions. The extinct flying dragons called pterodactyls might measure seventeen feet across the wings, and a few birds such as condors or albatrosses span not far short of this. About ten pounds body weight only can be raised high in air: anything beyond this spells forfeiture of aviation.

INSECTS AS LARGE AS RATS

Insects breathe by a complex system of tubes, and if the largest size known to be attained by any insect were exceeded, the entire structure would collapse. Insect giants are the Goliath beetles of Africa, and the South American Hercules beetle, all bulking about as large as rats. The Indian Atlas moth spans a foot across the wings, six inches less than the giant dragon-flies of the coal epoch.

Crustaceans, such as crabs and lobsters, breathe through gills and have tougher shells than insects, but these shells must be periodically cast, and the strain upon the creature's system limits its expansion. The giant sea scorpions of the coal epoch measured nine feet long, but the largest living crab, a spider crab of Japan, though spanning nine feet across has a body not much larger than a man's head.

SHELLS WEIGHING HUNDREDWEIGHTS

Sea water by its density reduces weight more effectively than fresh water, and so in the ocean we find sea snails with shells two feet long, such as the spindle snail of South Carolina, U.S.A., four times as long as any land or river snails. A shellfish living a sedentary life can afford to grow even larger, and on the Barrier Reef of Australia exist clams with shells over a yard long, and weighing many hundredweights.

The less skeleton or similar structure a creature possesses for the support of its soft parts, the greater restrictions are placed upon its expansion. Jellyfish seldom span over a yard, and only a few deep-sea anemones grow to six feet long, with a spread of tentacles covering two yards diameter. The largest single-celled animals floating in mid-ocean are about the size of one's finger nail.

WARFARE AMONG ANIMALS

THE old saying " There's nothing new under the sun " has more truth in it than is always realized. No animals other than man have yet perfected liquid fire or poison gas, relying in warfare chiefly upon such primitive weapons as teeth and claws, but some of our modern forms of frightfulness were anticipated by animals long before man devised his own ways of wrecking civilization.

ATTACKS BY POISON GAS

Poison gas of a kind is employed by some animals, but it is often uncertain whether their powerful odours, so unpleasant to ourselves, may not be attractive to their own species. The odour of the Canadian skunk is probably intended to be fully as offensive as it is. The skunk is dressed in black and white, a popular warning type of colouring amongst animals. Moreover it appears conscious of its dread powers, and though no bigger than a ferret refuses to give the road to larger animals. If a man is splashed by the fluid it ejects from glands under its tail, he has no alternative but to get a new suit of clothes.

The termites, or white ants, have devised a terrible weapon. Termites build huge cities underground, guarded by special termites called soldiers. When a foe appears, these ants rush out and spray the invader with an acid secretion which solidifies on contact with the air. A big animal thus sprayed is merely conscious of an unpleasant stickiness, but an insect is literally petrified and put out of action as completely as would be a man covered with a thick layer of plaster.

SMOKE SCREEN OF CUTTLE-FISH

Rambling about the countryside one may sometimes chance to turn over a big stone and be surprised by several little reports, followed by tiny puffs of acrid smoke. This is the barrage of the bombardier beetle. The beetle on alarm exudes a drop of highly volatile fluid, which explodes with an appreciable report—almost negligible to us, but powerful enough to throw another beetle on its back.

It is quite possible that one of man's latest camouflage devices, the smoke screen, has been copied from the common cuttle-fish. Cuttle-fish, octopuses, and similar molluscs when alarmed eject great quantities of ink, which so cloud the water that under cover of the artificial fog the creature can make good its escape. This ink, known as sepia, is widely used by artists, dried ink-sacs of cuttle-fish being imported into Great Britain in great quantities from abroad. A common sea slug, the sea hare, and various rock snails use a similar device, but baffle pursuers with purple instead of dark brown ink.

DAZZLING FOES BY LIGHT

In the darkness of the ocean abyss inky means of escape would have no effect. Deep-sea cuttle-fish, however, evade danger by blinding foes not with blackness but with light. Such cuttle-fish, and also various deep-sea prawns, squirt out rolling clouds of blue-green phosphorescent liquid that dazzles the foe as completely as an electric torch dazzles a rat or hare on a dark night.

Another device of animal warfare we have copied is the water gun. A small fish known as the archer, living in oriental lakes and rivers, shoots insects resting on bankside vegetation by directing a stream of water at them with such force that the insect is knocked off its perch and easily devoured. The fish's mouth is drawn out into a long spout, and no doubt inspired the anti-burglar water pistol as well as a similar weapon used by naturalists to kill such creatures as humming birds and large tropical butterflies.

HANDS AND FEET

SHERLOCK HOLMES, the famous detective, could take a client by the hand and say, "Ha! I see you are a bricklayer—or an artist—or a piano tuner "—as the case might be, and of course he was always right. The anatomist can do something of the same sort with animals, for the hand is the key to the creature's way of life.

WITH THIRTY FINGERS

The first hands appeared many millions of years ago when the fishes developed fins. A fin is only a hand, but with anything from ten to thirty fingers called rays. When fishes crawled out of the water, so many fingers were not wanted. Five, or even less, did the work just as well.

Frogs, newts and reptiles all have four or five fingers. There are five fingers covered up in the turtle's flipper. When the birds grew feathers and used them in flight, fingers could be discarded. Today only one bird, the Brazilian hoatzin, keeps during its early days two fingers with which to climb about the trees before it has learnt to fly properly.

HANDS AS CLIMBING HOOKS

The mammals have always relied upon their fingers and toes, and the former show wonderful modifications. Even the monkeys have found scores of different ways of using them. Most have kept four fingers and a thumb like ourselves, but the spider monkeys and orangutan use their hands largely as climbing hooks, and so the thumb has dwindled or even disappeared. The aye-aye, a lemur found in Madagascar, lives by picking grubs out of bamboo stems. To do this the fingers are drawn out like the legs of a spider, and the third finger, which does most of the picking, is as thin as a piece of wire.

Hands are still the best of all climbing tools, and some lemurs have mproved them by developing enormous pads on the fingers and palm. Tree frogs and gecko lizards have such adhesive pads that they can walk up window panes and over ceilings. One lemur, the African bush baby, improves its sucking pads by wetting them before climbing.

HANDS FOR WALKING

The cat tribe has developed finger nails strong enough to tear flesh. The bear's claws may be four inches long and can rip the toughest bark from a tree. The ant-eater has carried this a stage further. All its hand-power has been concentrated in the two middle finger nails, five-inch weapons that can tear down massive earthworks.

All the grazing and browsing animals, relying upon their lips and snouts for gathering food, employ the hands solely for walking. Thousands of centuries spent in trotting upon hard earth have centred the horse's hand-power in one central finger; the remains of the unwanted fingers are hidden beneath the skin of the foreleg. The pig, on the other hand, treading on swampy ground, has retained its fingers. They splay under pressure and so give a better support. Such hands could only support a beast of moderate size. The elephant, though keeping its five fingers for use on soft ground, subjects them to such enormous pressure that they have become welded to form a single solid base, enclosed within a wall of inch-thick skin.

Only a few mammals have returned to the water, whence all mammal life originally came. The whale, sea lion and walrus appear to have fins almost like those of a fish, but once they are stripped of their skin, the scientific Sherlock Holmes has no difficulty in recognizing them as well-formed hands—the hall-marks of mammals.

ARE THERE UNDISCOVERED ANIMALS?

THE Loch Ness monster, though not taken seriously by many people, is a reminder that man is always waiting for " something new," and in the newspapers one still often reads rumours of strange creatures in distant lands, monsters that as yet have not been shot, either with gun or camera.

STARTLING BEASTS FROM PATAGONIA

There is really no reason why new animals should not be discovered. Some startling beasts have come to light within living memory.

For instance, the giant ground sloths, sometimes as big as elephants, have always been regarded as having become extinct long before man was well established. But in 1899 a party of scientists in Patagonia stumbled on an amazing cavern. It was not only full of giant sloth skeletons, but great pieces of fresh skin, huge stacks of fodder, weapons, remains of fires, and other oddments showed that very skilful savages must have kept the sloths captive in the cavern, and slaughtered them for food as required.

FINDING THE OKAPI

Another argument in favour of some great animals yet surviving is that until actual specimens are obtained no verdict can be given, since the average man, with the best intentions of speaking the truth, is given to exaggeration.

Just after the giant sloth discovery, Sir Harry H. Johnston, a British diplomat in the Belgian Congo, sent home stories of a strange new donkey in the Ituri forest. Bits of skin which reached England decided scientists in saying that the animal was obviously some sort of zebra. But in 1902 a specimen of this new zebra was shot, and it proved to be the now famous okapi, which like the giraffe is a last survivor of a race of giant browsing beasts that once roamed Africa, Asia and Europe.

KENYA'S NANDI BEAR

Long before the World War, and for years afterwards, the Press published accounts of a dreadful monster in Kenya Colony. It was supposed to be a blend of man and hyæna, and was called the Nandi bear. Rumours became so numerous about 1930, that the British Museum circularized all responsible white persons in Kenya asking for skins or other remains, if obtainable. In due course skins and skulls arrived. Sometimes a parcel consisted of a leopard skull and a hyæna skin, sometimes vice versa, but the two never "belonged."

About eighty years ago there were such persistent rumours of the moa, a giant ostrich-like bird, still surviving in New Zealand, that the Zoological Society of London made strenuous efforts to obtain one, but though several persons declared they had seen it, no moa arrived.

ANIMALS THAT SHED LIGHT

SOME years ago a bear escaped at Whipsnade, the country home of the animals belonging to the Zoological Society of London, broke into the carpenters' shop, rolled in a tin of phosphorescent paint, and soon set flying rumours of a ghost bear. Though that is the largest luminous animal yet recorded, many smaller creatures are "lit up," and for a variety of reasons.

WORM WITH A GREEN HALO

The phosphorescence of the sea, which in tropic latitudes is sometimes almost bright enough to read by, is caused by countless myriads of living organisms, microscopic plants and the minute larvæ of crabs, shrimps, fishes and other creatures. In Great Britain's home waters this light is most apparent in late spring and early autumn, when the sea surface brings forth its two main "crops." What purpose—if any—the light serves these creatures is not definitely known, and it is equally puzzling as regards a big sea worm common on the south-west coast.

This worm, known as the parchment tube worm, makes a U-shaped tube about a foot long in the sand, with both ends showing at the surface. The worm living in the tube secretes a substance that gives off light, and makes a big halo of greenish light at the head end of the tube. The worm must be its own worst enemy, for the light attracts fish, particularly eels, which plunge their narrow heads into the tube and extract the worm, extinguishing its light for ever.

ATTRACTING PREY AND PARTNERS

The two principal and most obvious uses to which light is put by animals is the attraction of prey and partners. In the ocean abyss, where all is inky blackness, large numbers of fish are brilliantly illuminated, with greenish or blue light organs called photophores. They are worn on all parts of the fish; set in rows like port-holes, or the light may cover the creature's entire head, under surface, or tail. Bottom-feeding fish have their under sides lit up, or scan the floor by means of a luminous beard.

Some angler fishes carry a long fishing rod on their heads with a luminous bulb at the end by way of bait. In one West Indian fish the powerful light organs on its head attract prey within reach of its huge mouth. Fishermen know this, cut out the light organs and thread them on their hooks, where they continue to shine for many hours. Some deep-sea cuttle-fish carry a dozen or more lights—green, blue and bright red.

FIRE-FLIES AS ORNAMENTS

As an attraction to partners lights are chiefly used by insects such as glow worms and the tropic fire-flies. Both are species of beetle and are illuminated at all stages of development, even while still within the egg. The light is at its brightest in the adult female insect.

In South America fire-flies are worn by ladies on gala nights, besides being used to decorate ballrooms, and so on. The insects are collected in vast numbers, stored in moss until wanted, and finally threaded upon wires.

FISHES THAT GENERATE ELECTRICITY

IF a cat's hair, or that of some human beings, is combed in the dark, there is a crackling sound, accompanied by blue electric sparks. Strangely enough the only animals that have harnessed electricity are various fishes, and they have utilized our greatest mechanical aid in several entirely different ways.

BATTERIES IN ITS TAIL

The electric eel of the Amazon is really a distant cousin of the loach. Its eel-like appearance is superficial. Four-fifths of the fish is tail, and it contains three sets of electric batteries. A fish six feet in length can shock with a capacity of several hundred volts, the power being chiefly utilized to kill or stun the prey. Horses and men have been drowned by this fish as a result of being thrown headlong into the water.

The fish also uses its batteries in a crude telegraphy, announcing its approach to others of its species. Once a victim has been shocked, all other electric eels in the vicinity are attracted to the spot as a result of electric signals given out by their pool or river mate. There are two species of this fish, one of a reddish brown colour, the other and commoner a dark slaty blue with a lurid flush suffusing its body.

ELECTROCUTES ITS OWN KIND

The electric catfish of Arabia and the Sudan is a heavily built fish two feet or more long, yellowish with brown spots, and having eight long feelers depending from its lips. It is very common, often eaten by the Arabs, and called the raad or thunder fish.

The whole body is enclosed in one big electric organ, as in an envelope, and its powers, though less than those of the electric eel, are considerable. Whereas electric eels seem to be safe from each other's shocks, the electric catfish invariably kills smaller members of its own kind kept with it in a tank.

USED TO RELIEVE RHEUMATISM

The electric ray, or torpedo, is common in all warm seas. Most of the body is occupied by closely packed electric batteries, like small Leyden jars, hexagonal in shape and so placed that one end touches the fish's back. the other its belly.

The torpedo, known on English coasts as numb fish, and in France as Monsieur Touchez, flings itself at such delicate fish as the grey mullet, and then slowly engulfs them before they can recover. Like the electric eel it has been used in aquariums to light electric bulbs, ring bells, and otherwise turn its batteries to account. After several shocks the fish becomes exhausted and needs an hour or two to recharge its batteries.

In earlier times this fish supplied a crude form of vibro-massage for rheumatoid and other ailments. The patient stood on the fish for as long as the physician ordered or his own powers of endurance decreed.

ANIMAL TRAVELLERS

A NIMALS are notorious travellers. Millions make several journeys annually, often covering many thousands of miles in the course of their migrations, and millions more travel as parasites, but in this case they travel merely by accident. It does not matter whether they travel or not, since their main object is a meal, always provided by the unwilling host.

A small number of creatures travel because constant movement is essential to a fresh food supply and general well-being. An extreme example of this is sometimes provided by newspaper paragraphs recording how some small dog, not necessarily homeless or ill-cared for, has formed a habit of travelling about some great city on public conveyances.

London has several such four-footed tourists. The dog leaves home after a good breakfast, and spends the remainder of the day on bus or tube, lunching at drivers' or porters' shelters, and then blandly presents itself to its master in time for its evening repast.

USED FOR CATCHING TURTLES

Some creatures in the wild lead similar lives. The most famous example is the shark sucker, found in all tropic and sub-tropic seas. The top of the head of this fish bears a big oval sucking disk—actually a modified back-fin—which adheres to any tolerably flat surface with enormous power. By this means the fish, which is a slow and lazy swimmer, habitually travels attached to sharks, turtles, or the hulls of ships. It will even affix itself to the inside of some giant fish's mouth, and thus established picks up all kinds of oddments instead of hunting for itself.

From early times the shark sucker has been used to capture turtles. The fisherman keeps a number of shark suckers on the floor boards or sides of the boat, each fish having a long line attached to its tail. When a turtle is sighted basking at the surface of the sea, a sucker is put overside and soon makes for the quarry. Having attached itself, both are hauled aboard.

FREE LIFTS FOR BABY MUSSELS

Travel may be essential to the welfare of young and helpless animals, and they ensure themselves a lift in a variety of ways. In most slow-running rivers, lakes and reservoirs may be found huge numbers of the zebra mussel, which is very like an edible mussel, but prettily striped. The baby zebra mussels, shortly after being hatched, sink to the river bed, and there lie till a shoal of fish approaches. When this happens each baby mussel violently opens and shuts its two shells, which action forces upwards a long, sticky thread.

All being well the thread attaches itself to a passing fish, and the baby mussel, hauling itself up, burrows into the skin of the fish and there stays until big and strong enough to return to the river bed and start life on its own.

EXPLOITING THE WASP

Among the wasp's many enemies is a beetle whose babies cannot live unless they early contrive to make a long aerial journey on the back of a wasp. To make sure of this the beetle grub climbs to the top of a wooden post likely to be visited by wasps in search of wood pulp wherewith to make their paper nests. The grub fixes itself to the post by means of a sucker on its hinder end, and then rears itself aloft, waving its long legs in the air.

Here it stays until a wasp comes within reach: at once the grub climbs aboard, is carried back to the wasp's nest, and there makes short work of the wasp larvæ, eventually tunnelling into a wasp cocoon and so remaining until it emerges as a perfect beetle. Then the exploitation of the wasps begins all over again.

TUNNELLERS OF THE ANIMAL KINGDOM

TUNNELLING plays an ever-increasing part in our communal life. It is a convenient way of saving space. Railways and garages tend more and more to be placed underground. One crosses the street by going below it, and it is under the earth that man shelters from attacks made from above.

WORMS AS EXCAVATORS

The first tunnellers were worms. Their work as excavators is not only indispensable to their own safety but to the vigour of vegetable life, and as a result the lives of other animals. The little tubifex worm, common in all ponds, passes nine yards of soil through its half-inch long body in every twenty-four hours. The earth worm similarly tunnels by pouring earth through its system, swallowing all it meets at one end, ejecting waste at the other. The worms in an acre of garden soil swallow and bring to the surface about fifteen tons of earth annually.

Like worms, all animal tunnellers tend to be long bodied, whether they be Aberdeen terriers, ferrets, moles, mole crickets, clams or "leather-jackets"—daddy-long-legs grubs. Methods of tunnelling vary greatly. All mammals use the front feet for digging; the hind are simply employed as shovels to throw out the material excavated. In this way the African ant-bear can tunnel fast enough to keep well ahead of two men armed with pick and shovel.

UGLIEST MAMMAL IN THE WORLD

Tunnelling affects not only an animal's legs and general shape, but its outer covering. The Scottie has a short, tough fur not easily clogged with dirt. The mole's fur is so short and dense that no dirt can adhere to it for long. A few tunnellers, like the armadillo, have developed skin so hard that it forms overlapping plates off which earth slides like rain from a tiled roof.

One creature, the African desert rat, by persistent tunnelling in hot sand beneath a tropic sun, has discarded all hair and is as naked as a hippopotamus. It is probably the ugliest mammal in the world.

WASP THAT BORES THROUGH LEAD

Many other substances besides soil yield to Nature's expert excavators. The grubs of the death watch and many other beetles, and the huge caterpillars of the goat moth, tunnel wood exactly as a worm tunnels earth. They eject, not typical worm castings, but little heaps of loose sawdust. A death watch grub has been known to drill a tube-tunnel straight through a row of leather-bound volumes each three inches thick. The wood-boring wasp will even eat its way through a pine log wrapped in several inches of sheet lead.

The long, wide tunnels that often make timber, shale, and even the hardest limestone look like so much gruyère cheese are made in a different way. Here the tunneller is usually a species of clam which has a very finely sculptured shell. By means of a strong muscular foot the clam sets up a rocking action of the shell, and the fine but resilient hooks and ridges on its outer surface act like a file. In this way not only limestone but solid coral rock is broken down. Reefs are continuously demolished and renewed. These tunnelling animals of the sea cost us millions of pounds sterling annually, just as does the death watch beetle, which only a few years ago nearly brought to grief the magnificent roof of Westminster Hall, London.

In the old days of Britain's wooden walls, even the finest ship was sooner or later doomed. A very common tunnelling clam, the so-called ship worm, makes tunnels a foot or more long, lining them with hard, shelly matter as it goes. It was this little mollusc that eventually demolished Drake's *Golden Hind*, the survivor of so many tempests and cannonades.

HOW ANIMALS SLEEP

SLEEP would seem to be one of the simplest matters to define. Actually it is a matter of degree, and what is wakefulness in one may be profound slumber in another. The bigger and better the brain, the less it knows complete rest. Sleep is always ebbing and flowing in the brain, which accounts for the dreams, so apparent in ourselves and some other animals such as dogs and cats. Areas of the brain are always at work; the whole never closes down in normal health.

NO NIGHT STARVATION FOR LEMURS

The old saying, " Six hours' sleep for a man, seven for a woman, and eight for a fool," means nothing in the light of present knowledge. Some of the best intellects need only five hours in the twenty-four, others eight or nine, and many more average persons show an even greater range.

Animals, though not to be compared with man for brain-power, exhibit great variety in their needs for rest. Apes and monkeys appear to be very like ourselves, for they keep similar hours, becoming active with the daylight and feeling need for rest after dusk. Like our own night watchmen and market workers, certain lemurs have reversed the natural order, but still need about the same amount of sleep in every twenty-four hours.

Nomadic animals living in open country are less stabilized in their hours of rest. A cow in an open field during summer, though safe from foes, has not outgrown ancestral traits, memories of a remote time when every mouthful was snatched with one eye alert for possible approaching danger.

Most grazing mammals eat and sleep in short shifts; light and darkness do not necessarily dictate work or bed time. Elephants seldom appear to spend more than four hours in actual sleep, though they may remain in one spot for twice as long, " resting " in a strange way with ceaseless shiftings from foot to foot and a rhythmic swaying of the body.

DO WHALES SLEEP?

This question is unanswerable, since even when a whale remains for hours on the sea surface there is no guarantee that it is actually asleep. During the nine months that a small school of porpoises was kept under observation at the New York Aquarium there was never a complete cessation of their steady progress round and round their pool, although this non-stop swim showed a marked slowing down at night.

Possibly a whale continues to swim mechanically when at rest, just as many a soldier in the World War marched in his sleep. Some fishes appear to sleep. Surface species may sink to mid-depth or sea floor at night, and vice versa. The wrasse actually lies upon its side, like a dog, and many other common fishes lean against rocks, aquatic plants, and such like. Mullet normally swim in great shoals. At night the shoal breaks up, each fish points a different way, and all are still. A light at once brings them together, and again on the move.

WINTER SLEEP

The well-known winter sleep of the hedgehog and dormouse is accompanied by a much more marked fall in temperature than that which usually accompanies sleep. Some birds undergo a similar death-like torpor when asleep. Cold weather makes humming birds sleep so heavily that they can only be lifted from their perches by unwinding each toe separately.

The Australian frog-mouth, or morepork owl, sleeps so heavily that a companion shot beside it fails to arouse it. The bird can even be lifted from the branch and placed in a bag without waking.

WEAVERS IN THE FEATHERED WORLD

NATURE has anticipated so many of our complex machine-made necessities that one can only wonder if primitive man first conceived such things by studying their crude beginnings amongst the lower animals. Weaving, for example, rightly called an ancient craft, is more ancient than many suppose. It began long before the dawn of man.

BIRDS THAT "SET THE FASHION"

Two great classes of birds, living on opposite sides of the world, the American hang nests and the Oriental weaver birds, have practised weaving and attained considerable perfection. These little birds, which are never larger than thrushes, use dried grasses to build enormous communal nests, generally hung from high branches well beyond the reach of tree snakes, monkeys and other freebooters.

In America special sanctuaries have been supplied with coloured wool, with amazing results. The birds have used them in building their nests. Blue is a favourite colour, and certain birds having "set a fashion" others in time copy. The effect of a colony thus decorated is as though the trees bore huge rainbow-coloured fruits.

TAILOR BIRD SEWS LEAVES TOGETHER

The Indian tailor bird, a species of warbler, carries the art of weaving a stage further. Not content with a mere jumble of strands, it uses grasses to sew pendent leaves together, as one might lace together the two flaps of a boot. In the cup so formed a nest of grasses is placed.

Weaving of a sort enters into the construction of the edible birds' nests. The swallows building these nests on high cliffs in China reinforce the glutinous saliva which forms the bulk of the nest with grasses, hairs, and so on, much as we now reinforce various plastic substances for surgical splints and many other widely different purposes.

SILKS FOR SEALING

Silk is not a monopoly of the silk worm. Most moths, butterflies, and innumerable other insects employ silk to build cocoons wherein to shelter during the change from grub to chrysalis and chrysalis to perfect insect. The caddis worm, used for fishing bait, so seals up the mouth of its stone- or stick-built "case" prior to emergence as a caddis fly.

These silks are often very sticky. A race of tropical ants produces grubs that give out threads of a substance as adhesive as seccotine. The adult ants make nests of leaves, and use their grubs as living spindles to fix the leaves together. The ants arrange themselves in two gangs, one pulling the two leaves together, the other gang—each worker with a grub held in its jaws—fixing the edges so that they cannot fly apart.

CATGUT OF SPIDER SILK

Spider silk is spun to make webs either of the accepted pattern or funnel shaped, like that of the house spider, and may even be converted into a diving bell. The water spider so uses its silk, filling an inverted thimble-shaped nest with air, and laying therein its eggs. The best catgut is not of mammal origin but spider silk taken from large spiders whilst it is still in a semi-fluid state and then drawn out to the required length.

Quite as strong is the silk woven by molluscs with which to anchor themselves to rocks. It is strong enough to withstand all but the severest storms. A tuft of this can always be found in a freshly opened edible mussel. It is quite harmless, and not, as some people suppose, poisonous weed.

Off the Eddystone lighthouse in the English Channel lies a bank of fan mussels with shells a foot or more long. The silk spun by one of these mussels almost suggests a horse's tail. It has been used to make gloves and neck ties, but the quantity has never been sufficient to make such manufactures a business proposition.

LIFE-SPAN OF ANIMALS

MATTER is indestructible, and living matter potentially immortal. If a culture of cells (cells kept in a nutritive medium) is made from the body of a young and healthy animal, cell division takes place. If some time later another culture is made from the new growth, and so on, a part of the original animal can be kept going almost indefinitely—long after the animal itself has died.

But as it happens, no creature can of itself endure, so far as we know, for ever. Sooner or later, the cells of an organism do not necessarily decay, but some one part of the complex structure gives way, the whole is thrown out of gear and death results. Every animal is, so to speak, an unwitting suicide.

TIME-HONOURED FALLACIES EXPOSED

It is only during the last half-century that the subject of the span of life has come under serious consideration. Statistics of the life-spans of animals have been gathered from all quarters, such as zoological gardens, farms, and aquariums, and tabulated. Many arresting facts have recently come to light, and some time-honoured fallacies have been disposed of.

In the first place the life-limits of most wild animals must remain conjectural, and the figures furnished by creatures kept in confinement possibly exceed the normal limits. An animal under human supervision is protected from foes, disease, and all other chances of the wild.

BODILY WEAR AND TEAR

How long the body machine, whether of plant or of animal, will last depends largely upon wear and tear. A big body tends to wear longer than a small one. No animal is known to last longer than such a tree as the giant sequoia, which may outlive twenty centuries. On the other hand no one can place a limit to the potential life span of a sea anemone. One kept in the Nelson family for more than a hundred years shows no great change in size or vigour.

An anemone leads a tranquil life and knows few enemies. A lobster, on the contrary, exposes itself to as many hazards as a medieval musketeer. A giant lobster in the Millport Aquarium is known to be forty-four years old, and begins to show signs of senility. In addition to all the dangers of its own seeking, a lobster exhausts much energy in the periodic casting of its shell, an adventure sometimes costing the crustacean its life.

ELEPHANTS ARE AGED AT FORTY

Reliable records refer, not unnaturally, chiefly to beasts, birds and other creatures commonly kept in captivity. Few of these animals approach civilized man in length of years.

The elephant, though popularly supposed to live well over a century, generally shows signs of age after forty. Whales are often represented, on no particular authority, to far outlive the elephant. This seems questionable, since the elephant seldom becomes a parent before twenty, whereas a whale may do so at two and a half.

The donkey is another creature of alleged longevity, but it rarely survives a quarter of a century. Lions often live in captivity to forty years of age, much longer than an easily worked horse, and three times as long as most domestic cats. Big kangaroos tend to live twice as long as small species, bears twice as long as badgers and ferrets, but the supposed correlation of size and longevity receives another check when we consider dogs. A great dane and a pekinese enjoy practically the same number of years.

AGE IN THE FEATHERED WORLD

Vultures, eagles and owls outlive most other birds. Captive vultures of forty-odd are common, and the feathered age record is held by an eagle owl of seventy.

Poverty of feathers and an overgrown beak are often pointed to as guarantees of great age in parrots. Actually they merely indicate ill-health and neglect. A disreputable specimen once widely advertised in the newspapers as a double centenarian was proved at death to be only thirty-eight.

GREAT BRITAIN'S OLDEST FISHES

A few giant tortoises alone deserve the great ages attributed to them, and a few examples still living are known to have seen fully a century and a half. Reptiles, like fish, tend to grow rapidly for their first few years and then to continue growing with slowly slackening speed through the rest of life. Mammals and birds reach a maximum stature shortly after puberty, and so remain.

Fish, and possibly the shell-bearing molluscs, carry indisputable indications of age in rings of growth. In molluscs these are marked upon the shell, in fishes on the scales and so-called ear bones, the one always corroborating the other. The alleged centuries-old carp, subjected to this test, seldom proves to be much over thirty. Possibly the fungus often covering these fish lends a " rime of age " which earns for them a false reputation. The giant catfish in Woburn Park, Bedfordshire, however, are known to be over sixty, and the sterlets in the London Zoological Gardens are stated on indisputable authority to be forty-six years old. These are the oldest fishes known in Great Britain. Their nearest competitor is an eel in Ross-shire, which has graced a small tank for forty years.

As regards molluscs, the ridges on their shells usually mark where growth stopped for the year, winter being generally a period of relative quiescence. The average oyster brought to table is not more than four years old.

UNDERTAKERS OF THE ANIMAL KINGDOM

There comes a time when the longest-lived animal exhausts its resources. What happens to all the dead? One seldom sees dead animals in the countryside, though there is a noticeable mortality amongst the shrews in autumn, and a particularly hard winter proves fatal to many birds. Wherever the animal falls, Nature soon returns the nitrates and water of its body to the source from whence they came, and employs the dead to create and maintain life anew in the rising generation.

In the sea, bodies disappear even quicker than on land. Over 20,000 minute crustacea have been counted devouring a single dead sea-urchin. The dead which are not eaten sink at varying speeds and stop at varying levels according to their density. The last and heaviest remnants of this rain of dead matter finally reaches deep water, where no plant life can flourish, and feeds creatures which make their way into the blackness of the abyss. Here only a few small but voracious fishes live, alternately starving and gorging according to the mortality far above them.

On the arid plain a camel's bones are picked clean in an hour by jackals and vultures. In the depths of the forest other scavengers take over the same labour. Even the body of a dead elephant presents no problem. The animal, always seeking deepest seclusion wherein to die, attracts countless myriads of keen-scented burying beetles. They shovel away the earth from beneath it, and lay their eggs in the fast-rotting hide. Within a few hours millions of maggots, co-operating with the legion offspring of the flies, are fast reducing the five-ton corpse to a skeleton. Then acids bred of earth and moisture rot the great bones, and the ceaselessly growing vegetation closes over all.

Before long the tusks and a few hard, enamelled teeth, sunk deep in the soil, are all that remain of the largest of living land animals. The following season elephants are browsing on the vegetation nourished by the fallen giant. So life goes on.

CONCERNING THE HUMAN BODY

IT is computed that seven tablets of soap could be made from the fat in a human body weighing ten stone; two nails, each about three-quarters of an inch long, from its iron content; and enough sweetening matter for three cups of coffee from its sugar. Its carbon, converted into graphite, would provide the lead for 9,000 pencils; there is enough calcium to whitewash a fowl-house; and sufficient phosphorus to make 2,200 match-heads. The body produces enough hydrogen and oxygen gases to light the lamps of a street 500 yards long for two hours.

COMPOSITION OF THE HUMAN BODY

If all the spaces between the atoms in the human body were removed, and if its protons and electrons, namely all its smallest particles of substance, were joined together into one mass, it would just be possible to see this substance through a magnifying glass. The substance of a human body is said to be the thousand-millionth part of its volume and to consist of atoms the number of which is expressed by one with twenty-seven ciphers and which, in their multifarious combinations, form a cell-state of eight billion cells.

The human skeleton is composed of 206 bones, moved by means of about 750 striated muscles. A human body weighing approximately nine stone consists of approximately 40,694 grammes of water, 11,357 grammes of carbon, 1,694 grammes of hydrogen, 1,626 grammes of nitrogen, 3,682 grammes of oxygen, and 2,716 grammes of ash-constituents.

While the human body as a whole is sixty-five per cent water, the brain, the spleen and the spinal cord are seventy-five per cent water. Four-fifths of the blood consists of water, and the most watery organ is the vitreous humour of the eye, which is ninety-nine per cent water.

HOTTEST AND COOLEST PARTS OF THE BODY

The hottest parts of the body have been ascertained by means of the electric thermo-needle. The liver and the kidneys register the highest temperature; the heart is about 1°F. cooler, the lungs about 2°F. cooler, and the cerebellum or little brain is only 6°F. cooler.

The temperature of the skin is considerably lower. The instep registers 91°F., the lobes of the ears about 76°F., the tip of the nose about 70°F. If the body did not continuously give off heat, in twenty-four hours its temperature would be 185°F. instead of 98.4°F.

PARTS OF THE BODY LIVE LONGER THAN OTHERS

The length of life enjoyed by the various parts of the body is considerably shorter than that of the organism as a whole. A red blood corpuscle, for example, lives for ten weeks at the longest, a strand of woman's hair three to five years, an eyelash only four weeks.

ORGANS THAT OUTLIVE THE BODY

Dr. Carrell, Colonel C. A. Lindbergh's assistant, maintains that the heart, the kidneys, the glands, the arteries, and other organic parts of the body, when placed in a life chamber (a sterilized receptacle constructed by Colonel Lindbergh), could be kept alive and made to function, outside the body, for many hours (in some cases even days), and also gain in weight.

WORK OF THE LUNGS

Adults breathe sixteen to twenty times a minute, infants and the fever-stricken at a far higher rate.

The quantity of air inhaled per minute by an adult at rest is fourteen to eighteen pints, i.e., about one pint per breath. At a time of muscular exertion, twenty, forty or even eighty pints are inhaled per minute, as a result of the increased rate and depth of respiration. When completely unfolded, the total functional area of the lungs would cover an area of 156 square yards, sufficient standing room for 500 persons. During his lifetime a person sixty years old has drawn about 508,000,000 breaths, conveying into his lungs 9,600,000 cubic feet of air.

MAN'S STATURE

The weight of an ovum is only .004 gramme, whereas that of the fully-grown body averages out at about ten stone. Man decreases in stature after his thirtieth year; and after his sixtieth year in weight also.

The average Englishman is 5 ft. 7¼ in. high and weighs 11 st. 1 lb. The average Irishman is taller, 5 ft. 8 in., but weighs 2 lb. less. The tallest inhabitants of the British Isles are Scotsmen, who average 5 ft. 8¾ in., and weigh 11 st. 11 lb., and the shortest are Welshmen, who average 5 ft. 6½ in. and weigh 11 st. 4 lb.

The tallest men in Europe are to be found in Scandinavia; the tallest in the world in Africa, where also are found the shortest—the pygmies.

HUMAN BODY AS ELECTRIC POWER-HOUSE

An English scientist states that the body is covered with a network of " living dynamos " supplying the brain, the nerves, the muscles, and the heart with electric current, which in its turn acts as the connecting link between mental " orders " and corporeal reaction. These " living dynamos," says the scientist, are gigantic molecules (34,000-5,000,000 times larger than atoms of hydrogen), which form protein, the chief constituent of protoplasm. They are like magnets, the ends of which, loaded positively or negatively, may be termed bipolar ions (elementary particles electrically charged).

Something the nature of which has not yet been discovered, brings about the discharge of the positive pole of the dynamo, whereupon the negative load immediately moves towards the discharged pole of the adjoining molecule. Thus a regular current runs along the whole chain of dynamos, resulting in a muscular contraction. Other effects of the stimulus given by electric currents are the secretion of glandular fluids and the transmission of nerve-impulses.

The amount of heat given off by a man is almost ten per cent more than that given off by a woman. When standing, the human being gives off ten per cent more heat than when sleeping; when walking briskly, 200 per cent more; and when in violent exertion 560 per cent more. After a meal the emission of heat increases by forty per cent, during mental exertion by four per cent.

LIMITS OF TEMPERATURE

Professor Chaubert is said to have stayed on several occasions in a room heated to a temperature of 260°C. The oven in which the English sculptor Chantrey dried his moulds was heated to 174°C., nevertheless his workmen went in and out of its compartments with nothing on but wooden shoes. Some of them, however, felt a violent pricking in the lobes of their ears and in their eyes.

The lowest degree of cold ever measured was that recorded by the Polar explorer Schwatka, when leading an expedition in the track of Franklin's. One day in January he noticed that the thermometer registered 75°C. below zero. Undeterred, he continued to move his camp twelve miles further north every day.

HOW LONG CAN A MAN SLEEP?

The Cretan philosopher Epimenides is supposed, when looking for one of his father's sheep, to have slept in a cave for seventy-five years and then to have lived in the normal way until he died in his 137th year. This, however, is doubtless only one of the improbable stories for which the Cretans were notorious. A man of the name of Horms slept almost uninterruptedly for thirty years in his cottage near St. Charles in Minnesota, U.S.A. When his long sleep began his weight was fourteen stone; on waking, he weighed only about six stone. A railway pointsman from Dresden went to sleep for eighteen years after an accident. He died in 1899.

During an eight-hour sleep the human being changes his position at least thirty-five times. The shortest period of sleep is that which follows immediately after losing consciousness; it lasts fourteen minutes. The second and third periods are more intensive. A former national insurance official of Budapest was shot in the temple during the World War and since then has not been able to get a minute's sleep. His brain, as well as his other organs, have functioned normally with no sign of fatigue. Ordinarily, eighty-four hours is the longest period during which a person can keep awake.

HOW LONG IS IT POSSIBLE TO FAST?

In 1920, during the Irish struggle for independence, Terence MacSwiney, the Republican leader and Lord Mayor of Cork, on being sentenced to two years' imprisonment, went on a hunger-strike which terminated with his death seventy-five days after it began. In 1933, M. K. Gandhi, the *Mahatma* (Great Soul), fasted for three weeks, and very narrowly escaped death as a result. The New Testament tells us that Jesus fasted for forty days and forty nights.

It is said that in the latter part of her life, St. Rose of Lima took only a little bread and water daily. It is also reported that when she was "fasting" St. Rose ate orange pips instead of bread, and on Fridays only five of these. Towards the end of her life she shut herself up from Thursday to Sunday and ate nothing but the bitter leaves of the passion flower.

MAN'S SURPLUS GERM CELLS

From time to time publicists make much of the 2,000,000 surplus women. By this is meant that in Great Britain 2,000,000 women are unlikely to marry. How many realize that in another sphere there is a disparity between males and females, with the latter in an unsuccessful minority, which makes the two million figure extremely small? This disparity relates to the germ cells maturing in men and women after puberty has been reached.

In the female the eggs, or ova, go through their stages of development in what are known as the follicles of the ovaries. These are tiny pouches which at birth number some 70,000. When a girl has reached the age of eight she has lost about 30,000 of these. Of the remaining 40,000 approximately 200 survive to become true Graafian follicles. Every lunar month during the years between puberty and the menopause or climacteric, one of these Graafian follicles, in which one ovum reposes, comes to maturity, breaks through the walls of the ovary and reaches the Fallopian tubes. The Fallopian tubes are two canals, one on each side running from the uterus to the ovary itself. The figure then, for female germ cells, is one per month. In the same period the spermatozoa developed by a man reach the amazing total of (in round figures) 850,000,000,000.

HOW MANY CHILDREN CAN A MAN HAVE?

Tradition has it that Augustus the Strong, Elector of Saxony and King of Poland, had 350 children by his numerous mistresses. A Canadian living on Rhode Island had forty-one children as the issue of his three legal unions. His first wife repeatedly gave birth to twins, and on three occasions his second wife presented him with triplets. Thirty-six of these children survived.

At a census of large families in Italy in 1928, it was ascertained that a peasant living in Trettori, near Avellino, had thirty illegitimate children, twenty-six of whom were still living. In Canada an ordinary number of children per family is eight to ten, but eighteen children are not unusual, and sometimes twenty-five or more are born of one mother. It is not uncommon for five generations to be living simultaneously.

SEX DETERMINATION

According to the theory expounded by Professor M. Hartmann in 1935, the sex of all the higher animals is determined at the moment of fertilization.

The female, he says, has only one kind of ovum, which contains a female-forming factor. The male, however, has two kinds of sperm, some of which contain female-forming factors, while the others contain male-forming factors. When an ovum meets with a sperm which contains a female factor, the newly formed germ receives two female inheritors, the female substance predominates, and the result is a girl. When the ovum meets a sperm with a male factor a boy results.

FATHERS UNRELATED TO SONS

In many South Sea Islands a father is not reckoned to be a blood relation of his child. Because pregnancy lasts nine months the islanders do not connect the birth with any act which preceded it. When white men have attempted to give the Melanesians elementary education in these matters, the natives have refused to believe in the facts. Moreover, they have offered evidence to show that they, and not the whites, are correct.

They rendered their boars incapable of procreating but the sows farrowed. This greatly perplexed the investigators until they made the discovery that it was the practice for the sows to be allowed to root in the bush. Here they were mated with wild boars.

SKIN'S TWO MILLION PORES

The skin has approximately 2,000,000 pores—sweat glands, as they are called. In other words, each square inch of the skin averages some 500 of these. The palms and the soles of the feet have four times as many: 2,000 to the square inch. On a temperate day in summer a man or woman doing the least strenuous kind of work will rid himself of a quart of moisture, all of which except for one per cent of salt and a trace of urea, is water.

In very rare instances men are born without sweat glands. These unfortunates develop a temperature of 100 degrees and over on a hot day, or on any day when they work strenuously. Cases have been recorded when work of the lightest nature performed by a person lacking sweat glands has resulted in a temperature of 105 degrees.

SHIVER AND GET WARM

The skin has hot and cold points. The precise function of these is not yet known. If a breeze blowing on a bather's body makes the temperature of the latter fall below sixty degrees, the bather shivers. This is because the cold points have responded to stimulus, and set the muscles shivering. This shivering creates heat.

If a man immerses all but his head in a bath of water heated to 104 degrees, sweat breaks out on his forehead. If he then plunges one of his hands in a bowl of cold water, his forehead no longer sweats. The reason for this is that nerves leading to the sweat glands regulate the secretion of sweat; that in this instance the nerves running to the cold points of the skin make a greater response to the stimulus of the cold water than the hot points to the hot water.

HANDICAPS OF THE HORNY HANDED

For the scientifically minded there are many experiments which may be performed in the guise of parlour games. In these, children and those whose ordinary interest in science is small will willingly take part. Take, for example, a pound of lead shot, or screws, or nails. Ask a number of guests to put as much into their right hands as will weigh an ounce. In most cases, anything from one and a quarter ounces to two ounces will be the quantities taken.

Vary this by asking those taking part to put enough screws or shot into a box to make both contents and box two ounces. Normally a still greater error is made. When, however, the weight asked for is half a pound or a pound, the error is considerably smaller. Adults, at least, are accustomed to dealing with half-pounds of tea or pounds of butter.

The conclusion to be drawn from such tests is this: the sensations registered by the skin are of use when sense-judgments are made. For this reason a masseuse, for example, is likely to make such judgments more accurately than a horny-handed navvy; a doctor than a motor mechanic; a girl cashier than a scullery maid.

FAIR HAIR BECOMING RARE

In parts of France, in Germany, and in what once was Austria, the fair-haired are becoming fewer. In America, also, this holds good.

Mr. T. M. Baxter, statistical worker in the latter continent, concludes that among the dark-haired there is less liability than among those of fair hair to suffer permanent ill-effects from most diseases. Women with darker hair and darker eyes are more numerous than similarly dark men.

HAIRS GROW IN SETS

When a child kisses the downy cheek of its mother, it is unaware that in her fourth embryonic month that mother was, like itself, covered with such down. *Lanugo* as it is called, is the first fur coat a man or woman wears. Sometimes before, and always after birth, this, in the case of men and many women has been replaced by another and different coat. In some women *lanugo* is still found upon the cheeks.

"As numerous as the hairs on the head" is an expression not uncommon in the Bible. It has been left to the modern scientist to discover that both on the head and on the body hairs grow in sets of from three to five. These are a survival from our reptilian ancestry. Our remote progenitors had three, four or five hairs springing from beneath each scale of their scaly bodies.

FEELING THE WAY WITH WHISKERS

As cats today, so probably men in their sub-human past, felt their way by means of whiskers, or *vibrissæ*. The hairs of the brows and those that grow in the ears are, it is thought, variants of the whiskers from which they have descended.

More or less unaltered *vibrissæ* often appear, usually not till after men have reached their prime, as coarse, stiff hairs longer than their fellows, in the brows. With some unfortunates these sometimes grow in the ears and on the end of the nose.

WHY HAIR TURNS WHITE

It was the prisoner of Chillon who, if Byron be believed, found that his hair had turned white between dusk and dawn. Blonde or brunette, red or auburn, all hair turns white in the end, provided the owners retain their tresses.

There is no pigment in the hair of a white rat. Its whiteness comes from numerous tiny gas globules which, found in the hair, reflect the light. So it is with the Common White, that butterfly which gets its whiteness because of the reflection from infinitely small particles of uric acid—an excess of which gives humans such trouble.

And so with many birds and beasts. The brown stoat becomes the white ermine in the winter of northern latitudes. A ptarmigan in winter time gets its whiteness similarly. In man the hair grows first grey and then white with the onset of the years because, as the new hair grows, it is deficient in pigment and finally almost devoid of it. In the case of the prisoner of Chillon, however, as with every man or woman whose hair has been turned white by shock in a few hours, it is the sudden and excessive production of bubbles of gas. These cover the pigment beneath them.

REVEALED BY FINGERS

Women of all kinds and in all ages have sought to beautify their hands. Poets of every country and every century have lauded the loveliness of the hands of their beloved. In our own time fortunes are made as well as told, from hands. Yet whatever manufacturers of beauty preparations may place on the market, and whatever women may do to enhance the beauty of their hands, the structure of those hands remains unaltered.

Anthropoid apes, almost all negroes and many men have this in common : the index finger is shorter than the ring finger. In most women the index is longer than the ring finger. It is this which makes the shape of a woman's hand æsthetically more pleasing than a man's. Short thumbs belong to the earlier stages of evolution. To right the balance as between man and woman, the longer the index finger the more superior normally is the evolutionary stage. Pfitzer and others have advanced the theory that woman's longer index is due to the fact that she uses her forefinger more frequently than a man to gesticulate.

NATURE'S FOOT RULE

Most men have elongated feet with long and well-developed middle phalanges; while most women have shortened feet whose middle phalanges are shorter and not so finely made.

As men have longer thumbs, so they have, as a general rule, longer great toes than women. Relatively as well as absolutely longer, that is. Increased length of great toe and thumb is a recently acquired characteristic of the human race.

LITTLE TOES STILL LITTLER?

Unlike the outer toes and fingers which have three bones and are triple jointed, the great toe and the thumb have only two bones and are double jointed. Research shows that in an increasing number of cases the little toe also tends to have only two joints. In these the middle and end phalanges have become fused.

Investigation has revealed that while four out of every ten women have the two joints thus fused, this is true of only three out of every ten men.

DOUBLE-JOINTEDNESS

People who are " double-jointed " have a wider space between the first two toes as well as greater flexibility in the toes themselves. This condition is found in one out of every ten men, but in roughly three out of every ten women.

This is the more remarkable in that women rather than men tend to wear the narrow shoes demanded by fashion, and hence cramp their feet. Epileptics and idiots are, like members of the less-developed races, in many cases notably double-jointed.

CHILD'S FIRST CRY

A monkey weeps, an anthropoid ape shows all the signs of grief but sheds no tears. Elephants, as befits their size, weep copiously. Most human children do not really cry in the ordinary sense of the term before they are three months old.

Darwin's explanation of the origin of a child's first tears has yet to be overthrown. In brief it is this: When a child howls with hunger, or screams with rage, the blood vessels in the eye become gorged with blood. Muscles near the eye are affected by this; they contract, the lachrymal glands respond, tears are secreted in several ducts on the inner side of the upper eyelid, some of these fall by way of an aperture in the lower eyelid, through the lachrymal sac, into the nasal passages; others trickle down the cheeks.

GROWTH OF CHILDREN

In the second year of life the rate of increase in weight rises in the period September-December, sinks in January-April, and ceases almost entirely in May-August. With regard to increase in height the situation is very different: the maximum increase takes place in the period April-August.

At five years of age boys are usually taller than girls, at seven years the two sexes are equal. From their ninth to their twelfth year boys again grow more quickly, but they are overtaken by the girls between the ages of thirteen and fifteen. After fifteen the male sex retains its superiority in the further development of the body.

GROWTH OF HAIR AND NAILS

Children's nails grow more quickly than those of adults. For their complete renewal they need in winter a period of 132 days, in summer only 116 days. The nails of the left hand need ten days more than those of the right.

The hair on the chin of a man who shaves grows, as a rule, 3/25ths in. weekly, or about six inches yearly, so that an octogenarian who has been shaving for sixty years has grown the equivalent of a beard ten yards long.

ADULT AND INFANT

The human adult has a head only twice the length of the head at birth. The trunk of the adult almost triples itself, the arms are nearly four times as long, and the legs five times, in respect to the corresponding measurements at birth.

PRECOCITY THAT PETERS OUT

The runner in a long-distance race who starts with a fast sprint is usually the first to fall behind after a couple of hundred yards. Equally, in the race of life whose full span is some seventy years, the mental sprinter usually falls behind his slower-starting competitors. The child genius rarely stays the course, and before middle age is usually a mediocrity.

Among white peoples, however, the precocious child by no means always fades away into intellectual torpidity. But among coloured peoples, this is the general rule. The Australian aborigines, the Fantis and many other American tribes, the Cambodians and the Eskimos are often remarkably intelligent till they reach the age of fourteen. From puberty onwards there is a swift decline in intelligence. In this connexion it is of interest to note that the anthropoid apes, when young, are markedly more human in appearance and behaviour than they become in mature years.

THINGS WE GROW OUT OF

Many are sleepwalkers in childhood who in adult years are rarely or never subject to somnambulism. In this condition the higher centres are asleep while the motor centres function in response to stimuli.

The kind of sleep which hypnotism induces provides another illustration of the fact that what holds true of infancy does not necessarily obtain in maturity. Although the figures are in dispute, it is beyond doubt that children are more easily hypnotized than adults. Again, children generally recover more quickly than grown-ups from anæsthetics, and suffer fewer ill-effects from its administration.

SINS AND VIRTUES OF THE FATHERS

How far are those coming from tainted stock responsible for actions in the ordinary sense? American investigators have traced the records of the descendants of a woman alive in 1740, whose manner of life was thoroughly disreputable. In 1935 these descendants totalled 2,820. In 1915 of the 1,250 then alive, 464 were prostitutes, 118 criminals, 170 mendicants, 129 workhouse inmates and 181 habitual drunkards. Many of the rest were weak-minded in varying degrees.

Now for the other side of the question. Jonathan Edwards, the famous speaker and writer, in 1900 had 1,394 descendants. Of the men, 13 were university presidents, 65 university professors, 60 doctors, 60 authors of some standing, 130 lawyers, 75 army officers, 100 clergymen, and 80 who had held high official positions of various kinds. Plainly, it is more advantageous to come of good stock than to be born with the proverbial silver spoon.

TELEPHONE EXCHANGE OF THE BODY

Human brains vary considerably in weight. Among the more obvious weight-controlling factors are size of body, sex, age and race. Tall men generally have bigger brains than small men, and the average woman has a smaller brain than the average man because her whole body is smaller than the man's.

BRAIN-GROWTH IS NOT STEADY

A baby's brain is only a quarter the weight of that of an adult. During the first three years of life brain-growth is rapid; during the next four much slower; and slower still during the next thirteen years. At the age of twenty the brain attains its maximum weight. Thereafter it steadily loses about one gramme a year. The " average man " of one nation may be larger or smaller than the typical specimen of another, and brain sizes differ in the same way. The brain of a full-grown British male weighs approximately 49.6 ounces (1,409 grammes); that of his wife 44.5 ounces (1,263 grammes). If it falls short of 32 ounces its owner is an imbecile.

STRUCTURE MORE IMPORTANT THAN SIZE

It is generally accepted that large brains do not necessarily indicate great mental ability. Many men of exceptional capacity have had large brains while others, equally eminent, have had comparatively small ones. As an index of capacity, structure is more important than size. It is generally true to say, that the more highly-developed a brain is the more numerous and intricate are its convolutions. The surfaces of the brains of reptiles and birds—animals of very low mentality—are almost smooth; those of cats, dogs and monkeys—animals possessing a comparatively high degree of intelligence—are slightly convoluted; while those of man are very considerably convoluted.

Ivan Turgenev, the Russian author, had a brain which weighed over 2,000 grammes; Baron Cuvier, the French naturalist, had one of 1,830 grammes; Byron, the English poet, one of 1,807 grammes. All these were above the average in size. But the brain of Anatole France, the French novelist, weighed only 1,017 grammes; that of Schiller, the German poet, 1,580 grammes. Other distinguished men with light brains were Jonathan Swift, the Irish satirist; Robert Wilhelm Bunsen, the German inventor of the Bunsen burner; Menzel, the German artist; and Baron Justus von Liebig, the German chemist.

The brain-case of a gorilla measures 550 cubic centimetres, that of the ape-man of Java, 880 cubic centimetres; that of the Australian aboriginal, 1,200 cubic centimetres; and that of the " typical " European, 1,481 cubic centimetres. Dr. H. L. Gordon, who examined the cranial capacities of 3,444 natives of Kenya, discovered that the average cubic capacity of the adult male native is 1,316 cubic centimetres. The brains of 100 normal adult male natives weighed, on an average, 150 grammes less than the European average. This figure also represents the difference in weight between the average male and female brain of English adults.

A brain of 48 ounces is composed of about 14,000,000,000 nerve-cells or neurons, according to Professor Constantin Economo, and it was discovered by Professor Adolphe of the University of Rochester, U.S.A., that whereas all the other cells of the human body continually renew themselves, those of the brain remain unchanged. According to Sir Arthur Keith, " not one person in fifty uses his or her brain to half of its real capacity."

BRAIN MAY NOT BE THE CENTRE OF THOUGHT

In 1934, Professors Hagen, Hartmann and Schmick made a joint pronouncement that the brain was not to be regarded as an independent organ but as a mere basis for the functioning of an entity which is fundamentally distinct from matter.

In October, 1936, the Swedish brain-surgeon, Professor Olivecrona, declared that the supreme centre of the intellect was just as much unknown to the medical world as it had ever been. He was inclined to think that the " centre of intellect " was not in the brain, and that perhaps it was not physically present at all.

FISHING IN THE SEA OF THOUGHT

The bran-tub and similar devices have for many years played their part in giving amusement at parties. Just as diverting and considerably more instructive is what might be called the psychological bran-tub game. Fish for words in the bran-tub of the mind. This can be done

most simply. Ask four friends to write on slips of paper a given number
of nouns—twenty-five will do. Note the time they take to do this—for
then two experimental birds can be killed with one stone.

When the lists are complete, make an analysis of the words to be
found in them. This analysis can take many forms. Most will be
surprised to discover that almost certainly the majority of the total
number of words will appear on two or more of the lists. Whatever
men's occupations, they have a community of thought which outweighs
the differences that the daily round imposes on them. Note the nature
of the words listed; note too the dominant differences in those made by
women and those made by men. In the second the abstract will figure
more largely.

For mere amusement's sake get a friend to deduce character from this
lot or that. Thus, if Miss A's contains the list of a dozen fabrics, and
of various articles of clothing, an interest in personal adornment is fairly
plain. If Mr. B's, a score of foodstuffs and the names of half a dozen
drinks, this is probably a self-revelation made by his unconscious rather
than by his conscious mind.

SPEED OF NERVE IMPULSES

It has been estimated that a nerve impulse (a sense-impression
travelling to the brain) is conducted by the nerves at a speed of 115-265
feet per second. Hermann von Helmholtz discovered that the time taken
by a human being to react to an external stimulus is, on an average,
one-fifth of a second. The error in timing which is made, for instance,
in failing to catch a ball, amounts to about one-thirtieth of a second.

The virtuoso in violin- or piano-playing can execute ten to fifteen
distinct but systematically successive movements per second. The
professional speaker performs thirty movements of the speech organs
per second.

BLINKS IN THE MAKING

Despite the well-known scriptural passage, it is seldom necessary to
remove a mote from your brother's eye. Eyes are for ever being assailed
by motes; and motes, or the effect of them, are for ever being removed
by blinking.

Blinking is a reflex action. A mote is a stimulus exciting the eye. A
nerve-ending registered that excitation; a nerve conveyed it to the central
nervous system; the latter sent a message by a second nerve to the
muscles of the eyelid. Those muscles contracted. Their contraction, in
popular language, is a blink.

ACTIONS WE ARE NOT RESPONSIBLE FOR

Reflexes come by inheritance. The reflex which enables the hand to
grasp is present at birth. Within an hour of being born children have
been known to support the full weight of their bodies by grasping some
suitable object. It is thought that this is true of every normal child and

that this faculty may be a relic of those ancestors who swung from tree to tree to avoid the many dangers on the ground.

Every child can close its eyes on and after the day of its birth. Sucking and swallowing are reflexes that are as old as the man possessing them. Blinking does not begin until the third month.

HOW FRIGHT PARALYSES

A heroine rarely gets to the last page of a novelette without in the previous pages having been " paralysed by fright." Novelette writers often sin against every literary canon, but in this statement, at least, they are scientifically sound. Whether it is the villain's dishonourable suggestions, or the crook's threats, or the wild beast's threatened spring, the poor girl does, in fact, outside as well as inside the cover of novelettes, suffer a kind of paralysis. That paralysis is the result of fear. Fear, if sufficiently intense, is an emotion that temporarily deranges the nervous system. For a very brief space the heart will often cease to beat. As a result the brain lacks its ordinary blood supply.

It is for this reason that a rabbit will squat, unable to move, while a stoat creeps upon it; why a bird will allow a snake to dart upon it without stirring a wing feather; why a deer will sometimes remain in its lurking-place, motionless, although it is aware that its enemy has seen and is stalking it. So with the heroine.

That other novelettish phrase, " She fell as if her limbs were stone," is not by any means an inadequate description of all but petrification that occurs in man or beast when the emotion of fear is strong enough. A lamb or a sheep, if badly scared, can be lifted from the ground, when the animal's legs are found to be stiff, almost as if it were dead.

MADDENING AURORA

It has been discovered that where aurora borealis is, there for western Europeans lies, if not madness, at least nervous disturbance.

The Soviet Union has sought to cultivate that part of Siberia which lies within the Arctic Circle. Medical men went with settlers, and examined them at intervals to discover how the climate was affecting them. They ascertained that from twenty-four to forty-eight hours before the onset of a magnetic Arctic storm, the heartbeats of the colonists dropped till the ordinary rhythm was almost halved. The nervous system was compelled to make the necessary adjustment, and hence the sense of nerve tension which in extreme cases—and they are not rare, as any will know who have read biographies of the great Arctic explorers—ends in that condition which is called Arctic hysteria.

BRAIN AS CHEMICAL FACTORY

The brain-substance contains ammonia, which is formed by the activity of every organ, especially the muscles. It has been discovered from experiments made on persons who had just died that the ammonia content of the brain depends on the intensity of the brain's activity. In the case of dead epileptics the ammonia content was found to be double that of others.

Ammonia is plainly a chemical product of cerebral activity and of the active metabolism or chemical change of the brain-cells which takes place as the result of thought.

WONDERS OF HEART AND BLOOD

THE most efficient motor in the world is the heart. This machine never stops work so long as life lasts. It performs approximately 3,000,000,000 pumping actions over a period of seventy years. Every contraction takes .085 second, every dilatation .1 second, every interval for rest .4 second.

PUMP THAT NEVER CEASES WORK

The weight of the heart is about ten ounces. The daily work performed by it is equivalent to the energy required to lift a load of 40,000 pounds one yard, or an elevator containing three persons 100 yards.

Every twenty-four hours it dispatches into the circulatory system over 20,000 pints of blood. In doing this it uses about five per cent of the total energy conveyed to it, an amount that, converted into carbohydrates, is equivalent to about one ounce of sugar. The heart, therefore, could cover the energy requirement for its colossal task with six lumps of sugar.

VARIATIONS IN HEART-BEATS

The number of heart-beats per minute varies according to the size and, in the case of human beings, the age of the creature. The smaller the creature the quicker its pulse. Thus the heart of a sparrow beats 800 times a minute, that of a mouse 600, that of a rabbit 150, and that of a horse only forty times a minute. A human being's pulse is about 135 when newly born, 111 in its first year, 96 in its sixth year, 80 in its sixteenth year, 72 when fully grown, and only about 60 after its fiftieth year.

Napoleon's pulse beat only forty times a minute, and Justinus Kerner, the famous doctor and poet, could make his pulse beat faster or slower at will.

MILES OF VEINS AND ARTERIES

The veins and arteries of the human body, put end to end, would stretch for 350,000 miles, or fourteen times the circumference of the earth.

The human protoplasm or living matter is made up of twenty-five ingredients, which makes possible two and a half trillion combinations, The whole organism of the body consists of eight billion cells, all of which have developed from a single cell.

CIRCULATION OF THE BLOOD

The circulation of the blood was discovered by the English physician, William Harvey, about 1616; but he found himself unable to answer the question, "How is the blood conveyed from the arteries to the veins?"

The existence of the capillaries, the minute blood vessels that connect the arteries to the veins, was demonstrated with the aid of the microscope by Marcello Malpighi (1628-94), for many years lecturer on medicine at the University of Bologna. He found the first clue to their existence in a frog's lung. He also detected the existence of the red blood corpuscles. Other gaps in Harvey's account of the blood stream were filled in by Anthony van Leeuwenhoek (1632-1723), who is chiefly renowned as the first man to draw pictures of bacteria.

The amount of blood in the human body is equal to about five per cent of the total weight; the average man weighing something in the region of ten stone has about seven pounds of blood. In the whole body there are about thirty million red blood corpuscles, and about fifty million white. The blood freezes at a temperature of $\frac{1}{2}$ °C. and is destroyed at a temperature of $+60$°C. The extent to which the blood penetrates the various parts of the body is not everywhere the same.

In 1935, Professor Judin successfully carried out, for medical purposes, transfusions of blood from a dead body. Such blood, when unprotected, must not be more than six hours old, but if kept in sterilized receptacles it retains its virtue for three weeks and may be used at any time during that period.

FOUR BLOOD GROUPS

There is mention of the four human blood groups in a Chinese book of 1247, but it was not until 1900 that their existence was first scientifically demonstrated, in the Rockefeller Institute in New York.

Every living person belongs to one of these four groups, and it is a demonstrable fact that the individual's membership of one or other of them is not mere chance but that the groups are transmitted from generation to generation in accordance with a well-defined system. The stability of the blood groups has recently been demonstrated anew by Professor Thomsen of Copenhagen.

BLOOD AND DESTINY

The epoch-making discovery of the blood groups has led to conclusions the importance of which can hardly be realized by the layman. Professor Breitner of Vienna is of the opinion that the force that causes the blood corpuscles to adhere to each other controls the human life-curve, the greater or lesser expectation of life.

It would seem that membership of some of the groups connotes a greater expectation of life than membership of the others. But this strange force is inconstant. At present the best-known use of the knowledge of blood groups is in cases of disputed paternity.

FOR AND AGAINST TOBACCO

The pulse rate of smokers averages ten beats more a minute than non-smokers, because of the increase in the blood pressure due to the smoking.

When in the 17th century the plague was stalking through London and most parts of England, the boys at Eton were encouraged to smoke, since this was held to be a safeguard against the prevailing infection. Everywhere in the large towns and villages women and children smoked to keep the plague away. Modern research has shown slight anti-bacterial properties in tobacco smoke, but very much less than was believed in 1660.

In the past tobacco was often injected by means of an enema syringe in cases of dislocation. The effect was to decrease muscular spasm, and so to effect reduction of the dislocation. Tobacco was also used as an antiseptic in cases of wounds and ulcers. It was then applied externally, as it was to sufferers from various skin diseases, and to those who had cancer. After operations it was applied in order to relieve pain. Similarly it was held to relieve rheumatism, and intestinal trouble was treated by the application of tobacco to the nearest outward part. Present-day research goes to show that tobacco can, in fact, be absorbed by the skin. It finds, too, that bronchial asthma can be lessened by smoking tobacco.

FUEL FOR THE BODY FURNACE

THE food consumed by a human being in seventy years amounts to 44,000 pints of liquids, 265 cwt. of bread, 8,000 lb. of meat, 12,000 eggs, and 50 cwt. of vegetables—a total equalling the contents of twenty-five one-ton lorries.

WEALTH OUT OF WEEDS

Weeds and their uses are best illustrated by reference to wheat. In recent years the wheat field has seen more triumphs for science—and for humanity—than any battlefield. Genetics—the scientific study of heredity—is the baby of the sciences. Yet even so it has helped to feed human babies in ways of which, until recently, man had not dreamed. Fed them, both directly and, through the mothers that bear them and the fathers that are breadwinners for them, indirectly.

Wheat-crossing has been the magic making this possible; geneticists have been the magicians. As a result, a variety of wheat has been grown that ripens more quickly than any known to the world before. Naturally enough, with their sub-Arctic prairie lands to develop, the Russians have been some of the most prominent in the discoveries that have been made in this field—in the genetics field first as in the wheat field second. One Russian wheat ripens and can be cut in eleven weeks.

Nor is that the only kind of cross or the only kind of successful adaptation of Nature to the needs of mankind which geneticists have recently put to their credit and humanity's. For thin soils, wheats have been grown which can dispense with the richness of, for example, the good earth of East Anglia. Short-stalked wheats likewise are now grown that can face beating rain and violent wind without being too badly beaten down.

North Canada, northern Russia, the land of the Lapps, in some instances even the land of the Eskimos—all these either are already bearing wheat crops or will shortly do so. Against the debit that science shows in its inventions of newer and more horrible poison gases, is this credit of making not one, but many millions of wheat blades grow where no wheat blade grew before.

It has been left to one of those eminent men who are responsible for creating a number of scientific revolutions in Russia to take these triumphs of the wheat field one stage further still. Dr. T. Z. Tzitsin has discovered that it is possible to cross wheat with that coarsest and most vigorous and, hitherto, most reprehensible of grasses—the couch grass. A time may come when the couch fire, which has delighted the nostrils of many generations of Englishmen, will be a punishable offence.

Couch grass wheat gives weightier grain heads than any pure wheat has so far done. Moreover, a bushel of it produces more flour than a bushel of wheat as wheat. More notable still, it is not only heavy in its yield, it is perennial in its nature. Lastly, its roots are thick and matted. Because of this they hold the soil together and retain the moisture which the roots of pure wheat allow to escape them.

Weed-wheat has a rival in grass-milk. Two Americans have fed laboratory rats on a mixture of milk and juice pressed from ordinary green grass. The rats increased in weight and vitality. The latest records go to show that the vitamin content of milk can be increased by the addition of grass juice.

FRESH MILK—SIX WEEKS OLD

Milk, with or without grass juice, has a rich body-building content. Milk quickly turns sour. Sour milk may be as good for health as enthusiasts of it claim, yet for the majority its taste is repugnant. For centuries scientists have made use of the vacuum; recently they have put at the disposal of the dairy still one more use.

Milk is now ordinarily bottled. It can be—and often is—sealed in bottles with caps. If a jet of steam is puffed into the mouth of the bottle immediately before the cap falls into position, hermetically sealing the milk, that steam shortly afterwards condenses. A vacuum is formed, and, set in a refrigerator, the milk remains fresh for six weeks.

TANKS—AND TANKS

California has supplied the genius responsible for the first steps taken in the new agriculture—Agrobiology, as it is called. The man to whom the world may, in the end, owe its preservation is Professor Gerike.

The professor has set out to produce tropical or sub-tropical conditions with all the immense fecundity found in tropics or sub-tropics, in lands where the climate is temperate. Bottles of chemicals are set, each in a shallow water-filled tank. Electric wires, running through the water, keep the latter just warm. A wire-netting mesh holding fibre or moss or even sawdust supports the seeds over the bottles of chemicals.

And the results? They are the kind to be met with in the story of *Jack and the Beanstalk*, rather than in prosaic everyday life. From one water acre—tank acre—Professor Gerike has raised 75 tons of potatoes; and from the same area 217 tons of tomatoes.

BUTTER NOT GUNS

There are some who wish this business of food—whether choosing, cooking or eating—could be simplified by taking a capsule once so often. But if a person is not interested in food, either he is ill or he is unintelligent, for not to aim at eating such food as will keep the body in good working order is deliberately to neglect a good machine. One may not live to eat, but at least one must eat to live.

To live. Not merely to exist. Adequate nutrition is not a cure-all, but it has been established that when animals are inadequately nourished, but otherwise have good living conditions, they fall very readily to infection and recover slowly. Similarly this is true for man. It has been found that where a congested area in a town has been cleared and where the occupants have been transferred to a healthy spot in the suburbs, the health of that population has tended to go down. That seems a paradox. Fresh air, sunlight, clean open spaces the people now had. But now they had heavier train and bus fares—consequently less money available for food.

This does not mean that cheap foods are of little value. Many of them are of great nutritional value—brown bread, herrings, pulses and oatmeal, to take but a few at random. It does not mean either that a rich man automatically has the right kind of food because he need not limit the amount of money spent on it. Many rich men have a bad diet, and many rich men are in poor health.

What is required, then, is some understanding of what kinds of food give the best results for health.

Biologists have worked out that there are some forty-odd raw materials which the human body needs for its well-being. This sounds rather alarming. But, luckily, it is not necessary to know about the forty, for a good diet falls roughly into three large classes, which nearly everyone has some knowledge of. Roughly speaking these may be termed energy-producing or fuel foods; body-building foods and protecting foods.

In the first class, of which men who do heavy manual work will need more than any other section, we get such foods as contain fats, starch and sugars. The second class for body-building and repairing—growing children will need almost as much as an adult—is made up of those foods containing protein. Meat, milk, eggs, cheese, fish, peas, beans, lentils, nuts all come into the second class. The third class, protective or protecting foods, contains those mysterious, much abused and much-talked-of vitamins. Protective foods help the body to make up for the deficiencies in the rest of the diet. Nursing mothers, pregnant women and young children have a special need of this third class of foods, which are drawn from dairy products, green vegetables and salads and fruits and fat fish such as herrings.

MAN HIS OWN GRAVE-DIGGER

"You dig your grave with your teeth." The genius of our forefathers invented that striking proverb, which states in homely fashion a great scientific truth. Many people die before their natural span is complete as the result of excessive eating. It is difficult to collect statistics on such a matter as this. Men and women have very varying ideas as to what constitutes moderation in eating. But it is a safe generalization to say that so far as can be ascertained, most centenarians have been small eaters.

To Solomon's "Go to the ant, thou sluggard" there might well be a pendant exhortation : "Go to the worm, you glutton." This in more senses than one. If the man who overeats will take example from dieting experiments performed on planarian worms, he will moderate his eating, and live longer in consequence. For it has been found that planarian worms, when they have come to the term of their ordinary existence, can be rejuvenated by being semi-starved. Whether semi-starvation is a price worth paying for a few more years of life is another issue, and one which everyone must decide for himself.

INVALIDS AS WEIGHT LIFTERS

Calvin Coolidge, one-time president of the United States, was known as "Silent Cal." The silent calorie is, where energy is concerned, the chief executive of the White House of the body. What is a calorie? It is the heat necessary to raise one kilogram (approximately one quart) of water through one degree centigrade.

In the human body sugar is the great calorie manufacturer. The liver and the muscles are the principal storage rooms of the reserves kept that the body may draw on energy at the bidding of the brain.

The invalid, who, in convalescence, spends twenty-four hours each day lying on his back in a position of rest, uses up 1,700 calories in doing the work necessary to keep the heart beating, the lungs working, and the body at a fairly constant temperature.

The same number of calories represent energy sufficient to lift 200 tons through one vertical foot.

PUTTING ON WEIGHT

In childhood there are few who are not perplexed as to why the time taken by, for example, a calf, a colt, a lamb, a kitten and a human baby to reach maturity varies so greatly. Not a little light is shown on this subject by the following facts. To double its birth weight a lamb uses up 4,243 calories for every two and a half pounds put on; a colt 4,512; a kitten 4,554, and a baby 28,864.

In other words a baby weighing 8 lb. at birth needs to use over 92,300 calories of energy in order to increase the weight to 16 lb. Again, a man weighing 12 stone, whose weight remains more or less constant during twenty years, expends more than 18,250,000 calories in that time.

A woman weighing 6 stone who doubles her weight in twenty years has added 11 lb. of fatty tissue and 66½ lb. of fat.

HUMAN CANAL WITH MILLIONS OF MUSCLES

For most, conscious interest in canals began with a geography lesson that gave particulars of the Suez Canal. Yet, little conscious of the fact though he may be, each human being is a canal owner. Moreover, if he permit that canal to be choked with rubbish or to fall into a ruinous condition he loses his canal-ownership and with it his life.

The water-way in question is the alimentary canal, that thirty-foot long tube which, coiled up in the abdomen for the most part, is open at both ends. The muscles which coat its lining of mucous membrane expand and contract, doing the work of pistons in a man-made machine. They are, in fact, tiny engines, a million of which go to every half-inch of the alimentary canal. The full length of the latter, therefore, has some 720,000,000 of these small motors whose ceaseless task is to force the food forward in the canal. Their power is such that it takes one-tenth of a second only for food to reach the top end of the stomach.

LIVING TOWEL IN THE BODY

From the upper end of the stomach the less solid food, known as chyme, is driven onward by the ever-working motors to the stomach's lower or pyloric end. At once it reaches the small intestine. In this amazingly well equipped chemical factory, supplied as it is with bile from the liver, fluid from the pancreas, and that product of tens of millions of infinitesimal glands called the intestinal juice, the principal digestive processes are carried out.

The small intestine's lining of mucous membrane, lying permanently in numerous uneven folds, has a surface rather like that of an extraordinarily finely made towel. Four million tiny tips, known as villi, stand out from it. These make the progress of the food slower, since, as can be seen under a microscope, they wave to and fro and up and down, and so provide a check on the free passage of the food particles. The final processes of digestion take place in the large intestine, which extends for five or six feet and which varies from half an inch to five times that width.

At the end of the first part of the large intestine is the vermiform appendix, cause today of so many operations. It is thought that this small, worm-like tube may once have been a second stomach. It performs no useful service now.

MAN'S FIVE SENSES

MAN has five senses: sight, hearing, smell, taste and touch; but smell and taste are only two varieties of what scientists often call the "chemical sense."

EAR'S AUDITORY CELLS

The innermost membrane of the human ear possesses 13,000 auditory cells. Vibrations of a frequency as high as 32,000 per second are perceptible by man. In music no note is used which has more than 25,000 vibrations per second. Four hundred thousand vibrations per second approach the boundary of heat and, when transmitted by fine threads, which themselves remain cold, give rise to burns on the skin.

The famous conductor, Arturo Toscanini, is reputed to be able to distinguish eight-tenth tones from seven-tenth tones.

LEND ME YOUR EAR-DRUMS

A year or two ago, Professor J. P. Delstanche, a Belgian scientist, succeeded in making, out of paraffined tissue, an ear-drum that functioned, despite its artificiality. Deafness resulting from split or thickened drums will, if the professor's discovery can be commercialized, have been robbed of its terrors.

Moreover, when the din of the noisiest variety of pneumatic drill becomes unbearable, those with the necessary equipment will take out their ear-drums and face the noise-hideous world with the bland smile of blessed deafness.

TASTE AND TOUCH

In each of the tiny papillæ of the tongue are about 500 terminal fibres of taste nerves. A practical demonstration of the capacity of the sense of taste is afforded not only by wine-tasters but also by the experts of the Peking tea school, who can distinguish forty different kinds of tea with their eyes shut.

The sense of touch resides in 500,000 tactile corpuscles distributed in varying density over the skin.

NORMAL SIGHT IS UNUSUAL

Only one in fifteen persons has normal sight. The sense of sight enables us to see things, but to judge of them correctly is the task of the reasoning faculty. The eye is the messenger, the brain is the receiver and reader of the message.

Human sight is a hundred times stronger than that of the bee and a thousand times stronger than that of the fruit fly. The "twinkling of an eye" takes place in one-sixteenth of a second and is the quickest movement performed by man. Objects moving at a rate of 200 miles per hour are visible to the human eye only when they are more than 100 yards distant. The hawk's limit of vision is approximately one mile.

FEATS PERFORMED BY THE SENSES

An amazing feat reported by Cicero is that of the man who wrote down the whole of the *Iliad* on a piece of bark which could be fitted into a nut shell. A Greek of the name of Mermekydes made a four-horse chariot of ivory small enough to be covered by a fly, and a fully rigged ship no bigger than a bee. At a military review at Palermo in 1935 an infantryman showed that he was capable of hearing a whisper eighty yards distant, and the noise made by aeroplanes flying below the horizon.

The hearing locates a sound according to whether it is the right or the left ear which first receives the sound-waves; those which come from immediately in front reach both ears simultaneously. The smallest difference of time of which the human being can be sensible is 1/30,000th of a second.

WHAT IS THE SIXTH SENSE?

The so-called sixth sense, or sense of vibration, known in the medical world as " cutaneous palpitation," is of no great practical importance except for the hard of hearing and the deaf.

This is not the case in the world of the lower animals. For ants it serves as a means of identification; fish react even to the pitch of a note. The spider reacts to the struggling of the creature caught in its web, but only when two parts of its body are affected by the vibrations : that is to say when the difference in time gives it a sense of direction.

HEAT-SOUNDS

It is now possible to produce sound-waves of as many as 1,000,000 vibrations, thus crossing the boundary between sound and heat. They can cause to vibrate the thinnest possible sheets of quartz and spun glass, and these, without becoming hot themselves, can produce burns on the skin and kill small creatures. Under their influence water, oil, paraffin, quicksilver and other metals can be thoroughly and permanently mixed together.

PEOPLE WHO " HEAR " COLOURS

A few people of both sexes, on hearing a particular sound, at once with no volition on their part, become aware of a certain colour. The colour is always related to the sound in question. In the majority of cases, each vowel is associated with a particular colour. Thus in the sentence familiar to all students of shorthand, " Pa may we all go too," a person with this faculty sees six colours in succession, the dominating vowel sound in each instance giving the word its colour.

Because suggestion can more easily play a part in any experiment devised to test this sense, research workers are cautious in presenting statistics relating to it. Apparently it is more common in women than in men. In comparatively small groups of girl students, the percentage has ranged from 6 to 15.7.

THOUGHTS THAT TAKE SHAPE

A curious parallel to what is sometimes called "coloured hearing" is the phenomenon known as "number form." Many children and a smaller percentage of adults are aware of—to quote Sir Francis Galton, one of the earliest and still perhaps the greatest authority on this subject —"the sudden and automatic appearance of a vivid and invariable form in the mental field of view, whenever a number is thought of, and in which each numeral has its own definite place."

Teachers and psychologists who make children their special study, have long been conscious of the difficulty which young children find in drawing a distinction between the subjective and the objective world. This may in part explain why that particular faculty, like the power of retaining in the memory pictures that can be visualized in detail at will, diminishes and often disappears as the mind becomes stored with academic knowledge.

MEN ARE MORE SENSITIVE TO COLOUR THAN WOMEN

In our own day men, especially of European stock, and increasingly among Orientals, wear sombre-coloured clothing. Women now as all through the ages, almost irrespective of race and latitude, seek gay colours and variety of fashion whether in cut or in trimming in their garments. It would seem that from this could be argued the possession by women of greater colour awareness than by men. This is not the case.

Men and women, of ages ranging from fifteen to thirty years, have been tested as to their ability to classify colours—this apart from their ability to name the shades. Here are the results: To red, yellow and green men were respectively four times, twice and one and one-eighth times more sensitive than women. To blue, women were one and a half times more sensitive than men. Possibly it is for this reason that the most famous and successful of women's dressmakers and designers are men.

COLOUR BLINDNESS IS INHERITED

Colour sensitiveness must not be confused with colour blindness. With this handicap, which is inherited by boys through their mothers (who do not usually have the defect themselves but whose fathers had) the victims are unable to distinguish between green and red. Most people are familiar with the man who cannot see the poppies in a field of growing wheat.

Who are the colour blind? Considerable research has been done on this subject. To state the results in general terms: 30 to 40 out of each 1,000 males are colour blind, while only 1 to 4 females out of 1,000 are similarly afflicted. There seem to be variations between class and class as well as between race and race. Among public schoolboys colour blindness averages 2.5 per cent; among their lower middle-class fellows the average is 3.5 per cent. Sons of wealthy Irish families are just half as subject to the defect as those of Irish labourers. Quakers and Jews suffer from it in a bigger percentage of cases than other sectarians. Among American Indians colour blindness is almost unknown in the women and amounts to less than one per cent in the men.

SENSE OF SMELL KEENER IN MEN

Ask a dozen friends whether man or woman has the more delicate perception of odours, and the big majority will give women superiority in this. The facts are the reverse, as experiments prove. Whereas women could detect no more than one part of oil of cloves in 50,667 parts of water, men perceived one part in 88,218. For amyl nitrate, garlic extract, bromine and cyanide the figures were respectively:—

Men   : 1 part in 783,870; 1 in 57,927; 1 in 49,254; 1 in 109,140
Women :   „   311,300; „ 43,900; „ 16,244; „   9,002

It follows that while men are far more qualified to undertake such occupations as tea-tasting and wine-tasting, women can in hospitals, the slums and elsewhere, carry out duties among objectionable smells with greater efficiency than men, whose olfactory powers are more developed.

Use of perfumes and herbs and spice through the centuries has tended to blunt the feminine nostrils to their potency. As early as in the day of St. Clement of Alexandria (about A.D. 150-215) this was a matter of observation. In his *Pædagogus* he writes: "Let a few unguents be selected by women, such as will not be overpowering to a husband." Men, then, should be charitable when, in bus or tube or tram they suffer from something like nausea as the result of sitting next to some over-scented woman. For she, poor creature, is aware only of a sweet fragrance where her neighbour perceives a pungent smell.

WHENCE THOSE SNIFFS?

On returning from a holiday the housewife detects, it may be, an unpleasant smell in her larder. She sniffs, and sniffing, discovers that she has overlooked food that has gone "bad" in the interval. How is her sniff produced, and with what object?

She has inhaled with unusual vigour. The air thus drawn into her nasal chamber carries the smell from the decaying food to the olfactory patches, as they are called. Here are to be found the nerve cells that respond to smells. Man has sniffed through all the ages in which he has lived. The anthropoid apes, who according to some scientists were his ancestors before him, sniffed also; and so back through all the long ancestry of humanity; reptiles, amphibians, even the mud-fish before the amphibians, have used their lungs in order to detect the source of smells, whether attractive or unattractive. The process can be observed any day by watching a dog.

WEEDS MORE SENSITIVE THAN MAN

Even the most dragooned of nations should take Solomon's advice and go to the ant and realize that its discipline, its subordination of the individual to the community, is lamentably inefficient compared with the ant's achievement.

Turning from the ant heap, let man ponder for a moment either the bee or the spider. He prides himself on sensitivity as a quality peculiarly human. But is it? For delicacy of touch, the spider makes man look clumsier than a cart-horse by the side of a racer. For ability to distinguish the most delicate of smells the bee is to the man as a Whistler to a child who works with coloured chalks.

In man himself, physical sensitivity varies as between individual and individual. The fact of that sensitivity can be tested by a simple and easily performed experiment. Take a silver and a copper coin. Set these in the mouth, holding them in front of the tongue. Allow them to touch. A faint taste of acid will at once be perceived, because a tenuous electric current has passed between the coins. To such a discharge men of various Eastern races are 100 per cent more sensitive than a European, yet many common weeds have a sensitivity to the same electrical discharge which is four times as great.

MYSTERY OF HORMONES AND GLANDS

Without the hormone there can be no harmony or balance in the human body. Hormones are glandular juices, of which the slightest excess or insufficiency betokens death or incurable disease. They are not only of importance for physical functions but also influence moral and mental characteristics.

IODINE FOR THE BODY

Glands are secretory organs; those with ducts secrete sweat or saliva (to this class belong also the intestinal glands and the gall bladder); the ductless glands pass their secretions direct into the blood and lymph, which penetrate the whole organism, even to the tiniest cell. These secretions are the oil, as it were, which enables the various parts of the whole complicated organism to interlock and work harmoniously together.

Every three hours the thyroid gland produces a secretion containing a millionth part of a gramme of iodine and passes it into the blood stream. The removal of this gland puts a stop to the process of renewal and causes the whole body to decay. The iodine content of the human organism amounts to only one two-thousand-millionth of one per cent, but a little less turns a man into an idiot, and a little more induces Basedow's disease.

The pineal gland has a great influence on the germ glands; should it cease to function, the body falls a prey to sexual precocity and excessive psychical activity. The removal of or a defect in the hypophysis (an appendage to the brain consisting of three lobes of skin five grammes in weight, adjoining the base of the skull), arrests the development of the bones and stops growth.

All dwarfs suffer from this deficiency; the giant, on the other hand, owes his abnormal stature to a surplus of secretion from the hypophysis; in this case the chin, hands, and feet are particularly large. An operation performed in time can bring these symptoms to a standstill.

DREAMS PLEASANT AND OTHERWISE

Diseased supra-renal glands in the case of a young girl cause her whole body to be covered with hair, but on the removal of these glands the skin assumes a deep brown colour, the patient becomes mentally deranged, is seized with convulsions, and eventually expires. Without the products of the thymus glands it is impossible for the sex glands to develop.

Experiments show that injections of the hormone from the hypophysis bring on the most delightful dreams, whereas terrible nightmares result from injections of the hormone from the supra-renal glands. Hormones from the sex glands induce erotic dreams.

DETERMINES CONSTITUTION AND CHARACTER

The functioning of the various glands, and the preponderance of one or the other in the blood, vary with every individual. The mixture of the hormones determines the individual constitution; on it alone depend the proneness to disease, the character, and the general tone of the whole organism. The blood protects itself against a surfeit and is able to reduce it, but whereas in a particular case the blood breaks down the substance of the thyroid gland very rapidly, it is correspondingly less able to cope with the substance of the germ glands or supra-renal glands. By means of a process known as interferometry, carried out only by specialists, the strength of the hormone glands, their interplay, and their excessive or deficient functioning may be studied. This study may produce in the future most important results.

Plants have hormones which control their growth and others which control the division of cells. The cessation of activity of the germ glands in autumn and their reawakening in spring may possibly be the cause of the migration of birds.

HOSTILE AND FRIENDLY BACILLI

THE more common bacilli are roughly one five-thousandth of an inch in length, and about one twenty-five-thousandth of an inch across. If then the 16,000,000 germs produced in an eight-hour night were lined up in a row one deep, just over fifty-three feet would give them standing room. In a word, two semi-detached villas of an ordinary suburban size would provide (with no side gardens necessary) frontage enough for the 16,000,000 to stand end to end.

LYING IN WAIT FOR YEARS

The life of a bacterium consists of its active and its resting stage. When conditions are unfavourable for it, it can if necessary rest for years, and start up into activity at the end of that time.

In their resting state, bacilli can lie in wait in the air, where they are usually found on dust particles, in the sea, and in the soil. They have even been found in icebergs but have become extremely active when given good conditions for their growth.

BACTERIOLOGISTS' "COLONIAL QUESTION"

With agar-agar, prepared from sea weed found off China, as a medium, bacteria can be grown under observation and tests carried out for their identification. At first there is nothing but the smooth, clear surface of the medium to be seen. About a day later comes a change which is visible without the help of a microscope. There is a small cloudy mass, known to scientists as a "colony"—a colony of germs, those millions which have developed from the bacilli introduced with a bacteriologist's needle. This needle is really a short length of fine wire made of platinum. It is twisted into a loop and used to scoop up fluid containing germs, and to lower them into the agar-agar or other medium.

The bacteriologist then has a colonial question to consider. Are they hostile to mankind, innocuous or friendly? For strange as it may seem, there are some bacilli which definitely are friends of man and beast. The most obvious aid to identification is the colour of the colony. Some will be transparent, some translucent, some green, others violet, red or golden. There is also the shape of the bacilli in the colony, which must be ascertained with the aid of a microscope. The common rod-shaped microbe is referred to as a bacillus; a germ which is spherical is known as a coccus, while that with a curved shape is a spirillum.

BODY'S POLICE FORCE

Staphylococcus aureus, which causes a number of diseases, including that enemy of male adolescence, the common boil, has the colour of old gold in its colony and looks rather like some rich fabric, so tenuously beautiful is this golden germ-mass. A near relative is *Staphylococcus albus*, from which man has nothing to fear. Its nature is as white and unsullied as the pure white of its colony. The organisms belonging to both these families lie in clusters of tiny spheres, and resemble infinitesimal bunches of grapes, hence the Greek name by which they are known.

For most the term "pus centre" is associated with ill-health. Thus a boil is a pus centre on a large scale, but a boil which is already on the way to demolition. *Staphylococcus aureus* has caused the boil; the leucocytes or white corpuscles in the blood have rushed to the scene of action, and the pus is evidence that the *Staphylococcus aureus* germs have been devoured by this police force of the body.

EARTH'S SMALLEST KNOWN ORGANISM

The *Pyogenic coccus*—one relating to the formation of pus—asks for a very small place in the sun. For, in round figures, its cubic content is 1/700,000,000th of a milligramme. In other words, 1½d. would be the cost of posting to any address in the United Kingdom 33,600,000,000,000 of these microscopic living creatures.

A breakfast cup would give millions of them comparatively more room in which to live and move and have their being than the earth provides for its inhabitants.

BACTERIAL BEER IS BEST

It needs the imaginative genius of a great author to see the dramatic possibilities of a bacillus as an important factor in a play, for a case can be made out for the many bacilli which commerce employs in the service of mankind.

Centuries before men knew that bacilli existed, they used yeast in order to ferment alcohol or to cause bread to rise. Not until Louis Pasteur in the mid-19th century investigated the action of yeast was it discovered that the yeast cell contains bacteria whose growth results in the phenomenon known as fermentation. It is this fermentation that breaks down sugars to alcohol.

An alcohol manufacturer consulted Pasteur as to why his vats were producing not alcohol but an acid. Pasteur proved that a bacillus producing lactic acid had been active. When only the yeast with its organism was used alcohol was formed. Beer drinkers should drink to the health of the bacteria without which beer would be anything but best.

BACILLI AS NIGHT-LIGHTS

Why does bread rise? When yeast acts upon the carbohydrates found in dough, it causes fermentation. Carbon dioxide is liberated, and so the bread "rises," becoming pleasanter to the palate and more digestible.

The bacilli in yeast are beneficent. They bring about chemical changes, which are still not yet wholly understood. To produce these changes the chemist would need powerful reagents and high temperatures.

There are other organisms which are a bane to bread and bread makers, even as yeast bacteria are a boon. *Micrococcus prodigiosus*, for example, is aptly named. It is an excellent example of a self-coloured bacillus (coloured by itself). As it grows it becomes red. Attacking bread, it quickly gives a loaf the appearance of having been spattered with blood.

Marine bacteria have their peculiarities. From time to time a butcher living in a seaside town has a disconcerting experience that may do his business great harm. Customers passing his shop after dark see that every joint of meat in his window shines with a phantom phosphorescence.

At once they assume that his supplies cannot be fresh, and take their custom elsewhere. The unfortunate tradesman has, in fact, suffered because his stock has been attacked by bacteria from the sea and the foreshore.

Shellfish and jellyfish, sea worms and crustacea are in many cases phosphorescent. In a word they give out light without giving out heat because of the phosphorescent bacilli in them. It requires but an elementary knowledge of bacteriology to cultivate from any given sample of sea water bacilli remarkable for their phosphorescence. Kept in a glass beaker, they will remain alive almost indefinitely. When the beaker is shaken, the oxygen of the air increases the glow, till it is as bright as a night-light.

HEALTHY ONLY WHEN DISEASED

If the green pea had a slogan it might well be, " Love me, love my bacilli." Duck and green peas have long been associated on our menu cards. From the green pea's point of view the duck is superfluous. But not a certain little bacillus whose formal name is *Bacillus radicicola*. For the pea is only one of many living things which, to be healthy, must be diseased.

On the roots of peas and other legumes are nodules in which this particular bacillus was found for the first time rather more than fifty years ago. Because these bacteria can absorb nitrogen from the air, itself eighty per cent nitrogen, they are known as " nitrogen-fixers " or ozotabacteria. If peas be sown in a field where none has been sown before, their growth is poor. But if the field be treated with *Bacillus radicicola*, at once the plants become sturdier and the pods fatter and more numerous.

BACILLI AS FACTORY HANDS

As the farmer has unpaid hands in the nitrogen-fixers, so the industrialist who manufactures dairy food employs bacteria in steadily increasing varieties. If bacteria did not produce lactic acid in milk, milk could not be transformed into cheese. New cheese has to ripen. During the ripening process, the bacteria live on in the now solid cheese, and in the conditions provided by the manufacturer, increase in number.

At this point in the manufacture, the effect of the bacteria on the changed medium in which they find themselves is to alter the flavour of the cheese. Industrialists take full advantage of this. Although the question, "What is the difference between a Stilton and a Gorgonzola?" cannot be answered altogether accurately by the statement that, " It is the bacillus that accounts for the label on the box," this is in fact not far from the truth. True Stilton differs from other cheeses in being made from whole milk to which is added the cream from another milking. Nowadays, unfortunately, so-called Stilton is sometimes made from " single cream " milk, and so lacks the unique flavour of the genuine product.

CONTRAST IN THE SEXES

THE nursery rhyme in which reference is made to " sugar and spice " and " puppy-dogs' tails " is our earliest introduction to the fact that there are differences between the sexes. Sooner or later, a psychologist will doubtless do with scientific seriousness what literary men have already done with satiric humour; analyse the nursery rhymes and demonstrate how these typical expressions of folk-lore wisdom enshrine exceedingly ancient beliefs about, in particular, the relationship of man and woman.

WHEN MAXIMUM WEIGHT IS REACHED

Leaving aside the sugar and spice theory of the nursery rhyme as to the physical composition of the human female, let us consider other comparisons of the sexes. Analysis of physically mature men and women made immediately after death has shown that whereas in a man the relative weights of muscle and fat are as 42 is to 18, in a woman they are as 36 is to 28.

Women tend to put on more fat than men. Consequently a man reaches his maximum weight at the age of 40, a woman hers at 50.

WOMEN APPEAR TALLER

Observe a man and his wife when they are sitting side by side. Often there is little apparent difference in their heights. When they stand up, in most instances, the man is seen to be definitely the taller. This is because, relative to their heights, a woman's trunk is longer than a man's. If 100 represents the full height of the body, the height of the trunk of a European male is roughly 33.5 and that of a European female 34.0.

It is a fairly accurate generalization to state that in women, while the trunk is relatively long, the limbs are relatively short. It is true that the relatively shorter arms of the female cause her to approximate to the infantile condition more nearly than a man. But this fact is of no great value to the cynic who wishes to argue from it the inferiority of women to men. For the feminist can retort—and does—with justification that, since in the savage and the ape the forearm in particular is long, man is nearer to ape and savage than woman.

There is the further fact, equally disconcerting to the cynic, that woman's jaw is to man's as 79 is to 100; and that comparatively large jaws are characteristic of the lower human races, as of apes. It suggests also that, despite the contrary popular belief, men are bigger talkers than women.

DEPARTURES FROM THE NORMAL

The very short or thin man married to the very tall or fat woman is normally regarded somewhat as a figure of fun. The average male is fatter and heavier than the average woman. Because anything that departs too conspicuously from the normal is a matter for comment, a sense of the ridiculous is stimulated by such unusual departures. They are, nevertheless, nothing in comparison with others that exist in Nature.

In certain kinds of spiders differences in height and weight are enormous. Proportionately, if a man of normal size and weight were similarly mated, his wife would top the scale at 100 tons, and would need an eighty-foot front door if she were to enter her house erect.

MEN LIKE EGGS WALKING

The ancients had a saying that the human trunk is like an egg with a large end and a small end; that a woman is an egg with its small end at the top, and a man one with its large end uppermost. Put less picturesquely, a woman's shoulders are narrower in diameter than her hips; while the opposite is true of a man.

Dr. Sargent, who made an examination of young Americans between the ages of 17 and 20, found that, relative to her height, a woman's hips averaged four inches larger than a man's. At 20 the actual (but not relative) measurements showed a woman to be a half-inch smaller than a man round the hips. Yet when men and women of equal height were taken at this age the girth at the hips was six inches more in women than in men. Women with narrow pelves tend to have still-born or weakly children, and thus this defect is not transmitted to any appreciable extent.

TRUTHS ABOUT THE TEETH

Women get their wisdom teeth earlier than men: more girls get these teeth in their twenty-second year than in any other; while the twenty-third is the comparable year in the case of men. On the other hand, men suffer less from dental decay than do women, since women have more drain on their calcium supplies.

In women the two upper incisors are both relatively and absolutely larger than those of men of the same age. This is the more remarkable in that the female jaw is definitely smaller than the male.

SEX AND SENSIBILITY

Professor Jastrow, by experimenting on his students, both male and female, established a number of interesting facts about sensibility to pain. The professor mounted a light hammer on a pivot placed eight inches above a table top. The hammer was then allowed to drop on to the tip of the forefinger of each hand. The number of degrees through which the hammer had to fall before a sensation of pain was experienced varied considerably.

Feminine sensibility proved to be double that of masculine where the right hand was concerned (the figures given were 33.9 degrees for the men and 16.6 for the women). There was less disparity for the left hand; the results showing 22.7 degrees for the men and 14.8 degrees for the women.

ABILITY TO ENDURE PAIN

Sensibility to pain is one thing; ability to endure pain is another. At intervals during the past 100 years statistics have been collected which go to show that from the age of 5 to 15 children endure amputation better than adults, and women better than do men. How far physical and mental courage accounts for the lighter mortality following amputation among women than among men is a matter of opinion rather than of fact. Yet the implication of such figures as follow cannot be resisted. Amputation figures established that in a total of 1,244 cases of amputation in men, 441 deaths were recorded, or 35.5 per cent. In 284 cases of women 83 deaths, or 29.3 per cent was the comparable figure.

Equally difficult to estimate is the relation between pain resistance and death resistance. But it is significant that more girl infants survive birth and the difficult months which follow it than boy infants.

DURATION OF LIFE

A CCORDING to statistics, duration of life is definitely affected by one's profession. It is not only professional risks (accidents, handling of poisons, carrying out of experiments, infection) and unfavourable conditions of labour (unhealthy atmosphere, etc.), which influence duration of life, but also the rate and the mode of working.

AGRICULTURAL WORKERS LIVE LONG

Conditions are not favourable in hotels, restaurants, and public houses, in industries in which poisonous substances are dealt with or in which certain organs of the body are abnormally exerted, and in professions which involve irregular bursts of energy and excitement. Conditions are very favourable in agriculture, teaching, the Civil Service and the Church. After coal- and sulphur-miners, clerical employees, shop assistants, and machine-minders have the least expectation of life (thirty-eight years on the average). Then come printers with thirty-nine years, and musicians with forty. Manufacturers, shoemakers, painters, and brokers usually live till they are forty-three, jewellers and tailors till forty-four, street-hawkers, in spite of their being so much in the open air, till only forty-six, bricklayers, on the other hand, till forty-eight.

Butchers and carpenters are allotted half a century apiece. One year more is allowed to doctors, the prolongers of their fellow mortals' lives, and to calico-printers. These are followed by another curious combination: solicitors, hat-makers, and rope-makers, who in spite of their widely differing occupations all live to the age of fifty-four, while the clergy depart this life at fifty-six. Public officials, among whom are included bailiffs and postmen, die at the age of fifty-seven; coopers survive them for another year. Bank clerks and farm labourers reach the age of sixty-four, while for judges sentence of death is passed in the sixty-fifth year. Actors and astronomers live the longest of all. Thanks to social reform of various kinds, the expectation of life is rising.

WOMEN LIVE LONGER THAN MEN

Who may expect to live the longest? To trust the statistician, it is the woman born in spring, as vitality is supposed to be strongest in persons born in that season of the year, and it must be a female because the gentle sex, in spite of all its weaknesses, has been proved to have greater powers of resistance than the male. Should she happen to be an artist or, as anything is possible nowadays, an astronomer, then she has every chance of living longer than her masculine competitor.

According to the figures published by a British insurance company in 1935, and which vary in some particulars from the above, the average expectation of life for royalty is 58.8 years, for merchants, travellers, and land-workers 62.4, for artists and writers 66.9, for soldiers 67.7, for politicians and clergymen 66.9. German statistics for 1936 inform us that 210 of every 1,000,000 men, and 310 of every 1,000,000 women are centenarians. The duration of human life was first scientifically investigated by the astronomer, Edmund Halley, in 1693.

NO LONELINESS IN OLD AGE

Of 100,000 persons of the male sex born on the same day, more than half will be alive when sixty-six years have passed. Of 100,000 women the same is true when sixty-eight years have passed. More than a third of all men live till they are seventy-two, more than a third of all women live till they are seventy-five.

Of all those with whom we become acquainted when they are between the ages of twenty and twenty-five, a half will still be living fifty years hence.

INCREASE IN THE DURATION OF LIFE

In the 16th century, of every 1,000 Europeans 582 lived to be sixty, in the 17th century 655, in the 18th century 718, in the 19th century 757, and in the period 1900-35 no fewer than 806. The duration of life for the white race has thus increased very considerably in 350 years.

WOMAN'S LONGER LEASE OF LIFE

That women have been granted a longer lease of life is almost universally demonstrable. In England about 750 men out of every 1,000 reach the age of fifty, while 790 women in 1,000 achieve the half-century. The figures for centenarians are quite astonishing—fifteen out of every 100,000 men, but sixty-three in every 100,000 women. In France, out of ten centenarians seven were women; of twenty-one centenarians in the rest of Europe sixteen were women. In the United States, 2,583 women, as against 1,398 men, have been known to live for 100 years. Yet for a woman middle age is more dangerous than for a man.

For women the expectation of life is 3.3 years longer than for men. There are several reasons for this: women have greater powers of physical endurance; they worry less; and their lives are, generally speaking, much more sheltered.

HUMAN EXPENDITURE OF ENERGY

The daily expenditure of energy by human beings naturally varies with the nature of their tasks. Woodcutters and stonemasons have to exert themselves the most; after them miners, joiners and locksmiths. Little energy is used by tailors, clerks and men and women of leisure.

It is necessary for the human body to make up for this loss of energy. The daily requirement of a man of leisure is 80 grammes of albumen, 40 grammes of fat, and 360 grammes of carbohydrates (starch and sugar); the woodcutter needs only the same amount of albumen, but four times the amount of fat and double the amount of carbohydrates.

NATURAL DEATH IS NOT NATURAL

In a recent year in England and Wales there were 476,810 deaths, of which only 16,066 or roughly three and a third per cent were due to old age. Thus only one English person out of thirty dies a natural death.

The causes of unnatural death are legion. The commonest are diseases of the heart and the circulatory system: they claim two English people out of seven. Next in order of importance come cancer and other tumours, which claim one out of seven; the infectious diseases, including tuberculosis and influenza, with about one out of nine; respiratory diseases, including pneumonia and bronchitis, two out of nineteen; diseases of the nervous system, one out of twelve; of the digestive system, one out of nineteen. About 22,700, or one in twenty, died violent deaths; and one in thirty died in infancy.

An analysis of the violent deaths reveals some interesting figures. In a given year there were twice as many men as women in this category. There were 3,839 male suicides to only 1,711 female suicides. Over 1,800 of the suicides were by gases; 807 by drowning; 786 by hanging and 749 by poisons. Of the 226 persons murdered in that year 117 were women and 109 men. Eighty-three men died of " wounds of war." Of the nine people who were executed, only one was a woman.

Accidents accounted for 15,829, of whom only one-third were women. Over 7,000 died on " roads, railways and in the air "; 1,238 by burns; 642 in mines and quarries; 600 by drowning; 35 at games; 11 by lightning; 56 by excessive heat; 16 by excessive cold and 15 by hunger or thirst.

EPIDEMIC THAT KILLED 25,000,000 PEOPLE

Figures soar when whole countries and continents are ravaged by epidemics. The Black Death, for instance, which raged in the middle of the 14th century, accounted for 25,000,000 persons, half the population of Europe. In 1710-11, in Copenhagen, 23,000 persons died of the plague. Far greater numbers succumbed to cholera in Hamburg in 1890, and millions died of the spotted typhus which broke out in Russia after the World War.

Malaria claims 2,000,000 victims yearly. In Prussia alone, in 1816-75, cholera and smallpox accounted for 700,000 dead. Though modern Europe may be protected against these catastrophes by dint of various precautionary measures, we have only to cast a glance at Asia, the cradle of epidemic diseases, to see that plague and pestilence are as capable as ever of decimating whole nations.

DEATH ROLL CAUSED BY WILD BEASTS

Official statistics issued from Calcutta, for example, state that among the causes of 1,150,000 deaths that took place in the province of Bengal, 460,000 were due to malaria, 360,000 to other febrile diseases, 60,000 to cholera, 25,000 to smallpox, 30,000 to tuberculosis, and 25,000 to dysentery, whereas about 5,000 natives were killed by wild beasts.

The last-mentioned cause of death is still responsible for a considerable proportion of the total number of deaths, especially in India. For this reason the Government of India offers substantial rewards for the destruction of wild animals and has thus caused to be killed in one year 1,368 tigers, 4,390 leopards, 2,700 lions and 2,349 wolves, in addition to 57,116 snakes. In Borneo crocodiles have become such a plague that the Dutch Government has been forced to encourage their extermination by offering rewards.

NATURAL DISASTERS AND WAR

Not insignificant is the number of persons who meet their death as the result of natural disasters such as earthquakes and volcanic eruptions. Dr. Heron, the Indian geologist, calculates that 2,750,000 people have lost their lives in the great earthquakes that have occurred during the last 200 years. In this respect Japan perhaps suffers more severely than any other country; in Tokio, in 1703, 200,000 lives were lost in this manner.

The Peking earthquake of 1731 caused the loss of 100,000 lives and that in Sicily in 1693 accounted for a similar number. Over 25,000 persons were killed by earthquakes in Peru and Ecuador in 1868 and 80,000 by the eruption of Krakatoa in 1883. More than 100,000 lives were lost in the floods of the Hwang-ho in 1935.

The victims of war must also be included among those who die unnatural deaths. Some idea of the total destruction of human life through this cause will be gained from the fact that 2,500,000 men fell in the wars waged between 1850 and 1897, and that during the World War 10,000,000 were killed outright; 6,300,000 were badly wounded; 14,000,000 were lightly wounded. In the influenza epidemic that followed the conflict, and may have been caused by it, 10,000,000 people died.

DEATHS DUE TO TRAFFIC ACCIDENTS

Traffic accidents account for an enormous and terrifying number of deaths. In four consecutive recent years 26,376 persons were killed and 818,232 were injured on British roads.

Private cars are responsible for more accidents than any other type of vehicle in Britain. In a recent year they killed 1,906 persons and injured 72,441. The score of motor vans and lorries in the same year was 1,351 killed and 28,152 injured. Third in this ghastly list come pedal cycles, which were responsible for 1,249 deaths and 64,886 injured. Then solo motor cycles, with 1,136 deaths and 31,997 serious injuries. Motor cycle combinations, which are said to be the safest motor vehicles on the roads, caused only 176 deaths and 5,902 injuries. Deaths from street accidents in London in a recent year numbered 1,448.

VICTIMS OF THE RAILWAYS

In a recent twelve months only one passenger was killed on the railways of Great Britain, but in the same year the total number of deaths from railway accidents was 380. In six consecutive recent years the toll of the British railways was 2,187 dead and 135,377 injured, but of these only 2,793 were passengers, the figures being 49 killed and 2,744 injured.

These railway figures do not include trespassers, suicides and attempted suicides, nearly 1,000 of whom met their deaths in two consecutive years on British railways.

In Germany just after the World War, there was a startling increase in the number of suicides; of every 10,000 deaths 250 were self-caused. In the United States 500 persons are struck dead by lightning every year, in England about 10. The most horrible cause of death is murder. In the former country, out of every 100,000 persons 10 are done to death by violent means. In Prussia over 430 persons were murdered in 1927 alone, and about 50 criminals are executed every year.

BEST YEARS FOR HEALTH

The best years in the life of a man of sound constitution who lives temperately are between his thirtieth and fifty-fifth years, those of a woman between her twenty-fifth and fortieth years. The period of life in which people are most susceptible to fevers is between the fifteenth and the twentieth years.

On an average, the total time during which a man seventy years old has been ill amounts to twenty-four months, or about ten days per year. But according to statistics, up to his fortieth year he is ill for only half this time.

BULGARS ARE THE MOST LONG-LIVED PEOPLE

The wiry Bulgars have the reputation of being the most long-lived people; many of the peasants, thanks to their simple and sustaining diet (in which yoghourt, a drink resembling sour milk, figures prominently), live to an extreme old age. Much the same may be said of the Turks, the last census in Turkey showing a surprisingly large number of centenarians.

The distinction of having lived the longest life of all is claimed by a Turk, Zaro Agha by name, a casual labourer of Constantinople, who was not "discovered" till after the World War. He was taken to America, and the public took a lively interest in him. After successfully recovering from the effects of a motor accident, he died a few years ago at what seems to be the rather improbable age of 163.

MOST FRUITFUL YEARS OF LIFE

It is said that, generally speaking, intellectual maturity is not attained until the thirty-fifth year. Many notable achievements in science, art, literature and affairs can be credited to very young men, but the majority of the works and deeds that live in history have been accomplished by men well past their youth.

MIRACLES PERFORMED BY SURGEONS

A WOUND which when inflicted on a ten-year-old child would take six and a half days to heal, would take ten days in the case of a twenty-year-old; thirteen days in the case of a thirty-year-old; eighteen days in the case of a forty-year-old; twenty-five days in a fifty-year-old; and thirty-two in a sixty-year-old.

NEW FACES FOR OLD

Today a film star whose beauty does not approximate the standardized mould consults a plastic surgeon. She can then be made beautiful, as the cinema world knows the term. Noses seem to be the feature most frequently altered. Not quite so seemingly frivolous is the case of the boxer who has his nose disfigured or fractured. Under the care of a plastic surgeon he can have his nose repaired, with scarcely a mark to show the delicate work which has been done. Boxers and film stars then, mostly consult plastic surgeons in the interest of their work.

For every one film star, or boxer, there are hundreds of other patients drawn from less spectacular walks of life. Many of these are the victims of fire or accident. During the World War many men had their faces so badly mutilated that the rest of life could but be a living death. Their fate inspired Major (now Sir) Harold Gillies—that now famous plastic surgeon who was knighted for his work in this field—to begin a new and daring technique in human sculpture. Hence today there are ex-soldiers who are able to face the world with rebuilt features.

After much patient work and experimentation, plastic surgery has reached a wonderful peak. A woman may be hauled out of a fire or a car wreck almost unrecognizable. Cheeks, brow, ears, nose—all may be disfigured or almost destroyed. Yet after many operations, new skin will have been grafted; a new nose may have been built up, even new brows or lashes—though these involve a long process—will perhaps have been induced to grow. Probably the most astonishing part of all this is that the work is so skilful that as a rule there are very few traces or no trace at all of the repairs.

If we put a patch on a garment at least the stitching is visible. Bu plastic surgery usually does " invisible " mending. Naturally it take time for skin and bone to grow, and to settle down in new places, bu ultimately these new faces are as good as new, not just patched-u affairs.

GRAFTING A TOE TO MAKE A FINGER

Formerly to have lost one's nose was to have lost it. Certain ski diseases made life almost unendurable for many men and women. Now thanks to the small band of plastic surgeons practising today, new nose are possible. The bridge may be built up with bone taken perhaps fror the hip, or with cartilage from a rib, and skin from some suitable are where the scar will not be noticed when it has healed.

Children burnt by fire no longer are said to be ruined, so far as thei appearance goes. Skin can be grafted in quite large bits to the fac and neck, and by the time the child is adult, little or no trace of th disfigurement will be visible. The story of the princess in the fairy ta who was dropped and had her nose grotesquely bent out of shape s that her father the king ordered all mirrors in the land to be abolished no longer fits the facts. Today she would probably be scolded by he mother for spending so much of her time looking in the mirror admirin; herself after the surgeons had finished their work.

More prosaic but no less spectacular is the case on record of a woma who had a toe grafted to take the place of an index finger she had lost This operation was performed by a Russian, Professor Kuslik, in 1936

LOWLY CREATURES AID RESEARCH

THROUGH mice, geneticists like Professor J. B. S. Haldane are makin; valuable discoveries in their own particular field of genetics, th science that has to do with those genes which in mice as in men influenc both character and sex.

LEARNING FROM THE HUMBLE MOUSE

Sexually mature at about four months old, a mouse can have twelv litters in a year. The female offspring themselves begin to breed at fou months. In the course of a short time, therefore, several generations o mice can be studied. A sport (that is to say an animal with freal characteristics) can be observed and the extent to which it transmits it essentially peculiar characteristics. The effect of special diets, either lack ing in some particular vitamin or rich in it, can be watched on a numbe of generations. If malnutrition, that great social problem of our ow day, can be solved, it is likely that a laboratory of experimental mice fo feeding purposes will be one of the avenues explored. Therefore though it needs 5,000 mice to weigh as much as an average man, let no the mouse be despised. The needs of a mouse and a man are similar

Mice illustrate various interesting facts true of all mammals—of al warm-blooded creatures, in other words. These, when at rest, lose the same amount of heat from a similar area of skin. It follows that each mammal needs an amount of food that is proportional not to the weight but to the area of the surface of the skin. Accordingly, the mouse, with its skin surface (relative to its size) seventeen times that of a man needs, relatively again, seventeen times as much food as a man. In short, the food a mouse needs daily, for the most part used to keep it warm, weighs a quarter as much as itself.

Many women of considerable courage are nervous of such harmless creatures as mice. The women settlers whom the Soviet is inducing to make homes in the Arctic region of Siberia will have other fears, but no fear of mice. For in the Arctic there are no mice, nor any other tiny mammals. They cannot get sufficient food to enable them to resist the intense cold.

TOAD MENTALITY

Shakespeare refers to the old superstition that imagined the toad to have a precious jewel in its head. Like others before and since, the poet describes this attractively ugly creature as hideous.

One of the lesser jewels in the crown of scientific achievement during the past three years has been the feat of a German in transferring to frog-tadpoles the brains of toads, also in the tadpole stage of development. This successful experiment was performed at Breslau by Professor Giersberg. A few of the tadpoles he treated thus became full-blown frogs. These showed themselves to possess a number of toad characteristics. They hopped rarely and crawled rather like toads. Unlike frogs, which go to earth only with the coming of autumn, in full summer these toad-minded creatures buried themselves at short intervals. The toad, who is altogether a toad, is in the habit of digging himself in, in a similar manner at this season.

On the face of it, this is one of those apparently inconsequent experiments of which scientists perform so many. Such experiments often bring either the experimenter or some other whose thought they have stimulated, to the brink of a discovery which, once made, effects a revolution in this sphere or that.

HOT SALT BATHS AS MOTHERS

The breeding propensities of rabbits are proverbial. So far, however, it has been necessary to secure a mother rabbit before rabbit offspring were a possibility. If Dr. Pincus, of Harvard University, brings his experiments to a successful conclusion, most of mother rabbit's task will have been done for her.

He has taken ova from various unfertilized rabbits, and passed them through the first stages of their embryonic development by the simple expedient of giving them hot, salt baths. The single cell multiplied and formed a series of cells making a kind of tube—the first stage of growth.

THE VEXED QUESTION OF RACES

ONE of Germany's famous scientists in pre-Nazi days was Professor Günther, whose life work was a racial study of the German people. His conclusion was that in the north of the country tall, fair-haired, blue-eyed men of Nordic race were in the majority; that in the south the predominating dark-haired and dark-eyed people came from the Dinaric race; while all over Germany are those who spring from the Falic, Ostic and Westic races. Racial impurity, in other words, is not confined to the Briton or the American. Every civilized people comes of a mixed stock.

"ARYANS" WHO ARE NOT ARYANS

Rather more than a hundred years before the birth of Christ, the Teutons migrated from the Baltic lands, and as invaders entered Gaul, the Roman Empire and even Spain. In all these countries the Teuton warriors mated with the inhabitants. Racially, this improved the stocks. But it follows that the Germans, despite their pride in so-called "Aryan" ancestry, are some of the best-crossed people in Europe.

The Teutonic migration is but one of many in history. The extent to which these have taken place in the past century is realized by few. Take Germany itself. Between 1880 and 1890, 1,342,000 Germans left their native country for the United States. Again, the Russian Revolution of 1917 resulted in the migration of 6,000,000 Russians who now are scattered over most countries in the world.

In Berlin, for example, there were in 1919, 600 chauffeurs, all Russians of the aristocratic or bourgeois classes. How many of their wives opened hat shops, or craft shops, or set up as dressmakers, or milliners? There are no statistics to record. But it is obvious that Germany—and it is roughly true too of France—has received a considerable tincture of Slav blood in the past twenty years. During the century beginning 1821, European immigrants into the United States totalled 33,800,000.

MEN IN MELTING POTS

The United States has long been known as the world's melting pot. As substances fuse, so do racial stocks. The original British settlers have received into their ranks men of Irish, German, French, Italian, Swedish, Norwegian, Russian, Jewish, Chinese, and Negro blood. Intermarriage has been widespread. Meanwhile the Red Indian aborigines are rapidly dying out. And yet ethnologists have noted in hybrid Americans, whose inheritance of Red Indian blood is nil or negligible, a definite manifestation of the Red Indian cast of face and build of body.

So with the Jews. F. A. Forel gives his authority for the statement that in China the Jews resemble the Chinese; in north-western Europe the Nordics; and in Russia the Slavs.

BLONDE JEWS WITH BLUE EYES

According to Günther and Eugen Fischer the Jews are not one race but six—it may even be eight. The bases of these are two different and differing stocks, the Armenian and the Semitic. The Armenian stock has a prominent Nordic strain. The Semitic stock is, in tens of thousands of cases, almost indistinguishable from the Mediterranean peoples in Italy and Southern France (particularly Provence), among whom so many of them live.

In Germany, of 75,000 Jewish children examined, thirty-two per cent were fair-haired and forty-six per cent possessed light-coloured eyes. In Jerusalem, where a big section of the Jewish population is German though Polish in origin—the Ashkenazim, as they are called—four out of every ten were blondes, three out of every ten had blue eyes.

NORDIC RACE'S GODFATHERS

The term Nordic Race is not a great many years old. It was brought into use almost simultaneously by three men. Of these one was Houston Stewart Chamberlain (1854-1927), the son of a British admiral and a naturalized German; Count Arthur Gobineau (1816-82), a Frenchman; J. Deniker, a Russian, whose best-known anthropological work was published in 1900.

It was Houston Stewart Chamberlain who wrote: "The Aryans tower over the rest of mankind. With good reason, therefore, will they make themselves, as the Stagirite phrased it, the lords of the world." This may be compared with the first impressions of Europeans given in the following passage from the Tibetan authoress, Rhin-Ohen-Lha-Mo: "To our eyes Europeans in general are ugly. Your noses are too large, and project like the handles of pots. Your ears are as large as those of swine; your eyes are as blue as the marbles with which our children play; your orbits are too deep; and as for your foreheads, they stick out like those of monkeys." All of which goes to show that men create brains or beauty in their own image.

TRUTH ABOUT THE "MISSING LINK"

THERE are men and women alive today who remember the furious controversy which continued for a couple of decades after the publication of Charles Darwin's revolutionary books, *The Origin of Species* (1859) and *The Descent of Man* (1871). These works had to do with evolution, but they effected a revolution—a revolution in scientific thought, perhaps the greatest man has known in the mental sphere. The fury of that controversy has long since died down. Charles Darwin is no longer denounced as an atheist. Yet some of the ideas current on the subject of evolution are very vague. For instance, neither Darwin nor any evolutionist since Darwin's day has said that all monkeys have evolved into apes, all apes into anthropoids, all anthropoids into men. Yet this error still persists.

APES AND MEN AS SECOND COUSINS

The highest order of mammals are called Primates, of which there are six families. The fifth of these are the anthropoid apes, that is to say man-like apes; the sixth, men.

Apes that figure in music-hall or circus turns can add and subtract figures, smoke a pipe, use cutlery better than many people, put on and take off clothes as quickly as the best of us. If a biologist or a zoologist were to train two or three generations of apes, it is likely that they could be taught to fire machine-guns and loose poison gases, as it is certain that they could fling Mills bombs with a precision, and over a distance that no infantryman could equal. In short, it is undoubtedly true that apes could acquire many, if not most, of the arts which men sometimes reckon to be part of civilization. An ape Bach might be more difficult to breed than an ape bomber. But this is equally true of human beings.

Anatomically, embryologically, physiologically, even psychologically, apes and men illustrate the same scientific facts. According to the majority of scientists they are, if not first, then second cousins. They differ, but in degree and not in kind. Thus, the male gorilla may be no more than 5 ft. high, yet he weighs as much as 400 lb. Were he proportionately as long in the leg as a man, he would be 7 ft. tall. Were a man proportionately as strong as the gorilla, he would have a punch capable of giving the knock-out to three world boxing championship holders, taken on simultaneously.

APES AS ATHLETES

Again, the orang-utan, despite his dwarfishness compared with man—his height averages 4 ft.—can swing himself from branch to branch at a speed that a 6-ft. man, running his fastest, cannot equal on the ground. Then there is the chimpanzee. The oldest human skulls so far discovered are not unlike the chimpanzee's, as may any day be verified in a natural science museum. The gibbon is a foot shorter than the orang, and the gibbon has a volume of voice that even Caruso never possessed, although the gibbon's voice is not so melodious. The gibbon can make the best feat of a good athlete who specializes in long-jumping look somewhat childish. It takes a 15-ft leap almost in its stride, and often clears 40 ft. when the necessity arises. Even the diminutive marmoset possesses a brain that is scarcely distinguishable from that of a human embryo in the third month.

Contrary to popular belief, the "missing link" of which so much has been written, is to be sought rather between men and the anthropoid apes than between those apes and monkeys proper. For while the anthropoids yield results similar to men when blood tests are made upon them; and while they can be inoculated with many of man's diseases—and bacteriologists have found that they have about the same susceptibility to infection—the monkeys make no such response when their blood is tested, and only a very light response as regards infection.

Again, unlike the gibbon, monkeys do not normally or for long maintain an upright position, whether at rest or walking. And unlike the gorilla and the chimpanzee, monkeys have not developed large brains. Yet, from some aspects, in theory the monkey might well have evolved as big and as good a brain as the anthropoid ape. Like the ape, the monkey needs judgment each time he swings from one branch to another. But whereas the gibbon and his fellow apes often left the trees for the ground, the monkey remained arboreal in his habits.

It was his life on the ground that began to educate the anthropoid. Educated him in the exact sense of that word: it led him out. It led him on also. His progress made man possible. It is from stock similar to the gibbon's that mankind has sprung.

HUMANITY'S MARATHON BEGINS

When man's ancestor left his forest trees for the ground, and remained there for longer and longer periods, a definite stage had been reached. Very quickly Nature was forced to enlarge his brain in order to enable it to meet the many and varied demands that the exigencies of his now terrestrial life made upon it. Those demands increased steadily. On the ground he had a hundred foes which, when he was in the branches, could not attack him. Against many of them his only weapon was the brain behind the forehead.

When a housewife buys brains from a butcher she considers quality as well as quantity. Half a pound of brains in first-class condition is worth more than a couple of pounds no longer fresh. This is a rough-and-ready answer to the man who opposes evolution, and whose opposition is based on a different kind of objection. He concedes that if mental superiority is to be argued from the comparison of brain weight to body weight, then man whose brain is to his body as 1 is to 35, is superior to the ostrich (comparable figures: 1 to 1,200), the horse (1 to 500), the gorilla (1 to 120) and the lemur (1 to 40); but just as definitely inferior to the rat (1 to 28) and the humming bird (1 to 12). In the relationship between weight of brain and weight of spinal cord, man definitely leads all other animals: his own figures are 50 to 1; the gorilla's 20 to 1; the mammals apart from the primates, 5 to 1; fishes, 1 to 1.

WHY MAN'S ANCESTORS LOST THEIR TAILS

To return to man's family tree, and his probable emergence from apehood. To an arboreal beast a tail is, if not essential, of very great use in two supremely important as well as other less important respects. Swinging from tree to tree, the ape, like the monkey, used his tail as a fifth hand. When he leaped from one branch to another, it served as a rudder. In the course of generations of terrestrial life, with no longer the need for a tail that was as a fifth hand and with little need of a tail that was a rudder, since now his leaps were fewer and did not expose him to dangerous falls, man's ancestor lost his tail.

He lost more than that. He lost the power possessed by monkeys of today, even as it is lacking in apes of today, of clinging in babyhood with the toes (they do, of course, cling with the fingers) to their mothers. Again, the bodies of their mothers began to lose the long hair which had made clinging easier. Where the monkey had, and has, the ability to hang on to the monkey mother, the ape baby had to be carried. This put a responsibility upon its mother; almost certainly it increased the quality of mother-love. Take the human mother of our own day; the helpless infant-in-arms necessarily calls forth more solicitude than the toddler who, to a limited degree, can look after itself.

So it was with the ape mother. If her baby fell, she was responsible: she had been careless in the way she had carried him. Not so the monkey mother. If her offspring dropped and hurt itself she justifiably cuffed its ears for reprehensible carelessness. The monkey mother could go to her kind's equivalent of a party with an easy conscience. The ape mother could not. Hence the monkey mother remained in a mentally backward state. The ape mother metaphorically stayed at home and rocked the cradle. More literally, she rocked her child in the cradle of her arms, for there were no public crèches in which to leave her infant.

Man's ancestor, then, was now tail-less, walked more or less erect, and when of the female sex undertook the care of her children personally. When male, he had the greater need to guard his now more defenceless mate. Hence, if not the birth, at least the fostering of chivalry.

An ape mother, burdened with her nurseling, could no longer, when in need of protection from danger, run to her mate with the same speed as before. Thus arose the necessity for some means of communication other than personal contact. Almost every living creature has some kind of voice with which to give a cry of alarm—with which to call for assistance. But hampered as she now was, the ape mother needed the means of communicating not merely the fact of her peril and the whereabouts of herself, but many more details as to both. Nature, again called upon to supply a need, supplied it: the first crude accents of prehuman speech were heard. Thus, according to many eminent scientists, the anthropoid was evolved from the ape, the sub-man from the anthropoid, and man from sub-man.

MAN'S SUB-HUMAN ANCESTOR

There remains that other stumbling block which in the eyes of anti-evolutionists disposes of Darwin's theory. How is it that there are still apes, still anthropoids, still men who might rightly be labelled sub-men?

The answer can here be given only briefly. Broadly, the facts may be put thus: In the Miocene epoch of the Tertiary era—placed variously at from two to three million years ago—the *Dryopithecus*, a big-bodied ape, became man's sub-human ancestor. For reasons not yet understood, from his trunk as stock, two branches sprang. To one of these belong the *Paleopithecus* of India, as still belong the great apes of our own time. This branch remained arboreal. To the second branch, the branch whose members became terrestrial, belonged *Pithecanthropus*, Piltdown man and Heidelberg man. To this branch belongs every human being alive today.

WHERE MEN RESEMBLE PARROTS

Watch a parrot in its cage. A noticeable feature of the bird is its third eyelid—the nictitating membrane as it is called—which flickers swiftly back and forth over the front of the eye. Examine your own eyes in a mirror. On that side of each of them which is nearest the nose is a small fold. Running crosswise in between the lids, it is situated near the invisible opening of the duct that leads to the tear or lachrymal gland.

This is a vestige of the third eyelid which in the parrot, the pigeon, and some mammals of the lower orders functions as it once functioned in man.

WHEN MAN WAGGED HIS TAIL

Man has a tail concealed beneath the skin. In the embryo during the early stages of its development, this tail protrudes. In rare cases it still protrudes at birth today, though it is probably about 2,500,000 years ago since man lost his tail.

This skeleton of our tail is known as the coccyx; it consists of, usually, five rounded vertebræ no bigger than hazel nuts. In common with the apes we have the vestigial remains of muscles that once allowed us to put up the tail and wag it; blood vessels and nerves which gave it nourishment and connected it with the brain.

MAN'S DEBT TO REPTILES

When a man is fascinated by a snake, as has sometimes happened, it is not the kind of fascination which argues attraction. In fact, snakes are so little loved in any part of the world that the phrase, " a snake in the grass," has its counterpart in many languages, even as the term " reptile," sometimes used for purposes of abuse, has its parallels in the usage of many lands. Yet every human being is indebted to his reptilian ancestry for a biological inheritance of great value.

Not even in novels does a hero swear that he loves the heroine with all four chambers of his heart. It may be that the average writer of novels is unaware of the four-chambered nature of his own. For that particular kind of heart he is indebted to the remote reptilian creature which first developed it.

" The warm blood suffused her face and neck," the novel-writer is almost sure to say at some stage of his story. It would not have been warm blood but for that same reptilian ancestor of man's.

Again, but for that reptile of ages ago, our author might well have had to peck his way out of an egg before he could enter the world and begin his novel-writing. Instead, he lives for nine months in the most marvellous incubator of which man has knowledge. It was our alligator-like progenitor, the mammalian reptile, who dispensed with the allantois, the membrane about the embryo of a bird. Or rather, it changed its nature from that of a lung-like allantois to the placenta and the umbilical cord. Through the umbilicus the embryo was enabled to draw in oxygen and nourishment. The stored food provided by the yolk in the bird's egg was no longer needed. How much sharper than the serpent's tooth is man's ingratitude to—snakes!

NEW LIGHT ON ANCIENT MAN

MANY remarkable discoveries have been made during the last few years that shed light on prehistoric man. All over the world the spade of the digger has aided and abetted the pen of the historian in a united endeavour to shed light on the dark days of a remote past. From Maiden Castle in England to Choukoutien in China the anthropologist is constantly at work, and constantly rewarded by interesting finds.

METHUSELAH DIED YOUNG

In 1938, Dr. H. V. Vallois made known the results of his long and patient investigation into the length of life of prehistoric man. As a living person can be identified by his finger prints, so can the age of a prehistoric man be determined by his teeth and by the closure of the sutures of the skull.

Few will be surprised to discover that prehistoric man, fighting with his wits for the existence of his race against the overwhelming physical strength of the giant beasts of his day, seldom lived to old age. Most will be astonished, however, to find how very short was the life of the 187 subjects examined by Dr. Vallois belonging to the Neanderthal, the Upper Palæolithic, and the Megalithic periods (about 200,000, 30,000 and 15,000 years ago respectively). A table best shows the results of his investigation.

	Neanderthal (200,000 years ago)	Upper Palæolithic (30,000 years ago)	Megalithic (15,000 years ago)
Death before 20	55 per cent	34.3 per cent	37 per cent
Death between 20 and 40	40 per cent	53 per cent	58.5 per cent
Death between 40 and 50	5 per cent	10.8 per cent	1.5 per cent
Death after 50		1.9 per cent	3 per cent
	100 per cent	100 per cent	100 per cent

Of the very few who passed the fifty mark, not one reached three score years and ten. Contrary to expectation, in prehistoric days men lived longer than their mates. Below forty the female death rate was particularly high.

ENGLISHMAN OF 100,000 YEARS AGO

At the 1938 meeting of the British Association, anthropologists contributed papers on an unknown warrior, who, apart from the Piltdown man (believed by some to have lived 150,000 years ago, and by others 500,000 years ago), is the earliest known Englishman.

In 1935, at Swanscombe, near Gravesend, fragments of a human skull were found on the river bed of a stream whose course was near that of the Thames of to-day. Mr. A. T. Maryton, the discoverer of these remains, which are now at the British Museum (Natural History), London, gave it as his opinion that the skull belonged to a man who lived over 100,000 years ago, and who was therefore alive in the early Stone Age. Although there are indications that the head was permanently bent forward rather like that of certain apes, this skull did not belong to a species of the "missing link" kind, intermediate between man and the apes.

Three eminent scientists, Sir Arthur Keith, Professor W. E. C. Gros Clark and Dr. G. M. Morant, declared the age of the skull to be at least 250,000 years. Its owner, therefore, belonged to the mid-Pleistocene period, and was not only the one Englishman but the one European of that distant age known to our own. Having a brain capacity of 1,350 c.c., the skull was that of a member of one of the smaller-brained races of mankind. A number of the markings on the Piltdown skull were present on this of the Swanscombe man. Despite the smaller size of the brain, its ability—actual or potential—was not inferior to that of a human brain of our own day.

STONE AGE ORCADIANS

The year A.D. 1938 also shed more light on 1500 B.C. At Rinyo, on Ronsay Island in the Orkneys, a discovery was made of a Stone Age village. Mr. W. G. Grant, who found its site, proceeded with Professor V. G. Childe to investigate, and the results of their researches are expected to be more valuable than those relating to Neolithic villages previously excavated in Germany. Part of a beaker whose distinctive character clearly marks it as belonging to the transition period between the Stone and Bronze Ages, was found on a floor beneath which were the foundations and ruins of still earlier buildings.

The nature of those ruins suggests that many ideas hitherto entertained as to life in the early Stone Age will need to be revised. At Rinyo, Neolithic men did not live in pit dwellings but in roomy, stone houses. These had recesses meant for their beds of skins or dried grass. Still more remarkable are the remains of what was plainly something resembling a cupboard or dresser built in the walls. Fires were lit on open hearths, while a number of the houses had clay ovens —the first indication that Neolithic men baked.

For a decade or more the elaborate drainage system of the Minoans (people of Crete) has been marvelled at by our contemporaries. As in Crete, so in the Orkneys. For there are at Rinyo the remains of drains that are not mere channels but real attempts at an early kind of engineering. When these investigations of Orcadian village life are complete, knowledge of the Stone Age habits and customs, and of Stone Age community life, will be more authoritative and detailed than any to which we have had previous access.

COAL MEN OF THE BRONZE AGE

Excavations made by Sir Cyril Fox, director of the National Museum of Wales, in the neighbourhood of Coity, a village near Bridgend, Glamorganshire, has established that coal was, if not a king, a useful servant in Britain considerably earlier than has so far been believed. Of the two cairns brought to light, both of which are unmistakably of the Bronze Age, the Simondston cairn had buried in it two grown-ups and a child. The burials were made in about 1600 B.C. On the edge of the cairn were the cremated remains of five persons dating from thirty or forty years later. Fragments of coal found with one set of remains show that coal was the fuel used in these cremation burials. The coal must have been carried at least a mile and a half, since the nearest outcrop is that distance away.

Pond Cairn had a pit cut out of the rock at its centre. Among the stones of which the pit was full the burnt bones of a child had been scattered. In front of the burial urn was a basin, a projecting part of which was lined with charcoal. Around the cairn was a ring of thirty feet radius. Between this and the central turf-stack more charcoal had been trodden firmly into the earth by the feet of mourners or priests who had taken part in the cremation ceremony (or so it is conjectured).

This is but one more of the many modern discoveries which go to suggest that a number of civilized usages have had beginnings far more remote than has been believed till now. As tail-piece let it be stated that in a recent year the production of coal in the United Kingdom was 237,000,000 tons.

MUMMIES WITH ARTERIO-SCLEROSIS

Almost thirty years ago, M. A. Ruffer made an examination of ancient Egyptian mummies, dating back to the period between the years 1580 B.C. and A.D. 525. He established that among the Egyptians of those many centuries ago, arterio-sclerosis—one cause of which is popularly believed to be due to excessive smoking—was fairly common, and the Egyptians did not smoke tobacco.

Most of present-day knowledge of the effect of tobacco smoking is negative rather than positive in nature. Any arterial disease it may cause is brought about so slowly in the great majority of cases that it coincides with ordinary senility. Statistics are equally inconclusive, though rather more centenarians are non-smokers than smokers.

PEOPLES PAST AND PRESENT

THE pedigree of man is not a fixed genealogy. It is liable to be altered at any moment by new discoveries. Nature apparently made a number of experiments before arriving at the present type. Presumably they were failures, in so far as they all disappeared. As Sir Arthur Keith has said, "Our inquiries are but begun. There is so much we do not yet understand."

OLDEST TRACES OF MAN

Among the oldest traces of man that have been found in Asia, are *Pithecanthropus,* the ape-man of Java (500,000 years old), and Peking man (250,000 years old) found in 1929 by Dr. Davidson Black in China. The former, according to Dr. Alfred S. Romer, had a brain 300 c.c. greater than that of the gorilla but 400 c.c. lower than the lowest of existing races and 400 c.c. lower than *Eoanthropus* or Dawn man. Peking man, or *Sinanthropus* as he is termed by scientists, is a little nearer modern man than the ape-man.

In Rhodesia human remains have come to light whose age is estimated at 250,000 years. Traces have been found on the European mainland which show that there was human life in France at least 140,000 years ago. Heidelberg man is older still. According to Dr. Frederick Tilney he began to live in Europe from 150,000 to 200,000 years ago and continued to do so for 100,000 years. An entirely new theory has been formed about Neanderthal man, first found near Düsseldorf in 1856 and afterwards in Belgium, Austria, France, Gibraltar, Spain, Italy, Yugoslavia and Palestine, since Anders's discovery in Mongolia in 1928 of stone implements of exactly the same nature as those found in Germany.

Professor Granger is of the opinion that this primitive race, whose average brain capacity was slightly above that of modern man, moved from farther Asia westwards as Mongolia assumed its present desert character. Races related to that of Neanderthal man may once have inhabited Gibraltar, Malta, Jersey, Croatia, the Crimea, and Galilee. Perhaps they formed the original primitive race, if by this we mean a group of people who possess a common stock and consequently show a uniformity which distinguishes them from races of mixed blood.

UNEARTHING REMAINS OF PRIMITIVE MAN

During the last few years, pick and spade have unearthed skulls and fragments of bone which have led to considerable diversity of opinion. Placing the most primitive first, the usually accepted order of man, or near-man, is as follows : Java man, Peking man, Piltdown man, Rhodesian man and Neanderthal man. The first remains of Java man were discovered by Dr. Eugène Dubois in 1891-92, but the fossil skull of another and more advanced type was found in 1931 by C. Ter Haar, some twenty miles from the original site. To this the name *Homo Soloensis*, or Solo man, was given, the specimen having been embedded in the valley of the Solo River. A third Java skull was discovered in the Solo Valley in 1938.

Peking man was brought to light by Dr. Davidson Black, a Canadian palæontologist, during researches carried out between 1926 and 1929. A complete skull was found at Choukoutien, some thirty-seven miles from Peking (Peiping). Fragments of Piltdown man rewarded the labours of Mr. Charles Dawson and Sir Arthur Smith-Woodward in 1908-12. The skull of Rhodesian man, hidden in a cave in the Broken Hill Mine, Rhodesia, was brought to light in 1921, and is believed to have belonged to an individual closely related to Neanderthal man, the first remains of whom were found in Germany in 1856.

Dr. L. S. B. Leakey came across fossils of ancient men in Kenya in 1932. With an antiquity perhaps equal to that of the Java, Peking and Piltdown relics, Kanam man and Kanjera man are regarded by some anthropologists as standing in direct ancestral relationship to human beings of today. What was at first thought to be the oldest known skeleton of modern man, who is known as *Homo sapiens* by scientists, was found by Dr. Hans Reck at Oldoway, Tanganyika, in 1931, but was afterwards proved to be of more recent date than was originally supposed. The skull of the oldest Londoner was found in 1925 at a depth of forty-two feet, and was claimed by Sir G. Elliot Smith as of Neanderthal type.

MAN FROM APE OR APE FROM MAN?

It is not known how, why, when and where the apes and the early human stocks branched off—if they did. In the opinion of Sir Arthur Keith, " All the evidence now at our disposal supports the conclusion that man has arisen, as Lamarck and Darwin suspected, from an anthropoid ape not higher in the zoological scale than a chimpanzee, and that the date at which human and anthropoid lines of descent began to diverge lies near the beginning of the Miocene period. On our modest scale of reckoning that gives man the respectable antiquity of about a million years."

Professor Henry Fairfield Osborn holds a contrary opinion. " I believe in the evolution of man," he says, " but I do not believe that he came from the apes. He came along a path of his own, and never passed through an ape stage." At the opposite extreme of these schools of thought is Professor Westenhöfer, who declares that the ape evolved from man.

SECOND COUSIN TO MAN

Early in 1938, Dr. Robert Broom discovered in South Africa parts of an anthropoid skeleton, nearer in several respects to the human type than the chimpanzee or the gorilla. The bones were found in Pleistocene strata, that is to say, strata of a date at which human forms already existed. They cannot, therefore, represent the long-sought link between man and the ape, but the discovery is of supreme anthropological importance in that, according to Sir Arthur Keith, it had " destroyed the finger posts we had depended on hitherto for drawing the line between anthropoid and man." According to its discoverer the skeleton represents " the nearest approach to man that we have yet had in a fossil anthropoid." Its skull, jaw and palate were shaped more like those of a human being than of a gorilla or a chimpanzee. The type of anthropoid it represents can be regarded as " second cousin to man."

Dr. Broom is the discoverer of two very interesting skulls : that of the Taungs ape and that of the Sterkfontein ape. He deduces from these finds that " it is highly probable that man arose in Africa." He points out that Darwin and, more recently, Sir G. Elliot Smith, inclined to this view.

The Taungs ape is probably a Lower Pleistocene form, 500,000 or 600,000 years old; the anthropoid found in 1938 is probably Middle Pleistocene, 200,000 or 300,000 years old; and the Sterkfontein ape, Upper Pleistocene, 150,000 years old.

ANCESTRAL BUSHES INSTEAD OF TREES

Whereas formerly it was commonly thought that the human races had an ancestral tree, the present tendency is to agree that it is truer to speak of an ancestral bush, seeing that in the animal world there is never a sign of transition but always sudden up-springings and dissemination.

The transition from one species to another has never been observed or proved. It is only within species that manifold variations with a definite tendency are possible. According to some authorities the human race arose through the purposive erection of the body, the complete freeing of the hand, particularly of the thumb, the acquisition of the ability to speak, and the retention of a brain capable of structural development. The lineage of man goes back by way of the primitive type of mammal, the bird, and the amphibian to the earliest vertebrate, the dogfish.

ORIGINAL HOME OF CIVILIZED RACES

CONCERNING this question there is as much divergence of opinion as there is with regard to the situation of the original Paradise. Of the human races as they exist today the Australian aboriginal is the most closely related to primitive man.

In Australia, at once the most recently discovered and most ancient continent, the progenitors of the present animal world also have been preserved in their purest form. The Australian " black fellow " represents what may be termed the universal rather than the specialized type of man. Whereas, on the other hand, the black, red, yellow, and brown races have developed very one-sidedly, the white race has not diverged so far from the mean form of the primitive type. It has retained its mobility, and hardened by vicissitudes and environment, has become the most powerful and the most civilized race.

Except for remnants of various primitive peoples it is possible to trace back for some thousands of years before our era the homes of the great races. Mongolia and the Tarim basin are the seat of all the Mongolian peoples, who from this starting-point colonized eastern Asia and probably also the North American mainland. In their vicinity, possibly in the Altai region, were originally settled the related Altaic races whose descendants inhabit western Asia and north-east Europe as Lapps, Finns, Esths, Livs, and Turks. Some ethnographers think that the original inhabitants of India, the Dravidians, and that ancient civilized people of Mesopotamia, the Sumerians, also sprang from this same family.

According to a former theory, the Hamitic and Semitic races, originally related to each other, had as their first homes Armenia and Kurdistan, but now Arabia, the home of so many other nations, is allotted to them, and it is even maintained that the Sahara, which was a centre of civilization before it became a desert, was the first home of those races which spread from ancient Babylon, by way of Egypt, to Iberia (Spain and Portugal).

The question as to where the white race was originally settled is a moot one. In any case, so far as prestige is concerned, it is of no importance whether the white race originated in Afghanistan, the Ukraine, the so-called Lathamland (England, Ireland, northern France, and Lower Saxony) or Scandinavia.

One of the oldest civilized races is the Malayan, which probably spread from Madagascar to Easter Island and became known as the Viking race of the Pacific.

RACIAL REMNANTS OF THE PAST

Racial fragments, whose relationship to races now flourishing it is difficult to discover, and which through in-breeding and a restricted mode of living have become doomed to extinction, are to be found tucked away in holes and corners all over the world. Among them are the dwarf Miaotsze, the original inhabitants of China, the aborigines of Japan, and the Ainu on the northern island of Japan, which with the Chukchis, the Gilyaks, the Yukaghirs and others form the relics of the ancient Siberians.

The aborigines of India are the dark-skinned Mundas. In one of these tribes, the Ho, matriarchy (the social organization in which the mother, and not the father, is the head of the family) is still in vogue. Ceylon is still the home of the Veddas; on the Andaman Islands, in the Bay of Bengal, are aborigines who have, so it is said, not yet learnt the art of making fire, and on the Philippines are the pygmy Itaves. The original population of Siam is composed of the negrito Semang, another tribe of pygmies.

The average height of most of these aboriginal tribes ranges between three feet and six feet. The Puri and Barniri in the interior of Brazil, the Batwa on the Congo, who are intellectually inferior to the Nubian negroes, the Akkas of inner Africa, the Bagielli in the southern Cameroons, and the Hottentots, probably the oldest people in Africa, are all small in stature.

In South America there still survive the pygmy tribes of the Makako and the Inje-Inje, whose language consists of a few words. Of the inhabitants of Tierra del Fuego there are barely 500 left; the last Tasmanian woman died in 1876. The aborigines of Easter Island may have been removed, either by force or willingly, or drowned by a tidal wave. Professor Kollmann of Basle infers from five skeletons found near Schaffhausen that the Upper Rhine was once populated by pygmies. Prehistoric skeletons found near Gmünd in Austria in 1937 measured only four feet three inches. The fossil remains of a man only fifteen inches in height were found at Vadnagar, Baroda State, in 1935, thereby confirming, it may be, the description of Ctesias, the Greek physician of the 5th century B.C., of a race of pygmies in the heart of India.

ORIGINAL RACES OF EUROPE

Whereas Heidelberg man lived in the middle part of the Ice Age, Neanderthal man, who had probably made his way to Düsseldorf on the Rhine by way of Gibraltar, lived in the last part of the Ice Age, after a very warm climate had prevailed for several thousand years. Neanderthal man was only about five feet three inches in height and was probably related to the aboriginal Hottentots, seeing that he has been found in South Africa as well as in Germany. He is also known to have lived in Thuringia, Moravia, France, the Crimea and Palestine.

In the warm, dry climate which prevailed in Europe at the end of the Ice Age there came to Europe—probably from Asia—Cro-Magnon man, so called from the rock-shelter in France in which his remains were discovered; other traces of him have been found in Bohemia and elsewhere. His limbs were finely shaped, his nose was short and coarse, his eyebrows were not strongly marked. The cultural epochs into which his period is divided are termed Aurignacian, Solutrian and Magdalenian, all named after places where relics of his activities have been found. It was during the Magdalenian phase that superb works of art were engraved and painted in the recesses of caves. How, when, why or where Cro-Magnon man disappeared is a matter which has not yet been decided.

We do not know in which millennium before the Christian era the (probably Iberian) Basques, Sardinians, and Ligurians first appeared in Europe, nor do we know much of the origin of the Alpine-dwelling Rhæti, who have been brought into relationship with the Etruscans. It has been conjectured that the forbears of the Italians were once settled on the Neckar, those of the Greeks in Silesia, those of the Celts in Thuringia, and those of the Teutonic peoples on the Baltic.

ANCIENT EUROPEAN PEOPLES

The Albanians are the only racially pure relic of the Illyrians who settled in the Balkan peninsula in the Stone Age. Two sections of them, the Hellenes and the Macedonians, developed into independent civilized peoples, but another section remained in a mountain fastness and persisted in a semi-wild condition through every period of history. These Albanians supplied good soldiers to the Roman legions and the Turkish armies, in return for which they were left undisturbed, to carry on their blood feuds and enjoy their lawlessness up to the present day. An interesting feature of their history is that in the Middle Ages they settled the depopulated classical soil of Attica, without, however, occasioning a second blossoming of Greek civilization.

The only pure relic of the Basques who once, as the Iberians (who belonged to the Hamitic race, in its turn related to the Semites), inhabited the whole of western Europe, is now to be found esconced in a corner of the Pyrenees. The name " Basque " means mountain dweller, as also does " Albanian." The tiny state of Andorra is Basque. Modern philologists have attempted to establish a connexion between the language of the Basques and that of one of the many tribes dwelling in the Caucasus. It is true that in antiquity there were regions near those mountains in which dwelt peoples who were known as Iberians and Albanians, so that possibly the forbears of the two oldest relics of European peoples were once neighbours there.

Old as it is, the history of the Basque people, until the recent Spanish civil war, is singularly uneventful. Their only poem, based on oral tradition, tells of the inroads of the Romans. Their constitution was always democratic. Even now they use rudely-made, two-wheeled ox carts and ploughs of clumsy design. On the other hand, there is a tradition that lone Basque fishermen found their way to America in the earliest times. They are said to have brought back with them the word *bacaillabo* (codfish), which they had taken from an American Indian language. Pizarro (i.e., " the bearded one," whence our word " bizarre "), who conquered Peru four hundred years ago, was a Basque. Previous to the institution of strict immigration laws by the United States, many members of this, the oldest European people, found their way to the New World, where they were welcomed as industrious workers.

CRADLES OF CIVILIZATION

THE original cradle of civilization has been sought, either actively or speculatively, in the Gobi Desert, in Turkestan, farther Pomerania, Java, Brazil, Scandinavia, Honduras, South Africa, the Congo, Ceylon, North America, and even the Arctic. The place most favoured by modern scholars is Mesopotamia, the present-day Iraq, for it is there that the oldest remains of stone buildings have been found, and not far off, in the Caucasus, the first metal work.

CONTINENT THAT WAS SHATTERED

Eduard Stucken is of the opinion that the cradle is to be located, not in Mesopotamia, nor in the legendary continent of Atlantis, but in a sixth continent, that of Oceania, which has been broken up into the present archipelago of Polynesia, Micronesia and Melanesia by vast upheavals of Nature. The inhabitants of the east coast of this shattered continent are thought to have found a second home in America (there was possibly sea-borne commerce between the empire of the Incas and Polynesia), while the inhabitants of the west coast took ship for farther India, Mesopotamia, and Madagascar.

Not only the affinity of language between the Egyptians, the Sumerians, the Polynesians, and the South Americans, but also the custom of building pyramids have been cited in support of this theory. Words which were written on tablets in cuneiform script 6,000 years ago are still used in the Antipodes. To give but one example, the Sumerian word *kud* means to part, the Maori word *koti* means to cut, the Peruvian word *kutu* means to break a thread with the teeth, and the Mexican word *kokota* means cutter.

The former inhabitants of Oceania who had fled from their homeland may originally have settled in Siam or in the Sunda Islands. That the Sumerians and the ancient Egyptians were particularly noteworthy seamen has not been established, but the fact that many Sumerian words are still used in America and Polynesia compels one to look for other links. Another point to be noticed in this connexion is that finds have been made on the Peruvian coast which are reminiscent of ancient China. Incidentally the Sumerians were acclaimed as the forefathers of the Turks at the Pan-Turkish Congress held at Stamboul in 1936.

It may be that the cradle of civilization was in the Tarim basin in Central Asia, where Sven Hedin, the eminent Swedish traveller, has located an age-old centre of culture in what is now a desert. Possibly, when inner Asia began to assume its steppe formation before the dawn of history, the Turkish and Mongolian peoples spread from here to all points of the compass.

WERE THERE HUMAN BEINGS IN THE COAL AGE?

Professor Klaatsch argues that man could not have made his first appearance on the earth in the Ice Age because even the lowest type of man has never had the canine teeth of an ape. According to the theory propounded by Dacqué, the human being has developed and differentiated itself by the gradual rejection of all animal features, the process having begun with the appearance of organic life and continuing up to the present day. Accordingly there must have existed even in the Carboniferous Age (500,000,000 years ago) a pre-human being which, adapting itself to the geological period, was protected by a horny armour, ran about on all fours, and was devoid of personality and intellectual capacity.

In the Permian period, which followed the Carboniferous Age, this being is thought to have had an eye in the forehead (now dwarfed into the pineal gland) and to have begun to assume an erect position of the body, though in other respects it was still more reptilian than mammalian. In the succeeding Triassic and Jurassic periods this " man " became marsupial, with undeveloped hands, a semi-erect gait, and cerebral expansion, with the frontal eye stunted. From the foundering continent of Gondwanaland, which linked South America to Africa, India and Australia, he escaped to Lemuria (linking Africa and India).

In the Tertiary period (about 18,000,000 years ago) part of Lemuria also sank into the Indian Ocean and man took the first steps towards civilization on Atlantis, cultivating the vine and so on; then there set in a marked development of the human cerebrum, an erect gait, the cult of the sun, and astrology. The early Ice Age saw the late culture of Atlantis and the foundering of this continent. The Alluvial period (geologically the modern period, which has been going on for the last 500,000 years) saw the beginning of the later historical cultures.

PEOPLES ON THE MOVE

IT would appear that folk migrations are not racial characteristics but expressions of the fact that a certain condition of culture has been reached. We know only of the major folk-movements that took place within the historical period, and our knowledge of these is incomplete.

HORDES FROM THE TARIM BASIN

Even in the sixth millennium before our era the migration of the Hamites and Semites from North Africa—it is believed—to the Near East lay in the distant past. The departure of the Mongolian peoples from the Tarim basin between the Kun Lun and Tien Shan mountains of Central Asia, is allotted quite arbitrarily to round about the year 3000 B.C. As already mentioned, Dr. Sven Hedin avers that what is now a desert was formerly a cultural paradise. The Tibetan horde occupied Tibet, a second horde advanced across south China, where it established various states in 2000 B.C., to farther India, where in 220 B.C. it called into existence the empires of Champa and Cambodia.

In A.D. 1340 a second horde following on the first founded the empire of Siam. The Chinese horde left the Tarim basin at the same time as the Tibetan and occupied until 2000 B.C. the present provinces of Kan-Su, Shansi, and Chih-Li. The land between the Yangtze and the Hwang-Ho was settled by them in the period 1700-1100 B.C., but it was not until 220 B.C. that southern China was in their hands.

A third horde, that of the Tunguses, had left the Tarim basin with the Chinese and Tibetans and a part of it had migrated to America by way of north-east Siberia (a tribe living apart in south-east Tibet is wholly similar to the Indians of the western plains of North America). By 900 B.C. the Tunguses were in possession of Manchuria, Korea, and the Japanese islands.

COMING OF THE HUNS

About 1500 B.C. the Hunnic horde cut itself off from the original Mongolian stock and set up short-lived states in the dominions of the Chinese and Tunguses; three Hunnic empires were in existence about 180 B.C. The western Huns founded the Indo-Scythian Empire, which was destroyed by the Persians in 574 B.C., the central Huns split into the White and Black Huns and both sections moved into Europe, where their power crumbled on the death of Attila (A.D. 453). The empire of the eastern Huns was destroyed by the Tunguses and Chinese in A.D. 100.

It is possible that ages ago the Turkish tribes or West Mongols, who were related to the Mongolian hordes in the Altai Mountains, were supreme in India as the Dravidians, in Mesopotamia as the Sumerians, in Asia Minor as the Hittites, and in Egypt as the Hyksos. A section of them appeared much later (A.D. 400) as the Avars, who some 400 years later were subdued by Charlemagne in what is now Hungary. About A.D. 600 the Turkish tribes were split asunder by the Chinese; a few hordes were engaged as bodyguards by the Caliphs and in 976 founded an Indo–Turkish Empire, which was overcome by Tamerlane in 1398; the Turkish horde of the Petchenegs drove the Magyars out of Bessarabia into Hungary about the year 900. The Turkish Seljuks conquered Asia Minor, and the Osman horde pushed forward as far as Morocco and Vienna.

ORIGIN OF THE COSSACKS

Among the off-shoots of the Turkish tribes are the Tartars, who by 1468 had advanced as far as the Indus, and mingling with the Russians in southern Russia became the Cossacks. The Turks who stayed behind in Central Asia were driven out by the Mongols in 1209 and now live as the Yakuts in north-east Siberia. The Kirghis are another Central Asiatic Turkish tribe. The Turks proper, who were settled in Asia Minor, conquered the Balkans in the 15th century and maintained their position there until they were slowly forced southwards again in and after the wars of 1683-1699.

The hordes of the Buriats, Khalkhas, and Kalmucks, falsely called the true Mongols, who had lived apart from each other on the edge of the Gobi Desert for untold centuries, formed a confederation in 1175 for the purpose of founding an empire. They overran China, Persia, Siberia, Russia, and India, and maintained their supremacy in Egypt as the Mamelukes until 1800. In Europe there are remnants of them living in the Crimea.

About 4000 B.C. a Hamitic migration is thought to have taken place, moving from South Arabia, Nubia, and Libya into Spain and southern Europe and bringing into Europe the Iberians (Basques, Sardinians, Ligurians). At the same time a Semitic horde, known as the Akkads or Akkadians, wandered into Mesopotamia, where it adopted the culture of the Sumerians.

The migration from Arabia of the Canaanitish tribes in 2700-1400 B.C
poured over anterior Asia like a flood. Among them were the Amorites,
who succeeded the Akkads in Mesopotamia, while the Phœnicians, who
were also Semitic, occupied the Syrian coast of the Mediterranean.
About 600 B.C. the Semitic Chaldæans moved from Arabia into
Mesopotamia, and after 1,200 or 1,300 years there followed the occupation of North Africa, Spain, and anterior Asia by the hordes from
Arabia which had embraced Islam.

FROM SIBERIA TO TIERRA DEL FUEGO

American migrations are difficult to follow. Probably the Tunguses
crossed the Bering Straits about 2500 B.C. on hunting and fishing
expeditions, and received the seeds of a higher culture from Central
America. The Swedish ethnologist, Baron Nordenskjöld, points out
that there are features of the North Americans which show their
relationship to Asia on the one hand and to Central and South America
on the other, that is to say that there was once a connexion between
Siberia and the whole of America as far south as Tierra del Fuego.

The highly developed cultures of Mexico and Peru can only have
been brought about by a brisk maritime traffic between southern and
eastern Asia and Central America by way of the Pacific Ocean. From
Central America the culture was conveyed to the primitive American
Indians to the north and south. Thus the Mayas, for example, brought
culture from Honduras in Central America to Mexico about A.D. 500,
where it was adopted in 1325 by the Aztecs, who came from the north.
Similarly the Chileans received culture from the Peruvians, while in
the forests of Brazil uncultured tribes of aboriginals, about which little
or nothing is known, are still existing at the present day.

NEW HOMES IN THE NEW WORLD

In contrast to the migration of whole peoples as the manifestation
of a certain condition of culture, the emigration of small sections of a
people is the result of causes which are somewhat different, although
they, too, have either contributed to the culture and racial structure of
a nation, or have produced precisely the reverse effect.

In antiquity, emigration was a natural and acknowledged right, often
utilized on account of over-population or the desire to be rid of
obnoxious elements; this was how colonies originated. Similarly in
the Middle Ages a powerful stimulus was given to emigration by
commercial and military factors. The first check given to emigration
was by the later stages of the feudal system and serfdom. It received
a fresh impetus, however, in the age of discovery and in that of the
religious wars, when the adherents of religions that were not tolerated
in a country were expelled.

In 1819-1926 about 36,000,000 Europeans and some 800,000 persons
from other countries emigrated to the United States of America. In
1857-1915 the Argentine received 4,200,000 white immigrants, Brazil

3,300,000, whereas in 1861-1923 there were only 1,100,000 immigrants to Australia. In 1920-1926, 4,600,000 Europeans left their homes to settle oversea. After the World War 1,500,000 Greeks came back from Asia Minor, and 800,000 Turks went back from Europe to Asia. Until 1870 departure from Japan was punishable by death, but between 1870 and 1929 about 700,000 Japanese emigrated. In 1907-1929 some 100,000 Japanese set up new homes in Brazil.

In modern times Great Britain has consistently encouraged emigration, as has France since 1789. In 1830-1840 some 220,000 Germans emigrated to the United States.

TRANSPORTED TO CONQUERED TERRITORIES

The Jews moved out of Egypt in 1150 B.C., were carried off to Babylon in 722 B.C. and to Spain under the Emperor Hadrian, and in recent years have returned in large numbers to Palestine. They have met with ever-growing disfavour in Germany under the regime of Herr Hitler, and many of the sufferers have found new homes in France and Great Britain. The pre-Roman Italic tribes dismissed their surplus man-power every year, but the Romans transplanted the inhabitants of conquered territories hither and thither. Thus in 180 B.C., 40,000 Ligurians were settled in the depopulated Samnium, and in 8 B.C., 50,000 Dacians were similarly settled in Thrace. Trajan populated the present Rumania with settlers from Asia Minor. Hadrian settled Britons in the Odenwald, along the *limes,* the frontier of the Roman Empire against Germania.

In the 12th century, Henry the Lion transferred Dutchmen and Westphalians to territories on the right bank of the Elbe, which were inhabited at the time by Slavs. In 1200, Andrew II of Hungary sent to the lands of the Moselle and Rhine for settlers in Transylvania. Catherine II of Russia established settlements on the Volga with Franks and Württembergers who had emigrated.

Large numbers of negro slaves from Africa were imported into Haiti in 1505, and 40,000 Caribs (Central American Indians) from the Bahamas in 1550. Only a few years ago 5,000,000 northern Chinese settled in Manchukuo. The last descendants of the Assyrians, 24,000 souls in all, are to be transplanted from Iraq to their old home on the Orontes in Syria; and the Nubians of Upper Egypt, whose lands along the Nile have been flooded by the raising of the dam at Assuan, are finding a new home in the Sudan.

DRIVEN OUT OF SPAIN

The Jews (in 1492) and the hard-working Moriscos (Mohammedans from Morocco) were driven out of Spain for religious reasons. The town of Hanau on the Main was founded by Flemish refugees in 1579, and Freudenstadt was founded by refugees from Styria. The descendants of 1,600 Dutch Mennonites are still living in and around Danzig. In 1650 some 150,000 Bohemian Lutherans found refuge in

B.O.F.—L*

Saxony. After 1685, 1,000,000 Huguenots left France and brought huge sums of money with them into their new home in Germany. In 1690, Waldensian refugees founded a settlement near Maulbronn, in Württemberg.

The Protestants driven out of Salzburg in 1732 were settled in East Prussia, while their fellow-victims from the Zillertal were accommodated in three villages near Schmiedeberg. Inhabitants of the Erzgebirge have settled in Clausthal, in the Harz; Franks have migrated to the Oder. Spanish troops who served under Napoleon made a permanent settlement for themselves on the Danish island of Laaland.

France is strewn with villages whose names indicate a Sarmatian settlement; for example, Sermaize. Ancient Sarmatia included Poland and part of Russia. Alani settled at Valence, Huns at Orleans and in the Swiss canton of Valais, where there also settled in A.D. 930 detached bodies of Arabs. The descendants of the Teutonic Cimbri are still living in twenty different communities in the Alpine area of Northern Italy and continue to speak their own ancient language. In the Hasli-Thal in Switzerland there live the descendants of Normans who came up the Rhine in 840.

Saracinesco, in the Sabine Mountains, near Rome, was founded in the 9th century by Arabs who still only marry among themselves. Descendants of the Visigoths are living in various recesses of the Pyrenees; even after the year 1500 there were villages of Ostrogoths in the Crimea. In A.D. 798, after a revolt in Cordova, 1,500 Andalusians who were descended from the Vandals were driven out, to settle eventually in Crete. The Averser or Avner, the inhabitants of the Avers, an upland valley of the Swiss canton of Grisons, form a German-speaking island amid a population speaking a Romance language. They originated either in a body of Germans who came here from the Valais in the Middle Ages or in a garrison of Hohenstaufen soldiers who were left behind to guard the Alpine passes at the time of the Roman expeditions.

THREE PUZZLING RACES

THE origin of two civilized peoples, the Sumerians and the Etruscans, is still much debated. Some authorities consider that the Sumerians were West Mongols who entered Mesopotamia from the north-east in the sixth millennium B.C. Others hold that they were Hamites, others again that they were Aryans. From whence the Etruscans and the Gipsies derived is also subject to speculation.

MYSTERY OF THE SUMERIANS

The language of the Sumerians was probably Altaic. Sumerian words occur in Greek mythology: examples are siren, satyr, Tartarus and Dædalus. By reason of their inventing writing, the Sumerians rank as the first of the Asiatic civilized peoples. This picture-writing of theirs was converted into phonetic writing by the Semitic Babylonians. The Sumerian town of Kish, in Mesopotamia, was standing before 3500 B.C. Tombs have been found there containing two- and four-wheeled ox carts.

The Sumerian art-forms, with their bold, untrammelled lines, strike quite a modern note. The Babylonians adopted the Sumerian gods, prayers, and hymns in their entirety. To Sumerian literature we owe the *Epic of Gilgamesh*, the forerunner of the Greek *Odyssey*. Beautiful toilet cases, and pieces used in board games were fashioned by the Sumerians. Their political power lasted till 2700 B.C., their cultural influence till 700 B.C.

TEACHERS TO THE ROMANS

The Etruscans, who acted as teachers to the Romans, are reputed to have been the earliest of the civilized peoples of Italy. At the congress of Etruscologists at Florence in 1932 it was stated that they were certainly not Aryans, but that on the other hand their language was not Semitic.

Some scholars hold that the Etruscans were related to the Rhæti, who were domiciled in the Alps and who established themselves in Italy. It is quite likely that Hellenic mariners (the Tyrrhenians), landing on the coast of Etruria, constituted themselves their aristocracy, in the same way as the conquering Aryans in Armenia and in the empire of the Hittites in Asia Minor became a military caste. The earlier monetary system of the Etruscans, their alphabet, and their gods seem to be of Greek origin.

ARE THE GIPSIES EGYPTIANS?

A statement frequently made by the gipsies is that they were driven out of Egypt on account of their religion, and that they are the true children of the Land of the Pharaohs, to which they will one day return. This is why they are called " gipsy " or " gypsy " in English, from the word " Egypt," and *gitano* in Spanish, from the word *Egitto*, meaning Egypt. All that can be said in favour of this claim is that their ears are set high on their heads, a feature which has been noticed in Egyptian statues and mummies. On the other hand, it has not been possible to trace any linguistic relationship between them and the Egyptians.

What is the real origin of this curious people, which since the year A.D. 1417 has been wandering in bands through almost every country of Europe? Whence comes the name *zigeuner* (German), *czigany* (Hungarian), *zingaro* (Italian) and *tzigane* (French)? Professor Sampson seems to have solved the riddle. The gipsies, he says, left their country of origin, India, in the 8th century A.D., but only a portion of them, for the rest are still living in the south of the country and have Aryan-Dravidian features. In the veins of the gipsy flows the wild blood of the Indian Dravidians and Kolis (whence the wood " coolie ").

When the ancestors of the gipsies left India in A.D. 450, they wandered first to Persia, where they split into two groups, which were called after their speech-sounds " Ben " and " Phen." The Ben group wandered on to Syria and became the ancestor of the gipsies in Egypt and anterior Asia; the Phen group passed through Armenia and Kurdistan and appeared outside Constantinople in 810. The gipsies are next heard of in Crete (1322), Corfu (1346), and Wallachia (1370). From Wallachia they moved to Hungary; they were seen in Barcelona in 1477; and together with the Jews and Moriscos were driven out of Spain in 1492. They appeared in England in 1450. In the 16th century they were roaming through Poland, Russia, and Scandinavia. Everywhere they went they apparently adopted the religion of the country but soon reverted to their old mode of living, recognizing only the " moral laws " of their tribe.

At a congress of gipsy chiefs held at Lodz in 1933, under the presidency of the Spanish gipsy-king, Mateo, a Pole was unanimously elected king and as Michael II was given a palace in Warsaw.

HOW COUNTRIES GOT THEIR NAMES

THE origin of the names of countries varies greatly in different cases. The largest continent, Asia, takes its name from the district behind the town of Smyrna, and the name was familiar to Pythagoras as early as 550 B.C. America, the second-largest continent, on the other hand, is named after an otherwise little-known Florentine mariner called Amerigo Vespucci, who embarked on four voyages to America between 1497 and 1504.

Just as we refer to Asia as the Orient (the land of the rising sun), so the Phœnicians spoke of Europe as Eref, which is equivalent to the Occident (the land of the setting sun), and just as the name Asia was transferred from the district in Asia Minor which lay behind Smyrna to the whole continent, so the whole of Africa was so called by the Romans after a Hamitic tribe, the Afri, in Tunisia, which was already known to the elder Cato.

LAND OF THE SOUTH

By the Dutch navigators who landed in Australia, the great island-continent was called simply New Holland; it was not till later that it received its present name, which was invented as long ago as 150 B.C. by Ptolemy to designate a continent which he surmised to lie in the southern hemisphere. The word " Australia " means " the land of the south." The name of the country of the Nile, Egypt, is as old as its history. The old name of Turkey—the Sublime Porte—means " lofty gate." The name Abyssinia derives from *habesh*, " mixture " of peoples.

Rome, Romagna, Rumelia, Rumania, etc., contain the stem of the Aryan word for " flow " (Greek *rheo*, German *strömen*). Rome,

therefore, means "stream town" and is linguistically connected with
the names of the rivers Rhone, Rhine, Aare, Ruhr, Reuss, Rio, etc.
Italy (= *vitalia*) means simply "pasture land." Britain comes from
the Welsh word *brython*. Albion means "highland" (the Celtic *alb*,
alpen, *apennine* = high) and not "white land," as the Romans falsely
inferred from its chalk cliffs.

An Aryan word related to "Alb" gave the name to the Albanians
in the Balkans. Before France received its name from the conquering
Franks it was called Gaul. This Celtic G becomes W in the Germanic
pronunciation; thus Wales is *Galles* in French and is linguistically
identical with the Canton Wallis (Valais); there are common features,
too, in the names of the Spanish province of Galicia, and Portugal.
Belgium derives its name from the Germanic Belgæ who entered its
territory in 750 B.C. Spain was given its name by the Phœnicians, who
called it Shapan ("rabbit land"). Similarly the Canary Islands means
"dogs' islands," and the Azores "hawks' islands."

RUSSIA NAMED BY FINNS

Sweden and Switzerland, which are widely separated geographically,
are said nevertheless to have an historical-linguistic connexion, inasmuch
as in A.D. 867 a band of Normans settled in the Swiss valley known as
the Haslital and gave Switzerland its name. The Finns who dwelt on
the Dnieper and saw the river fleets of the Northmen called the latter
rodsen (rowers), whence came the name Russians and Russia. Canaan,
like Holland, means "Netherlands," i.e., low-lying land. Holstein is
so called after its inhabitants, who once dwelt in the *Holz* (German for
"woods"). Bohemia was once the home of the Celtic Boii, who,
mingling with the Avars, also gave Bavaria its name.

The Romans called all the Hellenes after a small tribe which was
the first to become known to them: the Græci, on the Adriatic Sea, and
it is a curious fact that in the Middle Ages the Greeks called themselves
Romai, namely Romans. Germany (which is called *Deutschland* by
the Germans themselves) was given this name (Germania) by the
Romans, while the French and Spanish called it after the German tribe
situated nearest to France: the Alemanni.

GERMANY'S DEBT TO ITALY

The people to whom the Gauls first applied the name of *Germani*
(Celtic "neighbour," Latin *germanus,* "related") were the Celticized
Germanic tribes of the Eburones, in the Ardennes. Professor Hennig
has explained that the word "Germane" means "dwelling near
thermæ," as, for instance, the inhabitants of Baden are called after the
springs of Baden-Baden, and those who dwelt near the springs of La
Mancha in Spain were called *germani* in antiquity. The word "warm,"
says the professor, is of Aryan origin and occurs in the names Wurms,
Bourbon, and the world-famous Thermopylæ (hot-gates).

There is little doubt about the Germans' own name for their country

—*Deutschland*. The word *deutsch*, which arose in the Frankish period, means etymologically "popular" (*theod, diot* = people; hence the adjective *diutisc*, Latin *teutonicus*) and originally denoted the vulgar tongue as opposed to Latin. The custom of referring to the users of this tongue as *deutsch* arose in Italy, whose destiny at that time was being shaped by the policy of the German emperors. The primary meaning of *die deutschen Lande* (which was first used in the 11th century) was the German-speaking territory of the Holy Roman Empire; it was not until the ecclesiastical-political disputes of the 14th and 15th centuries that the word *Deutschland* truly expressed the national consciousness.

LIFETIME OF STATES

THAT states are not exempt from the universal law by which everything on earth is subject to change and dissolution was the belief of Joseph Fouché, Napoleon's Minister of Police. There have been no states, he says in his *Memoirs*, whose term of existence has exceeded a certain number of centuries.

FRENCH REVOLUTION "INEVITABLE"

If the age of states were reckoned at from 1,200 to 1,500 years it would certainly be the limit of their existence, whence the inevitable conclusion that a state which had not received its death-blow within a period of thirteen centuries (France from the time of Clovis to 1789) could not be far from a catastrophe. Accordingly the French Revolution was nothing but an historically inevitable upheaval, albeit one of only the second magnitude, since the state was not entirely ruined but only made a forcible change in its constitution. Such upheavals are comparable to volcanic eruptions, which change the shape of the crater but leave the volcano itself in existence. It is quite another matter with historical upheavals of the first magnitude, by which a state is struck out of the book of history.

PATRIARCHS AMONG THE NATIONS

What is there to be said about the duration of some of the most famous states in history? Egypt, China, and Japan are patriarchs among the nations because their geographical position allowed them to live their lives to the full. The Land of the Pharaohs lived, unchanged in structure, through thirty centuries as the Ancient, Middle, and New Empires. Interrupted only by revolutionary crises, the first five dynasties of China, which held sway over only the north-east provinces, ruled for fifteen centuries. Another seventeen centuries elapsed between A.D. 220 and the fall of the last dynasty in 1912. China has always been a geographical entity with a uniform culture.

Even as early as 600 B.C. an ordered constitution for Japan was not difficult of attainment owing to its insular position, although the fertile plain of Kwanto around Tokio remained unconquered until A.D. 150.

For twenty-five centuries this political organism slumbered on, awaiting until our own day to become " the rising sun " for the East.

It was not until 1867 that Japan threw off the shackles of feudalism; but within the following ten years the most astonishing advances were made, and within forty years Japan had definitely taken her place as one of the great powers of the earth.

OLDEST THRONE IN EUROPE

Tropical states, such as the Indian, African, and Maya Empires, were like exotic plants, full of sap but short-lived. Similarly all other states which have played a part in the history of human civilization, with the exception of the city-state of Babylon, have enjoyed a comparatively short existence—for instance, Assyria, Media, Persia, and the Caliphate.

The Grecian system of small city-states was merged, like many other states, into the Roman Empire, which lasted for five centuries. Its existence was prolonged, however, by the East Roman or Byzantine Empire for ten centuries more. Its successors, Russia and Turkey, have experienced crises in our days which were all but fatal. The Holy See, which has maintained its independence for thirteen centuries, is now the oldest throne in Europe whose foundations were established in antiquity.

NUMBERING THE PEOPLE

The picturesque little mountain state of San Marino in northern Italy, the smallest and, as it claims, the oldest republic in the world, was traditionally founded by Marinus of Arbe in the second half of the 4th century A.D. Thirty-two square miles in extent, the territory of the republic consists largely of the precipitous and craggy hill known as Mt. Titano. The Pyreneean state of Andorra, which is about six times as large, dates traditionally from the reign of Charlemagne (742-814).

We have evidence that an extensive census was carried out in Babylonia about 2500 B.C. The children of Israel were numbered at the time of the Exodus, and David counted his warriors. Censuses were taken at an early date in China, Egypt and Persia.

In Rome censuses were held for the purpose of verifying the civil status of citizens and thus assessing their civic liabilities. The census was held every five years, and by the time of Augustus (630 B.C.–A.D. 14) had to come to cover practically the whole of the civilized world.

The modern census, which is based upon the Roman model, dates from the middle of the 17th century, the first to be held being in Quebec and Nova Scotia. The German states led the way in Europe, being followed by Sweden.

" FEAR OF DISTEMPER "

Great Britain was late in the field. Proposals were made in the House of Commons in 1753, but they were defeated, opponents expressing the fear that a census might result in " some great public misfortune or epidemical distemper." It was not until 1801 that the practice was established.

The last important state to adopt the practice of numbering its people was Turkey, which held its first census in 1927.

DISTRIBUTION OF MANKIND OVER THE EARTH

At the time of the birth of Christ the Roman Empire had probably about 50,000,000 inhabitants, of whom 7,000,000 were in Egypt. The number of the Teutonic peoples living between the Rhine and the Elbe at the beginning of the migration of the nations, by which time the population of the Roman Empire had appreciably diminished, is estimated at 6,000,000, for it appears from the latest researches that even in the time of Christ the number of West Germans alone amounted to something like 4,000,000

In the year 1350 there were 100,000,000 Europeans, in 1800 there were 175,000,000, which number had increased by 1936 to 500,000,000. The peak of the increase is expected to be reached in 1950. The population of the world increased from 775,000,000 in 1800 to 1,564,000,000 in 1900 and entered on the second thousand million in 1935. Of these the Malays have increased in 100 years from 11,000,000 to 67,000,000, the white races in Europe and America from 185,000,000 to 685,000,000, and the Chinese from 245,000,000 to 450,000,000.

HUMANITY MARCHES ON

An English statistician, after devoting much time and labour to the problem, has arrived at the conclusion that up to the present day at least 47,000 billion persons have lived on the earth. According to this reckoning, every square mile of dry land has been inhabited by 134,622,976 persons, which means five persons to every square foot. The present population is about 2,000,000,000.

EARTH'S POPULOUS FAMILY

The population of the world has increased in an amazing way during the course of the centuries. It has been calculated that at the time of its greatest expansion the Roman Empire contained a population of only 50,000,000, of whom about 7,000,000 were in Egypt alone. For centuries the population of the Land of the Pharaohs has maintained itself at more or less the same level, but the case with the European countries is very different. There the increase has been enormous.

Whereas in 1480 the population of England was only 3,700,000, in other words about half that of modern London and almost the same as that of modern Denmark, today it is about 40,000,000. In 1480 there were as many as 12,500,000 Frenchmen, but that number has only trebled itself (39,200,000, excluding Alsace and Lorraine).

In 1480 the population of Germany and Austria amounted to 10,500,000, whereas that of Russia is computed to have been only just over 2,000,000; now the latter country has fifty times as many inhabitants as then. The Spaniards have doubled themselves: in their most flourishing period (1480) there were nearly 9,000,000 of them; 100 years later (1580) the population of the mother country showed no increase, and even 200 years later the increase was only about 100,000. Italy, on the other hand, which at the time of its Renaissance (1480) had the same number of inhabitants as Spain, has now quadrupled itself and is the most populous country in Europe after Russia, Germany and Great Britain.

TOTAL POPULATION IS INCREASING

The total population of the world is increasing, but the birth rate is falling steadily in almost every European country except Russia. War losses make no appreciable difference to the rate of increase, although in the period 1850-1897 over 2,500,000 men were killed in war—a loss which in the World War was suffered by Germany alone.

The population of the world was about 775,000,000 in 1800; it had more than doubled itself (1,564,000,000) by 1900, and it must now be in the region of 2,000,000,000. Estimates of the maximum population the earth could support vary greatly. Some experts have put the figure as low as 3,000,000,000; others as high as 7,000,000,000. The Malays have increased more rapidly than any other race: from 11,000,000 to 67,000,000 in 100 years.

337

MOST POPULOUS COUNTRY

China, with approximately 450,000,000 inhabitants, is the most populous area on the face of the globe. India comes next with about 400,000,000; then Soviet Russia with 170,000,000 and the United States of America with 130,000,000. The population of Japan proper does not exceed 80,000,000, but that of the Japanese Empire has been put at about 100,000,000.

The most densely populated countries in the world are Barbados, in the British West Indies, and Java and Madura in the Dutch East Indies. Barbados has 1,100 people to a square mile; Java and Madura together have about 820. Belgium, with 705 people per square mile, is the most densely populated country in Europe. Next to it come England and Wales, which taken together have over 700 to each square mile.

AUSTRALIA'S TWO PEOPLE TO THE SQUARE MILE

Australia has only two people to each square mile. This is partly accounted for by the immense desert areas of that continent, but it could support many more people. In Africa the density of population varies from 555 persons per square mile in Mauritius, to one person in Libya, south-west Africa, and Bechuanaland. In the United States of America there are thirty-six persons to the square mile.

About two-thirds of the population of the world live on only one-eighth of its habitable area: China, Japan, India and part of Europe.

TOWNS MORE FAVOURED THAN COUNTRY

Within the last century more and more people have been moving from country to urban districts. In England and Wales, for instance, about forty per cent of the people live in towns with a population of over 100,000.

In Germany, the flow of population into the towns has been even greater. Fifty years ago, three-quarters of the population were living on the land. Today that position is reversed. After the World War, when the housing shortage was acute, overcrowding in the large towns in some countries increased so rapidly as to become a menace to public health. In London the average number of inmates per house was eight, in Philadelphia, U.S.A., only five, and in Paris as much as thirty-eight, but in Berlin no less than seventy-six persons were crammed into a single dwelling.

WORLD'S LARGEST CITIES

The population of capital cities has increased in a very remarkable fashion during the last seventy years. London, including Greater London, has the largest population of any city in the world—over 8,000,000 souls, yet it is little more than double the number in 1870. At the same date New York contained 900,000 souls. Today it ranks second in the list of the world's great cities, with a population of nearly 7,000,000. Next comes Tokyo, Japan, with 5,400,000. Berlin comes fourth with a population of 4,250,000, a tenth of the entire population of Prussia. In 1870 the city contained 800,000 souls.

It is said that the total population of the world, if massed together, could find standing room on the small Danish island of Bornholm and that were it necessary to pack the whole of the human race in one receptacle, with the object, shall we say, of shooting it off by means of a rocket to another star, a case 1,100 cubic yards in capacity would suffice.

MARRIAGE AND DIVORCE

More than a thousand people get married every day in Great Britain and Northern Ireland, where the average annual number of marriages is about 375,000. The annual marriage rate in the United Kingdom is thus about 16 per 1,000. Two people are born for every one that gets married, and three people die for every two that get married. The proportion of divorces to marriages in Great Britain is about 1 to 80. The average age of persons married in Britain is 29 for men and 26 for women. Widowers who re-marry do so at the average age of 50, and widows at 45. According to the last census nearly fifty-two per cent of Englishmen were unmarried; forty-four per cent were married and nearly four per cent were widowers. For women the figures were: fifty per cent single, forty-one per cent married and nine per cent widowed.

In every country of the Northern Hemisphere the busiest month for marriages is June. Deserving of special mention for his matrimonial activity is Robert Thieme, who died in 1935, at the age of 103, after outliving fifteen wives.

LARGE FAMILIES

In 1935 a monument in stone was erected at Bönnigheim in Württemberg, Germany, to a woman of the 15th century who had brought into the world fifty-three children (thirty-eight boys, fifteen girls). At Valladolid, Spain, in 1926, a woman sixty-eight years old gave birth to her twenty-ninth son. According to statistics, only one woman in every 3,300 has a child after the age of fifty years. In 1928 an Egyptian woman brought forth four girls and two boys at the same birth. In 1934 Mrs. Dionne, a Canadian, bore five girls at one confinement. The children are remarkable as being the only quintuplets on record who have survived early infancy.

Every year there are born into the world about 337,000 twins, 37,000 triplets, and sixty-five quadruplets: about 1,000 twins and 100 triplets daily, and quadruplets every five days.

BIRTH RATE AND DEATH RATE

The birth rate in England and Wales in 1935 was 14.7 per 1,000 of the population. Five years earlier it was 16.3 per 1,000 and in 1890 it was 30.2 per 1,000. It will thus been seen that the English birth rate has fallen by well over half in forty-five years. The death rate is also falling: in 1890 it was 19.5 per 1,000, in 1935 11.7 per 1,000.

The steep fall in the birth rate causes considerable misgiving among population experts, some of whom assert that if the fall is maintained the population of England in 100 years' time will be less than 5,000,000. The problem is not confined to England. Despite frantic efforts on the part of the authoritarian rulers of Italy and Germany, the birth rate remains at a very low level in both countries. In Italy it has dropped from 37.5 per 1,000 in 1890 to 23.3 in 1935; in Germany from 36.5 in 1890 to 18.9 in 1935. Austria has the lowest birth rate in Europe: it dropped from 37.8 in 1890 to 13.1 in 1935. Next to her comes Sweden, whose rate has dropped from 28.8 to 13.8 in forty-five years.

NEW ZEALAND HAS LOWEST DEATH RATE

The highest birth rate in Europe obtains in Russia, where in 1930 there were 30.1 births per 1,000 of the population. In British India the birth rate is very high: 34.9 per 1,000; but so also is the death rate: 23.1 per 1,000. India's infantile death rate is appalling: 164 per 1,000 births. The corresponding English figure—59 per 1,000 births—though much lower, reflects a thoroughly unsatisfactory state of affairs, when we remember that the figure for New Zealand is only 31 per 1,000 births and for Norway only 41 per 1,000 births. New Zealand, incidentally, has the lowest death rate in the world: 8.2 per 1,000, or one-third that of India.

Germany (excluding Austria and Bohemia) produces about 1,204,000 babies each year: more than twice as many as are produced in England and Wales (600,000) and about 480,000 more than are produced in France (722,000). At the other end of the scale is Norway, which produces only 42,000 babies a year, and Denmark with 65,000.

Norway's neighbour, Sweden, has the highest rate of illegitimate births in Europe: one birth in every seven is illegitimate. Next to Sweden in this respect comes Denmark with one in ten; then Germany with one in eleven. One English child out of twenty-three is illegitimate. In Belgium only one out of thirty-four is not legitimate. At the other extreme comes Chile with only seven legitimate births in every eleven.

ANCESTORS BY THE MILLION

Were it not that the further back we trace our ancestry the more marriages between relations we find recorded, we should have to presume that every person now living derived from a colossally large number of people. Taking thirty years as the average interval between generations, each one of us would have about 14 ancestors up to the year 1814, 126 up to the year 1740, 16,382 up to the year 1521 (fourteen generations), 33,554,430 up to the time of Barbarossa (A.D. 1180), 274,877,906,622 up to A.D. 800, and 36,892,000 billions up to the birth of Christ (sixty-four generations).

Since at this date there were only about 25,000,000 people living in the whole of the Roman Empire, it is obvious that among the ancestors of the world's present population many marriages between relations must have taken place, the degree of kinship varying according to race.

OLDEST GENEALOGICAL TABLES

Of the 2,000,000,000 now living there are very few who can trace back their ancestors beyond the fourth generation. Even when it came to setting down the dates of their great-grandparents they would find themselves in difficulties.

Only those of noble stock have tended their family trees for any length of time. The oldest English families pride themselves on being able to trace back their ancestry to the time of William the Conqueror.

It has always been the endeavour of families which have come into power to cast a halo of superhuman ancestry round their obscure origins. It was not only the rulers of Japan, Egypt, and Peru that declared themselves to be the "children of the sun god." Eleven tribes of Greece alone, not to mention the royal houses of Sparta and Macedonia and the Roman family of the Fabii, claimed Hercules, the son of the mother of the gods, as their first progenitor.

NAPOLEON'S ANCESTRY

Most of the princely houses of Germany asserted themselves to be the descendants of Odin. Cæsar built a temple in Rome to his reputed ancestress Venus, and resourceful genealogists presented Napoleon with a pedigree that went back to Cæsar; actually Napoleon's family came from Crete, where in the time of the Crusades it went by the Greek name of Kalomeros, the meaning of which is the same as that of the Italian form Buonaparte.

Even now there are family trees in Phana, the aristocratic Greek quarter of Stamboul, that go back to Aristotle, or even as far as Ulysses.

Pope Innocent X (1650), of the House of Pamphili, maintained that he had sprung from Numa Pompilius, the second king of Rome (600 B.C.); Maria Theresa of Austria, on the other hand, was supposed merely to have smiled when presented with a family tree that went back to Scipio, the conqueror of Hannibal.

ORIGINS OF EMPERORS

From Widukind or Widdekind, the opponent of Charlemagne, derive on the maternal side the Saxon emperors and, through Otto the Great's nephew, Hugh Capet, the royal houses of France. The princely houses of Anhalt, Brunswick, Oldenburg (Denmark), and Savoy (Italy) also claim Widukind as their ancestor.

The Merovingians, who founded the kingdom of the Franks in the 5th century, originated with Marobodius, chief of the Marcomanni (themselves related to the Suebi, the present Swabians), who had conquered Bohemia ("the home of the [Celtic] Boii") about the time of the birth of Christ. A branch of the Merovingians, who became extinct in France, ruled as a ducal house in Franconia. There is trustworthy evidence that from the elder line of this imperial family derives the house of Nassau-Orange, from the junior line that of Hohenlohe. From the latter the Frankish emperors were descended, and Henry IV's daughter Agnes was the ancestress of the Hohenstaufen. Further, there is to be found in all these families the blood of the Arsacids, those Armenian kings with whom Pompey was at war, for Henry I of France married a granddaughter of the Emperor Romanus II of Byzantium.

The year 1935 saw the death of the last female Palæologus (the Palæologi were the ruling family of the Byzantine Empire, overthrown by the Turks in 1453), who was a descendant of the Eastern Roman Emperor Andronicus III. After the Balkan War of 1911 she laid claim to the throne of Constantinople and was received with royal honours even in Greece.

3,000 YEARS OF ANCESTORS

The oldest authentic genealogical tree is possessed by the Duke of Kuefu. This goes back in unbroken succession, attested by memorial tablets, confirmed in their turn by documentary evidence, for seventy-seven generations, ending with Confucius, who for his part could trace his lineage back to 1151 B.C. At the present day there are sixty families directly descended from Confucius and retaining his name of K'ung.

WHAT THE ANCIENTS KNEW

IT would seem as though the saying, "There is nothing new under the sun" is nearly as applicable to the scientific world as to moral and ethical principles. It certainly happens often enough that a recently "discovered" truth is found to be based on old ideas, and a "new" invention or discovery to have its origins in the past.

"MODERN" INVENTIONS THAT ARE ANCIENT

Among the many "modern" things that were known to the ancients were turbines and pressure engines worked by steam. Printing and the making of books were known to them also. Long before the birth of Christ, Roman potters were stamping their names and devices on domestic utensils and vases by means of movable type, while the Chinese were engaged in block printing in the 9th century A.D. In ancient Alexandria there were advertisement pillars to which public notices were affixed with gum. The Romans had not only these but also huge boards painted with red and black letters as advertisements.

That asphalt and asbestos were used by the Sumerians in Mesopotamia before 3500 B.C. is proved by the discovery of these materials in Ur. Similarly building in cement and concrete was no secret to their descendants. The fire engine was invented by the Greek Ctesibius about 200 B.C., and there was an organized fire-fighting service in Rome in the last century before Christ.

UNBREAKABLE GLASS THAT DENTED

There were quite a number of automatic machines in the ancient world. In the temples of Alexandria, for instance, there were machines which produced a quantity of holy water when a coin was inserted in them. There was also a demonstration of a robot or automatic man before one of the Ptolemies of Egypt. There was unbreakable glass, which when dented could be hammered straight again; its mode of manufacture, though it was in common use in Rome, has not been rediscovered. It is only recently that modern science has produced fireproof glass, in which food can be baked and roasted.

MUMMY CLOTHS 3,000 YEARS OLD

The weaving and spinning of flax must have been an important industry in Egypt, even in the earliest period of its history, judging by the number of mummies which were wrapped in linen. In the Old Testament mention is made of the curtains in the temple and of the fine linen vestments of the priests. Mummy cloths 3,000 years old have preserved their original softness and pliancy, while their colours have remained fresh and unfaded.

In spite of complex and delicate machinery, modern weaving is not as efficient as that of the ancient Egyptians. On the other hand, the ancients had not that technical precision which can make threads 1,000th of a millimetre in diameter, nor had they the knowledge of the chemistry of colloids which can produce spun silk.

CLOCK RUN BY WATER POWER

Plato invented an alarm clock by fitting a siphon (a bent tube by which a liquid can be transferred from one vessel to another) to a water clock. As soon as the water was on a level with the top of the siphon, it ran down a tube into a vessel which stood below it so quickly that the air in it was compressed and escaped through a pipe with a loud whistle. Plato used this contrivance, which had to be set six hours in advance, to summon his pupils at four o'clock in the morning. The octagonal tower of a water-driven clock built in the last century B.C. still stands in Athens.

Incubators were in use in ancient Egypt; 7,000 eggs could be hatched simultaneously in one of these machines. They stood on little hearths which were heated with dung or straw.

LOUDSPEAKERS IN CÆSAR'S TIME

Vitruvius, who lived in the time of Julius Cæsar (102-44 B.C.) gives us a description of the loudspeakers, which were called *echea*, or "echo-strengtheners." They were bronze vessels fixed in small openings along the wall of a theatre or under a moulding. They re-echoed the sounds which came to them and conveyed them to the ears of the audience in a louder and more harmonious form.

Further amplifiers were fixed to pedestals sloping towards the stage to increase the volume of the sound-waves. They were of varying sizes and were so tuned that their range of sounds included the whole compass of the human voice.

The making of high-quality steel blades was known in ancient times. Swords and daggers were made of hard but flexible steel, and the marks that were made on their surface were ineffaceable. The secret of this process of hardening has been lost. Long before our era the Indians knew how to make rustless iron; an iron column erected in Delhi in 350 B.C., has resisted all the ravages of nature. This secret, too, has not yet been rediscovered.

The art of softening ivory by boiling in order to use it in gold and ivory sculptures has also been lost, but the method of producing the Roman red glaze of Aretine pottery (so called from the town of Arezzo in Tuscany) has been rediscovered.

CENTRAL HEATING IN ANCIENT ROME

Central heating was used in Roman houses long before our era. The warmth was created by hot air running below the floor which, being made of stone, would otherwise have been unpleasantly cold, and the walls, too, were heated.

Various mechanical devices were employed by the priesthood. For

massage, co
feet (in othe
Emperor A
Artificial
father of C
with an arti
Royal Colle
for a soldie
attached to
Lips, noses

BOILED W.
Curative
hills. Greel
treatment o
is with us,
that King
water kept
Nero never

The inst
Pompeii sh
women) mu
instruments
keenness ne
by means o
Cæsarean se
Guntramsd
had been pe

DISSECTION
Corpses
though Ari
animals and
Church Fat
The " Papy
in 1898) con
in Egypt in
Mummie
Egyptians p
which they
the patient
seeds, mixec
Even in
way of obta
rock crystal
mitted ultra
though of th

instance, the fire on the altar was used to expand the air in an extensive system of pipes and to cause metal birds to sing. By means of other devices the priests managed to make the images of their gods move. Thus, in the temple of Serapis in Alexandria, a magnet was so placed in the dome as to draw towards itself the head of the god, making him rise from his throne.

In many temples, beneath the hearthstone of the altar where burnt offerings were made, was an air chamber connected by means of an underground pipe with a vessel filled with water. When the water in the vessel rose as the result of being heated, it ran over into another vessel which was suspended alongside, and this, when it had become sufficiently heavy, opened the doors of the temple by means of a hidden system of rollers and wheels without making a sound.

WORKED BY EGYPTIAN PRIESTS

The Egyptian priests were certainly not ignorant of optics. A wonderful effect was produced when the face of the god, invoked by the faithful, suddenly appeared on the back wall of the temple. The head of the image, upturned, was held in front of a concave mirror which reflected it, lit up and lifelike, on the wall of the temple, which was kept in semi-darkness.

The statue of Apollo, the Greek god of light, which on his feast day was carried around in solemn procession and was shown to the people, was made to rise from its throne for a few seconds and then to float back on it again. The probable explanation of this trick is that it was a wooden figure with a thin covering in which was a sort of gas-filled balloon.

MASS PRODUCTION 1,500 YEARS AGO

In his De Civitate Dei (The City of God) St. Augustine, Bishop of Hippo and greatest of the Church Fathers, has something to say on mass-production methods.

" In a silversmith's, a little vessel passes through the hands of many workmen until it is finished, although it might be made by one man who is fully master of his craft. However, it is thought that most workmen are best employed by learning quickly and easily, one portion of the whole work, and in this way it is not necessary to give all a thorough training in every branch of the work in question, which would take much time and labour."

PRESIDENT ROOSEVELT FORESTALLED

President Franklin Roosevelt's Economic Plan of 1935, with its proposals for reserve stores of grain for crisis years, has its ancient counterpart in the plans made by Joseph when he was prime minister of Egypt.

In ancient Egypt there were " perpetual granaries " and all the usual business organizations connected with the economy of the harvest:

We know also of some of the medical fees that were paid in ancient times. Pliny tells us, for instance, that the physicians-in-ordinary to the emperor received a yearly salary of about £2,750 (excluding fees from private patients) and that the celebrated Roman physician, Galen, used to charge £50 for each course of treatment.

TABLE-TURNING IN THE LONG AGO

There is evidence that table-turning was practised by Egyptian priests, and the practice is referred to in the Bible: "Thou shalt not question the wood." In Egypt table-turning was carried on thousands of years before the coming of Christ. From Egypt it made its way to Greece. The Christians, especially at the time of their persecution in Rome, were accused of scandalous proceedings in connexion with " prophesying tables."

In a document of A.D. 370 we read that malcontents had plotted against the life of the Emperor Valens and had been discovered. On interrogation they confessed to having consulted a prophetic table. "Honourable judges," so ran their statement, "we crowned a little tripod with a wreath of laurels and sanctified it with talismans and mystical verses in accordance with the age-old ritual. We then set it in motion."

The Emperor Valens himself had recourse to " black magic." He made use of a cock, before which the letters of the alphabet were thrown on the ground, which was strewn with barleycorn. The first letter to be touched by the cock was the first letter of the required answer, and so on. Curiously enough, the letters touched by the cock were T, H, E, O, D, so that the emperor surmised that his enemy Theodorus was aspiring to the throne.

As it happened, the cock was both right and wrong, for on the death of Valens the throne was ascended by a Theodosius, to whom history afterwards granted the additional title of " the Great."

HYPNOTISM BEFORE MOSES

A practice to which the doctors of Egypt were addicted long before the time of Moses was self-hypnotism. To please their patients they put themselves into a trance and dreamt of cures for their ills. St. Augustine tells of a priest who could put himself into a death-like sleep whenever he so desired; in this state he was impervious to wounds and gave clairvoyant answers to questions put to him.

This may also have been the case with Pythia, the priestess of Apollo at Delphi, who, under the influence of an artificially-induced hypnotism, spoke in her sleep, while the secret forms of worship known as the mysteries of Eleusis may have been based on imperfectly understood electro-magnetic phenomena. There is evidence in both old and modern writers that the sibyls or prophetesses of ancient Greece and Rome allowed themselves to be mesmerized into a trance or state of clairvoyance.

RELIGIONS AND BELIEFS

EXACT statistics regarding the number of followers of the various faiths are unobtainable, but it is generally believed that the Christian religion has the most devotees, with an approximate total of 692,400,000. Of these 331,500,000 are Roman Catholics; 206,900,000 members of the various Protestant bodies; 144,000,000 Orthodox Catholics; and 10,000,000 Coptic Christians.

Of the other religions, Confucians and Taoists (mainly Chinese) total 350,600,000, of which it is computed that 350,000,000 are resident in Asia. Next come the Hindus with 230,000,000, practically all in Asia; then the Mohammedans, 209,000,000 with 160,000,000 in Asia and 44,000,000 in Africa. Buddhism has from 150,000,000 to 250,000,000 adherents, the vast majority in Asia; Animism and similar beliefs account for 135,650,000 mostly divided between Asia and Africa. There are 25,000,000 Shintoists, or adherents of the Japanese form of ancestor worship, and about 16,140,000 Jews.

PLACES SACRED TO MANKIND

Amongst primitive mankind the activity of deities and demons was confined within definite limits. The hearth was assigned to the gods of the household, the desert to the evil spirits, and the holy place, of whatever kind, was God's special throne. In the course of time the location of the holy place was extended to countryside, hills and groves.

Within the Mosque of Omar, which is said to stand on the site of Solomon's temple in Jerusalem, is still shown what is believed to be the Rock of the Apparition, where, according to the Bible, Abraham was on the point of sacrificing his son to God but was eventually directed to slaughter a ram in his stead. One can see the shaft with the runnel along which ran for centuries the blood from the burnt offerings of the temple sacrifices. After the time of Constantine the Great the Jews were allowed to return to Jerusalem, whence they had been banished, in order to anoint the sacred rock once a year.

The Mohammedans believe that Cain slew Abel here, that through this shaft Mohammed went up to Heaven, and that the rock hovers without support over the abyss which, for the Mohammedans, is the centre of the world. The Last Trump will be sounded here, and the Kaaba or holy stone which is the centre of pilgrimage, will be wafted here from Mecca. The columns round the rock are credited with the power of drawing together so as to crush to death any adulteress who sets foot inside the mosque.

HOLY CENTRES OF THE WORLD

At Delphi, in Greece, in the earliest times the oracle of Mother Earth (Gaia) was guarded by a dragon called the Python, which was slain by Apollo, the god of light and youth, who took on himself the consequent

"Go quicker." Jesus had replied: "I go, but thou shalt wait till I return." The pamphlet had an immense popularity, and the legend spread wherever Protestants had a hold.

Naturally, Ahasuerus was thenceforth seen quite frequently; he was reported from Salt Lake City, U.S.A., in 1868 and since then in Germany. The whole legend appears to arise from New Testament texts, Matthew xvi, 28, and John xxi, 22-23.

IDEAS OF A FUTURE LIFE

THE idea of an underworld is of ancient Egyptian origin. It was conceived as a second world, under the sway of the benevolent god, Osiris, lying beneath ours and likewise roofed over with a sky. It was divided into twelve parts corresponding to the hours of the night. A boat with the sun god on board sailed along the subterranean Nile and bore away the dead, who in the morning left the underworld and continued their voyage on the waters of Heaven.

This idea was taken over by the Greeks, who conceived the underworld, under the general name of Hades, as being under the earth, encircled by the River Styx. The souls of the dead, accompanied by Hermes, the messenger god of wisdom, were ferried across the Styx by Charon, the surly old boatman, to a place where Minos, the judge of the dead, directed them either to Elysium, on the right, or to Tartarus, on the left. Tartarus, a word of Babylonian origin, was a deep pit lying below Hades or Orcus, and shut off from it by doors of bronze.

HELL AND THE UNDERWORLD

Islam places the underworld beneath the holy rock in the Mosque of Omar in Jerusalem; here souls first enter Araf, the purgatory of the Mohammedans, where they await the Last Judgment in torment.

The Assyrians called the underworld Erishkigal, the land without a home. It lay in the darkness of the west, surrounded by seven walls and gates, in the centre of which rose the palace of the goddess of the dead and the lord of the tomb. The ancient Mexicans called the underworld the land of cold and gloom.

The word "hell" comes from Hel, the half-black, early-Germanic goddess of the underworld, who took only the souls of those who had died of illness or old age. The Christian hell was described by Tertullian, one of the great Fathers of the Latin Church, in terrifying terms. The horrors of hell and the pains of purgatory were brought home to the people in medieval Europe by paintings and carved judgment-scenes inside and on the exterior walls of churches, as in the north porch of Westminster Abbey and in the remarkable mural paintings in the interior of the little church at Chaldon, Surrey.

Paradise, from the old Persian word *paradaez*—park, is the bright side of the picture of the underworld, the abode of good souls, protected

from evil by ramparts. The Egyptians called their paradise Earu and
placed it somewhere in the middle of Arabia. There Thoth, the divine
judge of souls, weighed the human heart, after which the soul was
allowed to pass into the fields where the corn grew seven ells high.
For this reason an agricultural implement was put into the grave.

The Sumerians imagined that Paradise was on an island in the
Persian Gulf; the Babylonians placed it on Mount Ararat, in the
Caucasus. The Assyrians called it "the heavenly court on the silver
heights." Some Buddhists hold that Paradise lies to the west and that
there jewelled trees rustle in the scented breeze and the water laps
against a golden shore. The Mohammedan Paradise is at the sources
of the Nile, in a date grove decked with lotus flowers. For the Eskimo,
Paradise is a place bathed in perpetual sunshine, with a plentiful supply
of drinking water, where ball is played with walrus skulls.

ETERNITY OF DANCING AND FEASTING

The Javanese hope to reach Vavonango, the mountain of the blessed,
when they are dead. The inhabitants of Borneo believe that every
day a god on an iron ship carries souls through the vale of tears to
the blessed fields of Levamliau. For the Chinese, Paradise is in the
Kun Lun Mountains; for the Japanese, on the "island of dripping
ice." The Aztecs of Mexico considered that their nobles were received
after death into the "House of the Sun," where they lived a glorious
life, dancing and merrymaking. It lay in a mountainous country ruled
over by Tlaloc, the spirit of thunder and rain.

The early Germanic belief was that those who fell in battle went to
Asgard, the garden of the gods, which was shaded by the world-tree
Yggdrasill. In Valhalla, the hall of the fallen warriors, 540 doors led to
the tables served by the Valkyries, the maidens who had conducted them
there. The Persians thought that Paradise was "the lovely highland of
Albaj," which lay to the north, whence they had originally come. The
Celts imagined it to be on an island in the ocean called Flathykker;
the Greeks placed it in the "Islands of the Blest," the geographical
position of which has not been determined.

The Jews believed the Garden of Eden to be in the oasis of Er-Ruhebe,
east of Damascus, or by the Shatt-el-Arab, where it was destroyed by
the Flood. Hinduism looks towards a future attained only after
repeated re-births, sometimes described as extinction, but more properly
interpreted as a condition wherein the individual is lost in a wider
"cosmic" consciousness.

COCKAIGNE, THE LAND OF HEART'S DESIRE

Cockaigne, or Cocogna, the imaginary land of idleness and luxury,
also known as Severambia, the land of the perfect political constitution,
is a caricature from medieval times, current in most European
nations, of the paradisial conditions supposed to have prevailed in
pre-civilized times.

A similar idea was expressed in the ancient Greek comedy dealing with the age of Chronos, and in the Roman saturnalia, the forerunner of the modern carnival and possibly of some Christmas customs.

REINCARNATION AND TRANSMIGRATION OF SOULS

The idea of the perfection of the human personality through the transmigration of souls is found in the religious history of most civilized peoples. The Egyptian belief was that the soul, in the course of 13,000 years, was incarnated in every species of animal and, gradually leaving behind it all bestial attributes, eventually attained to human existence, which in its turn found perfection in the everlasting peace of the so-called Earu.

This conception, that the soul found its way back to the original source of all life by being purified in the bodies of animals and men, was communicated to the Greeks by the philosopher Pythagoras as early as 500 B.C. The opinion of the later Greek philosopher, Empedocles, was that the soul passed through plants also. These notions were given expression in the celebration of secret dramas in the Greek mysteries. The philosopher Plato was of the opinion that the migrations of the soul lasted 10,000 years.

Whereas Origen, the Greek Father of the Church, defended the view that the resurrection was already beginning in this life, through the process of uninterrupted spiritualization, other Fathers of the Church favoured the doctrine of " the resurrection of the body " on the day of judgment, when the earthly bodies of the just will reappear, though in some way transfigured. Islam also adopted the Jewish teaching, but gave it a more material interpretation.

The Persian belief was that at the end of the world the good spirit Ormuzd would lead souls back to their bodies and to everlasting life.

SHAPING OF FUTURE LIVES BY KARMA

The doctrine that every deed performed in this life is either punished or rewarded in a life after death is found in the Indian religions, in conjunction with the transmigration of souls. According to common Hindu ideas, an imperishable, purely spiritual soul constitutes the indestructible core of every living being, no matter whether it has a divine, demoniac, bestial or human body. On the death of the body, which resolves itself into its component chemical parts, the soul quits its habitation and passes into another body which is made afresh for it according to the sum of its good and bad deeds (*Karma*).

Buddhism has it that there is no unchangeable self or *ego* which clothes itself with material stuff in order to wander from one existence to another. On the contrary, the soul, like the body, is in constant process of formation. Just as the body is constantly changing, so the soul is subject to constant change and resembles a stream or a fire, which appears to someone glancing at them hastily to be a unity, but which is really assuming a different value every second.

This theory of the " non-existence of an unchangeable *ego* " is not absolutely opposed to the theory of the *Karma*, because it is also taught that the vital flame is not extinguished at death; in the form of the *Karma* it acquires fresh fuel, which enables it to go on living. It is only the saint, who ceases to produce a *Karma* because he has become conscious of the non-existence of his self and has consequently realized complete "selflessness" in his thoughts and actions, who reaches Nirvana and thus ends the chain of his compulsory rebirths.

The ancestor worship of the Chinese includes the doctrine of the existence of three kinds of human soul, which part at death. The first is buried with the body and is watched over by earth dragons; the second becomes a tutelary spirit of the household; the third enters the world of shades and is there invested with demoniac rank. A similar theory is part of the Shintoism of Japan.

PAGAN CUSTOMS ADOPTED BY CHRISTIANITY

RELIGIONS do not die, neither are they invented. They change their forms and their names but not their essence. The gods change their dress and their names, but not their meaning and significance. Religion has probably meant much the same thing to all men. Perhaps that is why certain of the best features of pagan cults were adopted by Christianity. The extent of these borrowings will perhaps never be exactly determined, but they are certainly much more numerous than is generally believed.

BORROWINGS FROM ANCIENT ROME

In ancient Rome the lights on the altars of the pagan gods of the household were transferred to the altars of the churches. The old incense offerings were adopted, but burnt offerings were forbidden. Holy water was used in the old temples. The cap of the pagan priests, now the bishop's mitre, was not adopted till the 4th century, by Pope Silvester I. Statues of the Virgin Mary, St. Peter, and others were ceremoniously clothed just as Greeks and Romans clothed their gods.

The custom of opening and closing holy doors was taken from the temple of Janus, the god of war, in the Roman Forum, the gate of which was kept closed in peace time. The making of images of divine beings and powers is found in the earliest forms of nature worship and was continued in Christianity, where first the figure of the Saviour, then those of the Virgin Mary, the apostles, and saints were depicted. An additional motive in the case of the Christians was that they wanted to mark the contrast between their manner of worship and that of the Jews and Mohammedans, which had no representations in stone or wood. The worship of images was forbidden at Byzantium from 730 to 843, but there was never any lack of support for it in Rome.

BIRTHDAY OF THE UNCONQUERABLE LIGHT

Friday, in spite of its being the day of Venus and Freya, was appointed a day of mourning and fasting; in Denmark, however, it is still customary to solemnize weddings on this day. On the Sunday of the Dead the pagan families of Rome went to the graves of their relatives, bedecked them with flowers, and ate a meal by them; the last part of this custom is still observed in the Greek Church. The fire of the goddess Vesta was solemnly kindled on May 1; similarly, in the Roman Church, on Holy Saturday, after all the lights have been extinguished, the priest solemnly lights the Easter candle, from which all the other lamps and candles are re-lighted.

The Ember Days are a relic of the pagan custom of imploring the help of the gods three times yearly for the production of good crops. January 6 was celebrated as the birthday of Osiris, i.e., as the festival of the solstice; the day was fixed 3,000 years before Christ. But as one day was lost every 128 years according to the calendar then in force, from A.D. 400 onwards the day was celebrated on December 24. As January 6 was not discarded, there arose a double feast, which is still kept as the birthday of Christ and the Epiphany (the manifestation of Christ to the Magi). By the Romans it was celebrated as the birthday of the unconquerable light, by the Teutonic peoples as "the happy tidings of the renewal of the sunlight."

PROCESSIONS OF LONG AGO

Concerning the feast of John the Baptist (Midsummer Day), Augustine wrote these words : "On this day, after which the days draw in, John the Baptist was born, that man might be abased; on the day when the sun begins to increase again Christ was born, that man might be exalted." In ancient Rome fire was kindled on June 24.

The age-old feast of the Lupercalia, when a procession with lights went round the Palatine for the purpose of expiation and the fructification of the land, was transformed in A.D. 500 into the feast of the Purification of the Virgin. Processions in honour of the gods, processions to the fields, intercessory processions, pilgrimages, votive offerings for cures, were all incorporated as customs of the Church.

Ascensions into Heaven, such as those of Hercules and Romulus and the Roman emperors (in their case called "apotheoses"), were revived in A.D. 993 in the form of beatifications and canonizations. The purple of the cardinals corresponds to that of the Roman senators. The nimbus round the head and the aureole round the whole body were known to the ancient Egyptians and Babylonians as the symbol of the sun; after A.D. 300 they were given successively to the Trinity, the Mother of God, the angels, the apostles, and the saints. The Sumerians were the first to give their mother of the gods, Istar, the titles Queen of Heaven and Our Lady; the Mother of God is thus addressed today in litanies of the Virgin. The Sumerians were also the first to conceive of guardian angels in female form.

The protection extended by the old gods to countries, cities, arts, and crafts, was superseded by that of the saints. Certain plants and animals were also sacred to them. Finally the churchyard wall corresponds to the ancient Greek *temenos*, the square which enclosed sacred buildings and was usually invested with the right of asylum.

THREE GREAT SACRED BOOKS

In the domain of religion and ethics the greater part of the human race is guided by one of three books: the Buddhist *Tripitaka*, Mohammed's *Koran*, and the Jewish Bible. After the Babylonian exile, that is to say from 597 B.C. onwards, the Old Testament was regarded by the Jews as an inspired religious document.

Until about A.D. 150, the Old Testament alone was held as the authoritative holy book for Christians, though due regard was to be paid to the new revelation. It was not until the expiry of direct tradition and the appearance of unauthorized Christian writings that the need was felt for the compilation of records according to the Christian revelation. The comparatively late and unco-ordinated nature of these texts, finally formed into what we know as the New Testament, is shown by various discrepancies, mostly of detail.

AGE OF THE NEW TESTAMENT

That the authors of the New Testament were aware of other versions of their narrative being in circulation is shown in the "preface" to St. Luke's Gospel: "Forasmuch as many have taken in hand to set forth in order a declaration of those things which are most surely believed among us. . . ."

St. Mark's version is the oldest, as a gospel; but it may have been preceded by those epistles of St. Paul usually dated A.D. 52-64. The earliest version of St. John's Gospel is probably a Greek papyrus of about A.D. 150, which has been in the possession of the British Museum since 1934.

TWO FOURTH-CENTURY VERSIONS COPIED ON VELLUM

The list of books accepted by the Church as forming the New Testament was closed about A.D. 400; the oldest extant version is that contained in the Bible known as *Codex Sinaiticus,* bought for the British Museum from the Russian Government for £100,000. It is an early Syriac translation in uncials, or capital letters, formerly in the convent of St. Catherine on Mount Sinai. The famous Biblical scholar, Tischendorf, discovered forty-three pages of it in a wastepaper basket in 1844; he took these away, and in 1859 secured the remainder. Some leaves, however, had been destroyed, and it now consists of 346 almost square sheets of vellum, some more pages, however, being in Leipzig.

The other 4th-century Bible manuscript is the *Codex Vaticanus,* also an uncial version but in Greek. It contains 750 almost square quarto vellum leaves; it is not complete in the New Testament, and has been retraced, to its great damage, by some 10th or 11th century scribe. The *Codex Alexandrinus* (British Museum) and the *Codex Ephræmi Rescriptus* (National Library, Paris) are both 5th-century versions.

TRANSLATIONS AND CIRCULATION OF THE BIBLE

The New Testament was translated into Latin in the 2nd century, and into Syriac about the same period. There was a translation into Gothic by Ulphilas (about A.D. 370). The Latin translation known as the *Itala* was the basis of the Vulgate version by St. Jerome, completed in 405, and of the first Anglo-Saxon translation.

The Bible was translated for the Slavs by the missionaries Cyril and Methodius in 850, and for the English by Wyclif between 1356 and his death in 1384. Seventeen German translations existed before those of Martin Luther and Dr. Eck appeared in 1522 and 1537 respectively.

The first English printed version of any part of the Bible was the translation of the New Testament made by William Tyndale and printed in Germany in 1525. Miles Coverdale's version of the complete Bible, published in 1535, was undertaken at the instigation of Thomas Cromwell. The third edition of Coverdale's Bible, printed in 1537, was published with " the King's most gracious licence," and was the first Bible to receive official approval. It was also the first complete printed English Bible and the first to divorce the Apocrypha from the Old Testament. The first " authorized " Bible was known as Archbishop Cranmer's, having a preface by him (1540). This, with revisions, continued to be the authorized version until 1568.

An edition based on Tyndale's appeared in Geneva in 1557-1560. It was known as the " Breeches Bible," since Adam and Eve are represented as making themselves "breeches" instead of the usual translation "aprons" (Genesis iii, 7). This was the most popular version of the Bible for sixty years.

AUTHORIZED AND REVISED VERSIONS

The authorized version which is now in general use in English-speaking countries was published in 1611. A revised version of the New Testament appeared in 1881; of the Old Testament in 1884; and of the Apocrypha in 1895. In carrying out this last revision the scholars to whom the task was entrusted aimed at retaining as much of the text of the 1611 edition as was consistent with accuracy. Their work was inevitably submitted to severe criticism on its first appearance, but now, after the passage of more than half a century, it is fairly generally recognized as a magnificent achievement.

The first Bible in German was printed in Strasbourg in 1466, and by 1500 a hundred more editions had been brought out. At the present day there are more copies of the Bible printed and circulated than of any other book. During the last 125 years 442,000,000 Bibles in more than 600 languages have been issued.

VALUABLE BIBLES OF THE PAST

One of the most valuable Bibles now in the British Museum, London, is a copy from the school of the learned Alcuin, which was presented to the Emperor Charlemagne in A.D. 800. It contains many illustrations in which the characters, as was the custom of the Middle Ages, appear in contemporary costume.

The National Library in Paris possesses a Bible in four languages (Hebrew, Chaldee, Greek and Latin) which was printed in 1514 to the order of Cardinal Ximenes as a gift for Pope Leo X. In the city library of Aix-la-Chapelle lies the Bible which was laid in the tomb with Charlemagne's body in 814 and was removed from it, together with other objects, by the Emperor Otto III. The four gospels are in gold characters on red parchment.

In the Middle Ages books were very dear, so that there were but few Bibles in circulation. In the year 1250 a good copy in the library of Nôtre Dame, Paris, was valued at 480 gold francs. In 1417 a convent pledged its Bible for 600 marks; in 1450 the normal price of a Bible was 340 marks. Illuminated copies fetched particularly high prices. In 1930 the Gutenberg Bible, printed on parchment, that belonged to the abbey of St. Paul in the Lavanttal, in Austria, was sold to the Congress Library at Washington for £375,000.

WORK OF THE HOLY INQUISITION

In A.D. 1200, Pope Innocent III ordered a crusade against the Albigensian heretics which exterminated practically the entire population of part of the Rhône Valley and wiped out a most distinctive local culture.

Following the rise of further heretical sects, the Roman Catholic Church established the Holy Inquisition in 1215; shortly afterwards its conduct was handed over to the Dominican Order, and its activities were most vigorous in Spain, where it warred against the Mohammedans and Jews, as well as sectarians. It is said that between 1481 and 1834 over 35,000 people were burned at the stake or otherwise executed.

VICTIMS OF INTOLERANCE

The massacre of St. Bartholomew's Day (1572) meant the death of 50,000 French Protestants, and this persecution only ceased with Henry IV's Edict of Nantes, 1598. In the next century persecution began afresh and before the Revocation of the Edict of Nantes in 1685 some four or five million Protestants had left France, to her great impoverishment in the industrial arts. From France and Holland thousands of dissenters reached England in 1567-1568. Not until two years before the French Revolution was persecution stopped by the Edict of Toleration (1787).

The numbers of the individuals who were executed on account of their beliefs during the reigns of Henry VIII and Queen Mary have been greatly exaggerated; they are trifling compared with the Continental figures. The lynchings in the more backward American states with which the fiercely Protestant secret Ku Klux Klan society has been associated, and the current persecutions of Jews in the dictatorship countries show that the spirit of persecution for race or religion is by no means dead.

BURNING OF WITCHES

In its later stages the Inquisition concerned itself especially with witchcraft. Paganism lurked in Europe as an organized cult until the Christian Church challenged it under the name of witchcraft, stigmatizing its cult as that of the devil and condemning its fertility rites as immoral orgies. In 1424 the first witch was burnt in Rome, and in 1484, Pope Innocent VIII ordered the severe punishment of witches; it is calculated that in Europe altogether over 300,000 persons must have suffered death for witchcraft, 100,000 of them in Germany.

In England, James I (1603-1625) who was a fanatical hater of witchcraft and wrote a book on the subject, stimulated the active hunting out of witches or "witch-smelling," as he had already done in Scotland. Hundreds of probably quite innocent old women were hounded to death. A frequent test adopted was ducking. The victim was fastened on a special chair or ducking-stool and cast into the village pond. If she floated she was guilty, because, so the theory ran, water was so pure that it would not receive a vile body; if she sank she might be innocent, but would probably drown during the proof.

The last trial for witchcraft that was legally conducted in England was held in 1712, though sporadic local witch-baiting still continued. Persecution, which began to reach serious proportions in Scotland after the killing of Lady Glamis for witchcraft in 1537 and reached its height under James VI, ceased there in 1722, as also in Prussia. An Act of Parliament abolished witchcraft prosecution as a legal process in 1736. France had abolished it some time before this date, though sporadic burnings still took place. In 1788 the last witch was burnt in Spain.

BELLS ANCIENT AND MODERN

CHURCH bells originate from the rites of the ancient Egyptians, who used little hand bells. These were adopted in the cult of Cybele, the earth goddess and fertility queen who was worshipped in Asia Minor, and for the cult of Persephone, the Greek goddess of the underworld. The Romans used house bells.

LARGEST BELL IN THE WORLD

The oldest bell tower is at Nola, in Central Italy. Rome's first church bell rang out in A.D. 604. In 871 bell ringing was adopted by the Greek Church. The largest bell ever cast is the "Czar Kolokol," at Moscow, which weighs about 220 tons and was cracked before it left the foundry. It is 19 ft. 3 in. high and about 22 ft. in diameter. It was never hung.

The second largest bell was cast in England in 1928 for the Riverside Church, in New York. Germany's largest bell, weighing 25 tons 6 cwt., hangs in Cologne Cathedral. The "Pummerin" of St. Stephen's, Vienna, which weighs 10 tons, has rung since the days of the Turkish invasion. "La Corda," at Toledo, Spain, was cast in 1753 and weighs 16½ tons. "Toni," which hangs in the church of San Omar in the Spanish seaport of Gijon, was cast as long ago as A.D. 817. The famous "Twelve Apostles" bell in the Vatican was hung in 1486. "Great Paul," in St. Paul's Cathedral, London, weighs nearly 17 tons. It is rung daily for five minutes at one o'clock, and is also used as the five-minute bell on Sundays.

CASTING OF BIG BEN

England's oldest bell foundry was established in London in 1576 and still possesses its old equipment. It was in this foundry that the famous bell of the Houses of Parliament, "Big Ben," was given its unique "cracked" tone, still characteristic of it, while it was being repaired in 1846, an error being made of four per cent too much tin in the alloy. It weighs 13½ tons, stands 7 ft. 6 in. high, measures 9 ft. across the mouth and cost £6,000 to install. It gets its name from Sir Benjamin Hall, who was First Commissioner of Works at the time when it was cast.

In Peking, in 1415, a bell 50 tons in weight and 15 ft. in height was cast to the order of the emperor and hung in the temple of Ta Chung Su. It is inscribed within and without with sayings from Buddhist religious books. The bell of the Shwe Dagôn pagoda in Rangoon, cast in 1775 and weighing 40 tons, fell into the water when it was being taken away by the British to Calcutta in 1872, but it was salvaged by the faithful and restored to its former position. The bell in the Olympic sports stadium in Berlin was cast in 1935 in Germany's oldest steel foundry, at Bochum.

Nearly all the big church bells are now rung by electricity, a notable exception being that at Nôtre Dame, Paris, which weighs 30 tons and is set in motion by eight bellringers.

LEGENDS ABOUT THE FLOOD

REFERENCES to the Flood are found in the legends and myths of countries widely separated from each other. These stories may have been inspired by the universal observation of the destructive forces of nature and by the discovery on mountains all over the world of sea shells and animals' bones which were actually deposited there by the rising and sinking of continents above and below the level of the sea during periods which lasted millions of years. Legends about the Flood are told in the most widely differing places: among the Chinese, the Indians of Asia and the Indians of the Orinoco. Similar legends are found in Africa.

BABYLONIAN ORIGINAL OF NOAH

If the Biblical story of the Flood is taken as a record of the overflowing of the Shatt-el-Arab, which is clearly reflected in the Babylonian legends, then it was a local affair. It was shown from geological remains by Professor Langdon, of Oxford, that this flood stretched no further than eleven miles from the east bank of the Euphrates. It was merely the overflowing of a river which washed away the ancient Sumerian towns on the Euphrates, including the capital, Kish, and Shuruppak, where Ut-Napishtim, a Babylonian who may be identified with Noah, was building his ark.

At Kish there is clearly to be seen, above a settlement-stratum of 5000 B.C., which contains no copper but only painted potsherds, the mud stratum deposited by the flood. The story is told in an epic found on a number of tablets found in Ashur-bani-pal's palace at Nineveh. Catastrophic floods still occur; in 1822, for instance, the town of Barisal, on the Ganges, was washed away, 50,000 people being drowned; and in 1883 the same fate befell 900 villages on the Bay of Bengal, at the mouth of the Hugli, causing the deaths of 60,000 inhabitants.

The Tigris, which joins with the Euphrates to form the Shatt-el-Arab, is during the greater part of the year a comparatively narrow river, but during the flood season it overflows its banks in places to a width of several hundred yards.

When the water recedes the Arabs plant melon and other seeds on the muddy foreshore, and, thanks to the fertility of the soil and the extreme heat, reap enormous crops in a very few weeks.

HOMES AND TEMPLES

THE ancient Egyptians and the Sumerians, who inhabited the area between the Rivers Tigris and Euphrates which now forms part of Iraq, share the distinction of having been the first architects. The oldest known brickwork, dating from about 3500 B.C., was constructed by the Sumerians, while the oldest surviving building of stone masonry, dating from about 2940 B.C., was erected by the Egyptian architect, Imhotep. This building, built as the tomb of King Zoser, is usually referred to as the Step Pyramid. About 200 feet high, it was surrounded by a group of limestone masonry buildings, two of which were tombs.

UNEARTHING SUMERIAN CIVILIZATION

Excavations have been carried out in two of the most ancient centres of Sumerian civilization, Uruk, also called Erech, and Ur, referred to in the Bible as Ur of the Chaldees. The foundations of the great temple of Uruk can still be seen. Built of sun-dried brick, possibly dating from about 3500 B.C., they cover an area 200 feet square. The outer walls, six miles in circumference, enclose an area of 1,100 acres.

A large part of a temple in Ur, once the home of the Biblical Abraham, is also standing. Built of bricks bound together with bitumen, the remains rest upon a brick-paved terrace 300 feet long and 174 feet broad. Their date has been fixed at approximately 2300 B.C., but other remains in Ur very considerably antedate these. The principal excavations here were carried out by Sir Leonard Woolley.

The temple was the centre of the life of a Sumerian town. In the temple enclosure lived numerous priests, whose activities included money lending, since the temple was also a bank, whose rates of interest were divinely controlled. The most famous of all the Sumerian temples was that built at Nippur in Mesopotamia, and dedicated to the god of the air.

THE TOWER OF BABEL

A lineal descendant of the lofty temples of the early Sumerians was the Tower of Babel, which, as we are told in the Book of Genesis, was begun in a plain in the land of Shinar. Its inception is there eloquently recorded : —

" And they said one to another, Go to, let us make brick, and burn them throughly. And they had brick for stone, and slime had they for morter.

" And they said, Go to, let us build us a city and a tower, whose top may reach unto heaven; and let us make us a name, lest we be scattered abroad upon the face of the whole earth."

This Tower of Babel has been identified with the tower temple at Babylon, an accurate account of which was discovered on a late cuneiform tablet in 1914. The word Babel does not, as had for long been supposed, mean confusion. It is derived from *bab*, a gate, and *iln*, a god, meaning the gate of a god, and so is identical with Babylon. The foundations of the tower temple were discovered by Professor Koldewey, the excavator of Babylon, and aided by the cuneiform inscription he was able to reconstruct the building on paper.

SOLOMON'S TEMPLE AT JERUSALEM

The Hebrew temple at Jerusalem was partly the work of Phœnician craftsmen who were lent to Solomon by his friend Hiram, King of Tyre. As the Hebrew acknowledged, " there is not among us any that can skill to hew timber like unto the Sidonians " (Phœnicians). Its building is described at considerable length in the First Book of Kings.

The temple was of wood and stone : " Hiram gave Solomon cedar trees and fir trees according to all his desire." "And the king commanded, and they brought great stones, costly stones, and hewed stones, to lay the foundation of the house." It was built about the second half of the tenth century B.C., and the work of construction is supposed to have taken seven years, and to have called for more than 180,000 men. This is all the more remarkable in view of the fact that the edifice was probably not more than 110 feet long.

Only thirty years after its completion it was plundered by Shishak, King of Egypt, but it stood for about four centuries thereafter, being finally destroyed by Nebu-Zaradan, the Babylonian, in 586 B.C. About seventy years later (516 B.C.) a second temple, twice as large as the first, was dedicated. This had been standing about 500 years when it was completely re-built by Herod the Great (74-4 B.C.), King of Judæa. The re-building took forty-six years and made the temple one of the wonders of the world. In A.D. 70, the Romans, under Titus, razed it to the ground, " and the site of it was made like a ploughed field." Today the site is occupied by the Islamic Mosque of Omar.

TEMPLE OF DIANA AT EPHESUS

The temple of Diana at Ephesus, to which reference is made in Acts xix, was erected by King Crœsus of Lydia (550-546 B.C.). Ephesus was one of the principal cities of Ionia, on the coast of Asia Minor. Diana, or more properly Artemis, was the goddess of childbirth and of wild life. One of the sculptured columns of this temple, bearing the name of Crœsus, by whom it was dedicated, can be seen in the British Museum, London.

In 356 B.C., on the day that Alexander the Great was born, the building was burnt down by a man called Herostratus. His sole object was to gain immortality, if only as a fool; but it was afterwards restored. Great pomp and circumstance attended the worship of the goddess, and her temple at Ephesus was magnificent enough to be ranked among the seven wonders of the world. According to Pliny, the Roman historian, it was 425 feet long, 220 feet broad and adorned with 100 columns, each 60 feet high. Some accounts tell us that it took 220 years to complete. Praxiteles, the great Greek sculptor, is said to have furnished an altar for it.

The silversmiths of Ephesus used to sell little silver models of the temple, with the image of the goddess enshrined in them. It was they who were most agitated when Paul declared " that they be no gods which are made with hands."

BUILDINGS IN THE ETERNAL CITY

FROM the points of view of the architect, the archæologist and the historian, Rome is by far the most interesting city in the world. Large sums of money have been expended during recent years in excavating and bringing to light the hidden treasures of the past.

ERECTED BY THE ETRUSCANS

Rome's first great buildings were erected by the Etruscans before 500 B.C. Among them was a magnificent temple to Jupiter, Juno and Minerva, on the Capitoline Hill. The Etruscans were handicapped in their architectural efforts by a lack of good building stone, and they therefore made extensive use of terra-cotta, a hard pottery, and of tuff or volcanic ash. The Capitoline temple had walls of tuff coated with stucco (plaster); and the figures with which it was adorned were of terra-cotta. In the course of time better materials were obtained.

Of a much later date (366 B.C.) was the temple of Concordia, the remains of which can still be seen. It was so called because it was built to commemorate a truce in the long-drawn-out struggle between the two great social orders of Rome : the patricians and the plebeians. There, Cicero (106-43 B.C.), the great Roman orator and statesman, delivered two of his speeches against the conspirator Catiline. The temple was of great architectural beauty and the repository of numerous works of art.

Among the most ancient ruins in Rome are those of the Regia, or royal palace, which is supposed to have been constructed by Numa Pompilius, the legendary successor of Romulus as King of Rome. After the establishment of the Roman Republic the Regia became the headquarters of the Pontifex Maximus, the religious head of the State. The Regia was destroyed and restored more than once before being finally reconstructed in marble in 36 B.C. In that year its walls were inscribed with the Capitoline Fasti, or lists of magistrates and triumphs, some of which are preserved in the Capitoline Museum.

DIVINITIES WHO BROUGHT VICTORY

Conspicuous among the many striking ruins of the Forum are three magnificent columns of the temple of Castor and Pollux, than which there was no more beautifully decorated religious edifice in Rome. The first temple on the site was erected in 484 B.C. to the Greek divinities who were supposed to have given victory to the Romans at the battle of Lake Regillus. The columns that can be seen today date from A.D. 6, when the temple was rebuilt by Tiberius Cæsar. The mad Emperor Caligula (A.D. 37-41), of whom it is related that he intended to make his favourite horse consul, made the temple of Castor into a portico of his palace in order that he might have the gods—or rather their figures— for doorkeepers.

Among the buildings of Rome that have survived more or less intact from an early date, few are more interesting than the temple of Fortuna, built during the period 70-50 B.C., and carefully restored in 1923. Its interest is mainly due to the fact that, having escaped reconstruction by Cæsar and Augustus—a fate shared by many of its contemporaries— it can be safely accepted as typical of its period.

PANTHEON THAT BECAME A CHURCH

The Pantheon, the old walls and arches of which still stand, was first built by Agrippa in 27 B.C., but largely reconstructed by Hadrian (A.D. 117-138). One of the most ambitious structures of ancient Rome, it was circular in shape and had a brick-and-concrete dome with a diameter of over 142 feet. The dome's only supports were the walls of the building. The walls were faced externally with slabs of concrete and were internally very richly decorated. The building was turned into a Christian church by Pope Boniface IV in A.D. 609.

Joseph Forsyth, writing in 1813, refers to the Pantheon in these terms: ". . . though exposed to repeated fire; though sometimes flooded by the river, and always open to the rain, no monument of equal antiquity is so well preserved as this rotunda. It passed with little alteration from the pagan into the present worship; and so convenient were its niches for the Christian altar, that Michelangelo, ever studious of ancient beauty, introduced their design as a model in the Catholic Church." It is referred to in Byron's *Childe Harold* as:—

> " Shrine of all saints and temple of all gods,
>   From Jove to Jesus . . . ."

The remains of the Colosseum, the largest Roman amphitheatre, are at the foot of the Esquiline Hill, east of the Forum. Its construction was begun by the Emperor Vespasian (A.D. 70-79), and completed by his successors. It was used for gladiatorial shows and the display of wild beasts; and it could be flooded for the presentation of mimic sea fights. Its marble seating afforded accommodation for 50,000 spectators. The arena measured 282 ft. by 117 ft. and the building 617 ft. by 512 ft.

OVER A CENTURY IN THE BUILDING

The Church of St. Peter, Rome, the grandest and sublimest Christian place of worship in the world, was dedicated by Pope Urban VIII in 1626, 120 years after the first stone had been laid. Its length, within the walls, is 613½ ft.; the width of the nave and the side aisles is 197¾ ft.; the height of the dome from the pavement to the top of the cross outside is 448 ft.; and the external diameter of the cupola is 195½ ft. St. Peter's is thus 93½ ft. longer, and 64 ft. higher than St. Paul's, London. The great dome was designed by Michelangelo, under whose control the building operations were placed in 1546.

Considered by many to be more beautiful than the church itself is the piazza which leads up to St. Peter's. It is surrounded by two semicircular colonnades, constructed by Bernini in 1667. Each colonnade is 55 ft. wide and is supported by four rows of columns, 48 ft. high, so placed as to leave sufficient room between the inner rows for the passage of two carriages abreast. Altogether there are 284 columns, surmounted by 192 statues of saints, each 12 ft. high. The area enclosed by the colonnades measures 787 ft. across. The colonnades do not stretch right up to the façade of the church : joining them to the building are two galleries, 360 ft. long and 23 ft. wide.

INDIA'S OLDEST ARCHITECTURE

At Mohenjo-Daro and Harappa are the remains of cities which date from about 3000 B.C. They are the oldest architectural relics yet discovered in India. The building materials used were brick, mud and gypsum mortar.

GREAT TEMPLE AT MADURA

One of the largest and most curious of the religious buildings of India is the Great Temple at Madura, which is said to have been built in the 16th century. Rectangular in shape, it is surrounded by nine ornamental towers, one of which is 152 ft. high. It contains the " Hall of a Thousand Pillars."

The largest Mohammedan place of worship in the world is said to be the Great Mosque (Jamma Masjid) of Delhi, which was built in the middle of the 17th century. It has three domes of white marble and is itself paved with marble. The greatest height of the mosque is 201 ft. and one of its courts is 450 ft. square. It stands on top of a rock and is approached by an imposing flight of steps.

LARGEST BUDDHIST TEMPLE IN CEYLON

In Ceylon there are a number of temples, known as *dāgobas* or *stupas*, which date from about 200 B.C. The *Thūpārāma dāgoba*, at Anuradhapura, is one of the most ancient. The man who was responsible for having it built planted in the same town a sacred tree which is still living, and which is probably the oldest historically interesting tree in the world.

The largest Buddhist temple in Ceylon is known as the *Laṅkātilaka*. The high-water mark of Hindu building is considered to be the triumphal tower at Udaipur, in India. It is 121 ft. high, and was erected in 1442. In graceful proportions, the Ran Gipri Mosque at Ahmadabad can bear comparison with any building of other traditions. The finest product of Rajput architecture in north-western India is the fortress of Jaipur, which was built in 1600.

Among Burma's architectural masterpieces is the Queen's Golden Temple in the capital, Rangoon. It is made entirely of teak, and is lavishly ornamented with carvings which illustrate the art of Burma at its height in the 'eighties of the 19th century.

CHINA'S LOVE OF WALLS

BECAUSE of the extreme antiquity of Chinese civilization one might reasonably expect to find a large number of ancient buildings in China, but the great majority of the earliest Chinese houses and temples were constructed of timber, a material which does not usually stand exposure to the elements for more than a few generations. The oldest surviving buildings in China are tombs, since the Chinese, venerating the dead, sought to give them lasting memorials, and made use of stone for this purpose.

The oldest pagoda in China is on Sung Shan, a sacred mountain in Honan. Built of mud and brick about A.D. 520, it has an eight-sided base and is just under 100 ft. high.

GREAT WALL OF CHINA

The most ancient, as well as the greatest piece of architectural construction in China—perhaps in the world—is the Great Wall which runs for 1,500 miles along the northern and north-western frontiers of the country. It was built before 200 B.C., mainly by Ch'in Shih Huang Ti, the first Emperor of China.

The Wall varies in height between 20 ft. and 33 ft. and in width between 12 ft. and 15 ft. Along its top runs a path some 12 ft. wide, and watch towers occur at intervals of 100 yds. The body of the wall is made of earth and stone, and it is faced externally with brick. Old when Christianity came to Britain, the Great Wall of China still stands, an impressive symbol of the enduring quality of the Chinese race.

SURROUNDED BY RAMPARTS

Walls are one of the outstanding architectural features of China. Surrounding the great cities are massive and beautiful walls, and practically no Chinese town or village is without its rampart. But not only do walls surround Chinese centres of population; they also divide them up into districts.

Few that exist today came into being before the 15th century. One of the earliest and best preserved is that which surrounds Sian, the capital of the province of Shensi, in north-west China. This is as it should be, since Sian is on the site of Kwan-chung, the capital of Shih Huang Ti, who was mainly responsible for the building of the Great Wall. Marco Polo, the Venetian adventurer, visited Sian (then known as Kenjanfu) in the 13th century, about 100 years before the present walls were built. Sian is of great historical interest and contains a number of magnificent buildings in the Chinese style.

ONCE CAPITAL OF THE MONGOL EMPIRE

Only thirty-five miles separate Peiping (Peking) from the nearest point of the Great Wall, and the lay-out of that city is a further striking illustration of the Chinese fondness for walls. Peiping consists of two main cities: the northern or Tartar City, and the southern or Chinese City. The former, quadrangular in shape, has walls fifteen miles long; the latter is oblong and has fourteen miles of walls.

Enclosed by the walls of the Tartar City, and having the same shape, is the Imperial City, with red-plastered walls six and a half miles long. Within the Imperial City is the Forbidden City, or, as it is sometimes called, the Purple City, from the colour of its two-and-a-quarter-mile-long walls. The Tartar City contains a number of the most famous Chinese buildings, including the temple of Confucius, the Lama Temple and the Hall of Classics.

Peiping has, in characteristic Chinese fashion, managed to retain much of the architectural grandeur conferred on it by Kublai Khan. After making it, in 1267, the capital of a mighty Mongol Empire whose western and eastern frontiers were Europe and the Pacific, he rebuilt it in a style at once sublime, fantastic and unique. It was no upstart city, for even when it became the capital of the Great Khan it could trace its history back for no fewer than 2,400 years.

CITIES HIDDEN IN JUNGLES

HIDDEN away in Central American jungles are the remains of ancient stone and concrete cities, some of which were built between A.D. 300 and 500 by a number of Indian tribes which are known under the collective description Mayas, a term signifying a unity of language but not of race. The Mayas had attained a high level of culture by about A.D. 200, but their civilization began to decline about A.D. 900, and was practically extinct by the time the Spaniards arrived in the 16th century.

BUILT WITH STONE TOOLS

The Mayas displayed an extraordinary skill in architecture and sculpture, despite that the only tools at their disposal were of stone. They knew nothing of iron and its uses, nor of the principle of the wheel, which means that they must have devoted an incredible amount of labour to quarrying, carving and transporting their building materials. Roger Fry, the painter and art critic, is of the opinion that the Mayas ". . . working only with Stone Age tools, have left us more master-pieces of pure sculpture than the whole of Mesopotamian, or than the majority of modern European civilizations."

Many of the Mayan buildings, and notably the temples, were built on top of pyramid-like mounds ranged round open courts. The mounds were stepped, after the fashion of the Egyptian pyramids. The exteriors of many of the buildings, sacred and profane alike, were carved and chiselled into forms of fantastic beauty. As a rule only small blocks of stone were used, but large blocks were employed for altars and stelæ, the perpendicular slabs on which inscriptions were carved or sculptures made. One of the largest of the stelæ is 25 ft. high.

RUINED CITY OF CHICHEN-ITZA

The ruins of the city of Chichen-Itza, in Yucatan, Mexico, are the most impressive surviving memorials of the Mayan civilization, and particularly of that branch of it identified with the Itzas. The name of the city means the Mouths of the Wells of the Itzas, since the inhabitants depended for their water on two great wells there.

The city was founded in the early part of the 6th century; abandoned in 668 and re-occupied by the Itzas in 964, soon after which year it was adorned with numerous beautiful buildings, including those known as the House of the Dark Writing, the Red House and the House of the Deer.

Early in the 13th century the Itzan inhabitants were conquered by a confederacy which included a Toltec-Aztec group. The Toltec-Aztecs further improved Chichen-Itza from an architectural point of view, erecting a great number of religious edifices. The main temple built by them was the Castillo, extending over an acre and having a height of 100 ft. The so-called Thousand Columns enclose five acres of temples, theatres, halls and terraces.

By the time of the Spanish conquest the glory had departed from Chichen-Itza. Some of the original inhabitants, after the loss of their city, made their way into the forested hinterland of Guatemala, where they kept their culture alive until 1697, when the Spaniards, bringing with them European civilization, destroyed their habitations and temples, as well as an invaluable Mayan library consisting of bark-fibre books in hieroglyphics.

Another great ruined centre of the bygone Mayan civilization is Uxmal, also in Yucatan. The temple of the Magician there stands on top of a pyramid 80 ft. high and with a base measuring 240 ft. by 80 ft. Among the other buildings, which cover an area of about 160 acres, are a number of great interest and beauty.

BUILT OF SUN-DRIED BRICKS AND EARTH

The Toltecs, who aided in the conquest of Chichen-Itza, had their own peculiar civilization, the greatest surviving monument of which is a pyramid at Cholula, in Mexico. This structure, the largest of its kind in the world, is composed of sun-dried bricks and earth. It covers an area of 45 acres and is 177 ft. high.

When the Spaniards under Cortés first reached Cholula in 1519, the pyramid was crowned with a magnificent temple. Cortés treacherously massacred its too friendly inhabitants, and destroyed much of the city, including the temple. The site of the temple is now covered by a chapel of the Holy Virgin.

EGYPT'S MIGHTY PYRAMIDS

THE oldest surviving building of stone masonry is the Step Pyramid. This was the forerunner by about half a century of the Great Pyramid of Gizeh, which was built about 2800 B.C. to be the tomb of King Khufu, or Cheops, to give him his Greek name. It covers an area of thirteen acres and contains 2,300,000 stone blocks, each of which weighs two and a half tons.

ERECTED BY 100,000 MEN

The quadrangular base of the Great Pyramid has sides 756 ft. long, and the top is 450ft.—originally 500ft.—above the ground. According to a Greek historian, the building of this pyramid occupied 100,000 men for twenty years.

The Great Pyramid is, as its name implies, the largest of the Egyptian pyramids. Next to it in size, and only slightly smaller, is that of King Khafre, also at Gizeh. The great pyramids are surrounded by smaller ones, the tombs of the nobles who owed allegiance to the kings.

There is an Arab proverb which runs: "Everything is afraid of time—but time is afraid of the Pyramids." So skilful was their construction that there is reason to believe that all would still be perfect were it not for deliberate damage.

FIRST LAMP-POSTS OF THE SEA

THE first lighthouses of which we have any record were built in lower Egypt at a very early date. They were towers in which fires were kept burning by priests. A Greek writer of the 7th century before Christ tells us of a lighthouse at what is now Cape Incihisari.

SEVENTH WONDER OF THE ANCIENT WORLD

By far the greatest and most famous of the early lighthouses was the Pharos, built on the island of that name about a mile from the Egyptian city of Alexandria in the 3rd century B.C. by Sostratus of Cnidus. It was destroyed by an earthquake in the 13th century A.D.

There is a good deal of doubt about the height of this seventh wonder of the ancient world. Some accounts make it as high as 600 ft.; others, only 400 ft. It appears to have been four-storied and the first of its stories is said to have contained 300 rooms. Fantastic claims were made about the distance from which its light was visible, but in all probability this did not exceed thirty-six miles.

OLDEST LIGHTHOUSE IN THE OPEN SEA

The first lighthouses in north-western Europe were those built by the Romans at Dover, England, and Boulogne, France. The *pharos*, or lighthouse, at Dover is near the castle. The Roman masonry in it can be clearly seen.

On a rock in the Bay of Biscay, near the mouth of the River Gironde, stands the Cordouan Lighthouse, built in the latter part of the 18th century. It is the oldest lighthouse now standing to be built in the open sea. It is a nine-storied building 196 ft. high.

MIGHTY FORTIFICATIONS AND RAMPARTS

THE Great Wall of China is not the only structure of its kind, although it is by far the greatest. In the same class is the Caucasian Wall, one end of which reaches to the western shore of the Caspian Sea. It was built by the ancient Persians to defend themselves against the Scythian tribes on the north. It is fifty miles long, and when first built was 29 ft. high and 10 ft. thick.

HADRIAN'S WALL

Hadrian's Wall, built by the Roman garrison of Britain at the orders of the emperor whose name it bears, extends for about seventy-four miles between Wallsend, on the Tyne estuary, and Bowness, on Solway Firth. It came into being at the end of the first quarter of 2nd century A.D., and it was manned by Roman legions until about the end of the 4th century.

The *Limes Germanicus*, the Roman frontier against the Germans, extending from the river Lahn to the Danube, was about 340 miles long and was defended by more than 100 forts garrisoned by 100,000 men. Broken through by the Alemanni tribes in A.D. 260, it was left unrepaired and ultimately abandoned by the Romans. Of almost equal importance was another Roman *limes* which protected Tunis and Algiers against the desert tribes.

MIGHTY MAGINOT LINE

The largest modern line of fortifications is the Maginot Line, which was built along their eastern frontier by the French after the World War, at an estimated cost of £150,000,000. It runs from Luxembourg to Switzerland. In places the fortifications go 400 feet below the ground. A similar line guarded the Czech-German frontier on the Czech side; it passed into German hands after the Munich Agreement of September, 1938. Buried forts known as the Siegfried Line and anti-tank devices constitute Germany's concrete and steel frontier on the banks of the Rhine.

Erected as a defence against rabbits, the longest fence in the world is in Western Australia. It is made of wire netting and runs from the south of the continent to the north-west coast, a distance of 1,062 miles.

EARLIEST TOWNS

PROFESSOR L. S. B. LEAKEY announced in 1935 that he had found a town near Ngaruka in Central Africa which he considered was founded about 20,000 years ago, but this is problematical. The oldest town sites of which we have any comparatively exact information are those of the Sumerians.

EXCAVATED SUMERIAN TOWNS

The Sumerians were settled at the head of the Persian Gulf before 3500 B.C. They gradually spread inland until they finally covered the whole of the area known to us as Babylonia. At a very early date they carried on trade with the civilized inhabitants of the Indus Valley and also with the Egyptians. They were accomplished metal workers, using copper, gold, silver and lead, and they understood the principle of the wheel, having both carts and chariots.

In the 26th century B.C., that is about 1,000 years after they settled on the shore of the Persian Gulf, the Sumerians were conquered by Sargon, a monarch of Akkad, and the Akkadians thereupon adopted Sumerian culture. In the course of time the Sumerian-Akkad cultural union gave way to Babylonia. The principal Sumerian towns hitherto excavated are Ur, Uruk and Nippur, which three have already been referred to; and Kish, Lagash and Adab.

BUILT BY NEBUCHADNEZZAR

Kish is now known as Tal-al-Uhaimer, which means "the little red mound." It derives its name from a great mass of ancient baked bricks, the red colour of which can be seen from a considerable distance over the plain. It was excavated after the World War by an expedition sponsored jointly by Oxford University, England, and the Field Museum, Chicago, U.S.A. Of this expedition, Dr. S. Langdon was a prominent member and he wrote prolifically on its work.

Kish was the centre of an important wheat-growing district. Its site is only a few miles from that of Babylon, which city came into prominence after Kish had ceased to be of paramount importance. Sargon, the great king under whom the Akkadians conquered the Sumerians, was himself a native of Kish. Among the very extensive archæological remains there are the ruins of fortifications erected by Nebuchadnezzar.

HELPED BY AN UNCOVERED TABLET

Nippur was situated in the very heart of the land of Sumer, and was therefore of importance because of its position. It was also the centre of the worship of the god, Enlil, who was greatly venerated by all the Sumerians. A very large number of records of all kinds, compiled by the priestly servants of Enlil, were unearthed there. They have proved of inestimable value to the archæologists and scholars whose laborious

task it has been to piece together the ancient history of this great people.
It was found possible to reconstruct the city of Nippur with the aid
of a tablet found there which gave full particulars of the lay-out.

TOWN-PLANNING IN THE ANCIENT WORLD

Karun, or Garun, near Lake Moeris, is held to be the first Egyptian
town to be regularly planned; its date is 2000 B.C. The first piece of
town-planning in the classical world was that of the Piræus, the
promontory harbour district of Athens, planned in broad, straight
intersecting streets in the time of Pericles (510-429 B.C.).

The first great city included in the Roman colonial empire to be
built according to such a check-board plan was Alexandria, founded by
Alexander the Great in 332 B.C. to supplant Naucratis, and destined to
become for a time the commercial centre of the Mediterranean.
Subsequently all Roman towns followed this design, among them
Trèves, Cologne, and Turin. After the Renaissance, Karlsruhe,
Mannheim, Madrid, and St. Petersburg were laid out in like manner.

In recent times, the new Bagdad, Ankara, Washington, Delhi, and
Canberra, the federal capital of Australia, have been town-planned.
The site of Adelaide was chosen by Sturt (1836); the design was entrusted
to a single man, Light. Today the city stands exactly as it was
rectangularly planned in London.

VENERABLE CHRISTIAN CHURCHES

THE ruin of a synagogue in the grounds of a Franciscan convent at
Capernaum has been identified as the site of the building where,
according to Mark i, 21, Christ first announced His message of salvation.
Until A.D. 335, the traditional upper room wherein Jesus instituted the
Last Supper was regarded as the centre at least of Hebrew Christianity,
whose chief was the Bishop of Jerusalem. It was utterly destroyed in
1219, and in 1900 the Benedictines erected in its place a copy of the
palace chapel at Aix-la-Chapelle.

VENERABLE MONASTERIES

The oldest existing monasteries, those of St. Antony and St. Paul,
lie to the south of Cairo; four Coptic monasteries, in the Egyptian oasis
of Menaa or St. Menas, date from the middle of the 4th century. The
oldest monastery in western Europe is Monte Cassino, half-way
between Rome and Naples. It was founded about 530 by St. Benedict
of Nursia on the site of a temple of Apollo and is the mother church of
his rule, hence of western monasticism.

The oldest church still standing is probably that which was built
about the year 300 at Etchmiadzin in Armenia. It is the ancient seat
of the Armenian patriarchs. The first of the larger churches were the
original St. Peter's in Rome and St. Sophia's in Constantinople
(Istanbul), which were built about the years 325 and 330 respectively.

The latter was cleared of surrounding encumbrances only in 1935. It is now a museum of Byzantine art. The enormous dome which is one of its chief glories was thoroughly repaired in 1926-1927.

CHURCH ARCHITECTURE IN ROMAN BRITAIN

Early churches in Britain are apt to be legendary. St. Joseph of Arimathæa is alleged to have brought the faith to Glastonbury in the first Christian century, and to have built a wooden church, which was later surrounded by a fine Norman one. Probably the earliest Christianity in the Far West was brought to Ireland in the early part of the 5th century; but no Irish churches of so early a date survive. They were probably built of mud and timber.

At Silchester a Roman basilica with some Christian details has been found, seeming to show a cult of the faith in Roman times. Basilican also was the church which St. Augustine was given in Canterbury when he arrived to convert the Kentish kingdom in 597.

CHURCH THAT BECAME A MUSEUM

Poland's oldest Christian church is the cathedral at Posen, which was built in the 10th century. Norway's is at Borgund, which has not been altered since it was first erected. The castle chapel at Wurzburg, consecrated in 706 and restored in 1936, is the oldest Christian chapel in Germany on the right bank of the Rhine. Russia's oldest church is St. Sophia's at Kiev, now a museum. The first distinctively Protestant church, that of St. Nicholas at Heilbroon, in Germany, was built in 1525.

GREEK TEMPLE THAT BECAME A CHURCH

The Parthenon on the Acropolis at Athens, erected between 447 and 438 B.C. as a temple of Athene Parthenos, " the maiden," is considered by many authorities to be the most beautiful building of antiquity. Long after the glory of ancient Greece had receded into the past this temple was turned into a Christian church and, later, into a Mohammedan mosque.

Built of marble, it was surrounded by forty-six Doric columns, each 35 ft. high. It was decorated both externally and internally with sculptured reliefs, the beauty of which has never been surpassed. Inside the temple was a magnificent gold-and-ivory statue of " the maiden," the work of Phidias, under whose direction all the decorative work was carried out.

In 1687, when the Venetians were besieging the Acropolis, which was held by the Turks, a shot was fired into the Parthenon, then used as a Turkish powder magazine, and very considerable damage was suffered by the historic pile.

Part of the frieze which ran round the outside walls, as well as some of the panels from the interior, were acquired by Lord Elgin when he was Envoy to the Sublime Porte in 1799-1803. They are now in the British Museum, where they are known as the Elgin Marbles.

MASTERPIECES OF ARCHITECTURE

THE tomb known as the Taj Mahal, at Agra, northern India, an exquisite memorial of an emperor's love, is generally recognized as one of the supreme achievements of the architect. It was begun in 1632 by the Shah Jehan, for his wife, and completed eighteen years later. It is an eight-sided white-marble building, crowned with a dome, and with a graceful minaret at each corner. Its setting is a superlatively beautiful garden. Each side of the tomb measures 130 ft.: its height is 210 ft. and the dome has an internal diameter of 58 ft. It is said to have cost £3,000,000.

The Pearl Mosque at Agra, northern India, built in 1648, is sometimes spoken of as Islam's noblest place of worship; while the Cave Temple at Karli, also in northern India, is the oldest and finest specimen of Buddhist architecture.

TEMPLES ON THE NILE

The finest example of early Egyptian architecture was the temple of the god Khnum at El-Kab, on the Nile, but it was pulled down by the Turkish governor in 1822. The glorious temples on the island of Philæ are now submerged part of the year owing to the construction of a dam. Built entirely of red granite, they are typical, in their charming extravagance, of the declining years of early Egyptian architecture.

The temple of Edfu, also on the Nile, a Greek adaptation of an Egyptian style, still stands as the noblest work of late Egyptian art. The forecourt is reminiscent of the Parthenon on the Acropolis at Athens, and the whole structure glows with colour.

ITALY'S MARVELLOUS CHURCHES AND PALACES

Italy holds architectural pride of place in Europe. Amongst her greatest architectural achievements is the church of San Zeno Maggiore at Verona, built in 1050, the finest Romanesque building in northern Italy. A stern simplicity is the first impression its front gives; but this is relieved by a great porch whose free-standing pillars are supported on crouched lions. A great wheel-window above lights the nave with its compound uncarved piers.

Santi Giovanni e Paola di Casamari, on the island of Ischia, near Naples, is an outstanding example of early Burgundian Gothic, unique in Italy. It dates from 1203. The cathedral at Arezzo, built in 1277, is the earliest example of developed Gothic in the country, where Gothic in the northern sense never really took root. The ducal palace at Urbino, a model of a Renaissance palace, was designed by Laurana, the master of the famous architect Bramante. A monumental staircase, sculptured drawings, friezes and chimneys are special features.

With the Carthusian monastery called the Certosa di Pavia, which was the finest product of the early Renaissance (1473), may be ranked the finest façaded building of the Renaissance, Bramante's Palazzo della

Cancelleria (the Apostolic Chancellery) in Rome, which was begun in 1495 and finished in 1505. The great cortile, or courtyard, 103 ft. 6 in. by 63 ft. 6 in., is surrounded by two stories of arcades of Doric columns from the old basilica of St. Lorenzo. The façade is well proportioned and quiet in treatment.

The Villa Madama, in Rome, a work of Raphael, is the first and best example of a country villa with gardens and park, and has a charming loggia. The Casino del Papa in the Vatican Gardens, which was designed by Ligorio (1560), is the classic type of an "antique" villa in the Renaissance style. Equally perfect is the Palazzo del Té at Mantua, the designer of which was Giulio Romano.

CALIPH'S PLEASURE PALACE AT GRANADA

The most striking achievement of Moorish architecture in Europe is the Alhambra at Granada. The pleasure palace of the new Western Caliphate, it was built between 1309 and 1354 to impress the conquered. A surfeit of surface decoration overspreads a series of courts, halls and apartments, of which the Lion Court (115 ft. by 66 ft.) is the most elaborate. Its material, however, is of little worth or durability, being mostly wood and plaster. It sustained considerable damage in the Spanish Civil War. The convent of Batalha, in Portugal, is another splendid Moorish creation.

Next to these two buildings the most notable monument of Moorish art is the Alcazar in Seville, a royal palace erected A.D. 1350-1369 on the site of a Roman fort. The mosque of Cordova, in southern Spain, built between A.D. 780-1000, has nineteen aisles, 1,000 coloured pillars in sixteen arcades, 10,000 lamps, and a silver floor. The prayer-chamber occupies 148,000 square feet. The decoration is extraordinarily lavish. Unlike St. Sophia's, Constantinople, a church which was turned into a mosque, this mosque has been turned into a church.

The cloisters of San Juan de los Reyes, at Toledo (1504), with their window traceries and canopied statues, and the Collegio de San Gregorio, at Valladolid (1488), with exuberant three-centred arches and twisted columns, are adjudged to be the most brilliant examples of Spanish late Gothic.

GLORIES OF MEDIEVAL FRANCE

THE most representative buildings of the Middle Ages are to be found in France, although the largest medieval cathedral in Europe—indeed, with the exception of St. Peter's, Rome, the largest church in the world—is Seville Cathedral, in Spain. The city walls of Carcassonne, in southern France, are the most imposing town fortifications that have survived undamaged the wear and tear of the centuries. Avignon is still girt with walls that extend for nearly three miles, and the Papal Palace there, built in 1316 by the exiled popes, is more impressive than any other medieval building of the kind.

WHERE KINGS OF FRANCE WERE CROWNED

France possesses the most beautiful churches in the pure Gothic style, the origin of which is disputed between England (Lincoln Cathedral: partly built by St. Hugh) and the Ile de France. Amiens Cathedral (1220-1288) is a glorious architectural harmony, both as a whole and in its details. Its chief glory lies in the choir stalls woodwork, which spreads like living foliage. The western façade is among France's noblest, with its ranks of statuary, culminating in the Beau Dieu d'Amiens, between the western doors. Above all a slender spire rises 180 ft. above the roof.

Chartres Cathedral (1194-1260) has without doubt the loveliest stained glass in the world. Its 130 windows are filled with 13th century work. Doorways and porches are crowded with carved figures, somewhat archaic but extremely interesting. The flying buttress rises in three arches one above the other.

Rheims Cathedral (1212-1241) was designed as coronation church for the French kings, with widened eastern half for ceremonial gatherings. In addition to statues of the monarchs, the elaborate western façade has some 500 statues in its recessed portals. Rose windows are a special feature, that over the central doorway being forty feet in diameter.

This shrine of French history was heavily mutilated during the World War by German shells, which made nearly 300 direct hits. It was completely restored in 1938 after twenty years' continuous work. The carving was reproduced, so far as possible, as before, M. Henri Deneux being the supervising architect. Mr. John D. Rockefeller gave 15,200,000 francs, and also paid for the restoration of the roof, carillon, upper gallery and flying buttresses. The total cost was more than £5,600,000. The use of reinforced concrete instead of wood for roof support has much lightened the new structure.

Beauvais Cathedral (1225-1568) represents the medieval cathedral-builders' most ambitious effort in respect of height. The openwork spire of 500 ft. above the transept crossing fell in 1573, and was not re-erected. The reconstructed choir and 16th-century transepts form the loftiest building of its kind in Europe, 157 ft. 6 in. to the vault—this being three times its span.

Held together internally only by iron tie-rods, the builders evidently realized they had attempted more than they could manage. Flying buttresses of immense thickness in triple tiers receive the heavy roof-thrust. Carved wooden doors, a flamboyant south transept, and stained glass of various centuries are other famous features.

CATHEDRAL LIKE A SHIP

Nôtre Dame, Paris (1163-1235), is one of the oldest French Gothic cathedrals. The wide, sombre interior contains many national monuments. The broad western façade is perhaps the finest in France, serving as model to many later churches. Encircling tiers of statued niches surround the three deeply recessed portals; above them stretches a band of statues of the French kings, and over it a 42 ft. wheel-window of great beauty.

The east end from the outside presents a graceful system of wide flying buttresses which has been aptly compared to a full-rigged ship. The buttresses are exactly designed to bear certain stresses, and together present a fine example of functional art. The Sainte Chapelle in Paris, in the building now used as the Palace of Justice, is perhaps over-delicate in its lace-like filigrees, but certainly lovely.

Other notable French Gothic cathedrals are Bourges (1190-1275), with picturesquely confused double flying buttresses and much 13th-century stained glass; Laon (1160-1205), early Gothic, on the Latin cross plan, with an English rectangular east end and a magnificent western façade; Soissons (1160-1212), early and austere Gothic; Le Mans (12th and 13th centuries), with an even more austere Romanesque nave and a vast choir; Bayeux (12th century), with twenty-two chapels and a huge 8th-century crypt; and Strasbourg (1250-1290, but additions during four centuries) with its elaborate west front.

ENGLAND'S STATELY CHURCHES

ENGLAND possesses many magnificent cathedrals, with features all their own. The typical English structures are relatively long, narrow and low, with very definite outlines, a square east end and a central tower. Being usually monastic in origin, they normally stand isolated in a close or on a river, not crowded with surrounding buildings as are so many French churches. Fan tracery vaulting and the whole of the perpendicular Gothic style were peculiar to England, as was the use of lead for covering the low-pitched roofs. English west fronts, with the exception of Wells, are not so deeply recessed or so richly carved, and there are fewer side chapels and flying buttresses.

ST. HUGH BEGINS AN ENGLISH STYLE

Durham (1096-1133) has the most impressive single monument of Norman work in its great nave (1099-1128). The round pillars, about the same width as the arches between, are channelled with flutes and spirals, and the vault is one of the earliest in England. Completed with a massive Early English transept and a Perpendicular tower, it forms on its impressive river site an architectural group with few rivals.

In Lincoln (rebuilt about 1185-1200) both the Early English and the Decorated or Middle English styles find their finest expression. Here St. Hugh started that grouping of small pillars around a central pillar which is the distinctively English Gothic manner. The Angel Choir (1256-1314) is the supreme expression of English Decorated in both proportion and carving, wherein Lincoln is peculiarly rich.

Salisbury (1220-1258) is the most uniform in style of English cathedrals; in its clear graceful outlines it is as completely typical of

Early English Gothic as is Amiens of French. Its Decorated spire is the loftiest in England (404 ft.). The wide level close makes a fine setting to what has been called the Palladium of English Gothic architecture. Views of it were painted again and again by Constable, that most typical English artist.

Canterbury Cathedral (choir 1174; nave 15th century) is the shrine of St. Thomas Becket, though the actual tomb of the prelate has long since disappeared. Flights of steps and wide ambulatories make an impressive approach to Becket's Crown Chapel. The fine central tower and cloisters are late Perpendicular.

Wells (1180-1425) is a very complete example of monastic lay-out, mainly Early English. Its chief glory is an immense double-towered west front (150 ft. wide), the finest in England, with rank upon rank of sculpture of the best period. The Decorated octagonal chapter house also is remarkably satisfying.

EUROPE'S LONGEST GOTHIC CATHEDRAL

Winchester (various dates between 1070-1486) has the double distinction of being the national church of the older English kings, and the longest medieval cathedral in Europe (560 ft.). Here are buried the remains of Saxon kings, including Alfred, and William II. The choir is the largest Early English one extant, and there is some fine choirstall carving.

Westminster Abbey was founded as a Benedictine monastery, 960, when its site was on an island. Partly rebuilt by Edward the Confessor 1055-1065, it was later almost completely rebuilt, in large part by Henry III (1245-1269). It has, in fact, grown with the national growth, and is filled with tombs and shrines, including those of the Confessor, Edward I, II, III, Henry III, V, VII and VIII, Queen Elizabeth, Mary Stuart, and the Unknown Warrior.

THREE LOVELIEST ENGLISH CHAPELS

Individual features of the Abbey are magnificent. Henry III's nave (102 ft., the highest Gothic vault in England) and transepts are fine French-influenced Early English; the Saxon-Norman chapel of the Pyx was for centuries the first national treasury; whilst Henry VII's chapel (1502-1512), together with St. George's Chapel, Windsor, and King's College Chapel, Cambridge, form a trinity that is the crown of the Perpendicular Gothic or Tudor style. The fan tracery of the vaulting and the canopied stalls of the Knights of the Bath combine to make Westminster Abbey unforgettably impressive.

York (12th-15th centuries) is the largest in actual area and in width (106 ft.) of English medieval cathedrals. The interior gives an impression remarkably clear-cut and spacious, the nave being second only to Westminster Abbey in height; whilst the 14th-century stained glass of the great windows is unique. The Five Sisters lancets in the north transept are windows each 50 ft. high by 5 ft wide.

MOTHER-CHURCH OF YORKSHIRE

Greatest of English monastic houses was Fountains Abbey, Yorkshire (1132), the mother church of the Cistercian Order in England, whose vast ruins and great tower still dominate the valley. The church must have been some 280 ft. long. The extensive and relatively complete remains give an excellent picture of what a great monastic foundation was like.

Amongst other great medieval churches are Glastonbury Abbey, supposedly the oldest English centre of Christianity; Exeter Cathedral, finest specimen of the Decorated style, rich in tracery and carving; Ely Cathedral, with remarkably delicate late Norman work, octagonal lantern and lady chapel; Carlisle, Augustinian Abbey with magnificent east end; Gloucester Cathedral, with early Perpendicular fan vaulting and immense windows; Oxford, actually the chapel of Christchurch College but now the Cathedral, with Norman triforium gallery; Peterborough Cathedral, second only to Durham as a Norman interior, with the oldest timber nave roof; St. Albans Cathedral, with the longest Norman nave in England, 284 ft.; and Worcester Cathedral, with the only circular chapter house in England and the chantries of King John and Prince Arthur.

LONDON'S OWN CATHEDRAL

First and greatest of cathedrals in recent centuries is the mainly 17th-century St. Paul's (1675-1710). Its free Renaissance style and ample dimensions give it a character all its own; many consider it the most beautiful church in the world, though in size it is but a quarter of St. Peter's, Rome (59,700 sq. ft. as against 227,000 sq. ft.). The exterior length is 515 ft., the internal 479 ft. The width across the transepts is 250 ft., and of the West Front 180 ft.

The great dome, 102 ft. across, begins 218 ft. above the paving, and carries the total height up to 365 ft. to the top of the cross. The weight of the dome is 67,270 tons. It rests upon twelve supports; 100 ft. up is the Whispering Gallery. Decorations include Sir James Thornhill's murals and Sir W. B. Richmond's mosaics Much of the carving is by Grinling Gibbons. Old St. Paul's was 586 ft. long, the longest Christian church in the world, and its spire had a height of 489 ft., the tallest in Christendom.

Cathedral building has continued in more recent years. The foundation-stone of Truro Cathedral, in Early English style, was laid in 1880, the architect being J. Loughborough Pearson. The Roman Catholic Westminster Cathedral of John F. Bentley was begun in 1895 in a modern Byzantine style.

Liverpool Cathedral (Anglican), remarkable for breadth of treatment and the influence of the Spanish school upon the architect, Sir Giles Gilbert Scott, was started in 1903. The Roman Catholic Cathedral in Liverpool, designed by Sir Edwin Lutyens, is also still in the making; and Guildford Cathedral (Anglican) is in its beginning.

ENGLAND'S HISTORIC HOMES

ENGLAND's historic houses, ranging over many centuries of growth, illustrate vividly the cultural achievements in home-planning of her formerly powerful aristocracy. Most complete and continuous in its development is Knole, a great house that may almost be called a village. The seat of the Sackville family, and mainly of the time of James I, the series of Jacobean interiors is unrivalled. Corresponding to it among palaces is Hampton Court, partly designed and built by Cardinal Wolsey (1515-1530), added to by Henry VIII (1532-1536) and considerably altered by Wren. The hammer-beam roof of its great hall and twisted Tudor chimneys are probably the best in England. It has the oldest tennis court in the world still in use.

BUILT FOR A FAMOUS GENERAL

The name of the great Duke of Marlborough is associated with two outstanding examples of English decoration. Marlborough House, in Pall Mall, a magnificent example of Wren's red brick, although altered appreciably, his rooms covered with Louis Laguerre's wall-paintings of the Duke's battles. The foundation stone was laid by the imperious Duchess in 1709, and she never failed to reassure both friends and enemies that the entire cost was borne by her husband. Sir John Vanbrugh, the playwright-architect, designed for him the most monumental mansion in England, Blenheim Palace, Oxfordshire (1705), 850 ft. long, with an 180 ft. long great gallery.

More nearly corresponding to the extravagant interior creations of the Continent was Fonthill Abbey (1796-1799), designed by Wyatt for William Beckford, the antiquary, on the strange lines of the extreme period of Gothic revivalism. It was made to appear a monastery merely adapted to domestic use. More famous is Strawberry Hill, Twickenham (1753-1778), erected for Horace Walpole, the letter-writer and essayist; here medievalism ran riot in a miniature castle of fantastic design.

Probably the longest late medieval room in England, and the finest panelled gallery, is in St. John's College, Cambridge (1511). It has an untouched moulded plaster ceiling. The Long Gallery of Montacute House (1580) is no less than 170 ft. long, and shows to what lengths the Tudor nobles would go in rivalling one another in their structures. It also has satisfying panelling and ceiling-mouldings. The gallery of Haddon Hall, Derbyshire (1567-1584) is, however, considered finer.

NEW USES FOR PALACES

MANY and various are the changes wrought by time in the uses to which famous buildings have been put. Communist representatives sit on the imperial throne of St. Andrew in the Kremlin; the throne room of the old Chinese Empire has been turned into a public tea-room where children are allowed to sit on the Dragon Throne.

CONVERTED INTO BARRACKS AND MUSEUMS

The castle of the prince-archbishops at Salzburg, the royal castles at Cracow and Pau, the royal palace at Prague, the castle of the Visconti at Pavia, the palace of the popes at Avignon, and the glorious Alcazar of the kings of Aragon at Saragossa are now soldiers' barracks. The Hall of the Knights in the castle of Dornburg, near Jena, once the meeting-place of the Imperial Diet, is now a government office.

The splendid pleasaunce of Medinat at Zahrâ, near Cordova, in southern Spain, became a lunatic asylum; the Sun Palace of the Great Moguls at Lucknow is a girls' school. The Castello dell' Ovo at Naples, built on the foundations of a villa belonging to the fabulously luxurious Lucullus, is now a military prison. The electoral palace at Trèves, finished in the 18th century, was a barracks from 1794 to 1930 and then became a museum.

Other palaces, by being converted into museums, have preserved some memory at least of their dignified past. This has very generally occurred in England, although only rarely is a palace entirely disused as a royal residence. Thus Holyrood House in Edinburgh, Hampton Court Palace and Kensington Palace are in a sense museums, but are also inhabited temporarily or partially by members of the royal family or by royal nominees.

Carisbrooke Castle in the Isle of Wight is the official residence of the Governor of the island; Walmer Castle that of the Warden of the Cinque Ports. The Tower of London still has its uses. The Naval Museum at Greenwich shares with the Royal Naval College the use of the sailors' hospital built by Wren on the site of Greenwich Palace.

FATE OF EUROPE'S CASTLES

Many of the famous castles of Germany are entirely ruined, others have been adapted to uses undreamt of by their builders. The ancestral castle of the Hohenstaufen dynasty lies in ruins; its stones were used to build a local government office at Goppingen. The castle of the Hohenzollerns was destroyed in the 15th century, being rebuilt in 1850.

The castle of Wettin (first built in A.D. 950), ancestral seat of the Saxon princes, was sold by Augustus the Strong in 1697 to pay for the cost of keeping the Countess Cosel in luxury. In 1925 the upper part of the castle was acquired by Herr von Waweren, while the lower part was purchased by the Thuringian Historical Society as a national home for youth; and in 1936 the castle was made a school for training National Socialist leaders. Gottorp Castle, near Schleswig, the cradle of the royal houses of Denmark and Russia, now houses a revenue office.

Similarly in England, Tintagel, legendarily King Arthur's castle, and certainly the early stronghold of the Earls of Cornwall, is a ruin; and Ludlow, the famous Norman seat of the Lords President of the Welsh Marches, where Milton's *Mask of Comus* was first presented (1634) and Butler wrote *Hudibras,* fell into decay in the 18th century.

SHIFTING MOUNTAINS OF MATERIAL

SINCE the first surviving building of stone came into being in Egypt some 5,000 years ago, whole mountains have been pulled down and myriads of stones have been hewn, transported, and piled up again into cities and monuments. An age of building in wood was followed by the age of stone, now being superseded by the age of iron and steel.

NEW CITIES THAT WERE SECOND-HAND

Entire cities have been rebuilt of old materials. Kairouan, the desert city, was built out of the ruins of Carthage, just as present-day Cairo was built out of age-old Memphis, and Renaissance Rome was built out of ancient Rome. Salerno, near Naples, was built out of the ruins of Pæstum in the 5th century.

Obelisks, which for thousands of years kept a lonely watch over ruined Egyptian temples, now stand in the busy streets and squares of great modern cities such as London, Paris, Rome, New York and Istanbul (Constantinople). St. Sophia's at Istanbul contains huge columns that once stood in the temple of Zeus at Cyzicus (Asia Minor), the temple of Diana at Ephesus (Asia Minor), and the Temple at Jerusalem. Worked into the dome of St. Sophia's are stones from Abraham's Well at Shechem and porphyry from the Sanctuary of the Sun at Baalbek in Syria. In the Piazza della Trinità in Florence stands a column which was brought from the Baths of Caracalla in Rome.

Four granite columns in Charlemagne's Minster at Aix-la-Chapelle were removed in 1794 to the Louvre in Paris; Charlemagne had originally had them taken to Aix from the palace of Theodoric the Great (king of the Goths about A.D. 500) at Ravenna. Other columns from his palace were removed by the German emperor, Otto I, to the cathedral he was building at Magdeburg, and others again were re-erected by the Venetians in the famous Church of St. Mark.

MOVING AN ENTIRE PALACE

Whole buildings, indeed, have been moved, and that not rarely. The delightful palace built at Moret, near Fontainebleau, in 1527 by King Francis I of France for his mistress, was transferred three hundred years later to the Quai de la Conférence in Paris. Parts of the palace of the Tuileries found their way to Corsica, where they were used to build a villa, and some of the columns were taken to Schwanenwerder, near Berlin. The Pont de la Concorde, Paris, was built in 1790 with stones from the Bastille.

Parts of the Mausoleum of Halicarnassus in Asia Minor are now in the British Museum, and the Altar of Pergamum and the market-gate of Miletus are in Berlin. The Gothic portal of the University of Cairo was taken from a Christian church which the Crusaders had built at Acre. The pavement of the Viceroy's palace at Calcutta is composed of stones taken from the Great Wall of China.

CAVE DWELLERS

LAKE DWELLINGS

EGYPTIAN DWELLING HOUSE

WOOLWORTH BUILDING NEW YORK

UNIVERSITY OF LONDON

CARNARVON CASTLE

Homes and Habitations of Man

TEMPLE OF ISIS, PHILÆ

TAJ MAHAL

DORTMUND CHURCH, GERMANY

TEMPLE OF ISIS, PETRA

THE BELFRY, BRUGES

Ideals of Beauty in Architecture

In 1935 an ancient temple of Buddha in Japan was transferred to Hsingking (Changchun) the capital of Manchukuo (Manchuria).

VAST STONES THAT MEN HAVE HEWN

One of the largest building stones in the world belonged to a temple in Peru of the pre-Inca period; it is 39 ft. long, and its weight is about 357,000 lb. Another is the keystone of the temple at Baalbek in Syria, which is 1,800 tons in weight, 75 ft. in length, 15 ft. wide and nearly 17 ft. in height.

Blocks of stone weighing 252,000 lb. were used for the Mycenæan castles of the second millennium B.C. The dome over the tomb of Theodoric the Great, King of the Goths, at Ravenna, is composed of a single stone nearly 36 ft. in diameter. It was brought to Ravenna by a ship from Istria. The Phœnicians are said to have brought earth to Malta, at one time an even barer rock than at present.

MOVING CLEOPATRA'S NEEDLE

The obelisk on the Thames Embankment known to every Londoner as Cleopatra's Needle is 68½ ft. high and weighs 180 tons. In its blackened state it is difficult to realize that it is of pink granite. It has no connexion with Cleopatra, being one of a pair of obelisks set up by the Pharaoh Thothmes III (about 1500 B.C.) at Heliopolis, many centuries before the beautiful Egyptian queen disturbed the Roman Empire. It was presented to England by the Viceroy of Egypt in 1819, and was set up in London sixty years later. It was lost for a time in the Bay of Biscay when being towed to Britain, and during the World War was damaged by a German bomb. The companion obelisk is in Central Park, New York.

The obelisk brought from Egypt to Rome by Constantine the Great weighs 412½ tons. It now stands outside the Lateran Palace. The granite basin which has been in the Lusgarten in Berlin for the last hundred years was hewn out of a block weighing 7,500 tons; there is room in it for forty-four people.

BUILDINGS THAT HAVE WON MEN'S AWE

AMONGST mysterious buildings which have impressed men's imagination must be included cave-temples, grotto-temples and catacombs. The vast structures, known as labyrinths, can be compared in extent to skyscrapers. Remains of the famous labyrinth of Crete, which gave its name to the type, were brought to light by excavations made by Sir Arthur Evans at Cnossos. It is said to date from about 1500 B.C.

Pliny, the historian, tells us that the labyrinth of Crete was built on an Egyptian model by Daedalus, Icarus's legendary flying instructor; indeed, a ruined labyrinth has been found in the Fayum, near the Nile, built by Amenemhet III about 1830 B.C. and restored 1150 B.C., which is thus the oldest labyrinth that we know of.

Herodotus the historian, and Strabo the geographer, who lived many centuries later, saw the remains of this structure and probably drew on their imaginations freely in describing what was no longer visible. According to them, its twelve temples and countless smaller chapels were linked together by 3,000 passages. The only material used was granite from Assuan. Flights of ninety steps, flanked by four pyramids, led to the shrines of the gods. In the centre of the vast building stood, they said, a statue of the supreme god Serapis, about 10 ft. high, carved out of a single block. The labyrinth was thus a pantheon of the Egyptian deities.

LABYRINTH OF THE MINOTAUR

In Crete, the place of the highest god, "fearful in his mysterious enthronement," was taken by the bull-headed idol called the Minotaur. It was approached by way of innumerable chambers, all of which were intended to work on the feelings of the visitor and heighten his sense of awe. From pottery and mural pictures it is evident that bull-riding and fighting were absorbing sports to the ancient Cretans.

Besides those in Crete and Egypt, Pliny makes mention of labyrinths on the islands of Samos and Lemos. Of the latter he relates that he saw 150 columns still standing. In Italy, the Etruscans, who were specially open to foreign influence, certainly had one building of a similar nature, for in describing the mausoleum of Lars Porsena, the Etruscan king, known to all readers of Macaulay's *Lays of Ancient Rome,* the Roman historian Varro refers to it as a labyrinth. "Each side of the square wall that enclosed the tomb," he writes, "was 325 ft. long and 55 ft. high. In the middle of the enclosure was the labyrinth itself, rising to a height of 162 ft., while at the four angles stood pyramids bearing caps hung with little bells which tinkled at every breath of wind."

In northern Europe, labyrinthine remains of buildings have been found, mostly of those which served religious ends—for example, the so-called "Trojan castles" or Troy-towns in Gottland.

MAIDEN CASTLE'S MIGHTY FASTNESS

England has an extremely fine prehistoric example which may rank as a labyrinth. Maiden Castle (perhaps derived from *mai* = strength, *dun* = hill), near Dorchester, covering about 160 acres, with a two-mile circuit, has six concentric rings of ramparts some sixty feet high, the entrance to each facing in an opposite direction from that outside or inside it, so as to force any invader to expose himself to a maximum of flanking "fire" from the defenders as he circled round from gate to gate.

The main settlement of the close-packed huts within the ramparts occurred, it is believed, in or about the 4th century B.C. The place probably sheltered 5,000 people or more. In the 1st century B.C. outworks were added, the rampart was reinforced and additional defences were erected. The place was abandoned during the Roman occupation in favour of the city where the county town of Dorset now stands.

ANCIENT PLACES OF WORSHIP

Carnac, in Brittany, having originally perhaps 15,000 massive menhirs or blocks of stone, provides us with the remains of another huge structure, prehistoric, and probably devoted to religious purposes.

Stonehenge, in Wiltshire, apparently a similar type of sun temple, but planned with more geometrical skill, is a much smaller affair of two stone circles and two horseshoes of stones and trilithons; the outer circle is unique in having morticed lintels. It was obviously an important centre, with a race-course and converging avenues.

PALACES OF GREAT RULERS

The Ramasseum, the palace of the Pharaoh Rameses at Thebes, built about 1250 B.C., covered an area of about 5,040 square yards. Its columns were eighty feet high, the floor was plated with silver, and the doors were covered with gold, studded with precious stones. Outside the ruins stand two of the largest sculptures in the world.

The dimensions of the royal castles in ancient Babylon, with their so-called hanging gardens or earth platforms supporting tiers of arches, were astounding. In A.D. 300 a complete town, Spalato, now renamed Split, on the Dalmatian coast, was built within the palace of the Roman Emperor Diocletian. The palace of the Potala, residence of the Dalai Lama, Tibet, is nine stories high, and the former summer residence of the Chinese emperors comprises twenty palaces. The largest palace of an Indian prince was built at Madura in 1623; the Moslem university of Ibn Tûlûn in Cairo occupies some 17,000 square yards, and the seminary at Salamanca, erected in 1617, is about 20,000 square yards in area.

The temple of Buddha at Boroboedoer, on the island of Java, was built in A.D. 750 on ten terraces, the uppermost of which has a chapel over twenty-seven feet high. The whole structure is adorned with nearly 500 statues of Buddha and bas-reliefs made up of 1,500 slabs. It bears a curious resemblance to the Maya temple at Palenque in Central America.

EUROPE'S IMMENSE MONASTIC BUILDINGS

Portugal's resources were exhausted by erecting the convent of Mafra, the largest in the world. It cost over £4,000,000, and was built in 1717-1730 by a German architect, Johann Friedrich of Regensburg, 45,000 workmen being employed on it daily. When finished it had 1,500 windows, 5,200 doors, nine courtyards and two towers, each 223 ft. high. It has a counterpart in the monastery-palace of the Escorial in Spain, which was designed in 1563-1586 by a pupil of Michelangelo at a cost of about £780,000. This has 1,672 windows, eighty-six staircases, eighty-nine fountains, and 100 miles of corridors. Its long frontage of

660 ft. seems to represent the cold spirit of rigid etiquette. Just as the Escorial is typical of 16th-century Spain, the convent of Mafra exemplifies the weak ostentation of 18th-century Portugal.

Germany also possesses a religious building of similarly monstrous size in the convent of Leubus in Lower Silesia, built in 1698. It is twice as large as the Winter Palace in Leningrad, which previous to the World War was inhabited by some 5,000 persons. The Leubus convent is four times as large as the town hall in Amsterdam. Its main front is even longer than that of the Escorial, while the length of its side façades is some 523 ft. Its Hall of Princes measures 97 ft. by 49 ft. and is 45 ft. high. The convent of Ottobeuren, in Swabia, has been called the German Escorial; and the convent of Weingarten in Württemberg is, after the palace in Berlin with its 365 windows, the largest baroque building in Germany.

LARGEST PALACE IN THE WORLD

The largest castle in Germany is Burghausen on the Salzach, which has a frontage of 3,250 ft. The palace at Mannheim, built in 1720-1760, is the largest in Germany, while Schloss Ludwigsburg, near Stuttgart, contains 414 rooms.

The largest palace in the world is the Vatican; and the largest palace in private hands is Count Waldstein's Palace in Prague, which is of huge dimensions and has a magnificent terrace.

QUAINTEST HOUSE IN ENGLAND

The quaintest building in England is the Triangular Lodge, built 350 years ago by Sir Thomas Tresham at Rushton. It has three floors, each with three windows, each window containing three rows of four triangular panes. Each floor has three triangular rooms, the walls of which are exactly 33⅓ ft. in length. At the point where the roofs meet rises a triangular chimney. On each of the three sides of the house is a Latin inscription composed of thirty letters, and over the entrance is another inscription in honour of the Trinity.

STEPS AND DOMES

THE highest flight of steps in the world is the 6,000 steps which ascend the sacred mountain of Tai-Shan, in China (5,000 ft.). The well-preserved stairway which leads up to the White Temple of Ur, in Mesopotamia, was built in the 5th century B.C., and is thus probably the oldest in existence.

OLDEST FLIGHT OF STEPS

Babylon has some ancient isolated flights of steps used, it seems, for observatories; India's Jaipur observatory (1718-1734) is perhaps the most famous of this type, its gnomon being 90 ft. high. The oldest flight of steps still in use leads to the church of Ara Cœli on the Capitol in Rome; it is made of marble from Carrara. Until 1348 it formed the approach to the temple of Serapis on the Quirinal, built in 272 in the reign of the Emperor Aurelian.

Among "trick" staircases, one of the most famous is the spiral staircase in the Château de Chambord, in France, which was built in 1530 by Francis I. It is so contrived that persons ascending and descending it do not meet each other.

FIRST DOMED BUILDINGS

The largest unsupported brick barrel-vaulting is that in the incomplete palace of Ctesiphon, built about 550 by Chosroes I of Persia, on the Tigris. The span is 82 ft.

The first domed buildings were the "nuragi," the mysterious structures found in Sardinia which date from about 3000 B.C. Huge domes covered the tombs and treasure-houses of Mycenæ in Greece (1200 B.C.).

The most famous of the domes of the classical period which have been preserved are those of the Pantheon in Rome, the church of St. George in Salonika (4th century), and St. Sophia's (A.D. 533). Michelangelo's stone-constructed dome in St. Peter's is still unsurpassed for beauty. One of the largest domes is that of the Central Market Hall of Leipzig, which covers an area of 61,473 square yards. The dome of St. Paul's Cathedral covers about half that area (32,684 square yards).

ARCHITECTURE NEW AND STRANGE

DIFFERENT indeed even from the most rococo palaces are the productions of our modern architects, inspired by the theories and imagination of the French architect Le Corbusier. Revolving, spherical, steel and glass houses have been fashioned. A stairless tower hotel, rather like a gasometer, has been devised and erected at Sestrières, in the Italian Alps, by the Duke of Aosta. The exterior of Grundtvig Church in Copenhagen, built in memory of the famous Danish poet, educationist and bishop of that name, resembles a gigantic pipe organ. America has distanced Europe in oddity by producing an all-glass house built of glass bricks.

HOTEL LIKE A GUN-TURRET

At the seaside resort of Constanta (Kustenje) in Rumania a hotel was built in 1936 in the form of a gun-turret. The church at the Press Exhibition held at Cologne in 1928 was made entirely of steel, copper, and coloured glass. The Friedenskirche (Church of Peace) at Frankfurt is snow-white in colour and entirely bare of interior decoration.

Some of the materials and forms in use today must be regarded as extravagant. In Kyoto, Japan, is a skyscraper constructed mainly of glass, and covered with Cubist paintings. Built alongside the town hall of Rustringen in Germany is a water-tower of multi-coloured bricks.

The Augustinian Church in Berlin was modelled on a newspaper office, a prominent feature of which is rounded glass corners, one above the other. A soap factory at Nowawes, near Potsdam, was built entirely in the style of a castle; the wireless station at Nauen resembles a theatre; the railway station at Antwerp a cathedral, and the public hall in the post office at Utrecht the nave of a church. One half of the Film Artists' House at Hollywood, a creation of 1936, represents a gigantic perfume bottle, the other half an ice-pudding.

HIGHEST IN THE WORLD

The Woolworth Building in New York was for some time the highest in the world (792 ft.). Now the highest skyscrapers are the Empire State Building (1,248 ft.) and the Chrysler Building (1,030 ft.). The Eiffel Tower in Paris (985 ft.) comes next, followed by the New York Radio Building (840 ft.) and the Bank of Manhattan (838 ft.).

The New Delhi of Sir Edwin Lutyens and Sir Herbert Baker is a spacious blend of Renaissance and Indian motifs. Within an immense circle three large interior courts separate the three Houses—the Council of Princes, Assembly, and Council of State. At the hub of the " wheel " is a circular library. The approach is by an avenue with a memorial arch flanked by office buildings.

DAMS ANCIENT AND MODERN

THE first great dam of which we have any record was built about 3,700 years ago by the Pharaoh Amenemhet III. It was an earth dam of the simplest type, depending merely upon facing earthworks with brick. A good modern example of earthwork dam construction is the Davis Bridge Dam, Vermont, U.S.A., which is 200 ft. high, and has earthworks 1,900,000 cubic yards in volume.

The largest European dam of this type is at Dortmund, Germany. Completed in 1934, it is 195 ft. high and some three million cubic yards in volume. Along the top of it run two tracks for pedestrians and one for vehicles.

BIGGEST MODERN DAM

The dam at Assuan, 750 miles from the mouth of the River Nile, is an irrigation-reservoir barrage. It is 1¼ miles long with a height of 173 ft., and holds 4,800 million tons of water. The Sennar or Makwar dam in the Sudan has formed a lake fifty miles long. The largest dam in the world, with the exception of the Grand Coulee, now in course of construction, is the Boulder Dam on the Colorado River, U.S.A., completed in 1935. A rampart 727 ft. high and 650 ft. thick at the base holds back the Colorado River and forms a lake 115 miles long, which holds enough water to cover an area of 5,000 square miles to a depth of 10 ft. The intake towers by the side of the dam are each 390 ft. high.

The Grand Coulee Dam on the Columbia River, U.S.A., will rank as the greatest man-made structure the world has ever seen. It will irrigate an area as large as southern England and give a livelihood on the land to 30,000 families. Moreover, it will produce twice as much electricity as the greatest hydro-electric plant in Europe—Dnieprostroi, Russia—and the greatest in America—Niagara—put together. Its planned dimensions are: height, 550 ft.; length, one mile; thickness, 500 ft. Twenty-three million tons of concrete will be required to build it. The dam creates a main reservoir 100 miles long and a subsidiary reservoir twenty-eight miles long.

HIGHEST BARRAGE IN INDIA

The Lloyd Barrage (1923-1932), built for irrigation purposes across the Indus at Sukkur, in the province of Sind, is nearly a mile long. Its seven main canals total 400 miles in length, and it will irrigate an area larger by 500,000 acres than the whole arable area of Egypt. At the time of its completion it was by far the most impressive structure of its kind outside North America.

At Bhatgar, thirty-two miles from Poona, in the Deccan, is Lloyd Dam, not to be confused with the Barrage. Completed in 1928 after fifteen years of labour, it makes possible the raising of about £4,000,000 worth of crops every year. The highest barrage in India is at Bhakra in the Punjab. Its crest will, when completed, rise 500 ft. from the foundations.

The highest barrage in Europe is the Dnieprostroi, on the Dnieper river: 2,500 ft. long and 200 ft. high, it forms a lake ten miles wide. Its primary object is the production of electric power.

GREAT AQUEDUCTS OF ANCIENT ROME

Modern engineers have yet to find a better method of building aqueducts than that used by the ancients. While excavating a stepped pyramid at Nippur, in Iraq (Mesopotamia), a party of American archæologists discovered at a depth of twenty-three feet the perfectly preserved vaulting of a drain dating from the fourth millennium B.C. It is the oldest known example of barrel-vaulting.

In the palace of King Minos on the island of Crete, the foundations of water-closets have come to light. The conduits made by King Hezekiah of Judah, and by Polycrates on the island of Samos, are mentioned elsewhere. The conduits to be found at Miletus, on the west (Greek) coast of Asia Minor, and the drainage system of ancient Rome reveal great ingenuity and skill on the part of their designers.

The daily water-consumption of a modern city of a million inhabitants is less than a fifth of the amount—220 million gallons—which ancient Rome was capable of receiving through its aqueducts in twenty-four hours. The first aqueduct was constructed in 312 B.C.; the second, forty-three miles long, in 272-269 B.C. Both of these were underground. A third, sixty miles long, and for about a twelfth of its length borne on arches above ground, was constructed in 144-143 B.C., and others were built later. Two of the ancient aqueducts of Rome—the Virgo and the Trajana—were put into service again between 1570 and 1611.

The Romans constructed many aqueducts outside Italy. Of these, the Pont du Gard at Nîmes, France, and the aqueduct bridge at Segovia, Spain, are the two most remarkable. The former is still standing, and the latter continues in use. The Pont du Gard was built by order of Agrippa some twenty years before the beginning of the Christian era. Consisting of three tiers of arches, the middle one having eleven arches each spanning 75 ft., it is 160 ft. high. The Segovia structure, which has 109 arches in two tiers, is 102 ft. high and 2,700 ft. long.

SCHEMES TO DRAIN LAKES AND SEAS

Modern engineering has achieved many marvels in the sphere of land-reclamation, but plans for the wholesale alteration of the distribution of land and water are not new.

In very early times Lake Copais in Bœotia, Greece, was drained by a subterranean aqueduct driven from sixteen shafts, the deepest of which went down 150 ft. This antique drainage system—it may be 2,000 years old—was renovated and extended in 1895, when a large area of lakeland was reclaimed.

In 1912 the water was drained off from the sacred lake of Guatavita, in Columbia, in the hope that the ancient sacrificial offerings of the Incas, which were thought to be worth millions of pounds sterling, would be discovered. Large quantities of beads were found, as well as pendants of gold, amber and stone.

The partial drainage of Lake Nemi, near Rome, was effected for a similar purpose. The level of the lake was lowered 71 ft. and some twenty-seven million cubic yards of water were drawn off, with the result that two Roman galleys of magnificent proportions, one a pleasure ship of the Emperor Caligula, were exposed to view. They had been submerged for 1,900 years.

In ancient times the Mareotis (Mariut), a coastal lake near Alexandria, was connected by canals with the sea and the Nile. Its basin was still full in the 17th century, but when the French arrived on the scene at the end of the 18th century, they found that it had practically dried up.

The British, who followed them there for the purpose of driving Napoleon out of Egypt, refilled the lake in 1801, but in so doing had to flood whole villages. In 1895 the lake was partially drained by Dutch contractors, and five square miles of land were reclaimed. This area now produces excellent vines, as it used to before it was flooded.

When the reclamation of the Zuider Zee is complete, Holland will have increased her fertile territory by one-tenth. The Zuider Zee originally covered an area of 800,000 acres, of which 550,000 acres are to be reclaimed. The total cost of operations is likely to be in excess of £80,000,000. The work began in 1920.

LANGUAGE: WRITING: FIGURING

INVESTIGATIONS into the origin of language trace it to involuntary, animal-like sounds prompted by interesting sights and feelings, and to attempts to imitate sounds heard. The ancient Greeks, who studied the question, could never make up their minds whether there was a natural connexion between sound and meaning or not. Some thought there was; others considered that language from the very beginning was a matter of artificial sounds.

HOW LANGUAGE BEGAN

In the 19th century the three main theories of speech origin may be summarized, following Max Müller, the great philologist, as (1) the "bow-wow," or onomatopoetic theory. When early man wished to indicate a dog or the action of a boiling pot, he imitated the sounds they made as "bow-wow" or "bubble," just as modern children call a train a "puff-puff." (2) The "pooh-pooh" theory derives language from the expression of emotions, love-cries, exclamations of anger, and so on. Wrath, awe, rush, might be suggested as examples. (3) The "Yo-he-yo" advocates believed rather in articulate sounds first accompanying action, such as the heaving at a rope or dancing.

Experts for a time generally imagined language as monosyllabic in origin, but nowadays primitive language is thought, by analogy with such primitive tongues as Eskimo, to begin with long sentence-sounds or word conglomerations semi-sung and with pronounced intervals, not unlike good Hebrew. Otto Jespersen, Danish author of many works on the structure of English, may be taken as opening up a new approach to origins. By tracing modern languages backwards he aims to reach eventually to a set of sounds existing before the evolution of speech.

PRIMITIVE LANGUAGE IS COMPLICATED

Contrary perhaps to expectation, the older the language the greater its irregularities of formation and variety of words for individual objects, the more concrete, and the less generalized and simple the thoughts conveyed. A comparison of the root words of varied language stocks shows that language is the common product of humanity as a whole.

Geographical, political or occupational divisions between an originally similarly speaking group led to dialect divisions also, and ultimately to different languages, the difference between dialect and language being one of degree, not of kind. Dialect is more a matter of pronunciation and grammar forms, language more of vocabulary.

"Foreign accent" occurs when two language groups come into close contact; it is a fertile source of sound-changes and borrowed words. English has been modified by contact with Scandinavian languages, Celtic Latin, Church Latin, Norman-French, and Dutch. Literature contributes largely to word borrowings from other languages.

INVENTIVENESS OF PRIMITIVE PEOPLE

The number of primitive languages is legion. Language invention is particularly marked in the most primitive folk; thus in Brazil, in a region 312 miles long, there are seven or eight completely different languages, the poorest of which in point of vocabulary is the Inje.

Children are always ready to invent new words. For this reason as long ago as 600 B.C. Psammetichus I of Egypt thought to discover the original language of his people by isolating a number of children.

Written and civilized languages change very slightly in the course of time. Once a people has entered the sphere of civilization its language gradually assumes permanent forms. The need for mutual understanding is increased in civilization by the brisk exchange of goods and ideas.

EARLY ALPHABETS OF MAN

The first two letters of the Greek alphabet, *alpha* and *beta*, came to denote the series of letters which the Greeks borrowed apparently from Phœnician traders, and from which our alphabet is derived.

Alphabets, even those more detailed than is ours, only give approximate indication of sounds. Thus in English the letter *A* may be sounded as in r*A*ther, as in v*A*n, or as in m*A*ke; that is, as a " Latin " *a*, a short *a*, or the broad " diphthong " *a* which is really the sound *ay-ee*.

Just as language is a clumsy garment for thought, so writing is a clumsy means to convey language. The more primitive the attempt the clumsier it is. Early attempts to convey meanings include sticks with knotted strings attached, notched sticks and, amongst the North American Indians, coloured wampum beads or deerskin.

When men began to use instruments to record pictures upon wood, stone, skin, and so on, three essential stages in the growth towards an alphabet may be distinguished.

At first come pictographs, which are crude drawings of objects to be conveyed; ideographs which represent ideas or combinations of these with certain formalizations, as in hieroglyphs. North American Indians and the ancient Egyptians well represent this stage.

In syllabaries the same picture symbol is used for an identical sound in whatever combination it occurs. The picture then degenerates in order to help in speed of writing, and becomes a mere symbol for a sound.

Between pictographs, ideographs, hieroglyphs and syllabaries come Sumerian writing and Babylonian cuneiform, whence our writing more directly derives. These added phonetic symbols and used both them and ideographs. From this stage derive Egyptian, Hittite, Chinese, Maya and Aztec writings. The Japanese, it may be noted, chose forty-seven Chinese characters to represent the syllables of their utterly different language, thus completing the transfer from meaning to sound representation.

In the alphabetic stage the letter has no value other than phonetic. Nations which have adopted alphabets have never returned to other conventions. The modern western alphabet of twenty-six letters has survived for some 3,000 years with little change among a great variety of languages.

OUR EGYPTIAN OR MINOAN ALPHABET

Theories about the origins of the alphabet are various. Perhaps most philologists incline now to favour a Semitic source, largely on the ground that the names of the letters, which have no meaning in Greek, have meaning in Hebrew and allied tongues.

The Moabite Stone (9th century B.C.) and a Baal-Lebanon inscription in Cyprus contained until recently the earliest known Semitic script. François Lenormant, the French archæologist, considered its origin Egyptian; so does Dr. Alan Gardiner, who found a missing link in the already alphabetic Sinaitic inscriptions discovered in 1906 by Sir W. Flinders Petrie, the greatest British Egyptologist.

Some think the alphabetic origins lie in Babylonian cuneiform; others, principally Sir Arthur Evans, the explorer of the buried cities of Crete, think them Minoan (Cretan). Sir Arthur believes that the Philistines took the alphabet from Crete to Palestine, whence the Phœnicians borrowed it. The evidence of four more recently found South Semitic alphabets, however, seems to favour an Egyptian origin.

Sir W. Flinders Petrie has put forward a theory of the evolution of the alphabet from a series of commercial signs in use in the Mediterranean.

It appears probable that the Greeks borrowed from Aramaic sources firstly the western or Chalcidic alphabet, from the south-east tip of Asia Minor, together with Babylonian weights and coins; then, secondly, a variant alphabet, the Ionic or Eastern, the Ionian Greeks borrowing this directly from Phœnician traders.

The Greeks used some of the twenty-two borrowed consonant letters for vowels, and added several letters. The Indian alphabets, unlike ours, are arranged according to sound: first the vowels, in logical order, then the consonants.

ROMANCE IN A TO Z

THE earliest Greek inscriptions date from the 9th or 8th centuries B.C., and were found in Thera Island. Some uniformity of alphabet was attained by the Greeks by the 4th century B.C.

A is the purest and the oldest vowel, often converted into E and Œ in the early languages, while in Sanskrit it represents twenty-seven per cent of the total number of sounds. It is consistent throughout the Greek alphabets.

B comes from the Phœnician *beta*, meaning "house." Some have derived it from the hieroglyphic sign for ladder, others from that for a crane.

The letter C is a late comer, being an offshoot from G. Its sound has varied from that to K and, latest of all, to S. C came from the Greek to the Roman alphabet as *gamma*, but when the distinction from G and K became obliterated, G was used for Q and K, e.g., in the Latin name "Gaius." Subsequently, when the distinction between G and K reappeared, G was reinstated by the elementary teacher, Carvilius, in 234 B.C., in place of the superfluous Z (*zeta*), and K was only rarely used (as in Kalendâe, Karthago, Kæso). C was pronounced as K, and it was not till about A.D. 700 that C before E, I and Y began to be pronounced as the English Ch. The pronunciation of the Latin C as K, now quite general in English schools, whereby, for example, Cicero is pronounced "Kikero," is therefore the more correct.

D has not been traced back with certainty further than the Phœnician and Hebrew alphabets, although it used to be customary to ascribe it to Egyptian and refer to the shape of the delta of the Nile, also a triangle.

HOW Z BECAME THE LAST LETTER

E originated in the combination of A and I. In the eastern Greek alphabet the letter represented a vowel, in the western an aspirate breathing.

In early Latin and Spanish, F, the same sound as the discarded Greek letter *digamma,* was often pronounced as H (Hernando—Fernando); whereas in other languages TH was pronounced as F e.g., " Feodor " instead of " Theodor " in Slavonic.

G, as has been said above, replaced Z (*zeta*), taken from the Semitic *zain*, which had become superfluous, and Z was relegated to the bottom of the alphabet. North European peoples have changed G into W, e.g., *Gallia* into *Wallia*, while, conversely, the southern peoples have changed W into G, e.g., *Welf* into *Guelfo*. The Czech language has no G.

H is especially common in North European languages, where it often appeared first before a consonant, though not in English, e.g., German *hrein*; then, as in Greek, after a consonant, e.g., rhubarb.

I in Greek is an adaptation of Semitic *yod*. In Norse languages I or E commonly replaces the southern A, e.g., Sanskrit *sapta,* English *seven*, German *sieben.*

J did not appear in Latin texts until about the year 1600; it was then adopted in many modern languages.

In Slavonic languages K becomes R, and C becomes Z. Its origin has been referred to under C. In medieval times it signified the number 250. In chemistry it symbolizes potassium.

L is related to R; it is unpronounceable for many orientals. Its derivation is very uncertain. It is the chemical symbol for lithium, and in the Roman numeral system stood for 50.

A final M was not pronounced in Latin; it never ends a word in Greek, and in many cases it was changed into N by the Teutonic peoples.

M has been thought to represent two pent roofs side by side. Belonging to the labial-nasal group of consonants, it converts easily into the nasal-dental N. M was used by the Romans to signify the number 1,000, and N sometimes to indicate 90.

O is the Phœnician letter *ayin*, which means "eye." In medieval times it signified the number 11.

Arabic having no P, has, for instance, Farsistan instead of Parsistan. In Hebrew, P means "mouth," the symbol being a rough outline of a mouth. In the Teutonic languages there was no initial P; it first appears in Old High German in place of B. In French, P was frequently replaced by V.

Q is a diphthong which the Romans borrowed from the Greeks of Southern Italy to replace their KW. In Slavonic it does not exist.

In early Aryan languages letters which are now L's were R's. In Greek, Sanskrit, and the Slavonic languages R was classed as a vowel.

MOST CHANGEABLE OF LETTERS

With regard to the sound it denotes, S is one of the most changeable of letters. In Greek, which took it over from the Semitic fifteenth letter *samech,* as sigma, it was in most cases equivalent to H, i.e., *hepta* was the Greek equivalent to Latin *septem.* In Latin it corresponded to R, and in English S before K becomes SCH, as in English *school.*

The origin of T is unknown; it may have derived from a hieroglyphic sign for arm-with-cake-in-hand.

The Romans gave U the function of W, which it still has in English and German when it follows Q (German *quelle* = English "well").

V occupied the sixth place in the Phœnician alphabet, and signified "nail." The Greeks invented another letter in its stead (Y), which in Latin did the work of U and W.

W, in Greek, either became H or dropped out altogether; in Romance languages it was replaced by V, and in Old High German it was pronounced U.

X was taken by the Greeks from the Samnite alphabet about 400 B.C., the Samnites being a sister nation of the Romans. It was used by the Romans only in Greek words. In English it is pronounced KS, in Spanish CH, in Italian SS, in French GS.

Y, which was *vau*, the sixth letter of the Semitic alphabet, was used by the Greeks to denote the vowel UE, into which U had developed. It was introduced into the Latin alphabet shortly before the coming of Christianity; formerly, Syria, for example, was written "Suria." There is no Y in Italian.

In the language of the Egyptians Z may have been a bird symbol which was adopted by the Phœnicians in the form of the letter *sain.* In Latin it was used only in foreign words and consequently dropped from the sixth place in the alphabet to the last. In Italian and ancient Greek it is pronounced DS. In English it has become in some words interchangeable with S, e.g., civilise—ize.

ZODIAC AND THE ALPHABET

Professor Hermann Wirth, the German archæologist, having compared the oldest legends and traditions of every people, considers that he has found therein common features which today are unintelligible unless considered in the light of the conditions which, according to recent researches, are said to have prevailed in the northern polar circle before the glacial period: that is, a temperate, fertile climate, with polar conditions of sunlight, having a midnight sun and a dark winter.

In this long night of winter the zodiac, the visible calendar, became the sole means of finding one's bearings and telling the time. It became, therefore, the chief theme of religious feeling and the real alphabet, for it was from one of these twice-twelve " runic signs of the heavens," which Professor Wirth claims to have discovered in the oldest bone and stone scratchings of every country, that the new light arose every year out of the winter night.

According to this theory the signs of the zodiac originated as the celestial timepiece of a people dwelling in the polar circle. At the same time, they provided the basis for all subsequent alphabets.

EUROPE'S ANCIENT RUNES

Amongst primitive scripts must be included the runic script of ancient Europe.

The Runic alphabet was formed by selection from the Greek or Roman alphabet in the 2nd or 3rd century A.D., with certain additions. The letters are modified for carving on wood or stone, and are therefore angular.

Runes occur on the Anglo-Saxon crosses frequently found in northern England. The signature of Cynewulf, an early English poet, in his 9th-century poems, is indicated by runes distributed over several lines. The mysterious Franks Casket (8th century) has runes surrounding its pictured sides.

The oldest runic inscription on stone comes from Karlstad, in Sweden; it is surmounted by a swastika and six ships arranged in pairs, reminiscent of the fertility rites of the Bronze Age.

CONQUEST SPREADS DIALECTS

The predominance of a state or city which is also an intellectual centre naturally promotes the spread of its own dialect. In Greece the dominance of Athens made general the use of Attic; in ancient Italy there was a similar diffusion of the Latin of Rome, as in medieval Italy Sicilian (until the 13th century), and as in modern Italy Tuscan (from the time of Dante, who died in 1321, onwards).

In England since the time of Alfred the Great (848-99) the Wessex dialect and its descendants have led the way in literature. The " best " English, in other words that standardized as the educated form in the 18th century, comes from the district between Oxford and London. The best French is supposed to be spoken in Paris and Geneva; the purest

Spanish in Castile. In Germany the Frankish dialect was supreme until the time of the Crusades; it was then succeeded by Swabian and finally by the dialect of Meissen. German, as a literary language, originated in that spoken in the courts of the Emperor Charles IV at Prague and of the Electorate of Saxony.

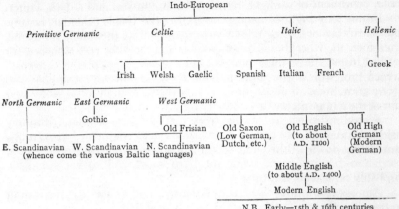

TABLE SHOWING DERIVATION OF ENGLISH

Indo-European

Primitive Germanic — *Celtic* — *Italic* — *Hellenic*

Irish — Welsh — Gaelic — Spanish — Italian — French — Greek

North Germanic — *East Germanic* — *West Germanic*

Gothic

Old Frisian — Old Saxon (Low German, Dutch, etc.) — Old English (to about A.D. 1100) — Old High German (Modern German)

E. Scandinavian — W. Scandinavian — N. Scandinavian (whence come the various Baltic languages)

Middle English (to about A.D. 1400)

Modern English

N.B. Early—15th & 16th centuries
Later—16th & early 17th centuries
Present day—from about 1650

Italics indicate conjectural languages of an intermediate type which have since perished.

HOW WE GOT OUR WORDS

ENGLISH is as clear as any other language in its traceable origins, complex as these are. It has been formed by the flowing together of several main streams of already-formed tongues.

The main stream is that brought by the Germanic tribes who conquered the island in the 5th and 6th centuries A.D. after its abandonment by Rome. Some dialects of islands off the German coast still form its nearest linguistic relations. The Celts were submerged politically, though to a decreasing degree from east to west of the country, and an independent Celtic kingdom still remained in Eastern England up to the time of the Danish conquest. To what extent Celts merged with or outnumbered their conquerors cannot at this date be determined except by the indirect evidence of language. The Celts had in their turn originally submerged a more primitive, short, dark people, traces of whom may be found in western parts of Scotland and Wales.

Each of these peoples added certain words to the language, with the possible exception of the primitive, short people conquered by the Celts; of this conquest we know so little that we cannot say if the Celts did in fact borrow any of their words or not. Celtic words, except those for rivers and other natural features, are not a numerous band, and those uncertain : *dun* (a hill) and *coomb* (small valley) are the chief of them.

OLD WORDS THAT PICTURE OUR ANCESTORS

Among the words found in English in common with Sanskrit, and therefore of high antiquity, are some which are very instructive as to the stage of civilization reached before the common ancestors of the early invaders of India and of the tribes that wandered westward, eventually to Europe, parted company.

The following list, for instance, gives a sketch of an early nomadic race, dependent on its flocks and herds for wealth : knee, foot, father, mother (and other relationship names), neve (nephew), hound, sow, goose, eoh (horse), ewe, wether, cow, ox, herd, fee (meaning both cattle and money), wheel, axle, yoke, wain, ore (meaning any metal), row, rudder, door, timber, thatch, mead (a drink made from honey), weave, tree, birch, withy, wolf, beaver, hare, mouse, feather, nest, night, star, dew, snow, wind, thunder, fire. The poverty of agricultural words and the absence of reference to the sea are significant.

Words referring to specific trees may refer to a later, definitely agricultural stage, not having counterparts in Persian and Indian roots, but dating from a European settlement. Beech, elm, throstle, finch, etc., also furrow, corn, bean, meal, to mow and to ear (plough), probably came from this time.

Our ancestors now also reached the sea, and so we find, according to this theory, mere (Latin *mare*, sea), salt, and fish.

ADDING TO THE VOCABULARY

After the Germanic peoples had separated from the later Mediterranean races, an enormous enrichment of vocabulary occurs, witnessing the growth of civilization, from which may be selected as typical : bowl, brew, broth, dough, loaf, hat, comb, house, home, borough (a fortified place), king, earl (a local lord), buy, worth, cheap, island, flood, cliff, strand, ship, steer, sail, points of the compass, hail, storm, and whale (used for any large sea creature).

We can tell what metals they had acquired by this time by the use of their names : gold, silver, lead, iron, tin, and even steel. Leech (a healer), lore (knowledge), book (a wooden writing tablet), and write (to cut letters in bark : German *reissen*) show clearly how far culture had progressed.

LATIN AND GREEK IN OUR LANGUAGE

The Roman conquest and settlement for some 400 years left singularly few words behind it in England. Cæsar (Kaiser) is perhaps the earliest Latin word adopted by the Teutons. Castra (Chester, camp), pavement and camp (used for a battle), are perhaps the only direct transferences that do not come via Norman-French. Some borrowings from Latin brought over by the Germanic tribes show clearly what elements of Roman civilization the Nordic peoples were capable of absorbing : street, drake (dragon), pile (javelin), mile, wall, toll, mule, cat, chest, ark (box), pound (the weight), inch, monger, mint (money), wine, ele (oil), pepper (from an Indian word, showing the use of distant trade routes), chalk (lime: showing use of mortar in building), pit (for a built-in spring), table, pillow, kettle, cheese, peer, plum, anchor.

It is notable that no words denoting Christian worship occur in these; and the reality of early Greek influence in spreading Christianity is shown by the curious little group of Greek words which the Faith contributed to the language: angel, devil, church (Greek *kuriakon*). But Rome soon asserted her sway, and all the words denoting organization are of Latin origin: alms, bishop, pine (pain or punishment), monk, minster (monastery).

Early missionaries were wise enough for the most part to use "native" words where possible; and all these are "heathen" words adapted to religious usage: God, hell, love, sin, rood (*ród*), and Easter (Eostre, goddess of dawn or spring). However, for many purposes Saxon words could not be found; and acolyte, anthem, apostle, deacon, disciple, epistle, hymn, psalm and stole were mediated through Latin from the Greek, and altar, candle, creed, nun, mass and shrine came from the Latin direct. A certain number, such as Sabbath, came from Hebrew adaptation.

NORMAN CONQUEST OF THE SAXON TONGUE

Before the Norman conquest the developed Saxon kingdoms had already borrowed many foreign words, as well as many from the Bible such as camel, palm, cassia, myrrh and crystal (ice, as well as the mineral). The more secular borrowings included chancellor, pride, cup, mat, pitch, fan (for winnowing), capon, lobster, trout, turtle (turtle dove), cole (cabbage), parsley, beet, fennel, radish, pine and box (the tree); also, rather curiously, India, Saracen and orange.

The brief Danish hegemony may be responsible for the considerable borrowings from that language; including such vital words as law, moot, hustings, and riding (county division).

For centuries Norman-French was the normal language of the governing class. Hence the vast number of English words of that origin. They are at first largely ecclesiastical, such as procession and charity. The rest are largely governmental, such as court, council, justice; or warlike, such as tower, standard, treason; or agricultural.

WORDS BROUGHT BY FRIARS AND KNIGHTS

Movements which have left their mark on English vocabulary include the Crusades, which contributed many Eastern words such as azure, damask (from Damascus), cotton, mattress; the coming of the preaching friars, which yielded patience, pity, anguish, salvation; and the formation of English legal institutions in the 13th century, which gave judge, assize, fine, felon, plea, heir, homage.

Only a few words can be selected from successive centuries, but the 14th century's absorption of most of the vocabulary of medieval

European culture, as well as a multitude of mythical zoological names, may be noted. The 15th century marks a halting space; the 16th century gave us the full riches of Elizabethan English, and a notable enrichment of Protestant Reformation words. The 17th century gives Puritan and Royalist terms, and the beginning of scientific definition and commercial vocabulary.

ARTIFICIAL AND ANCIENT LANGUAGES

IN recent times artificial languages have been evolved to facilitate international intercourse. They are all based on similar principles. In both Ido and Esperanto the vocabulary is made up of the commonest words in the chief civilized languages, and the rules of inflexion are, as in English, of the simplest.

Basic English is an adaptation, by C. K. Ogden, the well-known English psychologist and philologist, in which 850 words do the work of some 20,000. Evolved between 1928 and 1931 and partly based on the work of American language experts, its use is growing rapidly, not only in the English-speaking countries.

WRITING IN NUMBERS

G. W. Leibniz, the great German philosopher, experimented with the formation of a "logical ideal language," one of its features being the representation of elementary notions by prime numbers, and of combined notions by products of these numbers, so that combinations of notions would resemble chemical formulæ. He also considered the possibility of a simplified Latin in which there would be only adjectives and particles and two words for "be" and "thing," thus obviating the necessity for inflexion.

Although a universal language has not yet come about, a generally used script and numbers may be paving the way for it. As Thomas Carlyle said, writing is undoubtedly the most marvellous of all inventions. Our own Latin script has been adopted by the Turks, following which the Russian People's Commissar for Education has advocated its adoption. Japan, too, is now considering the same proposal.

GREATEST ADMINISTRATIVE LANGUAGES

In early antiquity there were already international and diplomatic languages. Thus the prevailing language in the Near East from 2000 to 1000 B.C. was the Semitic language of the Babylonians. The Pharaohs of Egypt corresponded in it with foreign potentates, and it was universally recognized in commerce. The discovery has been made in Canaan of a number of commercial treaties inscribed on clay tablets in the Babylonian language. Trilingual tablets, dating from the 2nd century B.C., have been found in the archives of the Hittite kings at Boghaz-Keui (Asia Minor), inscribed with Sumerian, Akkadian, and Hittite texts.

Greek, in its turn, was the international language of the Near East, especially from the time of Alexander the Great (356-323 B.C.), and it has maintained itself up to the present day as the principal commercial language of the Levant. In the Western world the language of Rome was for centuries predominant. It has continued to live in the Romance languages and as the language of the Church.

Latin was the language of the French law courts until 1539; but in England, Latin was mingled with Norman-French, English not again emerging as a governmental language until the time of Edward I. Latin was the language used in official circles in Hungary until 1836, and it is still used as such in Lithuania. As the language of the diplomatic world, Latin gave place to French about 1648.

PHŒNICIAN TRADERS SPREAD WRITING

Nearly all countries except those of the Far East, ancient America, and Oceania, have come within the sphere of the Latin script or its direct predecessors. The Babylonians took from the Sumerians about 300 symbols, which in ancient Persian were reduced to forty. The art of writing was probably transmitted by the Sumerians to the Egyptians, and probably thence to other peoples, through the medium of the much-travelled Phœnicians. They, needing a script to facilitate their world-wide commerce, simplified the Sumerian-Egyptian symbols and arranged them in an alphabet.

Both Egyptian and Phœnician letters are found in the earliest writings (still undeciphered) of the Cretans, Hittites, and the inhabitants of the peninsula of Sinai.

Among the direct offshoots of the Phœnician script are the Moabite script, formed in the kingdom of Moab, south of the Dead Sea, the Hebraic, the Carthaginian (from which derive the old Berber scripts and the Tuareg alphabet, still widely used in the Sahara), the early Syriac (in which was written an early translation of the Gospels), and finally the Greek alphabet.

WRITING FROM TOP TO BOTTOM

When the Greeks first began to write, they wrote the first line from right to left, the second from left to right, the third from right to left again, and so on. This method was known as *boustrophedon* or "turning like oxen in ploughing."

The Chinese write from top to bottom and from right to left, the Japanese also from top to bottom, but from left to right. The Mexicans write from bottom to top. Hebrew, Turkish, Arabic and Persian are still written from right to left.

Our modern or "Arabic" numerals also came originally from Mesopotamia. Both the Zend script of Persia and the Sanskrit of India were developments of the early Syriac script, and Sanskrit letters were turned into "Arabic" numerals in the course of the Indo-Arabic commerce. They were introduced to Europe at the time of the Crusades.

The art of writing enables man to make his knowledge less ephemeral than himself. Hence the god of wisdom for the early Near-eastern civilizations was at the same time the god of writing. The Sumerians called him Nebo, the Egyptians Thoth, scribe of the gods.

FROM STONE TO PAPER

THE first writing was on either a stone or a tree. Writing on stone is still practised in cutting inscriptions on memorials, while trees, as Shakespeare noticed, are still carved with the initials of sweethearts.

In the European-Asiatic sphere of civilization the need was soon felt for less ponderous materials for picture writing. For a time, recourse was had to dressed skins; but as these were required for other purposes also, they became too costly. As early as the days of Homer (about 800 B.C.), linen and thin wooden tablets were used, and scratchings were made on clay tablets, sheets of lead, wax, and other materials. The discovery of paper was made first in Egypt, then in China. The bast of the papyrus, a plant indigenous to Egypt, became the usual writing material. Egypt possessed a monopoly of it; a sheet of ordinary papyrus cost about 1d., a sheet of the best quality 8s. The famous public library of Alexandria obtained it free of charge.

PAPER FROM COTTON AND RAGS

A Chinese minister of agriculture is said to have succeeded in making paper out of cotton in the year 125 B.C., but subsequently in China it was made of straw and rags. When the technique of making paper out of fibre became known to the Arabs they set up a factory in Baghdad in A.D. 795 which was the first of its kind in the Near East. The process became known to Western Europe through the Crusades, and in 1290 the first paper factory in Germany was established in Ravensberg. "Rag paper" as made there is still considered to be of excellent quality.

The oldest piece of linen paper made in Germany dates from the year 1239; it is a document signed by Count Adolph of Schaumburg, and is now kept in Rinteln. Paper was first made in England in 1494; it was hand-made, but during the 18th century fibrous paper became too dear, owing to the great demand for it.

MODERN PAPER FROM WOOD

Wood-paper was invented at Regensburg in 1760 by the naturalist Schäffer, who, basing his experiments on observation of the wasps' nest, sifted sawdust and mixed it with water into a pulp. By the time he died, in 1790, his invention had been almost forgotten. It was rediscovered in 1806 by a master weaver in Saxony, who, independently of Schäffer, hit on the idea of imitating wasps, which make the material for their nests in much the same manner as wood-pulp is made.

The paper-making experiment was successful; it won widespread recognition. First esparto grass (from about 1860) then wood (from about 1880) came into general use, and in the latter half of the 19th century an endless stream of books was printed on wood-paper, which nowadays is used mainly for newspapers, good-quality paper being made of wood-cellulose. In 1853 so-called parchment paper or vellum was invented.

The modern paper-making machine was invented by a French clerk named Louis Robert in the Didot Paper Mills, at Essonne, France, in 1798.

Five years later the first English paper-making machine was set up at Frogmore, Hampshire, by Henry Fourdrinier and Bryan Donkin.

In civilized countries between 40 and 110 lb. of wood per head of the populations are used annually by paper mills. One of the results of the enormous demand for paper is a rapid decrease in the area of forest lands in North America and Sweden.

To help meet the ever-increasing demand, an area in America totalling about 156,000 square miles, was sown with maize in 1928. It produces an annual crop of 3,000,000 bushels. The new paper is being made of a pulp seventy-five per cent of which consists of maize and only twenty-five per cent of wood. Since 1929 several districts of Algiers and Tunis also have been used to produce the materials for this latest type of paper.

SUBSTITUTES FOR PAPER

Dresden has an interesting collection of writing materials used by peoples who lived outside the paper-using area. It includes a runic calendar written on six pieces of boxwood from Sweden (about A.D. 850); thirty-nine sheets made of compressed threads of the agave leaf and coated with plaster, which have preserved written documents of the Mayas in Yucatan; fragmentary writings from ancient Tibet, on blackened cotton-paper; palm-leaves inscribed with yellow characters, from eastern India; Siamese script in yellow on a black paper-like material; the Koran of Sultan Bajazet II, 433 pages of silk, inscribed in white Turkish characters on an azure ground; a letter scratched on gold foil by a Malay prince in 1696; and birch bark with the script of the Yukaghirs of north-east Siberia.

PENCILS AND PENS

Lead (graphite) pencils were in use as early as A.D. 1350, but it was not until 1761 that Kaspar Faber founded his famous pencil factory at Stein, near Nuremberg.

A pen of sheet brass was invented by L. von Wiese in 1579, and Samuel Harrison made a steel pen for Dr. Priestley in 1780. The marketing of quill-shaped steel pens began in 1803. They were 5s. each. Machine-made pens were first turned out by John Mitchell in 1822. James Perry is considered to have begun the manufacture of steel " slip " pens, but in 1828 Josiah Mason improved them. Patents for further improvement were taken out by Perry in 1830 and by Joseph Gillot in the following year.

Catherine the Great of Russia is said to have used a kind of fountain pen; but to go back much further, the early Egyptians used writing reeds which may be regarded as the prototype of the modern fountain pen, which was invented by Waterman in 1883.

ENTER THE TYPEWRITER

The first typewriting patent was taken out by an English engineer, Henry Mill, in 1714, but he did not manufacture his design. It is described as " an artificial machine or method for the impressing or transcribing of letters singly or progressively one after another, as in writing, whereby all writings whatsoever may be engrossed in paper or parchment so neat and exact as not to be distinguished from print." The pioneer American typewriter, which its inventor called a typographer, was made in 1829 by William Austin Burt, of Detroit. " Plees forgive al mistakes," he typed in the first letter that left his apparatus, " it is j est printed in a hurry on the new machene, amonge a crowd of people who are watching and arsking questions al the time."

Attempts to produce something generally satisfactory became numerous after 1860. In 1862 Jacob Peters of Copenhagen invented a typewriter, as did three American engineers, Carlos Glidden, Christopher Latham Sholes and Samuel W. Soulé, of Milwaukee, Wisconsin, whose invention was taken over and developed by E. Remington & Sons, gunmakers, in 1873. Sholes is recorded to have remarked, " I feel that I have done something for the women who have always had to work so hard. This will enable them more easily to earn a living." A woman, Queen Victoria, was the first ruler to admit a typewriter to a royal household.

SHORTHAND IN ANCIENT ROME

One of Cato's orations against Catiline, delivered in Rome in 63 B.C., was, we are told by Roman historians, taken down in shorthand by Tiro, the method being known as Tironian notes. Several stenographers, posted in the Senate, took turns at recording different parts of the speech and put them together at the end.

Luther's shorthand writer, a certain Dr. Cruciger, wrote down a report of Luther's disputation with John Eck which took place in Leipzig in 1519, and also took down Luther's speech before the Diet of Worms, one of the turning points in the Reformation in 1521.

A system of shorthand was invented in England in the time of Queen Elizabeth by Timothy Bright, and a similar one in France.

The most famous English shorthand manuscript is the diary of Samuel Pepys written in the period 1660-1669. Pepys freely adapted the system called " tachygraphy," which was invented by Thomas Shelter (1640) and expounded in his book of that name.

WRITING FOR THE BLIND

In antiquity and in the Middle Ages there was no writing whatever for the blind. The first beginnings were made in the 17th and 18th centuries.

Valentin Haüy, a French musician, devised the first system for embossing letters for the blind in the 17th century. The first book for the blind produced in the United Kingdom was that of James Gall, of Edinburgh (1827). The present system of writing and printing for the blind was evolved by the Frenchman, Louis Braille, in 1829.

MAKING MANY BOOKS

Owing to the numbers of slaves who could write, and were used for copying manuscripts, books in the Roman Empire eventually became nearly as cheap as they are today. A great centre was Alexandria with its library of over 400,000 volumes. Rome had a quarter largely devoted to book-copying shops. The rich Roman banker Atticus, a friend of Cicero's, was also a "publisher."

A collection of 340 of the biting verses written by the epigrammatic poet Martial (born A.D. 40) were sold for about 1s. De luxe editions cost perhaps 4s. 6d. Authors' royalties were unknown. Pliny was offered £5,000 for his collection of extracts from older manuscripts. Until A.D. 500 Rome was the centre of the world's book trade, and "publishers" had their representatives in the remotest Roman provincial towns. Although copyright did not exist, professional principles were upheld. That there were dishonest readers in antiquity is indicated by the discovery in 1936 in Trajan's Library in Athens of an instruction which ends with a request to the officials "not to lend a book out of the library to any visitor."

COSTLY BOOKS IN THE MIDDLE AGES

Book prices were higher in the Middle Ages than at any other time previous to the invention of printing. In A.D. 1150, for instance, an edition of Livy, an author then recently recovered from antiquity by the finding of a manuscript, cost 120 gold crowns, for which sum a fine estate in the country could be bought. Indeed a certain Antoninus Beccatellus did exchange his country estate for a copy of Livy.

Bindings were also at their costliest in the days preceding the invention of printing. There were Bibles studded with precious stones, bound in Babylonian leather, and with ivory pages. Hence the rebuke of the Church Father Jerome: "Your books are overloaded with precious things, whereas Christ died naked outside His temple," and that of the Persian poet Saàdī: "The Koran was given by God to men to make them better; but they think of nothing but to beautify its pages."

Movable type was used by the ancient Roman potters to imprint on their productions the names of their firms, but no one, apparently, thought of adapting the idea to printing books. In China, on the other hand, as early as 175 B.C., the texts of the Chinese classics were being engraved on wooden tablets from which impressions were taken, but it was not till A.D. 600 that separate wooden letters were used. By A.D. 1050 the practice of printing books from movable type had become general throughout China.

The first books printed in Europe were the "block-books" made by the Dutch on wooden tablets. The only relic of this phase of printing is the portion of a block, with raised letters cut out of the wood, which was discovered in the State Library in Munich in 1935.

GUTENBERG'S AND CAXTON'S PRESSES BEGIN

It was this block printing and the metal letter stamps used on book covers, many of which have been preserved, which gave Johann Gutenberg his inspiration. He did not know that printing from movable type had long been practised by the Chinese. The earliest of his productions dates from the fifties of the 15th century; his famous Latin Bible, called the Mazarin Bible, from 1456. The first book to bear the name of its printer, and the date and place of its publication, was the Mainz Psalter of 1457 The first Bible printed in German was produced by Mentelin in 1466.

William Caxton set up his press in England in 1476. His first known printed document in England, apart from his previous productions at Bruges, was only recently discovered at the London Record Office; it is an *Indulgence*, issued December 13, 1476, by Abbot Sant.

The first printing press at Rome was established by Pannartz and Sweinheim in 1464, and its various rooms are still on view. In 1470, Louis XI found accommodation for Gering's press in the University of Paris. Russia's first printed work, the Acts of the Apostles, appeared in 1564, whereas Brazil had to wait for its first press until 1811.

Lithography was invented by Aloys Senefelder, a Bavarian actor-dramatist (1771-1834), in 1796; the lithographic steam press appeared in 1846; the first iron printing press was constructed by the third Earl Stanhope (1753-1816) in 1800. The first modern rotary press, printing from a reel of paper continuously paid out, was made by an American, William Bullock, in 1865.

The first application of the three-colour block process of printing, now used so extensively for colour plates and catalogues, was made by Frederick Ives, of Philadelphia, in 1880. The photo-lithographic process evolved with the gradual application of photographic inventions to the old lithographical principle of the mutual repulsion of grease and water on a limestone or metal plate. Similarly, the colour-gravure process has evolved from photogravure.

Photogravure itself was determined in its basic principles by the experiments of Fox Talbot in England in the fifties of last century. Karl Klic, working on these, produced in England in 1879 an efficient and workable process.

CHURCH FATHER WHO WROTE 6,000 BOOKS

Origen, the prolific Greek Church Father who lived in the 3rd century, was responsible for 6,000 written works, the less famous philosopher Chrysippus for 700. Voltaire's writings fill seventy octavo volumes. The philosopher Jean H. S. Formey, who died 1797, left behind him 700 volumes. The Italian comedy-writer Goldoni wrote 200 plays, the Spaniard Calderon 127 comedies, 95 religious plays, and 1,000 *entr'actes*.

Lope de Vega, the Spanish playwright, left behind him no less than 1,800 theatrical compositions, and the German Hans Sachs 200 plays, 197 farces, 116 allegories and 272 tales.

RARE AND VALUABLE BOOKS

The greatest price ever paid for a single book was £100,000, given in 1933 by the British Museum for the earliest known copy of the New Testament, the Codex Sinaiticus, found in St. Catherine's Convent at the foot of Mt. Sinai in 1844 and sold by the Russian Government. It probably dates from the early part of the 4th century.

Among the most valuable books in the world is the hand-written copy of the Koran presented by the Emir of Afghanistan to the Shah of Persia. The binding alone is said to have cost £30,000, consisting as it does of gold plates embellished with arabesques composed of 398 gems, 167 pearls, 132 rubies, and 109 diamonds of the first water. In contrast to this there is the book which the Italian writer Marinetti ordered in 1935. It is made of thin leaden sheets which are printed and embellished with coloured letters and pictures.

The treasury of the library at Uppsala, Sweden, possesses a work of untold price in the *Silver Codex*, which is written on parchment in silver letters on a red ground. At an auction held in Berlin in 1930 a copy of the Mazarin Bible fetched £65,000. This Bible, with forty-two lines to the page, was the first book printed with movable type. The record price for a first folio Shakespeare is £5,250, paid by an anonymous donor of a copy to the British Museum. A small volume of the *Fables of La Fontaine*, illustrated by Fragonard, which cost 6 francs on publication, was sold by auction in 1936 for 2,000,000 francs.

BIG AND TINY BOOKS

The bulkiest work ever written is probably the Chinese dictionary printed to the order of the emperor in 1600; it consists of 5,020 volumes, each containing 170 pages. The largest single volume is the *Anatomical Atlas* in the State Technical School in Vienna; it is 74 4/5 in. high and 35 2/5 in. wide, and took the best part of five years to print (1825-1830). In 1936 the English miniature expert Gunner wrote a book on Windsor Castle which measures 7/20 in. by 14/25 in., and contains only ten pages; it was purchased by the King. Gunner's latest book measures only 31/125 in. by 37/200 in., and contains 100 pages. One of the smallest books in the world measures 2/5 in. by 1/5 in. It was printed at Padua in 1897 and comprises 208 pages; its subject matter includes a hitherto unpublished letter written by Galileo in 1615.

No other book has anywhere near so great a sale as the Bible. In a recent year a single institution, the British and Foreign Bible Society, circulated 11,318,575 volumes of Holy Scriptures and added twelve translations to a list which totalled 723.

LIBRARIES OF TABLETS AND ROLLS

The first libraries were formed in temples and state archives. The oldest of which we know is that belonging to the Assyrian King Sardanapalus at Nineveh (about 1900 B.C.); later that at Tel-el-Amarna in Egypt (15th century B.C.), and the library of the contemporary Hittite kings in Asia Minor. All bear witness to the high level of culture in those times.

The first public library in ancient Greece is supposed to have been that which was opened in Athens by the tyrant Peisistratus (510 B.C.) and afterwards pillaged by Xerxes. As time went on, more and more scholars formed their own libraries. The famous library of Alexandria, with its collection of over 400,000 manuscripts, suffered serious damage in the fighting between Cæsar's and Pompey's armies in 47 B.C. and at the hands of fanatical Christian monks in 391. The victorious Roman general, Antony, presented the beautiful Queen of Egypt, Cleopatra, with 200,000 books from the library of the kings of Pergamum in Asia Minor.

After the taking of Carthage in 146 B.C. the Romans gave the contents of the library there to the African kings who were allied to them. The first public library in Rome was established in the reign of the Emperor Augustus (63 B.C.-A.D. 14), in the temple of Liberty by the wealthy Roman Asinius Pollo. This was followed by the grand libraries opened one after the other by the emperors on the Capitol and the Palatine, which Pope Gregory the Great in his Christian zeal destroyed in the year 590, defending his action on the simple ground that everything that was not in the Bible was superfluous.

In the first centuries of their existence both Christianity and Islam waged a fierce war against all written traditions of the heathen past. In 728, under the Emperor Leo, the libraries of Constantinople were destroyed. Barbarian hordes, fire, and earthquake completed the destruction of the written memorials of antiquity.

REBUILDING OF CULTURE BY MONKS AND PRINCES

Reconstruction began in the monasteries of Western Europe. On the Continent, schools and libraries were founded by Charlemagne; in England by Alfred the Great (died A.D. 900). In the Arab world, fanaticism gradually died away, and princes collected books for mosques and schools and made endowments. The collections at Cairo and at Cordova, in Spain, were gradually increased until they eventually numbered 50,000 volumes apiece.

In 1362 the famous poet Petrarch established a public library in Venice. With the foundation of the universities from 1300 onwards and the coming of the Renaissance, interest in libraries naturally grew throughout the west of Europe, and with the invention of printing, new libraries were established everywhere. Lincoln's Inn contains the oldest library in London, it having been originally built in 1497.

FOUNDING OF OUR GREAT LIBRARIES

In 1449, Pope Nicholas V laid the foundation stone of the Vatican Library, and the rulers of Florence, the wealthy banking family of the Medici, established the libraries of San Marco and San Lorenzo. The libraries of Wittenberg, Dresden, Munich, and Vienna were founded in 1502. The old library of the University of Oxford was restored by Thomas Bodley in 1602. The library of Moscow, founded in 1650, went up in flames in 1812 when the city was burned during Napoleon's invasion of Russia.

The largest library in the world is that established at the British Museum, London, in 1753; it possesses about 5,000,000 volumes and 200,000 manuscripts. Probably the next largest is the United States Congress Library at Washington, with between 4,500,000 and 5,000,000 books. The Paris Bibliothèque Nationale has about 4,000,000 volumes and 500,000 manuscripts. The Berlin State Library possesses some 2,500,000 books. Larger figures are said to have been reached in Russia, where many copies of the same book are counted separately, whereas the above figures refer to separate works. Probably the total of books in American libraries is greater than that in any other country; most of the libraries with over 50,000 volumes are in the United States.

1,500 YEARS OF NEWSPAPERS

THE first "newspaper" in the world was the *Peking News*, which celebrated its 1,500th anniversary in 1863 and remained in existence until 1935. The *Kingpao* (court circular) first appeared in A.D. 750. The journalism of the Western world is considered to have originated in the *Acta diurna* (from the Latin *diurnus* comes our word "journal") which were published from Cæsar's time onward.

The first broadsheets reported, in 1482, "How the Turks assailed the Christian Churches" and, in 1493, in Vienna, "The Burial of the Emperor Frederick III." The word "newspaper" may conceivably be applied to the letter written by Columbus announcing the discovery of the New World, which appeared the same year and was translated into every known language.

FIRST PRINTED NEWS

The first printed newspaper, *Notizie Seritte*, also known as the *Gazetta* because a *gazetta* (a small coin) had to be paid by all who wished to read it, was published in Venice, but at irregular intervals. It confined itself to news of a sensational nature. According to Randle Cotgrave's *Dictionarie of the French and English Tongues*, published in 1611, the term referred to "A certaine Venetian coyne scarce worth our farthing; also, a Bill of Newes; or, a short Relation of the generall occurrences of the Time, forged most commonly at Venice, and thence dispersed, every month, into most parts of Christendome."

News of current events could be gleaned from the *Fugger Newsletters*, which were published between 1568 and 1604, and from the contemporary *Avvisi di Roma*. The former was a hotchpotch of news from all over the world, supplied to order by two agents of Fuggers, the famous trading house.

The first English weekly newspaper was the *Weekly News*, started in 1622 by Thomas Archer and Nicholas Bourne. England's first daily newspaper was printed on one sheet only and was called the *Daily Courant*. No. 1 appeared on March 11, 1702, three days after Queen Anne's accession. America runs this date close with the *Boston Newsletter*, a daily which began publication in 1704. Daniel Defoe, who wrote *Robinson Crusoe*, helped to start the *Daily Post* in 1719. The *Oxford Gazette* first appeared in 1665 and afterwards altered its title to the *London Gazette*, under which designation it continues to appear.

The first German occasional newspaper was published in the Rhineland in 1542; the publisher's name and the place of publication were kept secret for fear of prosecution. Its circulation was obtained by the personal recommendation of the few educated persons who could read, and it was issued only when an event of importance had taken place.

The first regular German newspaper—possibly the first in any European country—was *Avisa Relation oder Zeitung*, which made its first appearance in 1609. *Die Frankfurter Oberpostamtszeitung*, which was founded in 1615 and was superseded in 1866 by the present *Frankfurter Zeitung*, was another early German newspaper. The *Gazette de France* was founded by Cardinal Richelieu, the famous statesman, for the purpose of influencing public opinion, the Cardinal taking a personal share in its production. On one occasion Louis XIII was persuaded to write an article for it.

GROWTH OF THE LONDON PRESS

Modern English newspapers began with the *Morning Post*, 1722. It is now incorporated with the *Daily Telegraph*. *The Times* was started by John Walter in 1785 as the *Daily Universal Register*. The *Daily News*, now the *News Chronicle*, which Charles Dickens edited for a few weeks, started in 1846, then Colonel Sleigh's *Daily Telegraph*, 1855. The characteristics of modern journalism began to be developed in the last century. About 1890, W. T. Stead in the *Pall Mall Gazette* began to use interviewing of the modern type and give his journal a more popular tone as regards politics. *The Star*, founded 1888 by T. P. O'Connor, brought out the human element more fully.

Alfred and Harold Harmsworth's *Daily Mail* saw the real launching of the new journalism, 1896. The *Daily Mirror* was transformed from a daily for women into the first illustrated daily halfpenny newspaper. The *Daily Express* followed the *Daily Mail*; the late Sir C. Arthur Pearson founded it in 1900.

The *Daily Herald*, founded in 1911 as the official organ of the British Labour Party, was the first newspaper to maintain a sale of over 2,000,000 daily for five years. No British daily newspaper has yet achieved a 3,000,000 circulation, but among Sunday papers the *News of the World* and the *People* exceed this figure.

SACRED AND MAGICAL NUMBERS

MATHEMATICS, the science of numbers, has always exercised peculiar fascination over men's minds. At first the numbers themselves seemed to have something magical in them, and to be entitled to veneration owing to their properties. Thus Goethe calls the symbolic " 3 "—" the eternally ageless, the three-named, the three-formed." The Indian doctrine of the Trinity or Triad, known as Trimūrti, is that " He who is Vishnu is also Siva, and He who is Siva is also Brahma, one being but three gods."

"Everything is divided into three," said Homer, and Confucius said the same when speaking of the measure of time. The religious belief of the ancient Egyptians rested on the doctrine of the trinity of the gods Ptah, Sekhmet, and Imhotep which was taught at Memphis. According to this, God the Father does nothing, merely begets God the Son; but here, as opposed to India, the third person, Sekhmet, is a goddess.

THREE IN PHILOSOPHY AND SUPERSTITION

The deep-seated intuition of the Three in One is met with at every turn. The Egyptians believed in the three embodiments of the god Osiris; the basic vowels *i, a,* and *o* play a symbolical role in the late Greek philosophy called neo-Platonism. The fertility of the Persian Sun-god Mithras is threefold.

This last number was considered sacred, and to go beyond it was sacrilegious. This is probably the origin of the age-old dread of thirteen.

MAGIC SQUARES

To Pythagoras the Greek mathematician numbers were symbols of the ultimate mysteries. "Enter in, for there are gods here, too," said Heraclitus, the early Greek philosopher, concerning the science of numbers. Just as with letters games have been played, such as the fabrication of the " magic " word abracadabra, which is said to be readable in 1,024 ways, so with numbers. "Magic " squares, called by planetary names, were worn as charms.

This was the Jupiter logogram : —

16	3	2	13
5	10	11	8
9	6	7	12
4	15	14	1

In this astonishing square the sum of any four numbers forming a symmetrical group is 34. The sum of the numbers in the four horizontal, vertical, and diagonal rows is in each case 34; similarly each of the four quarters, e.g., the middle square

10	11
6	7

and the four corner num-

16	3
5	10

bers, 16, 13, 4, 1. Finally, the symmetrical groups 3, 2, 15, 14 and 5, 9, 8, 12 give the same result.

The following Mars square was worn as a protection against accidents. The sum of the numbers in each of its five vertical, horizontal, and diagonal rows is 65.

14	10	1	22	18
20	11	7	3	24
21	17	13	9	5
2	23	19	15	6
8	4	25	16	12

ZERO AND MINOR QUANTITIES

Zero was adopted in the 9th century from the Arabs. The minus sign was invented in 1202 by the Italian merchant Leonardo of Pisa to indicate his debts. The plus ($+$) and minus ($-$) signs were generally adopted in the 14th century.

ARITHMETICAL ODDITIES

When 37 is multiplied by 3 and multiples of 3 (up to 27) the results are 111 (37 × 3), 222 (37 × 6), and so on up to 999, while 3,367 multiplied by 33, 66, 99, etc. (up to 297) gives 111,111, 222,222, 333,333, etc., up to 999,999.

The latest magical number was announced by Professor Zervos, of Athens, in 1936 to be 142,857.

$$142,857 \times 2 = 285,714$$
$$\text{,,} \quad \times 3 = 428,571$$
$$\text{,,} \quad \times 4 = 571,428$$
$$\text{,,} \quad \times 5 = 714,285$$
$$\text{,,} \quad \times 6 = 857,142$$
$$\text{,,} \quad \times 7 = 999,999$$

It will be observed that in each case the product contains the same figures as the original, except in that of the multiplication by 7.

ART IN MANY FORMS

THE art of painting is at least 50,000 years old. Not one but many paintings of this age have been discovered in the cave-dwellings of northern Spain and southern France. The most celebrated collection is in the cave of Altamira, near Santander, Spain. They were found in 1879, but it was not until 1895 that archæologists accepted them as prehistoric, and it is only recently that their date has been put so far back as about 50,000 B.C.

Picturing animals of the chase, these works of art were first engraved on the rock walls of the cave and then painted in three colours—black, red and yellow. Displaying as they do a remarkable faculty for observation and a fine sense of colour and line, they rank among the world's great works of art. They were executed neither for decoration nor as means of self-expression, but because of the magical aid they were supposed to give to the hunter who was unlucky or losing his skill.

In the cavern of Les Combarelles, near Les Eyzies, in the south of France, representations of the reindeer, horse, mammoth, cave bear, woolly rhinoceros, wild ox, stag, lion and wolf have been incised by artists of long ago. For the most part human figures, often wearing ceremonial masks, are badly drawn. There are also rough sketches of huts known as tactiforms, probably representations of homes prepared for ancestral spirits.

PAINTING AT UR OF THE CHALDEES

Recent excavations and researches have fairly conclusively proved that Sumerian (Mesopotamian) civilization existed before that of Egypt. That painting was practised by the earliest Sumerians we know from the fact that painted pottery has been found at the lowest levels at Ur. The Sumerians were producing highly accomplished sculptures before 3000 B.C., and by about 2250 B.C. they were turning out their best work. One of the most remarkable existing products of their skill is the portrait head of Gudea in the Louvre, Paris.

Shortly after 2000 B.C. the Sumerians came under the domination of the Babylonians. As a consequence, their art lost all its life and originality. Neither the Babylonians nor the Assyrians possessed the artistic feeling of the Sumerians and the Egyptians.

EGYPTIAN ART OF 5,400 YEARS AGO

The art of painting was practised in Egypt in the pre-Dynastic period, that is to say, before 3400 B.C. Excavators have recovered an abundance of pre-Dynastic painted pottery which had been placed in graves for the use of the dead. Human beings, male and female; animals, ships: these are among the objects painted by the earliest Egyptians. Of a later date, but still pre-Dynastic, are the earliest wall-paintings.

By means of the wall-paintings found in the tombs of the age of the Pyramids, which began about 2900 B.C., we are able to make a fairly complete reconstruction of the life led by the Egyptians nearly 5,000 years ago. Of no other civilization of equal antiquity is our knowledge anywhere near so complete. These paintings are not pictures in the ordinary sense: the scene to be depicted was first carved in relief by a sculptor and then coloured with brilliant pigments by a painter. They may be called relief-paintings, or pictures in relief-sculpture.

These representations of the things of everyday life were executed because it was believed that their presence in the tomb in some magical way enabled the deceased to continue to use the wealth he possessed before death claimed him.

The deceased's fields, his flocks, his herds, his beasts of burden, his husbandmen, his craftsmen: all these are represented producing food, clothing and wealth for him. Death, for the Egyptian, did not mean the end of life as it is known on earth, but simply a continuation of it. Because these relief-paintings were executed to serve a severely practical end, there was no deliberate attempt to make them things of beauty. In so far as they are "works of art," they are so incidentally. While Egyptian sculpture may be said to have attained to something very near perfection, Egyptian painting remained to the end comparatively elementary.

EARLIEST PORTRAITS

From the ancient Egyptian tombs come the earliest portraits of which we have any knowledge. Again, they are not portraits in the ordinary sense, but carvings in wood or stone painted in natural colours. Many of them are extraordinarily beautiful and life-like. The Great Sphinx in the cemetery of Gizeh is a portrait—the largest ever made—of Khafre, the pyramid-builder. Carved from solid rock, the nose and beard now worn away, the head is 91 ft. in circumference and 19 ft. from the top of the forehead to the bottom of the chin. The height from ground level is 66 ft. The animal body is 172 ft. long.

Egyptian art went on until the Roman subjugation of the country in the last century before the Christian era. It thus had a continuous life of well over 3,500 years.

CHINESE ART OF ARTS

Chinese painting can only be traced back for 2,000 years, but it most probably had its birth more than half as long ago again. Painting, for the Chinese, is the art of arts. It is so much a part of their everyday lives that even their handwriting is a form of painting. Only an artist, and a skilful one at that, can write a good Chinese hand.

One of the earliest existing masterpieces of Chinese painting is the *Admonitions of the Instructress in the Palace,* a roll depicting life at court under the Ching Dynasty (A.D. 265-420), now in the British Museum, London. It is attributed to Ku K'ai-Chik, the artist who

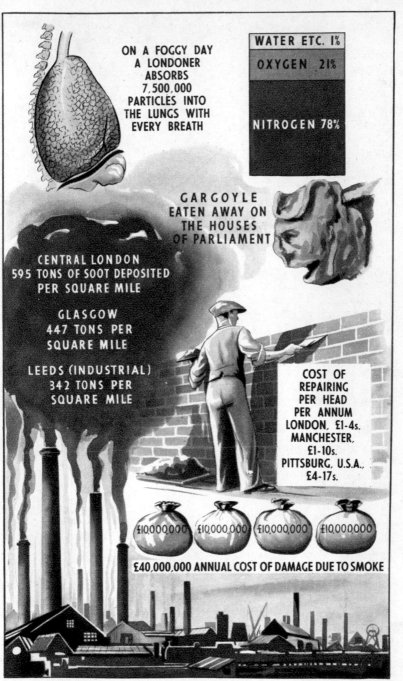

ON A FOGGY DAY A LONDONER ABSORBS 7,500,000 PARTICLES INTO THE LUNGS WITH EVERY BREATH

WATER ETC. 1%
OXYGEN 21%
NITROGEN 78%

GARGOYLE EATEN AWAY ON THE HOUSES OF PARLIAMENT

CENTRAL LONDON
595 TONS OF SOOT DEPOSITED PER SQUARE MILE

GLASGOW
447 TONS PER SQUARE MILE

LEEDS (INDUSTRIAL)
342 TONS PER SQUARE MILE

COST OF REPAIRING PER HEAD PER ANNUM
LONDON, £1-4s.
MANCHESTER, £1-10s.
PITTSBURG, U.S.A., £4-17s.

£10,000,000 £10,000,000 £10,000,000 £10,000,000

£40,000,000 ANNUAL COST OF DAMAGE DUE TO SMOKE

The Trail of Destruction Wrought by Smoke

ROMAN BRITON   SAXON   NORMAN

XIIITH CENTURY   XVTH CENTURY   XVITH CENTURY

XVIITH CENTURY   XVIIITH CENTURY   XIXTH CENTURY

British Costumes through the Centuries

is thought to have been responsible for another early Chinese masterpiece which is now in the Freer Collection at Washington, U.S.A. This
latter, whose scenes are laid in fairyland, illustrates a poem on a river
nymph.

The most eminent Chinese painter of all was Wu Tao-tzū, who lived
under the Tang Dynasty (A.D. 618-905). He painted an enormous
number of pictures, including more than 300 Buddhist frescoes, but
nothing of his has survived except a few designs engraved on stone.

Also of the Tang period were Wei-ch'ih I-sing (early 7th century)
and the portrait painter Yen hi-pēn, of about the same date. The first
great Chinese landscape painter was Li Ssu-hsün, born in the middle
of the 7th century. He used the colours green, blue and gold, and
painted scenes in which mountains and lakes or rivers figured
prominently.

The 8th century in China saw several great animal painters at work.
Foremost among them were Han Kan, who took horses as his subjects;
and Han Huang, who painted buffaloes. The first half of the 10th
century produced the flower painters Hsü Hsi and Huang Ch'uan,
and during the Sung period, immediately following (960-1260), the
painting of flowers became very popular.

PAINTING OF A MYSTICAL KIND

The most famous of the Sung Dynasty artists was Li Lung-mien
(about 1040-1106), who began by painting horses, but gave this up to
devote himself to Buddhist subjects. Immediately after the Sung
period landscape painting of a mystical kind claimed attention, and the
12th century is generally spoken of as the most fruitful for works of this
type.

In the Yüan, or Mongol period (1260-1368), lived Wu Chên, whose
paintings of bamboos were masterpieces, and who became known as the
"Priest of the Plum-blossom." During the Ming Dynasty (1368-1644),
Chinese painting tended to pay more attention to beauty of form and
line for their own sake than to the pictorial expression of delicate shades
of thought and emotion.

The last period of Chinese art is the Ch'ing or Manchu, which began
in 1644 and lasted until the early years of the present century. Landscape painting dominated in the 17th and 18th centuries. The most
famous flower-painter of the period was Yün Shou-p'ing (17th century).
The Chinese painters of the 19th and early 20th centuries, though
maintaining a high level of skill, were content to follow in the footsteps
of the masters, breaking no new ground.

PREHISTORIC INDIAN PAINTING

Prehistoric paintings of great antiquity have been found in numerous caves in north-central India. Like their European counterparts at
Altamira and other places, they include representations of the animals
of the chase. The long-dead artists have left us pictures of a rhinoceros

hunt, of a stag hunt, and of the giraffe, the horse and the deer. The technique employed is very similar to that of the Altamira artists.

The most remarkable existing early Indian paintings are on the walls of excavated Buddhist temples and monasteries at Ajantā and Bāgh. Some of them were executed during or before the 1st century, others date from the 6th and 7th centuries.

During the 11th and 12th centuries a famous school of painters existed under the Pāla Dynasty in Bihar and Bengal. Specimens of its work, consisting of painted wooden book-covers and illustrations in palm-leaf manuscripts, have been preserved.

From the 13th to the 17th centuries there existed a Gujarātī school of painters who specialized in the illumination of manuscripts of the Jain scriptures. The earliest existing production of this school is on palm-leaf, and was produced in 1237. The next earliest is dated exactly 190 years later and is, like the remaining Gujarātī works, on paper.

RAJPUT SCHOOL OF PAINTING

A number of Indian painting schools and movements have been grouped together under the general heading Rajput. The earliest Rajput painters devoted themselves almost exclusively to wall decoration. Fine examples of their work in this kind may be seen in the Old Palace at Bīkāner. A characteristic of Rajput paintings is the brilliancy of the colours used. In its earlier phases, indeed, it paid but scant attention to line and form. One of the most celebrated schools was the Kāṅgrā, brought into being under Raja Samsāra Cand in the latter part of the 18th century.

Many fragments of early rock-painting have been found in Ceylon, the art of which is closely related to that of India. At Sīgiriya there are a number of magnificent rock paintings dating from the 5th century. They represent full-bosomed women half-covered by clouds raining down flowers upon the earth. There are extensive but badly damaged early frescoes in the Northern Temple at Polonnāruwa.

CULT OF BEAUTY IN GREECE

Never has the artist been more highly regarded than he was during the 5th and 4th centuries B.C. in Greece. No bygone art has had so great an influence on the modern world. The sculptors and painters were interested primarily in the naked human body. The beauties of nature, of mountains, rivers and fields, were hardly considered by them; and of the kind of beauty with which a Rembrandt could invest a faded old woman they were almost completely ignorant.

No Greek paintings of the 5th and 4th centuries B.C. survive, save only those on vases. The vase-paintings suggest that, though the early Greeks knew more about the principles of painting than the Egyptians, they were yet far from mastery of the art.

One of the first of the great Greek painters was Polygnotus of Thasos (about 475-445 B.C.), who devoted himself mainly to depicting scenes from Greek mythology. He executed a number of large wall-paintings, two of which, the "Capture of Troy" and the "Descent of Odysseus to Hades," are described by Pausanias, who wrote a tourists' guidebook to Greece in the second half of the 2nd century A.D. The work of Polygnotus was admired by Aristotle (384-322 B.C.), the great philosopher.

Zeuxis of Heraclea (southern Italy) famous for his paintings of nude women, lived in the latter half of the 5th century B.C. Among his most celebrated pictures were one of Helen of Troy and another of a Centauress (a being half-horse and half-human) and her young. So skilful was Zeuxis, so it is said, that when one of his paintings of a bunch of grapes was placed in the open air the birds flew down to peck at it.

GREATEST PAINTER OF ANTIQUITY

The greatest of all the painters of the ancient world was Apelles, who was born at Colophon, Ionia, about the middle of the 4th century B.C. He specialized in portrait painting, being the first famous artist to do so. His most distinguished sitter was Alexander the Great, but he also painted many members of the Macedonian court. The greatest picture by Apelles was the "Aphrodite Anadyomene," in which he depicted the Greek goddess of love wringing the water from her hair after she had sprung from the sea, in which she was born. This picture was bought by Augustus, the first Roman emperor, for a sum roughly equivalent to £20,000 in present-day English money.

One day a cobbler criticized the way in which Apelles had drawn a sandal, whereupon the great artist altered his work. The next day the cobbler again ventured criticism, but this time of a leg, whereupon Apelles remarked that "a cobbler should stick to his last." Hence the proverb.

In the 3rd century B.C. Greek painting gradually declined, and in the 2nd century the Romans put an end to the independent existence of Greece, and incidentally to any hope of a renaissance, or new birth, of Greek art.

The Romans, an essentially practical people, had always despised art and the artist, but after their subjugation of Greece they carried off to Rome many masterpieces of Greek sculpture. These excited the admiration of the educated Romans; Greek artists were consequently employed in Rome, and thus Græco-Roman art came into being.

It was a poor thing in comparison with Greek art proper, simply because the Romans, notwithstanding their immense achievements in the realm of affairs, were barbarians beside the ultra-civilized Greeks.

ART TREASURES BURIED IN LAVA

The Greeks were not the first people whose culture had exercised a modifying influence on the Philistinism of the Romans. They had previously derived considerable cultural benefit from contact with the Etruscans, or Tyrrhenians, who lived in north-west Italy, and whose comparatively highly developed civilization owed something to Egypt, something to Mesopotamia, and a good deal to Greece herself. The Etruscans displayed a genius for making portraits in terra-cotta. What distinguishes these portraits from those produced by the other nations of the ancient world is that they were not idealizations, but had "character." Each portrait gave an impression of an individual person and not of a certain type of person. It was the blending of these three artistic elements—Greek, Etruscan, Roman—that gave Italy the genius for art which made the Italian Renaissance possible.

The Etruscans were responsible for the laying out of Pompeii, one of the towns that was overwhelmed by an eruption of Vesuvius in A.D. 79. The excavations there have disclosed a large number of interesting wall-paintings. They depict scenes from the ordinary life of the people of the time, as well as from history and mythology. From the artistic viewpoint these paintings are not particularly noteworthy, but this is not surprising in view of the fact that Pompeii was an unimportant country town.

Much richer in works of art is the neighbouring town of Herculaneum, which was likewise overwhelmed by the eruption of A.D. 79 and buried in lava that in some parts was 120 ft. deep. The finest of these are the statues and busts which, to quote Mrs. E. R. Barker, "give us types, either originals or copies, of works of art ranging from the 6th century B.C., in an unbroken series down to almost the end of the 1st century of our era." Hundreds of frescoes, some of which display skill, imagination and good taste, have also been recovered.

FIRST GREAT ITALIAN MASTER

The first great European school of painting was the Florentine, and the credit for bringing it into being is usually accorded to Giotto (about 1266-1337), the first of the Italian masters. Giotto was also the father of the Italian Renaissance, or new birth of art, which lasted from the end of the 13th century until the beginning of the 16th century.

Giotto devoted most of his time to wall decoration and altar-pieces. Some of his frescoes can be seen in the vaulting of the Lower Church at Assisi, Italy. Painted in honour of St. Francis, they are: the "Marriage of St. Francis to Poverty," the "Allegory of Chastity," the "Allegory of Obedience," and the "Vision of St. Francis in Glory."

Works by Giotto survive in Rome, Padua, Florence and other towns of Italy. The greatest of these is the series of frescoes with which he covered the internal walls of the chapel of the Arena at Padua in 1306. The pictures include a representation of the Last Judgment and scenes from the life of Jesus. Giotto also excelled as an architect. His bell-tower of variegated marble, with its statues and reliefs, at Florence, is not the least of the works of a man who first sought to study art by scratching a representation of a sheep with a flint. His "canvas" on this occasion was the ground.

CREATOR OF THE "MONA LISA"

The most arresting figure of the Italian Renaissance was Leonardo da Vinci (1452-1519) who was at once painter, sculptor, architect, inventor and poet. His most famous paintings are the " Mona Lisa," also called " La Giaconda," and the " Last Supper." The former is in the Louvre, in Paris, and the latter on a wall of the refectory of the convent church of Santa delle Grazie, in Milan.

A contemporary of Leonardo da Vinci was Michelangelo (1476-1564), who was primarily a sculptor—the most gifted that ever lived—but who produced paintings which rank among the greatest of all time. The most tremendous task accomplished by Michelangelo was the decoration of the vaulted ceiling of the Sistine Chapel, Rome. It took him four years, during the working hours of which time he had to lie on his back. Often enough paint dripped on to his face. The Renaissance in Germany produced Albrecht Dürer (1471-1528), probably the world's greatest engraver on wood or copper. The friend of Erasmus and of Luther, Dürer was the son of a goldsmith and one of eighteen children. A deeply religious man, he took Nature as his guide, and produced over 1,250 works.

MOST PROLIFIC PAINTER OF ALL

The greatest painter of the Flemish School was Peter Paul Rubens (1577-1640), perhaps the most prolific artist the world has ever seen, for his canvases number some 1,300. Rubens visited England, where he executed a number of works, including a magnificent decoration for the ceiling of the Banqueting Hall (now the United Services Museum) in Whitehall, London. The National Gallery has two of his best pictures: the " Rape of the Sabine Women " and a " Holy Family."

Anthony Van Dyck (1599-1641), Rubens's greatest pupil, was almost as prolific as the master himself, despite that he died at the early age of forty-two. Van Dyck spent the last ten years of his life at the court of Charles I, and during that time exercised a very beneficial influence on English art.

Rubens had advised him to devote himself to portrait painting, and then to make a thorough study of the Italian masters. As a result, not only did he become one of the supreme masters of portrait painting but he succeeded in grafting on to what Rubens had taught him some of the best characteristics of the Italian masters. His influence is seen in the great English portraits of the 18th century.

AMAZING POWER OF REMBRANDT

Standing head and shoulders over all the painters of the Dutch School is Rembrandt (1606-1669), whose full name was Rembrandt Harmensz van Rijn. Among his greatest works are " The Night Watch," which is in the Royal Museum at Amsterdam, and the " Good Samaritan," in the Louvre, Paris.

A wayward genius who took any and every type of humanity as

a model, who painted his own portrait at least fifty times so as to transfer his emotions to canvas, who quarrelled and loved with equal zest, Rembrandt died in poverty, as independent in his garret as he had been when numerous wealthy patrons applauded him as the Shakespeare of painting.

SPANISH PRINCES OF THE PALETTE

Spanish-bred was the magnificent genius of Velasquez (1599-1660), one of the greatest portrait painters of all time. So great was his mastery of the technique of painting that he has earned the title of the " painters' painter." Velasquez was very unlike the popular conception of an inspired painter who, in a fine frenzy of genius, almost throws a masterpiece on to a canvas. He was one of the most gifted men who ever lived, but he took infinite pains to achieve mastery of his art. The hand that held Velasquez's brush was guided more by intellect than by emotion.

It is said of Francisco Goya (1746-1828), another Spaniard, that he has had more influence on modern art than any other master. He himself was to so great an extent an original genius that he cannot be said to have followed in the footsteps of any one else. Everything he did he did in a new way.

Ranked with Velasquez as a painter by some critics, he was also an etcher of vigour and originality, though the meaning of some of his works is not too obvious. It is said that he painted when he was well and etched when he was ill, which may account for his obscurities.

FAMOUS ARTISTS OF FRANCE

The first great French master was Nicholas Poussin (1594-1665), whose greatest triumphs were his landscapes. His countryman and contemporary Claude Lorrain (1600-1682), was also a landscape painter of genius. Among the many great French painters who followed them in the 18th century are Antoine Watteau (1684-1721), and Fragonard (1732-1806), both of whom gracefully delineated country scenes.

Outstanding French painters of the 19th century were Eugene Delacroix (1798-1863), Jean Ingres (1780-1867), J. B. C. Corot (1796-1875), Manet (1832-1883), Degas (1834-1917), Paul Cézanne (1839-1906), Renoir (1841-1919), and Paul Gaugin (1848-1903).

ENGLAND MARRIES ART AND MORALITY

In England William Hogarth (1697-1764) sprang into fame by the publication in 1732 of a series of engravings called "A Harlot's Progress." They, like most of Hogarth's other works, are singular in being at the same time great works of art and moral lectures. They drew attention to the brutality with which women were treated in Bridewell Prison. Similar in type are the series known as "A Rake's Progress," " Marriage à la Mode," " Four Stages of Cruelty " and " The

Election." Hogarth was the first and greatest of the caricaturists, but he was also a first-class portrait painter.

He was followed by four portrait painters of genius: Sir Joshua Reynolds (1723-1792), Thomas Gainsborough (1727-1788), George Romney (1734-1802) and Sir Thomas Lawrence (1769-1830). Reynolds, the son of a poor Devon schoolmaster-clergyman, was the first President of the Royal Academy, founded under the patronage of George III in 1768, and also the first British artist to be knighted. A prodigious worker, in one year this great biographer in paint had no fewer than 150 clients, to each of whom he probably gave six or seven sittings. He produced nearly 4,000 canvases. John Ruskin placed Reynolds among the supreme colourists of all time.

Gainsborough preferred landscape painting to portraiture, but excelled in both. Quick of temper, he quarrelled with Reynolds, but on his deathbed sent for the friend from whom he had been estranged. "We shall meet again," he whispered, "and Van Dyck will be of the company." Romney, who first raffled his pictures or sold them by auction in an attempt to earn a living, started life as a cabinet-maker. Lawrence's sitters included kings, statesmen, soldiers, literary men and many famous beauties. Although his income sometimes reached as much as £20,000 a year, and twelve months before his death he could still demand 700 guineas for a portrait, he was not what is called "a good business man." As a consequence his life was haunted by the grim spectre of debt. And just as he neglected the financial side of his affairs, despite his stipulation that half his fee should be paid in advance, so he often neglected to complete portraits he had begun. Among his unfinished pictures may be mentioned that of William Wilberforce, the friend of the slaves; and of Napoleon's son, the ill-fated King of Rome, whom he sketched during a visit to Vienna in 1819.

The English school of landscape painting also includes John Constable (1776-1837) and Joseph Turner (1775-1851).

PICTURES WORTH A KING'S RANSOM

WITHIN the last forty or fifty years some extraordinarily high prices have been obtained for pictures. In most cases they far exceed the fees paid to the painters, who as a general rule were not " good business men " but devoted to art mainly for " art's own sake."

£100,000 FOR A CANVAS

In 1895 the " Welsh Funeral " by David Cox was sold for £2,520, or exactly 126 times what it had cost. The year before Sir Joshua Reynolds's "Lady Betty Delmé " had fetched £11,550. In 1876, Thomas Gainsborough's " Duchess of Devonshire " was knocked down at £10,500; twenty years later Romney's " Ladies Spencer " fetched £11,025. In the present century an American paid £54,000 for Gainsborough's " Harvest Wagon."

In 1900, £24,250 was paid for two Van Dyck portraits; and in 1908 Turner's "Mortlake Terrace" made £13,230, while Lancret's "La Ronde Champêtre" reached £11,200. In 1913 Rembrandt's "Bathsheba" was sold for £44,000.

Gainsborough's "Blue Boy" fetched thirty-five guineas the first time it was sold; sixty-five guineas the next time, and about £100,000 in 1921, when it and Reynolds's "Mrs. Siddons as the Tragic Muse" fetched £200,000 together. In 1926 two Gainsboroughs fetched £46,200 apiece, and Lawrence's "Pinkie" 74,000 guineas. In the following year Reynolds's "Lady Ann Fitzpatrick" made £19,425.

PURCHASED BY THE NATION

In 1919 Franz Hals's "Old Lady" was sold for £27,400; a "St. Eustace," ascribed to Carpaccio, fetched £33,600; and Romney's "Beckford Children" £54,600, or exactly 520 times what the artist was paid for the canvas. Romney's "Anne, Lady de la Pole" once made £41,370, while Hals's "Portrait of a Gentleman," reckoned to be worth about £3 in 1884, fetched £9,000 in 1913. Hals's "Portrait of a Woman" fetched £27,400 in 1910.

In 1923, £29,400 was paid for Van Dyck's "Portrait of Anton Triest." Three years later £60,900 was paid for Romney's "Mrs. Davenport"; £77,700 for Lawrence's "Pinkie"; £46,200 for Romney's "Lady de la Pole"; and a similar sum for two Gainsboroughs.

Among the highest prices ever paid by the National Gallery, London, are £122,000 for the "Cornaro" Titian; £90,000 for the Wilton Diptych and £72,000 for Holbein's "Duchess of Milan."

THREE LARGEST PAINTINGS

The largest oil painting in the world hangs in the Great Hall of the Doge's Palace in Venice. It is Tintoretto's "Paradise," which has a length of 82 ft. and height of 33 ft.

Mignard's wall-painting, also of "Paradise," in the Val de Grâce convent in Paris, contains more than 300 figures, each three times life-size. The "Last Judgment," by Peter Cornelius, painted in 1836, in the Ludwig Church in Munich, is 59 ft. high.

GLORIES OF STAINED GLASS

THERE were stained glass windows in French churches as early as the 7th century. The art of glass-painting spread to England about the year 1000 and to Germany about 1200. The oldest glass in the latter country is in Bamberg Cathedral. Most of the old stained glass in churches was made between 1400 and 1600.

Among the loveliest windows in the world are the two in the cathedral of Chartres, in France, which depict the death of the Virgin and the story of St. James. This cathedral also possesses two most beautiful rose-windows and 100 other windows containing the figures of 5,000 persons. In the palace chapel at Dijon are some smaller pieces of stained glass which are not only wonderful works of art but of historical interest in themselves; they were made by the skilled hand of King René of Naples, who lay in captivity here in the 15th century.

In contrast to the essentially religious subjects usually depicted in old stained glass, the sports window in the cathedral of St. John the Divine, in New York, is notable. In it polo, cycling, tennis, football and other recreations are represented.

STATUES OF RENOWN

PROBABLY the oldest sculpture in the world is a group of bison modelled in clay by early man. It was discovered in the Tuc d'Audubert cavern at Montesquieu-Avantes, France. The famous Venus de Milo was discovered by a French naval officer, Dumont-D'Urville, in the island of Milo. The young officer came across a peasant laboriously digging up a statue broken into three pieces, and on the Marquis de Rivière, French Ambassador at Constantinople, being informed, he purchased it for 1,500 francs. It was presented to the Louvre, Paris, by Louis XVIII in 1821. The much-praised statue of Hermes, by Praxiteles, who lived in the 4th century B.C., was found at Olympia, Greece, in 1877.

The largest statue is that of Liberty enlightening the World, which stands on Bedloe's Island, outside New York Harbour. It is 150 ft. in height and mounted on a pedestal 177 ft. high. The giantess weighs 100 tons and is made of copper on an iron framework, the 350 pieces being hammered into shape and riveted together. There is room for twenty people in the head.

The work of Frederic August Bartholdi, the interior contains a staircase designed by the builder of the Eiffel Tower in Paris. Presented to the United States by the French people, the statue was dedicated in 1886, the address being delivered by Ferdinand de Lesseps, of Suez Canal fame, and the acceptance made by President Grover Cleveland.

MYSTERY STATUES OF EASTER ISLAND

Easter Island was so called by the Dutch Admiral Roggeveen because he came across it on Easter Day, 1722. Lonely and desolate, it belies its attractive name. Used by Chile, to whom it belongs, as a convict station, it is about twenty-nine miles in circumference and some 2,300 miles west of the mainland. The redeeming feature of this volcanic rock is a vast collection of statues made of larva cut from the crater of a volcano. They number over 550. Some are estimated to weigh over 100 tons and are 70 ft. high. Others are smaller. Many of them are recumbent and partly buried, staring with unseeing eyes at the sky. The gaunt figures have puzzled investigators from the first day they were seen, and the secret of their erection remains a mystery, although some interesting theories have been brought forward.

Professor J. Macmillan Brown, for instance, suggests that Easter

Island is the remnant of a ring of archipelagos that disappeared beneath the waves between 1586 and 1722, and was a great Pacific empire. That there are submerged islands in the neighbourhood was confirmed by soundings taken by the research ship *Carnegie* in 1928. Indeed, Easter Island itself has been reported missing on several occasions, notably in 1923. It may be that the famous men of the empire were buried there, and that the grotesque statues commemorate them. " The whole island is one vast sepulchre," reports Captain H. V. Barclay, R.N. " Look where you may, dig where you like, human remains are sure to be found." Another authority, M. Henri Lavachéry, believes that the first inhabitants were Maoris who settled there between 1000 and 1200.

The features of the statues are identical. All have eyes wide apart, with deeply sunk sockets, thin and stern lips, wide noses and nostrils, and long ears.

TAPESTRY AND CARPETS

TAPESTRY is a very old form of art, for the ancient Babylonians, Egyptians and Greeks made use of it. The cartoons of Raphael (1483-1520), one of the greatest painters of the Renaissance, were specially designed for reproduction by this means. They were made at Arras, Flanders, and afterwards hung in the Vatican, Rome, the master weaver being Peter van Aelst. The first establishment of the Gobelins, a name associated with the best tapestry, was a dye works started by Jean Gobelin in Paris about 1450. Henry III of France purchased a house owned by the family and installed weavers in it. Louis XIV gave the establishment the title of Manufacture des Gobelins in 1662. Four panels of Gobelins tapestry were sold in London for 15,000 guineas in 1918. Rubens and Van Dyck painted designs for the manufactory founded at Mortlake, near London, by Charles I.

The Bayeux Tapestry, made to commemorate the victory of Duke William of Normandy at the Battle of Hastings in 1066, is 230 ft. 9 in. long and 19½ in. wide. It is to be seen in the museum adjoining Bayeux Cathedral, and is still in a wonderful state of preservation. A magnificent set of tapestries which decorated the old House of Lords was destroyed in the Great Fire of London in 1666. In it was depicted the defeat of the Spanish Armada by the English fleet.

CARPETS THAT HANG ON WALLS

Few things are more decorative than an oriental rug or carpet that has not been made on mass-production lines. Certainly there is nothing more delightful to walk on. The pile is fashioned of innumerable little tufts of wool, and there are only two types of importance without this thick and yielding surface. The exceptions are the Kelims, made by the Kurds of Asia Minor, and the Cashmeres. They are used in their country of origin as wall coverings, blankets and tent hangings. In Scandinavia rugs are often hung on walls for decorative purposes.

There are still families in Anatolia, Persia and Syria, which retain their own individual design, handed down from generation to generation. Moreover, they possess well-guarded secrets regarding dye-making, and their vegetable colours are fadeless. If the family is Mohammedan, geometrical and conventional forms are invariably used.

MUSIC'S MYRIAD CHARMS

MANY thinkers have endeavoured to explain the nature of music. The mere statement that it is the language of emotion is no longer held to be sufficient. Today, when we know that secret powers lie hidden, not only in the universe around us but also in ourselves, music may be regarded as the expression of an enigmatic " something," the form and shape of which completely escape us. Music ranks as the deepest, the most intangible, and the most moving of all the arts. " True music," says Sir Walford Davies, " is a picture painted on time."

NATURE'S OWN ORCHESTRA

An earthquake in 27 B.C. brought to the ground part of a colossal statue of Amenhotep III erected near Thebes in 1300 B.C. The air streamed into the cracks that were formed in it, and, becoming hotter as the sun rose higher, produced that tone of lament which was first recorded by the Greek geographer Strabo. About 200 years later the Roman emperor Septimus Severus had the figure repaired, whereupon the sound ceased for ever.

Other natural phenomena, such as the " Cradle Song of the Sahara," the " Enticement of the Kalahari Desert," the " droning " in Chile, the " wailing " dunes of Hawaii, the " whistling " dunes of the Hebrides, the " moaning " of the fallen on the White Hill near Prague, the " wailing " of the Arabian Desert, and the " singing of the sand mountains " of Nevada, are all due to the rubbing together of millions and millions of grains of sand, often mixed with grains of salt, which form a kind of air-tight membrane that acts as a sounding-board.

The grains of sand rubbing together, either above or below this membrane, produce sounds similar to those emitted by a violin when its strings are vibrated on the bridge of the instrument.

SCALE AND COUNTERPOINT

The scale of twelve semitones is said to have been known to the Chinese as long ago as the third millennium before Christ. Huang-Ti, called the Yellow Emperor, is stated to have commanded one Ling-lun in 2700 B.C. to work out the principles of music. This the philosopher succeeded in doing, according to tradition, by listening to the voices of nature as he sat in solitude on the bank of the River Hoang Ho.

The Egyptians played from written music on lyres, harps, nofres— guitars with long necks—flutes, trumpets, drums and sistrums. The

Jews sang in choirs, and the inhabitants of ancient India were acquainted with both song and instrumental music. Of wind, string, and percussion instruments they had rich variety. In the British Museum is a piece of Babylonian music dating from 1800 B.C.; it is written on clay tablets, with Sumerian words and a Babylonian translation of the same. It is similar to Chinese music, with its avoidance of semitones and its use of five intercalated scale tones. In the accompaniment, provided by an eight-stringed harp, free use was made of double fingering.

DANGER OF "BAD" MUSIC

The British Museum also possesses a document of baked clay giving details of the eight campaigns of Sennacherib, King of Assyria, from 705 to 681 B.C. Following the siege of Jerusalem, the record adds that Hezekiah made submission and paid tribute with treasure that included gold, silver, precious stones, eye-paint, ivory couches and thrones, hides, tusks and precious woods, " together with his daughter, and the women of his palace and male and female musicians."

The Greeks, though no doubt versed in the theory of music, mainly confined their attention to choral singing and string music. The flute was also popular, and was taught in schools. Plato (427-347 B.C.), fully appreciated the value of music, though he qualified his approval by drawing a sharp and dividing line between what he held to be " good " and "bad." Pleasing music, according to him, was not necessarily the noblest, and bad music was " more dangerous than anything else." " Music," said the philosopher, " should render men noble and good. Nothing penetrates the soul and dwells therein so much as rhythm and harmony; therefore good music makes the listener good and refined, while bad music spoils him."

Brass instruments have been used by the military from time immemorial; the Romans, however, used them also for religious services. At first, the Christian Church used only *musica plena,* chorals consisting of full tones; it was not till about 1100 that " mensural " singing came in, with its long and short notes. Discords and their resolution were introduced as early as the 13th century by Franco of Cologne.

The first experiments in the modern art of counterpoint, the " geometry of music," namely the rendering of several melodies at once, were made by the Dutchman Dufay (15th century) and the Italian Costanzio Festa (16th century). Opera originated in Italy about 1600.

MUSIC OF THE EARLY BRITONS

Of music in the British Isles in early times little is known. The harp appears to have been introduced in Ireland about 1000 B.C. The horns of animals were used for sounding signals of alarm, and incidentally as drinking cups. In A.D. 609 Venantius Fortunatus made mention of the crotta or crwth of the Britons, which was played with a bow. Writing on the music of the Welsh, still far famed for their singing, Sir Frederick Gore Ouseley says: " Probably no race of men has preserved so much, unaltered, from the great storehouse of the past as these Cambro-Britons; and it is, therefore, not unreasonable to conclude that in their oldest tunes we may have the remains of what was anciently the music of this country long before the Roman invasion under Julius Cæsar." The Romans naturally introduced their own musical instruments, as did the Saxons, Danes and other intruders. In the Anglo-Saxon epic poem called *Beowulf* we are told that " There was song joined with the sound of music."

SAXON PART-SINGING

Giraldus Cambrensis (1147-1220), Bishop of St. David's, thus refers to Anglo-Saxon singing: " In their musical concerts they do not all sing in unison, as is the custom of other nations, but in different parts, so that as many as you see individuals, so many melodies and various parts you hear, all ultimately smoothly uniting under the softness of B flat into consonance and organic melody (in other words, in harmony). And, moreover, in the northern parts of Britain, beyond the Humber, in the neighbourhood of York, the Angles in singing employ a similar kind of symphonious harmony, using, however, only two parts, one deeply murmuring in the bass, the other delightfully warbling in the treble.

" Nor is this an acquired custom among the nations," adds the prelate, " but by long usage is, as it were, converted into their nature; and has now taken such root in the constituent prejudices of both peoples, that neither among the former, where the custom of singing in several parts prevails, nor among the latter, where they sing in two parts, can a simple melody be well performed. What, moreover, is more remarkable, children from their earliest years observe the same custom. Since, however, among the Angles this method is not universally observed, but only by the more northern inhabitants, I conceive that they have borrowed their method of singing, as well as speaking, from the Danes and Norwegians, who were more frequently accustomed to occupy as well as longer to retain possession of those parts of the island."

MUSIC IN CHURCH NOT WANTED

John of Salisbury, a contemporary, grumbled that the " rites of religion are now profaned by music; and it seems as if no other use were made of it than to corrupt the mind by wanton modulations, effeminate inflexions, and frittered notes and periods, even in the *Penetralia,* or sanctuary itself. The senseless crowd, delighted with all these vagaries, imagine they hear a concert of Sirens, in which the performers strive to imitate the notes of nightingales and parrots, not those of men."

FROM HARP TO ORGAN

The oldest harp in the world, made of gold, tortoise-shell and lapis lazuli, was found in 1934 in Ur, the capital of the ancient Sumerian empire. In the following year the discovery was made of the oldest organ in the world, at Aquincum, an old settlement of the Romans near Budapest, and it dates from A.D. 150. It had fifty-two pipes. The Greek scientist Hero of Alexandria is said to have built an organ with seven stops in the year 100 B.C. In Constantinople organs were played only in the hippodrome and the palæstra (wrestling school).

Cassiodorus, Consul of Rome under Vitigas the Goth, describes an organ of the early part of the 6th century as " composed of divers pipes, formed into a kind of tower which, by means of bellows, is made to produce a loud sound, and, in order to express agreeable melodies, there are in the inside movements made of wood that are pressed down by the fingers of the player, and produce the most pleasing and brilliant tones." Bishop Aldhelm of Sherborne, who died early in the following century, is stated to have introduced " a mighty instrument with innumerable tones, blown with bellows, and enclosed in a gilded case."

In A.D. 757 the Emperor Constantine V presented King Pepin the Short, Charlemagne's father, with an organ which Pepin handed over to a church, and which thus became the first church organ in Western Europe. Pepin, who was evidently a lover of music, also received a pneumatic organ from Harun Alrashid, Caliph of Baghdad. In a Latin poem written by a Benedictine monk named Wulfstan, an organ erected in Winchester Cathedral by Bishop Ælfheah in 951 is described almost like a modern specification. It had twenty-six pairs of bellows, and the united efforts of seventy men were required to keep the wind at the necessary pressure.

" Like thunder," we are told, " the iron tones batter the ear, so that it may receive no sound but that alone. To such an amount does it reverberate, echoing in every direction, that everyone stops with his hand his gaping ears, being in no wise able to draw near and bear the sound which so many various combinations produce. The music is heard throughout the town, and the flying fame thereof is gone out over the whole country."

QUEEN OF INSTRUMENTS

By 1174, when Canterbury Cathedral was burned and the organ with it, there is reason to believe that the " queen of instruments " was installed in many churches. In the accounts of Ely Cathedral for 1407 there is a long list of items connected with the building of such an instrument, including lead, tin, glue, horses' hides for bellows, and boarding the builder for thirteen weeks.

In 1589 Pope Clement presented the church of the Lateran with an organ built by the so-called " Master of Perugia "; it has 500 pipes, the largest of which weighs 2 cwt., while the keyboard is made of ivory and ebony. It was left unused from 1834 to 1934 and was reconditioned for the first time in 1935. The organ in the Court Church at Innsbruck was a present from Pope Julius III. The organ of Nôtre Dame in Paris, built in 1750, has 5,266 pipes and eighty-six stops. One of the largest organs in the world is that at Passau Cathedral: installed in 1928, it has 17,000 pipes and 208 stops.

The largest church organ in Great Britain is in Liverpool Cathedral, with 168 speaking stops and 10,690 pipes. It is operated by electricity and was built by Willis, who was also responsible for the organ of St. Paul's Cathedral, London, which has eighty-seven speaking stops and over 10,000 pipes, some of which weigh a ton. Probably the most unusual memorial to the fallen heroes of the World War is the organ built on a rock at Geroldseck, Kufstein, in Northern Tyrol. The pipes are placed in a round tower and the console or keyboard in a hall over 300 ft. below. It was completed in 1931.

The number of combinations of sounds which it is possible to produce with the aid of organ-registers is incalculable, so that it is no wonder that musicians acknowledge the organ to be the " Queen of Instruments."

STRINGED INSTRUMENTS DOWN THE AGES

The earliest legends of Ceylon tell of a certain Ravana who invented the first stringed instrument 5,000 years ago. It is described as a stick, to one end of which was attached a small cylinder of sycamore wood, across which ran two strings fastened to both ends of the stick. Apollo is said to have invented the lyre by stretching strings over a hollow tortoise shell. The kithara, apparently a development of the lyre, was a more elaborate instrument, and its playing was mainly confined to professional musicians.

The Arabs developed the string-instrument in all directions; they had taken over the whole art of Persian music and possessed fourteen different kinds of stringed instruments alone. Nevertheless, of this abundance nothing has been preserved for us but the rehab and the kemangeh. In Europe, into which Arab culture penetrated deeply, we have already in the 9th century an illustration of a gigue or giga, and in 868 the monk Otfried, author of the *Harmony of the Gospels,* speaks of a fidula (fiddle). As is seen in a relief in the museum at Rouen, by the year 1066 the angular rehab of the Arabs had already assumed the rounded form of the violin. It had three strings and was played with a bow.

The 'cello was no more " invented " than the violin; both are the result of slow development. About the year 1560 violins of a wonderful tone were being made by a native of Bavaria settled in Lyons, and also at Nuremberg by Dürer's father-in-law, Frey, while in the Italian cities of Mantua, Cremona and Brescia other masters were at work whose art was handed down to succeeding generations. With the introduction of printed music and the music of the Netherlandish school there arose that band of technically well-equipped composers who ousted the looser forms of composition formerly in vogue and undermined the previously unchallenged popularity of the human voice.

In the 17th century instrument making reached its zenith. It began with the violin makers Amati and Gaspar da Salo and ended with Guarneri, Stradivari, and the German masters at Mittenwald, by whom the making of stringed instruments was brought to a state of perfection. Perhaps the most wonderful of all these instruments is the violin used by Paganini, which was made in Cremona and is now preserved in a museum at Genoa. The Stradivarius used by the violinist Vecsey cost about £3,250; the Amati used by the Spanish virtuoso Paolo Sarasate was a gift from the Queen of Spain and is now in a museum in Madrid.

EARLY WIND INSTRUMENTS

The Jewish shophar or shofar must be one of the oldest of wind instruments. It is usually made of a curved ram's horn, and is used in synagogues on certain occasions to this day. In ancient times it was also blown as a signal in peace and war. By it Saul announced his victory over the Philistines. The chazozrah was a trumpet, probably of a type used by the Egyptians during their enforced stay in the Land of the Pharaohs and copied from them by the Hebrews. Jubal is referred to in Genesis iv, 21, as " the father of all such as handle the harp and organ." The latter was the ugab.

FASHION'S MYRIAD FANCIES

WHAT first prompted man to devise a means of covering his body is open to question. It may possibly have been simply love of ornamentation, but it is more likely that the custom arose from the need for protection against climatic conditions.

Once clothing was generally accepted its character was certainly determined in the first instance by climate. The peoples of cold countries found their requirements best served by clothes that were shaped to the limbs and close fitting, while those who lived in hot climates adopted the more suitable loose and flowing garment.

Another determining factor was occupation. People engaged in tilling the soil naturally required a covering that would give the greatest ease and comfort, while those who led a predatory life affected a style of dress more suited to an active existence and which gave protection from the dangers of fighting.

FIRST ATTEMPTS AT STYLE

Wide as is the difference in range and style between the dress of primitive man and the people of our time, there is yet one remarkable similarity—the extensive use to which are put the skins of various animals. But the skin " costumes " of the early people of Britain and other countries were far from being the things of beauty that are temporarily the joys of today, and their chief merit lay, not in their shapely outlines and attractiveness, but in their serviceableness as a protection from the cold.

Even in those remote times, crude efforts were made at tailoring this skin attire. The pelts were not just wrapped around the body, but fashioned into a kind of tunic or coat, with leg wrappings to match.

BRITONS DRESSED IN ROMAN GARMENTS

With the coming of the Romans, the early Britons were induced, perhaps against their better judgment, to adopt the more classic dress of their conquerors, and the closer-fitting apparel to which they had accustomed themselves rapidly gave place to the more attractive, but less suitable, flowing toga.

It was from the Gauls, many of whom became settlers in Britain, that the early Britons learned the art of dressing skins, and spinning and weaving fabrics. They also acquired a knowledge of dyeing, at which they soon displayed exceptional skill; and they began to produce both coarse and fine cloths of many and varied colours, from which were fashioned tunics and trousers of a pattern not unlike the Scottish plaid, and mantles of a single colour, usually blue.

It was the fashion to add to the general appearance by wearing a band or belt of gold or silver around the waist, while smaller bands adorned the neck, arms, wrists and fingers.

Although for the most part both men and women went bare-headed, the masculine attire was occasionally rounded off with a cone-shaped covering of cloth known as a " penguwch," which was later adopted by the women, when their menfolk declared in favour of a form of hat.

TUNIC, MANTLE AND GOWN

These fashions, which included shoes of cowhide that met the long trousers at the ankles, underwent considerable modification at the dictation of the invading Romans. The braccæ, or long, loose-fitting trousers, were abandoned, and in their place reigned the Roman tunic, which reached to the knees, while the cloak, or mantle, which still retained its name of sagum, was changed only in the manner in which it was worn, being thrown across the left shoulder, leaving the right exposed to view, instead of being fastened in front by a heavy brooch as hitherto.

Changes in fashion appear to have been a greater concern to men than women, for the garments of the latter were allowed to remain practically unaltered. The women affected a short garment or gown, which was thrown over the tunic, and which differed little from the mantle of the women of Rome. The Roman influence was also apparent in the manner of dressing the hair.

SAXON LOVE OF COLOUR

The Saxons brought the Frankish habit to Britain, a tunic that was short and sleeveless, over which was worn a mantle. They are frequently represented with the legs uncovered, and it is uncertain, therefore, whether they wore the braccæ of the early Britons. Their feet were invariably shod with boots made of a coarse, hard-wearing leather; these were black, and were the only part of their clothing lacking colour, for which they displayed a great fondness.

The tunic, reaching to the knees, was thrown open at the neck, the bondsman's being distinguished from that of his master by a slit at the side. Chiefs and members of the higher ranks had their tunics embellished with gilded leather, or ornamented with coloured embroidery. Generally the dress of all ranks was similar in style, but the upper classes wore their tunics longer. The longer the tunic the higher the station of the wearer. At this period was introduced the forerunner of the stocking of our own time, the lower part of the leg being covered by cross-bands of cloth, linen or leather.

LUXURY OF SILK

The costume of the women in Saxon times was but slightly changed from that of the Britons—the two-piece tunic and gown—the increased length of the gown being the principal variation. Only the sleeves of the tunic were exposed to view, and these, worn tight to the arm, were full length, with a bracelet at the wrist.

There was no attempt at shaping the mantle, which was of a different colour; it was simply a broad piece of cloth which could be conveniently made to enwrap the form in various ways. Both mantle and gown of the higher ranks were ornately embroidered with silk and gold thread. This ornamentation and the length of the gown were the chief differences between the attire of the richer and poorer classes.

As early as the 8th century silk had been introduced into Britain, but its excessive cost allowed only the more wealthy classes to enjoy its luxury.

BLUE AND PLATINUM HAIR

The present-day custom among women of bleaching their hair platinum, or dyeing it, is not by any means an innovation, if we can accept as authentic the colouring of Anglo-Saxon illuminated manuscripts. In many of these the hair of both youths and men is tinted blue.

Marked change in dress styles occurred in the Norman period (1066-1154). The tunic was given extra length, the legs were clothed with hose, a form of breeches, while on the feet short boots were worn. A sleeveless surcoat was worn over the tunic, and over this a rich and flowing mantle, to which was attached a hood to cover the head. Short hair, with the head sometimes shaven at the back, succeeded the long flowing locks that were formerly favoured, and the face was completely shaved. Those best favoured by fortune lined their hats with expensive fur, and added to their grandeur by decorating them with fine jewels and other costly ornaments.

POINTED SHOES DUE TO A DEFORMITY

Not all the modes of the Norman period were dictated by the whim of fashion. At least one dress variation, which became the vogue for about three centuries, was brought about by the necessity of hiding a malformation of the foot. It is said that Count Fulk of Anjou was much perturbed in mind by the inconvenience and unsightliness of bunions on his feet, and knowing of no sure means to remedy these he exercised his inventive genius in devising a style of footwear that would hide the swollen joints from inquisitive gazers. The result of his deliberations was the introduction of pointed shoes, the toes of which extended well beyond the feet.

The style of hairdressing during the Norman dynasty was frequently changed. The short hair and shaven faces gave place to curled and scented locks—which were sometimes bound with ribbons—and flowing beards. On one occasion when short hair had fallen into disfavour wigs were introduced, but their vogue was of short duration.

KING WHO ORDERED CURLS TO BE CUT OFF

The various changes from long to short hair were not always occasioned by the urge of fashion. Once the clipping of curls was made compulsory by a royal decree of Henry I. When in Normandy this monarch had listened to, and was much affected by, the preaching of a prelate named Serlo against the iniquity of wearing long hair. The preacher took advantage of the emotion caused and forthwith proceeded to crop the entire congregation. Whereupon, on his return to England, Henry I forbade anyone to wear the hair long.

The fashion was, however, revived, but about forty years later was again relinquished as the result, so it is said, of the dream of a young soldier. He said that someone came to him while he was asleep and strangled him with his own luxuriant locks, which reached almost to his knees. Such was the effect upon him that he at once had them trimmed to a normal length. Many of his companions followed his example, and when the story of his dream began to spread among the people, superstition gripped them so firmly that the fashion in hair-dressing once again underwent a change.

BRAIDED WITH GOLD WIRE

About the middle of the 12th century we find the quality of the material used for clothes becoming richer and the colours brighter. The men's tunic in the upper ranks of society was made from a silky kind of stuff imported from the East called siclaton, or siglaton, and set off by a jewelled girdle, fastened with a clasp from which hung a tiny ornamental dagger. The mantle, richly embroidered with gold thread, was more gorgeous still, and a jaunty cap surmounted a head of curling ringlets of hair.

The ladies of the day wore a full-flowing gown with a long train, and around the waist a magnificent embroidered girdle glittering with embedded gems. Their hair was almost entirely embraced by a bright-coloured kerchief, just enough being left showing to disclose that it was braided with gold wire.

WINSOME WIMPLE OF THE PLANTAGENETS

The typical dress of the woman of noble birth consisted of a heavily embroidered gown, with a collar of miniver, a species of squirrel, turned back to display the neck; extremely wide sleeves, scalloped out in an attractive leaf pattern, and a wide border to the gown about eighteen inches from the bottom. The girdle was broad and made of gold, and from it dangled three long tassels.

Many were the styles of head-dress, but one that had much favour was the wimple, of silk or cloth, which was wrapped round the head and throat right up to the chin, rather like the head-dress of a nun of of the present day. Fur was generously used, the pelissons, or cloaks, of the women and the mantles of the men being lined with sable, ermine or miniver.

Women of good figure looked very becoming in their "spencers," short jackets trimmed with fur and worn over long skirts, but these fashions were entirely unsuited to tall, gawky women and those possessed of more than an average covering of flesh.

There was an extremely wide gulf between the costume of the nobility and that of the middle and lower orders. The latter wore garments of fustian, frieze, kersey, or some similar coarse and relatively inexpensive cloth, their winter clothes, nevertheless, being frequently lined with fur, such as sheep skin and lamb skin. The more fortunate middle classes indulged in more costly clothing, and were often resplendent in elaborately embroidered gowns, tunics, and silken fillets, which were heavily decorated with expensive ornaments.

WHEN CARPENTERS WORE RUSSET BROWN

During the Plantagenet period there was a greater variety in dress than hitherto, largely accounted for by the distinctive styles adopted by members of different trades. The merchant, the haberdasher, the carpenter, the dyer, each and all could be recognized by the livery affected.

A man in a sombre gown of grey or brown, with hood and girdle, would advertise himself as a merchant; the carpenter would be known by his blouse of russet brown and the flat cap upon his head. Even the juggler could be told from the minstrel, the serving-maid from the poorest tradesman's daughter, by some little characteristic in the style of dress or the quality of its material.

PUNISHED FOR WEARING INCORRECT DRESS

Later there was an attempt by the less wealthy to imitate the styles adopted by the moneyed classes. This led to the introduction of sumptuary laws in the reign of Edward III (1327-1377) which restrained private excess in dress, and gave specific direction as to the cost and style of costume to be worn by persons of different status. Under these laws any person wearing dress of a quality or shape that was reserved for those of higher station was punished by the confiscation of the offending garment.

A further distinction in dress was brought about by the institution, out of the craft guilds, of the livery companies. Each company adopted its own particular livery, for which a special licence had always to be obtained.

Among the abuses against which ordinances were published was the dressing in livery of noblemen's servants and dependents, a custom which was extended by the wealthy to their tradesmen and other persons over whom they had influence, and of whose support in the event of disturbances they thus felt assured.

DAWN OF THE MODERN STYLE

IN the early years of the 15th century there was much confusion of style, long and short gowns, doublets and tunics, hats and hoods being worn indiscriminately, the only notable feature being their extreme showiness. If there was at all a characteristic tendency, it was towards a shortening of the dress, the classic style, with its long gown, hanging sleeves, and toga-like mantle, surrendering its influence to a gown displaying fewer draperies and graceful folds, and a doublet. The transformation was slow, but it signalled the knell of the antique style and the dawn of the modern.

ORNAMENTED WITH PLEATS

The doublet was a short jacket reaching below the waist, around which was fastened a girdle. The lower part of the jacket was ornamented with pleats; the sleeves, their fullness reaching to the wrist, were slashed to their full length, so that the white under-sleeve of the shirt could be displayed. Extra breadth or fullness was obtained by padding the shoulders. Sometimes the doublet was ornamented by being slashed or laced across the front; at others it was open to display a stomacher, in distinctly feminine taste, which was frequently beautifully embroidered and adorned with jewels. The material of the stomacher was generally the same as that used for the doublet, though occasionally it was made of linen.

Long hose were still favoured, and were fastened to the doublet by points or latchets. Pointed shoes remained the vogue, the points of the nobility being as much as two feet in length. These had to be looped up and secured at the knees. The reign of this exaggerated type of footwear was, however, fast drawing to a close, and it was not long before it gave place to the duckbill, a shoe that was almost as ludicrously broad as its predecessor had been long. Other styles followed; in fact, during this period there was a greater variety of footwear than ever before.

BOOTS SHORT AND LONG

Henry V (1413-1422) favoured a short boot in keeping with his military outfit, while his successor Henry VI (1422-1461) saw the introduction of a high boot, which reached to about the middle of the thigh and was turned over at the top. Both short and long boots were made of leather, the extended legs of the latter being of a softer and more pliable skin than the part which enclosed the feet.

Meanwhile, women, apart from their head-dresses, were not radically altering their own fashions, the noticeable modifications being confined to details such as the changing of the waistline and the lengthening of the train. As in modern times, the shape of the neck was always a matter demanding attention; the prevailing fashion was to cut it on the square. The sleeves displayed no set style, but were of varying length, with a leaning towards the trailing jagged-edged style, which had for long been greatly favoured.

There was a movement towards a closer-fitting gown, showing something of the outline of the bust, and many women displayed a preference for the two-piece mode of spencer, or bodice, and gown, the two being of contrasting colours, with the dividing line, to which

the spencer reached, at the hips. Later, a marked change was introduced
in imitation of the shortening of men's garments, the train of the gown
being dispensed with, a fringe of fur instead giving an attractive finish
to the edge of the garment. This was an unconscious indication of
the shape of things to come—the introduction at a later period of the
short hooped-petticoat.

HEAD-DRESSES THAT LOOKED LIKE STEEPLES

Many and marked were the changes wrought to the head-dress.
One style that attracted much notice, and not a little ridicule, was the
horned head-dress, which required the hair of the devotee to be gathered
in a network on both sides of the face, while from this there projected
a two-pointed frame having a quantity of fine white linen stretched
upon it.

No less startling was the tower or steeple, which originated in
France. This style had the effect of producing a similarity of features
among all who wore it. Rising to a height of about two feet above
the head, the " tower " consisted of rolls upon rolls of linen, which
narrowed to a point at the top, and from which was suspended a long
and plentiful veil of a light, gauzy material.

Among many other types of head-dress of the 15th century were
the cloth caps worn by women of the middle classes and a variety of
Turkish turban, the latter being formed of several widths of material
wound round the head with the end fastened up to form wings. Men
wore hoods, hats and caps of many varieties and often of fantastic
shape, and they even extended their taste in headwear to a type of
bonnet. Gradually, however, the fashion assumed greater uniformity,
and a smaller and more jaunty looking cap became the vogue.

FINED FOR WEARING VELVET

During the reign of Henry IV (1399-1413) dress was very largely
affected by the various sumptuary laws. This monarch looked askance
at the increasing fondness for display among his subjects, especially
those who were less able to afford the expense of moving with the
fashion, and he therefore issued a number of edicts, partly to save them
from themselves, but chiefly to effect rigid divisions between the classes
and the masses.

There was an order against the wearing of cloth of gold, velvet, and
other rich materials by anyone beneath the rank of a baronet; fox, otter,
and coney were the only furs allowed yeomen; and even the wearing
of a girdle or a dagger was strictly forbidden to any person possessed
of less than £20 a year or effects to an aggregate value of £200.

Restrictions were also placed upon the points of " poulaines," a
development of the original pointed shoes. Knights were forbidden,
on pain of a fine of forty pence, to wear boots or shoes having points
that exceeded two inches in length.

Such regulations did not apply to royal or noble personages. Into their wardrobes now came new and richer materials, including velvet and satin. Linen was also becoming an increasingly important item of wear among the nobility. In the wardrobe accounts of Edward IV (1461-1483) we find reference to the washing of sheets, shirts, stomachers and kerchiefs. Men often were entrusted with the laundering, but when a woman was engaged for the work it would appear that she was employed also to make the articles.

MODERN STYLES STARTED IN TUDOR DAYS

There is little similarity between present-day dress and that of the 16th century, yet the styles of today had their origin in those of the Tudor period. Both men and women of that time decided to emerge from the antiquity of loose, flowing garments, and enter a new world of fashion that decreed style of costume which, although not following rigidly the natural lines of the body, at least showed some pretence to marking the outline of the figure.

This change was not foreshadowed during the early years of the century, when the costume of both men and women displayed little alteration in style from that of the second half of the previous century. True, the long hanging sleeves were seldom seen, but the gowns of the women were still short-waisted, and the necks retained their square cut. The artificial shape of the bodice had not yet been introduced, but the train had definitely departed, except for its use on state occasions, and the gown was somewhat shorter. Stomachers remained in vogue.

Masculine attire still consisted of the doublet and cloak, the appearance being enhanced by a lace-trimmed shirt of fine lawn, embellished with coloured silk embroidery and dainty ruffles in which gold thread was neatly interwoven. These shirts were usually a most expensive item; one of the choicest quality incurred the wearer in an outlay of something like £10. Caps, attractively adorned with large plumes, were placed jauntily on the head, and Milanese bonnets of satin and velvet, set with jewels, were also worn. A sword generally completed the outfit.

REVOLUTION IN DRESS

DURING the reign of Queen Elizabeth (1588-1603) there occurred what can only be described as a complete revolution in dress. The loose, flowing folds of the women's gowns, exposing something of the contour of the figure, were relegated to fashion's scrap-heap, and in their place reigned a style that first necessitated the placing of the figure in a frame of whalebone so that the costume it supported stood out erect and stiff.

This was the age of the farthingale, or verdingale. This amazing fashion was first adopted in France about 1530, and was introduced into England from Spain about 1550, though it did not find general favour until Elizabeth became queen.

The farthingale consisted of a petticoat made of canvas or cloth sewn with graduated hoops of whalebone or cane, and covered with taffeta or other material of the kind. In its later form, it was greatly distended at the hips, giving a much greater circumference there than at the bottom of the garment.

The style was more suitable for tall women, but short women were equally slaves to the fashion. Their incongruity was frequently commented on by writers of the time. Montaigne derided them, saying: "To become slender in the waist, what pinching, what girdling, what circling will they not endure. Yea, sometimes with iron plates with whalebones and other such trash their very skin and quick flesh is eaten in and consumed to the bone."

Farthingales were worn either with a single-piece dress or with a separate pointed bodice and skirt, and the artificiality of woman's costume increased as the century advanced, the bodice being extended and made more pointed.

CORSETS OF IRON

The art of tight-lacing was largely practised, the use of whalebone corsets being a means to this end, and waists of no more than eighteen inches were achieved at the expense of much discomfort. Catherine de' Medici so compressed her body in an iron two-piece instrument, which fastened at the sides, that she was able to boast of a waist whose circumference measured no more than thirteen inches.

Another innovation, dating from a little before the time of Elizabeth, was the ruff. At first the fashion was confined to men, and was quite a modest affair. The full dignity of this adornment was not to be acquired for some time. For a while ruffs were too expensive as general wear for other than the wealthy classes, since after being worn a few times they lost their elegance of shape and had to be discarded. The fashion called for about a yard and a quarter of linen.

It was the custom of women to throw their ruffs well back and expose the throat, but Queen Elizabeth always wore hers close because her throat was yellow.

FASHION ALTERED BY A CRIME

The ruff fashion received a great fillip in 1564, when the art of starching was introduced into England. It was the wife of the queen's Dutch coachman, a Mrs. Dinghen, who brought from Holland this stiffening process, which she applied to the queen's ruffs with such success that soon everybody was desirous of having their ruffs similarly treated.

A practical-minded woman, Mrs. Dinghen promptly established herself in business, and was soon prospering greatly, starching the ruffs of the nobility, and teaching her new vocation to apprentices at a fee of £5 a head.

Both white and yellow starches were favoured, but when the

notorious Mrs. Turner, condemned to death for the poisoning of Sir Thomas Overbury in 1613, went to her execution wearing a ruff of yellow, this colour lost much of its popularity.

The distinguishing features of the ruff were its many pleats, which were kept in position after being starched by treatment with a heated iron stick somewhat resembling a goffering-iron. Additional strength was given to the stiffening by the use of wires, which were covered with silk or gold and silver thread, and were passed around the neck below the ruff. These not only assisted in keeping the ruff in position, but also lessened the weight which had to be supported.

The French ruff, an even more elaborate composition than the English type, was so constructed that the courtiers of Henry III of France (1551-1589) are stated to have experienced the utmost difficulty in eating and drinking, since they were scarcely able to bend the head forward. It is on record that one lady of the court overcame the difficulty of eating soup by employing a spoon with a handle two feet long.

CHILDREN'S HAIR FOR ADULT CURLS

The introduction of the ruff made necessary a drastic change in the method of dressing the hair. The lofty style of coiffure did not harmonize with the imposing array of ruff, and it was found that there was already sufficient weight to support without the addition of a tall head-dressing. It became customary, therefore, to arrange the hair in an elaboration of curls, which were strikingly set off by strings of pearls, divers jewelled ornaments, and beautifully wrought wreaths of gold and silver.

Dyeing and tinting the hair also became prevalent, the favourite hue being golden, after the colour of Queen Elizabeth's hair. False hair was largely in demand for curls and twists; many women of the lower orders were induced to sell their hair, while children often had their hair cut from their heads by people who found a ready sale among fashionable hairdressers for the stolen locks.

Wigs, of many different colours, were very much in evidence among royalty and the nobility. It was quite common for a wealthy person to possess a dozen or more; Queen Elizabeth had a collection of more than eighty.

We are apt to think that the use of cosmetics is a modern innovation. It is at least as old as the ancient Egyptians. In the days of Elizabeth women applied colour to their faces and used a variety of face-washes. There was also considerable use of perfumes.

Referring to the make-up practices of the time, a contemporary writer comments: " She hath a fair hair if it be her own, a rare face if it be not painted, a white skin if it be not plastered, a full breast if it be not bolstered."

It was during Elizabeth's reign that the fan became a part of every fashionable woman's ensemble. This was another of fashion's many importations from France, into which country it had been introduced from Italy by Catherine de' Medici.

Many fans were of costly and elaborate design, their handles of gold, silver and agate being studded with precious stones. Queen Elizabeth is said to have possessed a collection of twenty-seven, valued at many thousands of pounds. The carrying of fans was not confined to women only, young men often carried costly ones made from ostrich and peacock feathers, with richly decorated handles of gold and silver.

Another fashion to reach England from Italy was the wearing of perfumed gloves. Henry VIII is said to have worn a pair, but they were not in general use before Elizabeth's time.

GLOVES WORN IN BED

At that period it was more usual for men to wear gloves, though women also adopted the fashion. The queen was graciously pleased to accept the gift of a pair, embroidered with gold, from the University of Cambridge, but there is no evidence that she ever kept them on when retiring for the night, as was the custom with the ladies of France.

That gloves about this time could be purchased at prices ranging from threepence to three shillings suggests cheapness, but it must be borne in mind that money had then a far greater purchasing power.

Queen Elizabeth was frequently to be seen wearing gloves, it being customary for the sovereign and the nobility to have the hands covered in this way on ceremonial occasions. Her collection was unequalled, but then she was ever famous not only for the quality but also the quantity of the articles forming her extensive wardrobe. The number of her gowns alone is said to have exceeded three thousand.

QUEEN'S PRIDE IN SILK STOCKINGS

Good Queen Bess was especially proud of her silk hose. The queen's first pair was a present from her silk-woman. John Stowe, the chronicler and antiquary, records the incident thus:—

" In the second yeare of Queene Elizabeth, her silk-woman Mistress Montagu, presented her Majestie, for a new yeare's gift, with a pair of black silk knit stockings, the which after a few days' wearing, pleased her highness so well, that she sent for Mistress Montagu, and asked her where she had them, and if she could help her to any more; who answering said, ' I made them very carefully of purpose only for your Majestie, and seeing them please you so well, I will presently set more in hand.' ' Do so (quoth the queene), for indeed I like silk stockings so well, because they are pleasant, fine, and delicate, that henceforth I will wear no more cloth stockings.' And from that time until her death the queene never wore any more cloth hose, but only silk stockings."

The customary attire of the lower orders was made from kerseys, russet cloth, broadcloths, friezes and other coarse materials. Apprentices were distinguished by the gowns they wore, which were not unlike the blue gowns of the boys of Christ's Hospital, the similarity being heightened by the yellow stockings which were also frequently worn. The usual head covering was a flat cap of cloth. About this time, refugees from Denmark began to produce beaver hats. These were costly, and favoured by the upper classes only.

The women of the humbler classes were clad in simple cloth gowns, with a full skirt that easily cleared the ground, over which they wore a short spencer, or bodice. An alternative style was a short kirtle with a gown over it.

COMING OF THE CARTWHEEL RUFF

Towards the end of Elizabeth's reign there was a tendency for the cut of women's dresses to become lower. They became even lower during the early years of James I's reign (1603-1625), the front being cut so that the whole of the breast was exposed to view. The practice was soundly rated by the moralists, Stubbes, who was especially severe, commenting strongly on " the laying out of their hairs, the painting and washing of their faces, the opening of their breast and discovering them to their waists."

With the lower cut of the dress came the wearing of the cartwheel ruff, but this style was soon replaced by one in which the ruff framed the sides and back of the dress. Difficulties in starching led to the introduction of tall, wired lace collars, which rose high at the back and finished in a point on either side of the bodice. Before the ruff was entirely superseded by the new collar, there was a transitional stage during which both were worn together.

INHERITED QUEEN ELIZABETH'S WARDROBE

The fashions of the early years of the Stuart period, which began in 1603, showed comparatively little modification of the established dress of Elizabeth's time, and history records that Anne of Denmark, the consort of James I, made free use of the splendid wardrobe which her husband's predecessor had accumulated.

The farthingale still reigned supreme, and what difference there was between it and that of the previous reign was to be observed in the even lower cut, which was also extended to the back. The long pointed stomacher, which reached some distance below the line of the waist, also remained in favour, while the ruff was somewhat modified, being made to stand up fierce and stiff round the back of the neck.

WORN AS A PROTECTION AGAINST ASSASSINATION

James I displayed a great fondness for the stuffed and quilted doublet and hose, since he regarded these as a protection against the hand of the assassin. The trunk hose had by now developed into breeches, which were fastened immediately below the knee with ribbons. The full costume was completed by stockings, the nobility and gentry affecting silk, the lower orders worsted, which was fast ousting cloth from favour, and boots, which were now almost universally worn.

The queen herself appears to have shown little interest in dress, nor did James attempt to influence the fashions of his time, although his love of pageantry and magnificent display was pronounced. Yet he was enforced on at least one occasion to issue an edict regarding the wearing apparel of women. The royal command was against the wearing of the farthingale at court, since this "impertinent garment took up all the room."

This prohibition of its use arose out of an incident at one of the amateur dramatic performances known as masques that were frequently held at Whitehall. There had been a somewhat unseemly struggle among the ladies for the best positions, in which four or five of them had found themselves inextricably wedged together in the passage. Their immense farthingales had become so involved, and their release had been such a difficult and lengthy process, that by the time they had freed themselves the performance was half over and many of the audience had not yet been able to take their places.

PASSING OF THE FARTHINGALE

About the year 1623 fashion decreed the passing of the farthingale. The only resemblance to it in the gown that took its place was in the manner of padding the hips. The gown hung in heavy, ungainly folds from the pads, and reached to the ground. Within ten years this style also had ceased to exist, and a new and more graceful creation at long last relegated the monstrosities of padding, whalebone, starch and wires to the waste heap. The new mode embodied the freedom and grace of the ancient gown, while being entirely shorn of its severity.

France, as so often before, gave the lead, the first move in the transformation being the discarding by women of the ruff and its replacement by a soft and more elegant fichu of muslin and lace. Next followed the adoption of the new style of gown, attended by a much more attractive dressing of the hair, which was done in small curls about the temples and ears and fell intriguingly in ringlets about the neck.

The gowns of this period either consisted of two pieces—skirt and bodice—or were made as a single garment which opened over a petticoat. In the two-piece style, the skirt was given considerable fullness, while the bodice was freely supplied with folds by means of large pleats, or a number of gathers at the sides.

The sleeves of the gown were cut extremely short, and beneath it, and showing a little above the neck to form an edging, a chemisette was worn, having wide lace or muslin sleeves extending below the sleeves of the gown.

In spite of the growing simplicity of women's dress, it was far from being less costly, since the full folds were as rich and elaborate as had been those which covered the farthingale; and the free use of lace was an expensive item. The expenditure on jewels, fans, perfumery, and cosmetics, and the need for efficient lace-women and tire-women combined to make the maintenance of an adequate wardrobe an exceedingly costly business.

A further item of dress that now had to be given attention was the peruke or wig. This artificial head of hair, in imitation of the periwigs worn by men, was fast becoming fashionable, not only among women of the higher circles, but also the lower ranks.

BLACK MASKS WORN BY WOMEN

A curious fashion at this time was the wearing of little black masks by women when walking abroad. These masks were shaped to cover the upper part of the face down to the mouth, and were kept in position by two side wires and one which was passed over the top of the head. As an alternative to the mask, a large green fan was sometimes used to serve the same purpose—the protection of the face from disfigurement by the sun.

The fan was inseparable from the general ensemble, as was also the muff, and an additional adornment was a bejewelled watch, usually attached to the waist.

SPLENDOUR AND SIMPLICITY

THE attire of the gentlemen of the days immediately preceding the Commonwealth can be imagined by a description of that affected by Charles I (1625-1649). He is said to have worn " a falling band, a short, green doublet, the arm-part towards the shoulders wide and slashed, zig-zag turned-up ruffles, very long green breeches, tied far below the knee with long yellow ribbons, red stockings, great shoe-roses, and a short red cloak, lined with blue, with a star in the shoulder."

Many of the gallants of the day were resplendent in doublets and hose richly slashed with satin and lace with gold, with satin-lined cloaks of rich velvet, gold and jewel-embroidered velvet girdles or belts, beaver hats of black, ornamented with a plume of ostrich feathers, and coloured boots with trimming of point lace. Extravagant garters formed part of the costume of both men and women, and the cavaliers of Charles I carried a rapier which was hung from a beautiful sash passed over the right shoulder.

HENCE THE NICKNAME OF ROUNDHEADS

During the Commonwealth (1649-1660) a marked change took place in the prevailing dress. The Puritans of both sexes displayed a characteristic simplicity in both their attire and their manners. For the first time in England two entirely differing styles of dress existed side by side.

The sombre clothing of the Puritans was not assumed at the dictate of fashion, nor because the wearers were unable to afford the expense of more extravagant wear—it sprang in the main from their abhorrence of all forms of adornment. There were among them many who, in the ordinary course of events, would have been prepared to follow any fashionable and expensive style of attire, but the more zealous and earnest carried the more worldly with them, and the few who were overcome by the desire for greater display were soundly reprimanded for their carnal longings.

Perhaps the most uniformly distinctive feature of the Puritans was the closely cropped hair. It was from this custom that they acquired the nickname of Roundheads, which is stated to have first been applied to them by the consort of Charles I.

DRABNESS OF THE PURITANS

The man's costume consisted of coarsely woven doublet and hose of a drab colour; a heavy cloak of an equally sombre hue, wrapped completely around him; stockings of thick worsted; and a stern and forbidding high-crowned hat, broad in the brim and without trimmings of any kind. The neck was wrapped in a wide band of plain ribbon, called a falling band.

The costume of the Puritan woman was equally plain. Usually grey in colour, it lacked all such trivialities as embroidery, ribbons and lace, but was not infrequently made of good-quality silk. The sleeves of the gown were always long and lacking in fullness; no good Puritan woman was ever guilty of exposing any part of her arm.

The neck was covered with a fold of white cambric or a muslin kerchief, and the outdoor attire was completed by a severely plain hood fastened below the chin, or a high-crowned, broad-brimmed felt hat. In spite of its plain severity, there was nevertheless a certain fascination about the costume of the Puritan woman, engendered by its simplicity and neatness.

FACE PATCHING BECOMES THE RAGE

One remarkable craze that became fashionable during the reign of Charles I was face patching. Women of all ages were to be seen with their faces bedecked with every conceivable form of " patch," from black spots designed like the sun, moon or stars, hearts or crosses, to the elaborate design of a coach and horses stretching right across the forehead. The fashion was immensely popular for many years, and lapsed only towards the close of the century.

IN THE PERSIAN MODE

With the end of the Commonwealth, the stage was set for a return to an even greater extravagance and luxuriousness in dress than was the case in the earlier Stuart period.

One noteworthy feature of the reign of Charles II (1660-1685) was the introduction of a garment which has, with some modifications, persisted in male attire down to the present day. This was a straight, collarless coat which reached to below the knees and was buttoned from the neck throughout its entire length. It was girdled by a broad sash fringed at the ends, and had short, close sleeves with deep, turned-back cuffs, from which peeped the lace ruffles of the shirt sleeves. It was a fashion which had been imported from Persia. The costume was completed by a long waistcoat, hidden from view except when the coat was allowed to remain partly unbuttoned, and full breeches that fitted closely at the knees.

Charles II is said to have adopted this style of dress in the interests of economy and thrift.

GARMENTS MODIFIED BY THE FRENCH

The new fashion was accepted with avidity but soon underwent modification, and once again the lines of English costume were being based on those of the French, so that the new garments lost much of their peculiarly English character. The coat was worn longer, the sleeves became fuller, while those of the waistcoat remained tight. There was a tendency for the waist to become more pronounced, allowing a greater fullness to be lent to the skirt, which was given fan-shape pleats to carry the greater expanse.

The breeches became a tighter-fitting garment, the " petticoat " style being out of harmony with the fullness of the skirt of the coat. They still fastened below the knee, and for a time the garter, with its trimming of ribbon and lace, was retained. A later fashion decreed its departure, the stocking then being extended to cover the knee and extremity of the breeches. The outdoor cloak was no longer thrown over the shoulder in the Cavalier fashion, but hung from the band which was tied round the neck.

BATTLE OF THE WIGS

Although Charles II had adopted the French custom of wearing a periwig, his example was not generally favoured, nor did the male fashion of hairdressing display any distinctive style. It was left to the 18th century to provide full play for the periwig. There was never any attempt to foist it off as a natural head of hair; on the contrary, it was always worn unashamedly as a distinct and separate article of dress; and if, in fact, there was cause for shame, it was in not being possessed of this style of head-dress and being so undignified as to expose the natural growth of hair to view.

In the reign of Louis XIV of France (1638-1715) the full-flowing wig was the vogue, but this type soon gave way to the three-part wig, consisting of two side pieces called cadenettes and a middle section which formed a queue, or pigtail, at the back.

The full wig was gradually ousted by the tie-wig, or Ramillies wig, of which the peculiar characteristic was a plaited tail, tied at top and bottom with ribbon bows, the upper bow being the larger of the two. For appearing at court in one of these wigs, Lord Bolingbroke received a scathing rebuke from Queen Anne (1702-1714), who remarked that she might expect to see him appear in his nightcap the next time he was summoned by her. The continued wearing of the tie-wig by the noble lord resulted in its final approval and acceptance.

WIGS FOR EVERY PROFESSION

In the reign of George II (1727-1760) it became *de rigueur* among certain classes to affect a wig made in imitation of the natural hair. This was the bob-wig, and there were two distinct types—the major and the minor. They were both made short and close, the bob minor being worn by apprentices, while the bob major, or Sunday buckle, to which were attached several rows of curls, was the mode with the citizen.

There were numerous other styles of wig in favour, for there was a different style for almost every profession or trade, each having its particular name. That adopted by university students was specially fashioned, being flat on the top, to take their stiff, cornered hats, with a large bag at the back. This peculiar style is said to have originated among French serving-men, who inserted their hair in a black leather bag as the best and quickest means of disposing of it in a tidy manner. The bag-wig enjoyed some prestige among the English gentry, but they found it more in keeping with their station to have the bag made of silk. Although a presentable wig was obtainable for a guinea or two, it was by no means unusual for the wealthier classes to pay as much as forty or fifty guineas.

THIEVES WHO SPECIALIZED IN WIGS

Thieves found in wigs a great temptation, and many a costly specimen was snatched from the head of an unsuspecting wearer. They even went so far as to cut holes in the backs of the slow-moving hackney coaches to reach the occupants. Another device was for the thief to carry on his head a basket in which was hidden a small boy, who at a given signal would raise the lid of the basket and purloin the wig of a passer-by.

HATS WORN UNDER THE ARM

About 1770 the tie-wig passed definitely out of fashion. In its place reigned the towering macaroni, a wig which reached to an enormous height and had a very large queue; it required the hair to be extremely long. Its name was derived from the Macaroni Club, founded by a number of young bloods on their return from travelling in Italy, and a rival to the famous Beefsteak Club, to which belonged the reputed wits and notabilities of the time.

The hats which accompanied this fashion were modelled on extremely small lines, for it was impossible to carry one of normal size on the summit of such an edifice. Generally, the hat was a toy affair designed not as a head covering, but to be carried under the arm, and much attention was therefore given to its ornamentation. When placed on the macaroni, the " pretty black beaver " hat was frequently fixed to the side of it, and when lifted in greeting a lady, raised by means of a cane, or the point of a sword. Such costly oddities were regarded as essentials of full dress, and continued so for a time even after the bell-shaped beaver came in under the Prince Regent early in the 19th century.

Many people wore a sort of compromise between the macaroni and the natural hair called the "tower," a variety of half-wig, which was specially suitable for those whose hair had become very thin on the top. The "tower" reached as far as the crown of the head and the back of the ears, where it joined up with the natural hair and thus gave the impression of being part of it.

PUT A TAX ON POWDER

The powdering of wigs was a flourishing branch of the hairdressers' calling. With a view to increasing the national revenue, William Pitt put a tax on powder, much to the hairdressers' annoyance and discomfiture, for it had the immediate effect of reducing the quantity used. The amount of the tax was a guinea a head, which led to the Tories—who continued the use of powder—becoming known facetiously as "guinea pigs."

By the close of the century the wig had been almost entirely discarded, except for use on state occasions, its retention being confined to the learned professions and the clergy.

TOWERING HEAD-DRESSES

Not to be outdone by their male contemporaries, the women adopted a number of truly remarkable head-dresses. The style at the end of the 17th and beginning of the 18th century was known as the "commode," or "tower," which, according to the *Lady's Dictionary* of the time, consisted of "a frame of wire two or three storeys high, fitted to the head, and covered with tiffany or other thin silks; being now completed into the whole head-dress." The wire frame, which formed the front part, was fastened to a linen cap, fitting tightly on the back of the head.

These monstrous affairs could not be obtained except at heavy cost, and it is not surprising that this type of coiffure suddenly changed to a graceful and simple style that was extremely low on the head. The front hair was neatly combed back from the forehead, the remainder of the coiffure consisting of a number of long curls. A further change was soon to be made. The new vogue was brought about by a desire for conformity with a variation in the style of dress, the hoop having by now made its appearance. The low head-dress was not, it was felt, in keeping with the roundness of the skirt, since it made the head appear disproportionately small.

So fashion once again reverted to the towering head-dress, which grew to even greater heights with the decline in the girth of the hooped skirt. In the reign of George III (1760-1820) the extravagance and folly of women's head-dresses reached a peak that had never before been achieved. They involved an enormous preparation, being kneaded with pomatum and flour, brought up over a cushion of wool and twisted into a profusion of curls and knots, the whole being embellished with artificial flowers and ribbon tied into bows. Such elaborate preparation made it necessary for the " head " to remain unattended often for weeks.

One result of this fashion was that drivers of hackney carriages found their takings rapidly dwindling, since it was almost impossible for women to enter these vehicles. When the head-dress did allow of riding, it was necessary for the fare to sit hunched up, with her elbows resting on her knees throughout the entire journey.

"HALF AN HOUR OUT OF FASHION "

Many were the ingenious methods of ornamenting these lofty head-dresses, small flower gardens, masses of many-coloured ostrich feathers, and bunches of fruit being common. For evening wear the decorative effect was even more striking; it was a common sight to see the " tower " surmounted by a coach and horses, a ship in full sail, or a lighthouse.

With such a towering mass to support, it would seem that hats were unnecessary. Yet no woman ever walked abroad without this addition to her costume. Nor was it a creation that lacked size. Hats were, in fact, magnificent in their proportions. They were adjusted a little towards the back of the " head," in order not to detract from the appearance of the frizzed hair in front.

Many of the hats were shaped like turbans, with the central part of the crown trimmed, while others were wide-brimmed, low-crowned affairs, the brim being turned up to take a finishing spray of flowers. They had to be considered in conjunction with the type of head-dress affected, and thus the style was ever changing. Headwear styles changed so frequently that it was once announced satirically in the press that a certain noble lady was " more than half an hour out of fashion."

IN IMITATION OF THE CABRIOLET

About the middle of the 18th century there was a craze for headwear in imitation of the cabriolet or post-chaise, which had recently taken its place on the streets. It consisted of a large cap with wheels at the sides. Another style of cap which won much popularity was the fly-cap, fashioned to represent a butterfly and edged with garnets and brilliants. There was also a fashion in crownless or brim hats, not unlike a style of recent times. This was specially favoured in sunny weather.

The great "calash," the invention of the Duchess of Bedford in 1765, was a tremendous round cap stiffened by whalebone, which could either be worn over the forehead or thrown back. It was secured below the chin, and when worn in the forward position had a barrel-like appearance.

ADVENT OF THE DEVONSHIRE HAT

One more than usually attractive style was the "Devonshire hat," made of chip straw and delicately trimmed with white feathers. It was named after the beautiful Duchess of Devonshire, who was then a reigning beauty, and its general popularity led to the rapid passing of the cap from favour.

With the advent of this hat came a change in the style of hairdressing, the "false chignon" being discarded, and the natural hair, in long, powdered curls, being allowed to fall loosely about the shoulders. This permitted the head to be adorned with a more modest and intriguing form of head-dress—an unpretentious bandeau of feathers and a few precious stones.

Not everybody was induced at once to cut away from the long-established fashion of lofty head-dresses, and *The Times* in 1794 had occasion to comment upon the great length of the feathers that were worn, declaring that a lady was " twice as long upon her feet as in her bed."

PETTICOAT AS AN OUTSIDE GARMENT

One of the most revolutionary changes in women's dress came in the 18th century with the introduction of the hoop. It did not suddenly descend upon the English world of fashion, but developed out of the pannier, a looping-up of the gown which had become the vogue in the declining years of the previous century. The country of the pannier's origin is uncertain, the most likely possibility being that it was a German development of the old wheel farthingale, which had survived among the Teutons long after its passing in England.

The pannier, which caused the re-introduction of the tight-waisted stomacher, was a skirt which had the material bunched around the hips. The gradual enlargement of the panniers necessitated an increase in the number of petticoats required to carry the greater width and weight of the skirt, so for greater comfort the hoop petticoat was devised, and its popularity was such that it remained the mode for nearly 100 years.

Like all new creations, the hoop petticoat became extremely exaggerated, and eventually attained an enormous size. It was not a petticoat as we now understand the meaning of the term, but an outside garment.

In France, where the hoop petticoat was acclaimed with enthusiasm, it assumed as alarming proportions as it did in England. When the queen and the two princesses attended the opera they were compelled to occupy five seats between them, leaving a vacant one on either side of the queen, as complaint had been made that when they sat in three adjoining seats the hoops of the princesses completely hid her majesty from view.

During the reign of Queen Anne the hoop petticoat increased to such an immense size that in the narrow streets of London it became a great impediment to free passage. One unfortunate lady encountered a flock of sheep as she was gaily tripping along, and a ram, running on to the footway, became entangled in her hoop. The chronicler of this distressing incident relates that the lady " in her fright let the hoop down, which still the more encumbered the ram, as it fixed upon his neck. . . . Down fell the lady, unable to sustain the forcible efforts the ram made to obtain his liberty. At last the driver of the sheep came up and assisted in setting free his beast, and raising the lady; but never was finery so demolished. . . . The rude populace, instead of pitying, insulted her misfortune, and continued their shouts till she got into a chair and was out of sight."

EMBROIDERED IN GOLD AND SILVER

The complete dress of the wearer of a hoop consisted of the hoop petticoat itself, which was actually a skirt stiffened by whalebone, and a gown which opened in the front, and sometimes had a long train. The bodice of the gown was laced up over a stomacher, or, alternatively, stays of an attractive design were worn on the outside. The stays of the period, which were never an under garment, resembled a deep-pointed waistband, with shoulder straps, and often they were cut no more than six inches in length. The tall stays were most unattractive and usually uncomfortably tight.

Among the varied materials of which the petticoat was made, damask was largely favoured, and the woman of fashion would pay as much as £12 or £14 for a hoop petticoat in this material embroidered in gold and silver. There were also petticoats of velvet, silk, cloth and chintz, but few except the most wealthy were able to include an ermine petticoat in their wardrobes.

RESEMBLING JOSEPH'S COAT

Almost every item of a lady's costume was of a different colour, a petticoat of black having embroidery possibly of red; the stays might be cherry colour with blue and silver trimming; the gown of red and dove-coloured damask, beautifully flowered; a yellow satin apron trimmed with white; while the head cloths, ruffles, scarf and hood would also be of contrasting colours.

Trains were frequently worn, and some were exceptionally long. The hoop petticoat itself never reached to the ground, and some were criticized for being too short, one critic even declaring that " the ladies wear their petticoats up to their knees." This was a gross exaggeration of fact.

PATCHES OF POLITICAL SIGNIFICANCE

Patching of the face continued throughout the century. One critic somewhat impolitely wrote of this strange decorative art, " I have often counted fifteen patches or more upon the swarthy wrinkled phiz of an old hag, three-score and ten upwards."

The practice of patching even had political significance in the time of Queen Anne. Addison refers to its employment for this purpose; at the Haymarket Theatre he observed two parties of women who were patched in different ways: " The faces on one hand were spotted on the right side of the forehead, and those upon the other on the left. I quickly perceived that they cast hostile glances upon one another; and that their patches were placed in those different situations, as party signals to distinguish friends from foes. . . . Upon inquiry, I found that the body of Amazons on my right were Whigs, and those on my left, Tories."

BEAUTIES WHO REFRAINED FROM USING SOAP

The treatment of the face was an elaborate process. Cosmetics in great variety were in use, rouge and white lip-salve and wash being only a few of the requisites of a lady's toilet table. Various oils were also required, and lard scented with orange and jessamine was essential for correct face treatment.

Many beauties of the day refrained from using soap; they did not wash, but depended entirely on creams and pastes for their facial charms. The modern fashion among some women of plucking the eyebrows and wearing false eyelashes had its counterpart in the 18th century, when it was the custom to wear false eyebrows.

Fashion demanded constant change in the colour of women's hair, and consequently there was a big business in hair dyes. When golden hair went out of favour in 1775, ladies were much concerned to discover the best method of changing its hue. They found a solution to the problem in the use of elderberries and red wine.

STAIRCASES BUILT TO ACCOMMODATE DRESSES

In the second half of the 18th century small hoops became the mode for ordinary dress, the large hoop being reserved for full dress, but the change was not of long duration, and within a few years large hoops came into their own again. They became so immense at one time that architects had to make allowance for them in designing staircases, the balusters being made to bulge outwards.

It was not until the closing years of the century that the hoop petticoat passed definitely out of fashion. It gave place to a classic style; from being ridiculously wide the gown assumed a narrow, clinging style. Ease was now the dominant note, and all indications of fullness were abandoned, the figure being defined by the bodice, while not being in any way compressed.

GRECIAN DRESSES AND MOROCCO SHOES

Many dresses affected the Grecian model, the chiton being buttoned at the shoulders, and the hair dressed in keeping with the classical style. The gown in ordinary everyday use was not extravagantly long, and the train was worn only with court costume. Morocco shoes were correct daytime wear, satin taking their place in the evening. The former were worn with a chintz gown, a short satin cloak of black, and a bonnet of the same colour. Other articles of apparel at this period were the pelerine, a long narrow cape or tippet, the ends of which were knotted at the back, and a short mantle or cape which just covered the shoulders and at the back tapered to a point at the waist.

According to a fashion journal of the period a winter walking-out costume comprised a white muslin dress, a pink silk cloak covered with black crêpe and trimmed with black lace, a fancy hat with ribbons, and a brown bearskin muff.

MEN'S GLOVES TRIMMED WITH LACE

A description of the special features of the dress of the typical town-bred bachelor at the beginning of the 18th century is "flowing wig, brocaded waistcoat, rolled silk stockings and clouded cane." The coat would be extremely long-skirted, reaching almost to the ankles, and with moderately baggy sleeves and wide cuffs. The waistcoat, too, was very long, somewhere about the length of a modern tail-coat.

A gentleman's shirt was made of the finest white lawn, and was trimmed in front and at the wrists with lace ruffles. His cravat was of point lace. Such was the fondness of the gentlemen of the period for lace, that they even had their gloves trimmed with it.

The knee-breeches were almost completely hidden from view by the coat, but the coloured silk stockings were in glorious evidence. The attire was completed by shoes, wig, and hat, although the last-named was more often than not carried rather than worn. It was an article of considerable expense, and regarded as worthy of being left to one's successor.

When the hat was worn, great attention was given to the "cock" at which it was tilted, among the styles being the military cock, the Denmark cock and the mercantile cock.

Many were the shapes given to the hats of the day, for the fashion was constantly undergoing change. At one time they would be round, a year or two later they would "rise behind and fall before"; they would be large for a time, then of medium size, then small. Cocked hats were the invariable wear of boys; three-cornered cocked hats held sway until the French Revolution, which had a considerable bearing on English dress styles.

RULERS OF FASHION AND MANNERS

The typical male figure of the 18th century is the beau, or macaroni, whose business, as Misson says, was to hunt after new fashions. The original macaroni was described as "the worst gallant in nature; with the airs of a coquette, the manners of a clown." But there were famous beaux of the 18th century and early 19th century, who ruled manners as well as dress. Such were Beau Nash, who went to great pains to reform the manners and dress of the frequenters of the Assembly Rooms at Bath; and Beau Brummel, for many years the favourite of the Prince of Wales (later George IV), who was regarded as the best-dressed man of his day.

Among the changes of fashion introduced by the macaronies was a reduction in the size of the waistcoat to waist length. The coat also was shortened and cut square in front, with tails at the back, a style that can be seen in the modern evening-dress coat. This was a drastic modification, which received considerable adverse comment, not lessened by the adoption of white as the correct colour for the evening waistcoat.

The fashionable colour for both the day and evening coat was blue. This colour Beau Brummel invariably assumed, his pantaloons, which buttoned all the way down to the ankle, being black. The colour of the coat was frequently changed; in turn claret, brown and other hues had their day. Cold weather always required the man of fashion to carry a muff, which was suspended from his neck by a ribbon and decorated in the centre with a bunch of ribbons. A long sword, with a jewelled hilt, was an inseparable part of the attire.

SHAPING THE SHOE TO THE FOOT

Fashion in footwear was periodically changing, especially in women's shoes, but not until the last quarter of the 18th century do we meet with any attempt to shape it to the feet. Up to then boots or shoes could be worn indifferently on either foot, but about 1785 they began to be fashioned to fit the individual foot, greater attention in this respect at first being paid to the high boots then being worn.

After the wide skirts of the coat had given way to long tails, and the double-breasted style had been generally adopted as the prevailing fashion, buttons became the accepted form of ornament. They were on the large side, and varied greatly in shape and design. Though introduced as an adjunct of men's dress they were soon favoured by women as well.

JEERING AT UMBRELLAS

An item of dress which attracted inordinate attention when it was first introduced for men in 1756 was the umbrella. Its advent caused no end of ridicule to be heaped upon the venturesome Jonas Hanway when he first unfurled the strange article of equipment in the streets of London. It did not create a fashion, however, and some twenty years later, when an equally intrepid footman named John Macdonald flourished an umbrella of silk—Hanway's had been an oilskin affair—he, too, had to run the gauntlet of jeering from rude boys.

In spite of the derision evoked by the early use of an umbrella, its utility came gradually to be appreciated, and it was accepted as a necessary complement of the general costume.

EQUALITY IN STYLE MAKES A START

THE fashions of the London beau and his lady were eagerly accepted by all classes in a modified and less expensive form. Nor was there now such a strong dividing line between the attire of the aristocracy and members of the middle classes. There was more equality in dress, especially in women's clothing, the poorer classes being quick to affect the styles of the wealthy.

It was in the material, its quality—and age—rather than the style that the greatest differences were observed. This was specially noticeable about the train; many a poorer woman who was unable to afford a new one retained the old until it was bedraggled and torn, or renewed the train when the petticoat itself was scarcely fit to be worn.

RUFF REVIVED AND MODIFIED

No drastic changes in costume heralded the advent of the 19th century; the classic revival of the latter part of the previous century continued its influence. The so-called Empire mode bore considerable resemblance to the styles of earlier years, the flowing robes, devoid of pressure on the figure, and the short waist being still in evidence, the only difference, if any, being that there was less tendency to elaboration. The keynote was rather simplicity, the gown lacking flounces and furbelows, and falling in simple yet graceful folds throughout its length, with a moderate train to finish it off.

In addition to the pelisse, variously coloured long and flowing cloaks were worn when walking and driving, and in warmer weather short cloaks and mantles and the inevitable spencer were correct wear.

In the first decade of the century a modified form of an old fashion was revived—the wearing of a ruff. Not nearly so imposing and uncomfortable as the ruff of Elizabethan days, it was made of broad lace gathered into a band to fit the throat, and mounted on muslin.

VEILS LONG AND SHORT

Veils were in general demand, but the manner of wearing them varied considerably. The original fancy was for a short white veil, which was soon followed by a much larger variety, negligently thrown over the hat or bonnet, and hanging loosely about the neck. With full dress was often worn a long veil suspended from the back of the cap, not unlike a bridal veil. A few years later the short veil again returned to favour; it reached only to the throat, and was worn in a carefree manner, the sides hanging out instead of being carried round to the back.

There were many and varied styles of hats and caps in request, and almost as many different fashions in hairdressing. When an open-trimmed hat with ostrich feathers was worn it was customary to have the front hair done in curls, a most becoming fashion. Generally speaking, the style of coiffure decided the style of hat.

BOOTS WHICH LACED AT THE BACK

The waist-line was occasionally experimented with, but the short waist was in favour for a number of years, any attempt at lengthening it being met with accusations of barbarism. It was not, in fact, until about 1820 that a tendency to conform to the natural waist-line became evident.

There was little alteration in the style of footwear, which remained low and fanciful. The introduction of ankle boots laced at the back was little if any improvement, and gained no favour. Tan gloves, the colour generally matching that of the shoes, were popular; they were long, reaching up to the end of the short sleeves.

From now on to about 1830 no drastic modifications occurred in women's dress. There were many variations in style, but no severe departure from general lines.

MEN'S ATTIRE GROWS PLAINER

A characteristic feature of men's attire at the beginning of the 19th century was its growing plainness. The cocked hat, except for full dress, was conspicuous by its absence. For morning dress it was customary to wear the high-crowned silk beaver hat, with a rather large and curling brim. Gone, too, were wigs and powder, while knee-breeches, except for evening wear, were also a thing of the past, pantaloons, made of a plain, light-coloured cloth, having completely ousted them from favour.

Shoes were still more or less generally worn, but the Hessian boot, a high boot with tassels, was frequently to be seen and gradually becoming the mode. Coats and waistcoats displayed a variety of colours, among them brown, green, olive and buff, though the correct colour for the evening coat was blue, with gilt buttons, the waistcoat being of white Marseilles quilting. Trousers were regarded as not in the best taste for evening dress, but were not entirely inadmissible.

The morning coat was still short and cut square in front, but by 1824 its shape had assumed something more akin to the frock-coat of later years. The overcoat, which fitted tightly at the waist, had a fairly full skirt and a heavy fur collar.

Pantaloons were still the general wear with the frock coat, but they were soon to give place to trousers, which differed chiefly in being looser fitting. They were neither tight nor baggy, and straps were usually worn, these being of silk for full dress. With a high collar, muslin and silk cravats were worn.

PARIS INTRODUCES THE BALLOON-SLEEVE

The most remarkable feature of women's costume in the third decade of the 19th century was the importation from France of the enormous balloon-sleeve. This was so gigantic that there was little else of the bodice to be seen. The balloon was confined to the upper part of the sleeve, that from the elbow to the wrist fitting tightly.

At its inception there were two styles, the one, called *en gigot,* being as above described, the other being a kind of double sleeve—a short puff sleeve of the material used for the dress, with a covering sleeve of gauze extending from the shoulder to the wrist. With the balloon-sleeve there came also an increase in the girth of the skirt.

The first quarter of the 19th century saw a number of minor changes in women's attire. One of these was the introduction of the yoke, which came in because of the tendency of the existing style of dress to fall off the shoulders. The purpose of the yoke, which was at first made of muslin and later of the same material as the dress, was to keep the shoulders in position, and while it was more or less successful in achieving this object, its unattractiveness was so marked that the style never received general approval.

The hats of this period were on the large side, in consonance with the large sleeves, the favourite trimming being feathers. Greater attention was given to footwear, leather and black glaze being favoured, while in the winter months warmth was obtained by the wearing of gaiters.

COMING OF THE CRINOLINE

Towards the middle of the century, though the voluminous sleeve had disappeared, the skirt had assumed such remarkable girth that it was necessary for the wearer to clothe herself with many starched petticoats to enable the skirt to stand well out. To permit of a reduction in the number of petticoats, and at the same time retain the enormous width of the skirt, a modern substitute for the hoop was introduced. This forerunner of the crinoline, being extremely ungraceful, had a short life. But the skirt continued to be of excessive width and extremely ungainly.

The introduction into England in 1854 of the crinoline was preceded by a rumour from Paris that a revival of the pannier and hoop petticoat of earlier days was to take place. Crinoline petticoats, made from a stiff, unpliable material, were already being worn to make the dress stand away firmly from the figure, but there was a decided aversion to anything in the shape of a revival of the hoop.

Accordingly, when the crinoline did make its appearance, it was received with great misgiving and regarded as little short of a crisis by the world of fashion; but the example set by the Empress Eugénie could not be ignored and it remained the mode for many years.

SKELETON OF STEEL HOOPS

The crinoline consisted either of a skeleton of steel hoops or of a complete petticoat. Whichever form was adopted it obviated the need of supporting the weight of numerous petticoats. It therefore came to be generally welcomed, although there were those who preferred to retain the load of underclothing they were accustomed to wearing, the weight of which must have been borne with considerable discomfort.

For ball dresses the crinoline was found to be unsuitable, and a number of flounced petticoats were worn instead. In 1856 a fashion journal recorded that "many belles now wear fourteen in evening dress. They go to a ball standing up in their carriages, and stand between the dances for fear of crushing their dress and fourteen petticoats."

The crinoline varied in form and make, but the correct pattern was stated to consist of "four narrow steels each covered with tape, and run into a calico slip; the steel nearest the waist should be four nails from it, and should be one and three-quarter yards in length. The remaining three should be only two and a half yards, and placed, one at six nails' distance from the upper steel, the other two each at two nails' distance from the second steel. None must meet in front by a quarter of a yard except the one nearest the waist."

DRESSED IN THE BREADTH OF FASHION

Women of this period were referred to as dressing not in the height but in the breadth of fashion, a breadth that was enhanced by the quantity and variety of the trimming of the skirt, which was flounced up to the bodice, the flounces being as much as sixteen or seventeen inches deep. To add to the effect of width the sleeves were also flounced, not only at the wrists but on the upper part as well.

One of the most popular forms of outdoor wear with the crinoline was a short, black silk jacket, while shawls were also much in demand. The jacket was later developed into a masculine type of waistcoat, which long remained the vogue.

VOGUE OF THE BUSTLE

With the passing of the crinoline about 1868 the fullness of the dress passed from the front to the back, a change which eventually led to the introduction of the bustle, a small whalebone cage covered with linen or cotton and fastened to the waist by tapes. The vogue of the bustle lasted for about ten years; then it went temporarily out of fashion, but a few years later it regained its former popularity. With its revival came an increase in its size.

The bustle went out of favour finally about 1890, its place for a time being taken by looped half-circles of steel which were sewn into the back of the skirt. These were gradually reduced in both size and number until they were discarded altogether, the fancy for fullness at the back having passed.

The dress was now designed to adhere more closely to the hips, and the skirt, popularly called an umbrella skirt, was freely gored and spread out widely around the feet. Large sleeves once again became the vogue. These developed by stages first into the leg-of-mutton sleeve and then into the freer and fuller bishop's sleeve. Balloon sleeves were also revived for a time, but there came a gradual reversal to a half-size "leg-of-mutton" for day attire and a modified puff sleeve for evening dress.

HOBBLE AND SEMI-HOBBLE

For some time after the death of Queen Victoria in 1901 there was little attempt at creating new styles of dress, and apart from slight modifications, dress remained more or less standardized until about 1908, when the bell-shaped skirt, which had remained unchallenged for some twenty years, gave place to a tight-fitting garment, the famous " hobble " skirt. In appearance this certainly had the merit of smartness, but it restricted freedom in walking. To overcome this the skirt was often slit on one side. A few years before the outbreak of the World War in 1914 there was a move towards a wider-bottomed skirt. The gigantic, high-crowned, shallow-brimmed hats, often carrying an excess of trimming, which had a vogue contemporaneous with the tight-fitting hobble, also began to disappear. Then followed a smaller-crowned, wider-brimmed style.

DURING AND AFTER THE WORLD WAR

The four years of the World War proved an effective deterrent to drastic modifications of fashion. These years, however, witnessed one revolutionary change. Women began to cut their hair short. The first style adopted was the " bob "; later came the " Eton crop," and these two were followed by many similar styles of hairdressing. Succeeding years saw the introduction of permanent waving and a partial adoption of styles of long and semi-long hair.

NO REVOLUTIONARY CHANGES

Except for variations in length and fit—the skirts a few years after the War were often only knee length—there have been recently no really revolutionary changes in women's dress, although spasmodic attempts have been made to re-introduce in modified form some of the awe-inspiring models of other centuries. A revival of the crinoline has occasionally been threatened, and even in 1938 a modification of this Victorian craze made a half-hearted return. Except for evening wear, the dress continues to be about three-quarter length.

STANDARDIZING MAN'S ATTIRE

WHILE women's clothes were passing through a succession of changes during the middle and later years of the 19th century, the attire of men was at last showing inclination to become more or less standardized. Trousers had definitely arrived by 1830, and had become the correct accompaniment of the frock-coat.

The latter item of dress was subjected to many changes in the course of the next twenty years. From the tightly-fitting waist and flared skirt there emerged a style presenting an appearance of greater ease and comfort, by reason of an increase of fullness at the waist and considerably less expanse of skirt. The fur which had been a favoured trimming on the hem was no longer in evidence, and the neck was now finished off with a collar which was provided with turn-back lapels. The correct colour of the coat for morning wear was blue, the trousers being of white drill.

Apart from an occasional change of colour and modification in its length, the frock-coat was the rational dress for men for the next fifty or more years. By the end of the first half of the century, there was a decided leaning towards a more sombre colour scheme. Black was generally adopted, the trousers being of a large check pattern, tight fitting and strapped under the instep.

FLORENCE CREATED THE TALL SILK HAT

About 1840 the beaver hat found a competitor in the tall silk hat, which had taken several years to find its way into England from Florence by way of France. In both shape and height it has undergone much change since its first appearance, but for upwards of sixty years it remained a part of full dress, and although its popularity declined with the adoption of less formal dress it is still the correct head-gear for ceremonial wear.

By 1860 there was a reversion to the former loose-fitting trousers, with considerable fullness in the upper parts, tapering gradually to a rather tight-fitting ankle. Their appearance gained them the somewhat appropriate name of "peg-tops." The instep strap was now no longer in use.

For outdoor wear in cold weather, an overcoat cut in the double-breasted style, usually reaching to the knee, with buttons throughout its entire length, made its appearance. This was the nearest approach so far to the overcoat of the present day.

SIMPLICITY BECOMES CORRECT FORM

There existed now a wide gulf between the male attire of the time and that of scarcely fifty years earlier. It was considered an invitation to ridicule to attract attention by any richness in dress, and extravagance was akin to barbarism. Laces and velvet, except for court occasions, were regarded with the strictest disapproval, as was also an exceptional display of jewellery. Simplicity was the keynote.

The tail-coat was always worn for evening dress, at first with a white waistcoat and trousers of a light material, though a later style demanded a black waistcoat and dark trousers. With the former style went a cravat, with the latter the correct wear was a starched shirt and a low tie.

WARDROBE OF MANY SUITS

During the last quarter of the 19th century it became necessary for the well-dressed man to possess a considerable wardrobe. Mrs. Humphry, in her *Manners for Men,* gives an indication of his requirements : " For morning wear the morning-coat or jacket or tweed suit is correct. After lunch, when in town, the well-dressed man may continue to wear his morning-coat or the regulation frock-coat, with trousers of some neat striped grey mixture. . . . The Park suit may consist of a grey or light brown frock-coat, with waistcoat and trousers to match. The 'pot' hat and brown boots are permissible with an overcoat, under which there may be a tweed suit."

For some time the tail-coat lost its popularity, but it regained its erstwhile prestige at a later date, and by 1880 was as much in demand for general wear as the frock-coat. It was about this time that men turned to the jacket or tweed suit for morning wear.

During the next forty years the frock-coat and the tail-coat ran a close race for popularity, but the former was waging a losing contest, from which it finally retired a few years before the World War. The tail-coat was by then finding strong competition from the jacket for general daily wear.

"BOWLER" AND "BOATER"

With the gradual decline of the frock-coat and tail-coat for day wear in favour of the jacket, the tall silk hat was superseded by the hard felt "bowler" and later by the soft felt hat, while for summer wear the "boater" straw hat was a favourite for many years. Nowadays popular fancy is in favour of soft felt and cloth hats for day wear.

For evening dress, the tail-coat has held its position throughout, but the colour of the waistcoat has alternated between black and white, while the shirt collar has also shown a tendency to change. The high collar gave place after a fairly long life to the "butterfly wing."

A new departure in evening dress was the adoption towards the end of the last century of the dinner-jacket. It is said to have been devised for the greater comfort of frequenters of the gaming tables, who found the tail-coat somewhat tiring. For private and country wear it has almost entirely taken the place of the velvet smoking-jacket so popular in Victorian days.

SPORT AS FASHION DICTATOR

The great development in the playing of outdoor games in the present century has led to a miniature world of fashion in sports attire. Some sixty years ago, with the advent of the bicycle, an attempt was made to introduce standard attire suitable for this new means of locomotion. It consisted of a tweed jacket, rather tight-fitting trousers with a wide braid strip on the outside of each leg, and Hessian boots, the head-wear being a bowler hat, in the band of which was inserted a tiny feather to give it a sporting appearance.

A few years later saw the introduction of the Norfolk jacket, a pleated tweed garment which became very popular for shooting and walking. King Edward VII frequently wore one, and it is possible that it received its name from his custom of wearing one when shooting on his Sandringham estate in Norfolk. The present-day tweed jacket developed from the Norfolk style.

For all sports, present-day costumes are more appropriate than ever before, the golfer in his slacks or plus-fours, the footballer in his short knickers and jersey, the cricketer in his loose shirt and flannel trousers obtaining greater freedom of action than was ever enjoyed by participants in outdoor games in the not very distant past. Ski-ing and indoor ice-skating have also given the sporting world of fashion the opportunity to exercise its ingenuity in creating suitable and attractive costumes for enthusiasts.

MRS. BLOOMER AND RATIONAL COSTUME

The development of rational dress for sportsmen and sportswomen would have received energetic support from Mrs. Amelia Bloomer had she been living today. She was a pioneer advocate of rational costume for women; as long ago as 1851 this American lady set the world of fashion in a tumult by endeavouring to induce her women contemporaries to discard the unbecoming crinoline for the revolutionary pantalot or bloomer costume.

This costume consisted of a skirt reaching well below the knees, the normal jacket, and wide trousers gathered in at the ankles. Mrs. Bloomer organized and addressed many meetings in the United Kingdom in an effort to introduce and popularize it. Organized opposition and vehement ridicule compelled her to relinquish the campaign, but only after a long and strenuous fight.

NATIONAL COSTUME IS DISAPPEARING

WITH the modern tendency for all peoples to dress more or less uniformly, at least in most of the countries of Europe, national costume, except for special occasions, is slowly but surely disappearing. Peasant men and women of many lands display a growing desire to adopt the fashions of their city cousins.

PLUSH TROUSERS IN SPAIN

In most countries there was always a fairly wide range of styles according to the province or other division of the country inhabited. In Spain, for example, the national dress of the men and women of Valencia displays distinguishing features from that of the natives of Galicia, Catalonia or Leon.

In Valencia women wear a close-cut bodice trimmed profusely with lace, a short, full skirt with many lace flounces, and an apron adorned freely with spangles. Across the shoulders is thrown a small shawl, which has fringed edges and is tucked into the belt of the apron in front. The men wear white shirts with full sleeves, sleeveless coats, loose white linen drawers reaching to the knees, and broad, coloured sashes.

The Catalonian woman's costume is less striking than her Valencian cousin's. It consists of a skirt reaching to the ankles, a tightly fitting bodice almost hidden by a decorative shoulder shawl, and a white veil for head-dress. The footwear is quite simple in style in both provinces, and the colour of the stockings is generally white.

The male Catalonian wears high-fitting plush trousers drawn well up under the arms, a jacket that is correspondingly short, and a head-covering of red or purple wool called a *gorro,* and resembling a stocking-cap. An extra garment is the heavy woollen top-coat, or *gambeto,* which is worn in the cold weather, like the *manta* of the Valencian, a length of striped cloth which is flung about the shoulders.

In Leon the man displays a fondness for bright colours in his waist-coat, under which he wears a finely embroidered white shirt. His breeches are made full at the knees, and on his low shoes he likes to wear silver buckles. The woman wears a short velvet bodice over her blouse, a short loose skirt, while around her waist and hips she wraps a long, drab-coloured cloth. A mantilla is worn in an attractive fashion, and she is proud of her heavy necklace and cross.

WOODEN SOLES IN PORTUGAL

In Portugal the women wear a blouse partly covered by a velvet corsage, a short, full skirt of black material, and a quaint, broad-brimmed black velveteen hat over the kerchief which drapes the head. Much jewellery is worn, including rather large hoop-shaped earrings. On ceremonial occasions wooden-soled shoes, with embroidered heels and toes, are worn. A characteristic of the women's attire is the brilliantly coloured head shawl.

The men wear long trousers, short coats and high vests, the colour of all three garments being either brown or black. A red silk sash relieves the general sombreness, and either large felt hats or long bag-like caps are worn.

ITALIAN MEN WHO DON RIBBONS

The national costume of the Italian male peasant is chiefly notable for the small buttons on all the garments, which include a short, double-breasted coat, waistcoat and knee breeches, a coloured sash, and tall boots which almost completely hide the coloured stockings. The hat, with its small, upturned brim and cone-shaped crown, from which trail a number of long ribbons, is a distinctive feature of the dress of the Calabrian.

Just as distinctive as the hat of the male Calabrian were the detachable bodice sleeves that were until recently so popular with the women. The bodice was of silk or cloth, and was worn over a chemise or blouse of white linen, while the skirt was full and long. These garments, together with a long apron gathered into the waistband, still form the costume of the peasant woman, who in some parts of Italy continues to display a fondness for the folded shoulder shawl. In many parts a turban-like head-dress is worn, but another favoured style is the *tovaglia,* a long length of linen, half of which is folded about the forehead while the other half hangs down to the waist.

As in other lands, the French peasant costume shows considerable variation in different parts of the country. Perhaps the most familiar is that of Brittany, where both men and women still display a great fondness for the old styles of dress.

"BRAGON BRAZ" OF BRITTANY

The male Breton wears either the characteristic breeches, called *bragon braz,* which were specially popular a few centuries ago, or long trousers fitting rather loosely from the thighs to the knees. The upper garments include a short cloth jacket and a double-breasted sleeveless cloth vest of varying colours—blue, brown or red being the most favoured—over which is worn a bright sash or a wide leather belt. The vest is decorated with a double row of quaint silver buttons, extending from the neck to the waist. When breeches are worn they are accompanied by long garters fastened at the sides, the footwear being either leather shoes or carved or decorated wooden sabots.

HUNDREDS OF VARIETIES OF COIFS

The Breton woman affects a close-fitting bodice, finished at the neck with a figured fichu and a broad white linen collar. The skirt is extremely full, accentuating the smallness of the waist, and extends to the ankles, the front being covered by an embroidered apron. The sleeves are generally of wrist-length, with turned-back cuffs. On ceremonial days an embroidered bolero-like jacket is added to the dress.

A characteristic dress feature of all Breton women is the white coif, usually made of linen or net, the latter being embroidered by hand. There are hundreds of different varieties of coifs, the varying styles being an indication of the wearers' places of residence. Usually the coif is the only head-dress, but in some districts a small round hat, trimmed with ribbons and tied below the chin, is also worn.

In Normandy the most noticeable feature of women's costume is their caps. Their hair is entirely hidden by these starched muslin head-dresses, which rise well up from the head and have wing-like projections on either side. A bell-shaped skirt, with numerous pleats caught at the waistband, is worn, with a tight-fitting bodice, and a kerchief about the shoulders. Around the waist are wound several lengths of finely embroidered silk or wool to form a belt. The men adopt a white homespun jacket and long trousers, the former being decorated with a number of gilt buttons.

CLOTH JACKET FOR FESTIVE OCCASIONS

In Scandinavia there is, apart from a few minor peculiarities, little difference in the national costume of the people. The men are dressed in short coats having a double row of buttons, knee breeches, long stockings, and shoes ornamented with large silver buckles, while the women have a laced bodice with elbow-length sleeves, a skirt reaching to the ankles, an embroidered apron, and a fringed shawl thrown over the shoulders. Distinctive marks of nationality are a decorated silk or velvet bonnet, with long streamers, and an ornate metal belt.

In Norway and Sweden the picturesque old national costumes have been largely replaced by more modern clothing. In some districts of Norway the peasant men can still be seen in their dark brown trousers reaching almost to the arm-pits, with a cloth jacket for festive occasions and week-ends.

STYLES VARY ACCORDING TO DISTRICT

Norwegian women have one dress characteristic in common—the wearing of a full-sleeved white blouse gathered in at the wrist. In some districts may still be met the quaint, heavy cloth skirt reaching from just below the arm to a little lower than the knee. It is kept in position by shoulder-straps or embroidered braces, and its ornamentation consists of a few bands of similar material of different colour around the bottom, or as an alternative some coloured-wool embroidery.

Caps are usually worn, the styles varying according to the district. The head-dress typical of the beautiful Hardanger region is the *skaut,* a square of white, starched linen, with numerous tiny pleats, which is folded and tied on the head in a curious and intricate way. The women have a taste for brightness in stockings, which are generally of red, blue or some other coloured wool.

APRONS OF DISTINCTION

The Swedish woman is very proud of her apron, the striped design of which is an indication of the district to which she belongs. It is worn over a homespun dress, which allows the full, white sleeves of the chemise to be seen. In some districts the head-dress is a closely fitting linen cap decorated with lace, in others a kerchief is the head covering, the ends being tied below the chin. Like the apron, the cap also advertises the district from which the wearer hails.

Men wear knee-length leather breeches of brown or white, a homespun coat of blue, black or white reaching to the same level as the breeches, and blue or white woollen stockings. A round hat of felt is the customary head-wear.

DUTCH WHO THINK OLD FASHIONS ARE BEST

The quaint and picturesque costume of the Netherlands is fast being superseded by the conventional modern clothes of other parts of Europe. Only in certain districts, where the people cling desperately to the old fashions, are the typical long, full trousers of the men to be noted. Their colour is generally blue, while red is a popular colour for the short, double-breasted jacket which is worn with it. In some parts of the country full knee breeches are preferred to trousers. A deep fur cap or a cloth peak cap is variously worn, and sabots are the footwear.

Women find comfort and ease in their wide skirts and picturesque striped and flowered bodices, the sleeves of which reach about midway between the elbow and wrist. Extra girth is given to the skirt by the use of a bustle, and over it is worn a brightly coloured apron. The somewhat complicated head-dress fits closely, and consists of a layer of muslin trimmed with lace or embroidery and some coloured cotton, on top of which are two caps of lawn or muslin, and over all a close cap of cotton print. When out walking the feet are enclosed in *klompern*, which are exchanged when entering the home for square-toed leather shoes with fancy buckles.

GERMANY'S WIDE RANGE OF HEAD-GEAR

In Germany a short coat, vest and breeches are usually the three main articles of men's attire, the chief regional distinction being in the elaboration of the garments. One garment that is generally worn in nearly all parts of the country is the cloth top-coat, with its full pleated skirts reaching variously from below the knees almost to the ankles. Its collar is high, and it has large revers.

A very wide range of head-gear is worn, from the tall felt hat in Baden and Württemberg and the tricorne hat of Hesse to the cloth cap and visor that is favoured in some parts of Prussia, and the high-crowned, small-brimmed felt hat in Bavaria.

There is more uniformity of style in the dress of the women. It consists of a pleated skirt of heavy cloth, having plenty of width, and a spencer type of jacket, under which is worn a short-sleeved bodice, generally white, but sometimes of a dark material. Colour is presented by the figured calico kerchief, enwrapping the chest and shoulders, and the elaborately decorated stockings.

The head-dress of the Spreewald woman is the most characteristic item of her costume. Triangular in shape, it is made of printed material, and is worn with the central point of the triangle drooping down at the back of the neck, the two side ends being knotted below it.

Ribbons are a prominent feature of German peasant attire. In Württemberg and Bavaria they are used for lacing the velvet corsets and also for keeping the head-dress in its place. In the former district the neat and attractive bonnet, with its fan-shaped decoration rising from the back, has ribbons hanging from it; these not only keep it in position on the head but are also a decoration.

RUSSIA INFLUENCED BY CONSTANTINOPLE

In Russia the peasant costumes were originally largely influenced by the style of dress prevailing in Byzantium (Constantinople), and many traces of the fashions of that ancient city can still be observed. The principal article of women's dress was, until recent years, a full pleated or gathered skirt of rich brocade joined to a short sleeveless bodice. This was worn over an underbodice having a very full width of sleeves at the top, which narrowed from the elbow to the wrist. The sleeves were generally of a much more attractive material and of a different colour from the *sarafan*, as the outer garment was called.

Garments were often made more suitable for withstanding the cold by being trimmed with fur, and a necessary possession of every woman was a long, full cape heavily trimmed in this manner.

The chief glory of the Russian woman's costume was the elaborate head-dress, which entirely enclosed the hair. Made in a variety of shapes and styles, it had a foundation of cloth strengthened with wire, and this was covered with cloth of gold, silk or velvet to form the background, which was then made to assume the shape of a simple but attractive cap, a bonnet of fez-like appearance, a striking tiara, or a widespread fan formation rising above the head and about the sides. Whatever the desired shape, it was freely decorated with metallic-thread embroidery or profusely ornamented with pearls.

Beautifully embroidered veils were thrown over the head-dress when out of doors, and the costume was completed by carrying in the hand a *chirinka,* an embroidered square of silk or muslin, finished off with gold tassels or fringe.

IVAN'S SOMBRE GARMENTS

The costume of the Russian men, in comparison with that of the women, was sombre and unattractive. It consisted of a long, white linen or coloured cloth blouse, falling over the trousers and tightened at the waist with a belt. From the neck to the waist the blouse was opened on the left side, and this opening, the narrow collar, and the cuffs of the sleeves, which were full and banded, were embellished with coloured embroidery, as also was the bottom edge of the blouse.

The trousers, the ends of which were thrust into the top of high leather boots, were made of homespun or hand-blocked linen, and fitted loosely about the legs. For outdoor wear the simple unfashioned cloth kaftan, or top-coat, was added to the outfit, and in winter the rigours of the climate made it necessary to wear long sheepskin coats or fur capes.

FLOWERS FOR THE FAIR IN THE UKRAINE

The women of the southern country dress far more simply than their cousins of the higher latitudes. Their skirts are usually made from homespuns and linens, and the ornamentation is worked with silk and linen threads instead of gold and silver. The head-dresses are less elaborate, there being no display of pearls or other jewellery.

The women of the Ukraine pay special attention to the embroidering of the apron, which is gathered into a waistband, and of the blouse, of which the sleeves are large, ending either at the elbow or the wrist in a narrow cuff. For head-dress the elder women have a tall cap, from which a very long veil falls almost to the ground, while the young ones place on their coiled hair a wreath of flowers, from which long coloured ribbons are suspended.

REVOLUTIONARY CHANGES IN TURKEY

In the East, Western influence is making itself increasingly felt. In Turkey, China and Japan, especially the last-named, the national dress is surely, if gradually, taking second place to Western fashions. The richly embroidered mandarin robe of the Chinese passed away with the establishing of a republican form of government in 1912, since when this Europeanizing of dress has been slowly progressing, and the traditional kimono of the Japanese, both men and women, is slowly falling a victim to the more prosaic and uniform costume of the West.

In Turkey, under the post-War rule of Kemal Ataturk, European ideas of dress were introduced, one revolutionary change being the substitution of the cloth cap or felt hat for the red fez. His decree that women should dispense with the veils that covered their faces when in public was almost equally revolutionary.

DRESS REFORM THAT HELPED TO CAUSE A REVOLUTION

Although most Asiatic countries have shown a tendency to accept European ideas, there are nevertheless exceptions, and one of them is Afghanistan. Here an attempt was made by King Amanullah in 1928 to introduce various changes based on Western customs, including the fashioning of dress after the styles he had observed during a tour of Europe, but his efforts met with determined resistance and led to revolutionary action which compelled him to abdicate the throne.

But this rebuff to the spreading of European conceptions of dress in the East is insignificant by comparison with the progress made in other lands of greater extent and infinitely greater importance.

TRAVEL AND COMMUNICATIONS

"GETTING there and coming back," is both an ancient and a modern need, applying alike to primitive and civilized man. Travel has taken many forms. Trudging with aching feet and bent back along an unbeaten track, clambering across a fallen tree to span a stream, floating on the air-filled skin of an animal to reach the opposite bank of a river; lounging on the deck of a luxury liner, reclining at ease in an express train, speeding above land and sea on the back of a mechanical bird—these are but a few of the many means of transport. In its varied ways, communication now places almost every part of the globe in touch with the remainder. Even the polar explorer in the realm of the ice king is not remote from the busy haunts of more hospitable climes. He is linked by radio. The far has become the near.

HOW MAN CAME TO KNOW HIS WORLD

THE oldest maps in existence date from about 2300 B.C. They were made in Babylonia, and are clay tablets, circular in shape. The British Museum, London, possesses a specimen showing Lower Babylonia.

In the museum of antiquities at Turin, Italy, are several Egyptian papyrus maps more than 3,000 years old. These, like the Babylonian maps, are regional only. The first attempt at a world map, so far as we know, dates from the 6th century B.C.

SCILLY ISLES AS END OF THE EARTH

This is said to have been the work of Anaximander of Miletus (611-546 B.C.), who is also credited with being the first Greek author to write in prose. He made the Ægean Sea the centre of a circular world whose extremities were the Caspian Sea in the east and the Cassiterides, or Tin Islands (probably the Scilly Isles), in the west.

That other people were also drawing world maps in these early days is evidenced by the scornful comment of Herodotus (about 484-425 B.C.), the "Father of History," who wrote that: "For my part, I cannot but laugh when I see numbers of persons drawing maps of the world without having any reason to guide them."

Herodotus, who was consumed by an insatiable curiosity concerning men and matters, was a great traveller who in addition had inquired into the travels and explorations of others since the earliest days. He could afford to laugh at those stay-at-homes who pictured the earth as a cylindrical slice of land entirely surrounded by ocean, or who, like Anaximenes, the pupil of Anaximander, conceived the earth as an oblong rectangle.

PTOLEMY'S GEOGRAPHY

Yet such ideas persisted for centuries, in spite of journeys by land and sea which showed them to be erroneous. Other conceptions were more enlightened. Crates of Mallus, a Greek who died in 145 B.C., represented the earth as a globe divided into four habitable quarters—though many centuries were to elapse before the American and Australian continents were to become known to Europeans.

The most famous of the map-makers of the classical world was Ptolemy, the Greek astronomer and geographer of the 2nd century A.D. His map covers all Europe, the greater part of Asia, and a large part of Africa.

Ptolemy's map was actually in large part a copy of one now lost, which was drawn by Marinus of Tyre (about A.D. 120), and which Al Masudi, the 10th century Arab traveller, considered a superior work.

Ptolemy's map certainly suffered from grievous defects. Apart from its omissions, he drew Great Britain, which he called Albion, more or less upside down; he made Ceylon many times its correct size, and he pushed India northwards into the Asiatic mainland.

These and similar errors were not altogether excusable. By Ptolemy's day quite considerable portions of the globe had been explored. It was unfortunate that, when his work was rediscovered during the Renaissance, his map was given a higher authority than it had enjoyed during his lifetime. This fact proved very embarrassing to many a Renaissance explorer.

" EXPANSION OR EXPLOSION "

Exploration of a sort, of course, began as soon as man learned to think coherently. The migrations of tribes may be regarded as explorations; but such movements were neither systematic nor were they impelled by scientific curiosity. They had their origin in hunger.

Scientific exploration is largely a product of modern times: exploration for commercial purposes is very old. The outstanding exponents of this latter type in the ancient world were the Phœnicians.

Masters only of a narrow strip of rocky and sandy territory along the coasts of what are now Palestine and Syria, it has been said of the Phœnicians that they " had to go overseas or go underground." Present-day statesmen, faced with a similar necessity to find outlets for the productivity of their peoples, have coined the yet more striking slogan of " Expansion or explosion."

As early, perhaps, as the 12th century B.C., the Phœnicians were carrying on an extensive maritime trade in the Mediterranean, and thereafter for several centuries they made themselves indispensable to their neighbours, both great and small, in peace and in war.

Their success, due primarily to their courage and the resolute way in which they kept secret their trade routes, was enhanced by the fact that the ancient world as a whole dreaded the sea, and for the most part embarked upon it only when compelled to do so. The nations, though they came to hate the Phœnicians for their avarice and their capacity to drive hard bargains, were willing enough to let them do their overseas fetching and carrying.

COLONIES AND TRADE DEPOTS

The military empires, Assyria, Babylonia, Persia and Egypt, came to them for fighting ships and transports: Solomon invoked their aid when building his temple, and nations far and wide depended on them for imports and the disposal of exports.

This maritime monopoly which the Phœnicians built up rested on secure foundations. Their navigators were prepared to go anywhere, to trade in anything, to perform any service and to undertake any commission.

From the start they consolidated their position by a far-seeing policy of establishment of overseas bases. Gades (Cadiz) in south-west Spain is said to have been founded by them in the 12th century B.C., along with Lixus and Utica in north-west Africa. Carthage, most famous of all Phœnician colonies, dates traditionally from 813 B.C., Massilia (Marseilles), most enduring as a centre of commerce, from about 600 B.C.

Malta, Sicily, Corsica and Sardinia were occupied by the Phœnicians, who colonized also the greater part of the African coast of the Mediterranean and much of the Spanish littoral. From Gades they ventured out into the Atlantic, reaching certainly the Cassiterides, and quite probably the Azores and Madeira.

Eastward they penetrated by land—for they did not confine themselves entirely to sea routes—to the Euphrates and the Tigris, and by sea, so it is believed, to India. Southward they had overland routes to Arabia, and land and sea routes to Egypt and probably beyond.

CIRCUMNAVIGATION OF AFRICA

According to Herodotus, in the 7th century B.C., Necos, King of Egypt, dispatched a Phœnician fleet from the Red Sea with orders to return by way of the Pillars of Hercules (Straits of Gibraltar), and three years later this fleet returned as ordered, having completed the circumnavigation of Africa. Various details in Herodotus's account incline modern authorities to believe that the voyage was actually accomplished.

ADVENTURER WHO EXPLORED BRITAIN

Individual explorers were rare in the ancient world. Solon, lawgiver of Athens, visited Egypt to see its wonders—even in his day memorials of antiquity—and other Athenians did archæological research in Arabia. Alexander the Great, though interested mainly in conquest, had investigations into flora and fauna made in territories he overran, while Seleucus Nicator, one of the successors to the Alexandrine territories, had anthropological research done in India.

The most intriguing explorer of antiquity is Pytheas of Massilia, about whom, unfortunately, next to nothing is known, all our information concerning his astounding exploits being contained in a brief paragraph or two in a Latin author.

Believed to have been a sea captain who lived about 300 B.C., Pytheas set sail one day from Gades, crossed the Bay of Biscay, passed up the English Channel and landed in Britain. The inhabitants he found "simple in their habits, and far removed from the cunning and knavishness of modern man." This judgment was based on no superficial observation, for he is said to have "walked all over Britain."

He calculated the length of its coastline, discovered its shape, and traded with its inhabitants in places as far apart as Kent, Cornwall and North Scotland. In Scotland he heard of the island of Thule, six days' voyage distant, where "is neither sea nor air, but a mixture like sea-lung, in which earth and air are suspended."

Thule may have been Iceland, or the west coast of Norway, each of these places being subject to dense sea fogs. Whichever it was, Pytheas visited it, and further explored the coasts of western Europe for some 7,000 miles. It was a couple of centuries before any one followed in his wake.

HOW THE SILKWORM CAME TO EUROPE

The Roman Empire did little to advance exploration as such, but from the 6th century A.D. comes one of the most romantic stories in the history of industry. From an early date silk goods had been brought from China to Europe, but the Chinese jealously guarded the secret of the manufacture of silk, with the result that this material was in the West literally worth more than its weight in gold.

Then two Persian missionaries, long domiciled in China, came to the Roman emperor Justinian (A.D. 485-565), and told him how silk was made. Justinian sent them back to China to obtain silkworms, and after a long and adventurous journey they returned, bringing with them the precious insects concealed in a bamboo staff. From these few silkworms originated the European silk manufacture.

The official conversion of the Roman Empire to Christianity proved an enormous stimulus to travel. Every year thousands of pilgrims journeyed to Jerusalem, and to the holy places, real or invented, which Palestine, Syria and Arabia offered in abundance. Disputes between Christian and Moslem over the ownership of these places led to the Crusades, which, beginning as armed pilgrimages, deteriorated later into commercial exploitation. But one of their results was a continuous penetration of unexplored territories by missionaries, not only Christian but also Moslem and even Buddhist.

The *Arabian Nights* are not pure fiction; Sindbad the Sailor had his origin in Suleiman the Merchant, who about A.D. 850 voyaged to India, Ceylon and China. Arab fleets are said to have reached Japan, while Al Masudi travelled on land all over North Africa.

VIKINGS DISCOVER AMERICA

About the same time the hardy Norsemen of Scandinavia were pushing across the wild and frozen seas north-west of Europe to discover new homes for their ever-increasing population. In the 9th century they rediscovered Iceland—reached first some centuries previously by

Irish Christian missionaries—and towards A.D. 1000 they found and settled upon the coasts of Greenland.

A few years later one of the settlers, voyaging from Iceland to Greenland, was driven off his course by storms until he came to an unknown land far to the west. His description of this land excited the curiosity of one Leif Ericsson, who fitted out an expedition to explore it. He was successful in his search, and spent the winter in Vinland (Wineland) as he called it, which may have been Newfoundland or Nova Scotia or some other place, but was certainly part of the North American continent.

ACROSS THE GOBI DESERT

Tradition has it that Viking ships continued to visit North America until the 14th century; but the eyes of men in Europe were turned towards the east. Knowledge of the western hemisphere was lost, and it was left to Christopher Columbus to rediscover the New World.

In the 13th century news of the rising power and terrible ferocity of the Mongol Khans began to reach Europe. Hearing that they might be disposed to listen to the Christian teaching, in 1245 the Pope sent a Franciscan friar, John de Plano Carpini, to visit the Grand Khan.

Carpini's journey occupied him sixteen months, and took him across the Gobi Desert into Mongolia. Seven years later he was followed by William de Rubruquis, also a Franciscan friar, whom Louis IX dispatched as envoy to the Grand Khan.

Some few years after de Rubruquis's return, that most famous of all Eastern travellers, Marco Polo, set out on the journey which was to keep him seventeen years in China and later to furnish Europe with a flood of information concerning the Far East.

MARCO POLO'S "LYING TALES"

In 1260 Nicolo, father of Marco, and Maffeo, his uncle, jewellers of Venice, set out upon a business expedition, and some three or four years later found themselves in Peking. Here they were graciously received by Kublai Khan, who sent them back to Europe to secure from the Pope "some hundred wise men, learned in the law of Christ and conversant with the Seven Arts."

The Polos did not secure the hundred wise men; they got only two Dominican friars (who quickly lost heart and turned back), but they set out on their second journey nevertheless. With them was young Marco, who shortly after his arrival in China was taken into the service of the Grand Khan, and who spent some fifteen years as a Chinese official. During this time he journeyed throughout the empire, visited the borders of Tibet, Cochin-China, Siam, India and Japan, and gleaned information concerning lands as far apart as Siberia and Abyssinia.

When he returned to Europe he was induced to put the story of his experiences in a book. It was received with incredulity and regarded as a collection of "lying tales."

ROUND THE CAPE TO INDIA

In the 15th century the Portuguese began to emerge as the foremost maritime explorers of the world. Between 1415 and 1460 Prince Henry of Portugal, known as Henry the Navigator, sent expedition after expedition down the west coast of Africa, opening up Madeira, the Azores, and the coasts of Guinea, Senegal and Gambia.

Henry's death interrupted only temporarily the progress of discovery; within twenty years the Equator had been crossed, and within thirty the Cape of Good Hope rounded. This last feat was carried out in 1488 by Bartholomew Diaz, who would have pushed on farther had his crew not lost heart.

Ten years later Vasco da Gama, sailing in ships designed by Diaz, set out to find the way to India by way of the Cape. When his crew mutinied he clapped the ringleaders in irons and flung his navigating instruments into the sea. " If I do not find information of what I have come to seek," he said, " I do not return to Portugal."

His crew gave in, and on May 20, 1498, da Gama landed at Calicut in India.

DISCOVERY OF THE PACIFIC

Six years previously, Christopher Columbus had robbed the Atlantic of its mystery by sailing across it and landing in the West Indies. Twelve months before da Gama reached India, John Cabot, Italian-born mariner domiciled in England, had reached the mainland of the North American continent.

Both Columbus and Cabot believed they had touched the eastern coasts of Asia. The fact that a vast expanse of ocean lay between America and Asia was discovered in 1513 by Vasco Nuñez de Balboa. In 1518, Ferdinand Magellan undertook the conquest of this ocean.

After a vain endeavour to reach it by sailing up the River Plate in South America, he rounded the extremity of that continent, made his way through the straits which now bear his name, and then with supreme courage voyaged across the unknown waters for ninety-eight days, during which he sighted no more land than two uninhabited and barren islands.

On this passage—surely one of the most daring on record—Magellan and his companions suffered incredible privations; but the constant gentle breezes which bore their ships along, and the placid waters through which they sailed, earned for the ocean over which they passed the name it has ever since borne—the Pacific.

Magellan was killed in a small native war in the Philippine Islands, but Juan Sebastian del Cano, his lieutenant, continued the voyage, and finally, with thirty-one men, returned to Portugal. For the first time in history, the globe had been circumnavigated. Its extent was now known; henceforth exploration became a matter of filling in the gaps.

The exploration of North America was begun by the French and continued by the English. A French expedition under a Florentine,

Giovanni da Verazzano, surveyed the coast south from Newfoundland about 1524; Jacques Cartier (1494-1557), the discoverer of Canada, sailed up the St. Lawrence and carried out important explorations near its shores. Cartier was followed in 1603 by Samuel de Champlain, to whom more than any one the creation of Canada is due.

NORTH-EAST PASSAGE

About the middle of the 16th century certain English merchants took up the project of pioneering a sea-route to China and other points of the Far East by sailing along the northern shores of Scandinavia and Russia. The North-East Passage, as this route was called, was first attempted in 1553 by an expedition of three ships under the command of Sir Hugh Willoughby and Richard Chancelor. Two of the ships, including the one in which Willoughby sailed, were lost, but Chancelor "came at last to the place where he found no night at all, and it pleased God to bring them into a certaine great Bay"—the White Sea. Chancelor went no farther east, but travelled overland to Moscow, where he entered into negotiations for the development of Anglo-Russian trade. His efforts resulted in the formation of the Muscovy Company, the first of the great English chartered companies.

The North-East Passage was first achieved in 1878-1879, when N. A. E. Nordenskjöld made a great voyage from the North Sea to Bering Strait. He was followed in 1913-1914 by Vilkitski and in 1918-1920 by Amundsen. But it was not until 1928, when the Soviet ice-breaker *Sibiryakov,* captained by V. I. Voronin, made the voyage from Archangel to Bering Strait in just over two months, that the passage was opened up to commerce.

NORTH-WEST PASSAGE

In 1576 began the search for a route to the Far East by way of the waters between Canada and the North Pole—the North-West Passage. The first attempt was made by Martin Frobisher, who set out in 1576 but got no farther than the northernmost part of Labrador. In 1585, and again in 1587, John Davis made unsuccessful attempts to find the passage. The quest was taken up by Henry Hudson, who died in 1610 in the great bay that is called after him. Five years later Hudson Bay was explored by William Baffin, an intrepid navigator who, in the following year, came very near to finding the passage.

It was not until the middle of the 19th century that the North-West Passage was completely explored, and then—tragic irony in view of the terrible toll in men and material of its exploration—it was found to be worthless as a trade-route. In 1848 Sir John Franklin's Expedition, which had set out 120 strong three years earlier, was lost in the Arctic, having—as was long afterwards said—"forged the last link of the North-West Passage with their lives." Sir John Franklin's men discovered the passage, but the first to navigate it was Roald Amundsen, in 1903-1905.

AUSTRALASIAN PIONEERS

The pioneers of exploration in Australasian waters were the Dutch. In 1614 the Dutch East India Company, founded twelve years earlier, sent out an expedition under Jacob Lemaire to discover a south-west passage to the Pacific south of Magellan Strait. Lemaire rounded Cape Horn in 1615, and then sailed across the Pacific to New Guinea and on to the Moluccas. In 1642 Abel Janszoon Tasman, one of the greatest of the navigators, was sent to explore the southern continent of which little-known Australia was supposed to be a northern projection. He discovered Tasmania and New Zealand, and then voyaged on to the Fiji Islands, returning by way of New Britain, New Guinea and Batavia. In the following year he explored part of the Australian coast.

LEGEND OF SOUTHERN CONTINENT

James Cook's first expedition to the southern seas lasted from 1767 until 1770. Cook sailed round New Zealand and carefully explored part of the east coast of Australia. On his second expedition (1772-1775) he established the non-existence of rumoured habitable areas south of Australasia, the Indian Ocean and the Atlantic. His third expedition (1776-1780) was sent out to discover the North-West Passage by sailing from Bering Strait to the Atlantic. He got no farther than Bering Strait, the way being blocked with ice, but he carried out valuable surveys in the North Pacific. After his failure to make the passage of the Bering Strait, Cook returned to Hawaii, where he was killed by natives in 1779.

By the beginning of the 19th century it was possible to draw a map of the world showing the outlines of all its great land masses, but there were immense blanks on the maps of South and Central America, Africa, China, Australia and of the Arctic and Antarctic regions.

REACHING THE NORTH POLE

In 1827, W. E. Parry (1790-1855), who had some years previously made an unsuccessful attempt to find the North-West Passage, tried to reach the North Pole by water. He failed to do so, but he attained 82° 45' N., thereby setting up a farthest-north record that remained unbroken until 1875, when Albert Markham, a member of the Nares Expedition, reached 83° 20' N. by sledge. Eighteen years later Dr. Fridtjof Nansen reached 86° 12' N. by sledge and kayak (Eskimo canoe), after leaving his ship, the Fram, frozen in the ice. The Fram remained in the ice for nearly three years, during which time a vast amount of scientific work was done.

The only person who has ever reached the North Pole on foot is R. E. Peary. His wonderful journey across the ice ended on April 6, 1909, nearly 550 miles from the ship that had carried him into the Arctic regions. He was accompanied on the final stages by four Eskimos and a negro.

In 1897 Solomon August Andrée, a Swedish scientist, tried to float over the North Pole by balloon; Roald Amundsen, a Norwegian, tried to reach it by aeroplane in 1925, but failed. In 1926 Captain (later Rear-Admiral) Richard Evelyn Byrd, an American, flew over it by aeroplane a few days before Amundsen passed over it in the airship *Norge.* In 1928 an Italian airship, the *Italia,* under the command of General Umberto Nobile, flew across the Pole but was wrecked, and Amundsen lost his life in gallantly attempting rescue.

The conquest of the North Pole was completed in May, 1937, when four Soviet aeroplanes landed there.   They left behind them four scientists, who occupied a drifting ice-floe until February, 1938.

EXPLORING ANTARCTICA

The region of the South Pole began to attract explorers only in recent centuries.   It was a long way from Europe, and there did not seem much worth looking for.   Some geographers thought that Antarctica was an ice-gripped continent; others believed that there was no continent but only islands surrounded by a frozen sea.   Pierre Bouvet, with his mind set on finding the real or supposed land, came across the island which bears his name, over 800 miles from the Antarctic Circle, in 1739.   Thirty-two years later Yves Joseph Kerguelen found the Isle of Desolation, a name which he bestowed on it in sheer despair.   Not until 1773 was the Antarctic Circle crossed with deliberate intent, although luckless mariners may have done so unknowingly.   The navigator was Captain James Cook, his ship the *Resolution,* and they reached 71° 10′ S.   Between 1819 and 1821 a Russian, Fabian von Bellingshausen, discovered Peter I Island and Alexander I Land, the first territory found in Antarctica.   James Weddell in the *Jane,* sailing in 1823, collected specimens of the fauna of the region.

In 1831-1833 John Biscoe, in the *Tula,* made extensive land discoveries, as did John Balleny in the *Eliza Scott.*   French and American expeditions starting in 1840, under Dumont D'Urville and Charles Wilkes respectively, did useful work, the one discovering Adélie Land, the other passing very near to the magnetic pole and tracing extensive coast lines.   In 1841 the British explorer James C. Ross reached 78° 10′ S. and took formal possession of the continent, although many other nations have staked claims since then.

Between 1900 and 1930 some twenty expeditions in all worked in the Antarctic.   The Norwegian, Roald Amundsen, with a party from the *Fram* reached the South Pole on December 14, 1911.   On January 16, 1912, the British Captain Robert Falcon Scott, with four colleagues from the *Terra Nova* also reached it, but all perished on the return journey.

Ernest Henry Shackleton had already approached within ninety-seven miles of the South Pole in 1909.   The Shackleton-Rowett Expedition of 1921-1922, which sailed in the *Quest,* carried out an immense amount of hydrographic work, but Sir Ernest, as he had become, died on the island of South Georgia. Commander Frank Wild continued the work.

Between 1928-1930, and again in 1933-1935, Byrd explored parts of the south polar regions systematically by aeroplane, in which he flew over the South Pole in 1929, making a trip of 1,600 miles in nineteen hours.

PRECIOUS METALS IN ANTARCTICA

Moreux, the French geologist, believes that in the Antarctic there are immense treasures of precious metals dating from every period of the earth's history, since it is still in a state of volcanic activity. It is probably part of a very ancient continent that was once linked up with South America. In September, 1936, Australia annexed over two million square miles of Antarctica, in view of its potential mineral wealth. The existence of coal has been proved.

DOWN THE CENTURIES BY ROAD

"Next to the general influence of the seasons, upon which the regular supply of our wants and a great proportion of our comforts so much depend, there is perhaps no circumstance more interesting to men in a civilized state than the perfection of the means of interior communication." Thus the Report of a Committee of the House of Commons in 1808.

"If you wish to know whether society is stagnant, learning scholastic, religion a dead formality, you may learn something by going into universities and libraries; something also by the work that is doing on cathedrals and churches, or in them; but quite as much by looking at the roads. For if there is any motion in society, the Road, which is the symbol of motion, will indicate the fact. When there is activity and enlargement, or a liberalizing spirit of any kind, then there is intercourse and travel, and these require roads. So if there is any kind of advancement going on, if new ideas are abroad and new hopes rising, then you will see it by the roads that are building. Nothing makes an inroad without making a road. All creative action, whether in government, industry, thought or religion, creates roads." Thus Horace Bushnell, the famous American thinker.

MAN AND DOG AS BEASTS OF BURDEN

The first beast of burden was man himself, and in this capacity he performed notable feats. The great buildings of antiquity—pre-eminent among them the pyramids—came into being through the strenuous toil of thousands of human pack and draught animals.

No one knows which of the beasts of the field was the first to be enslaved by man and made to bear his burdens. Probably the dog. It is a little difficult for the inhabitants of modern Britain to think of dogs as draught animals, but not many generations ago they were so used

Height and Depth in the Old World

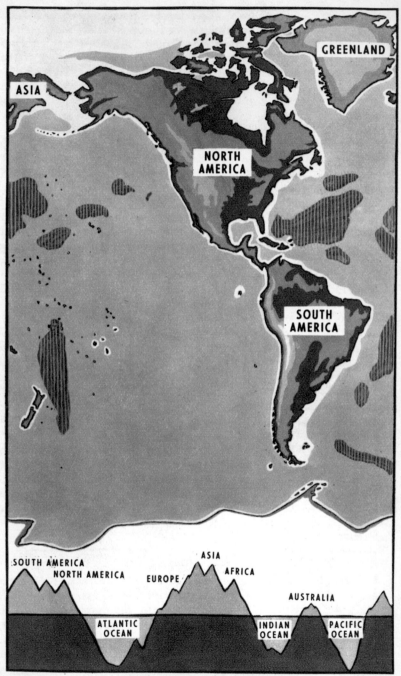

Height and Depth in the New World

in that country, and even today many dogs feel the weight of the harness in Belgium and in northern latitudes. In Europe they are made to haul small wheeled milk or bread carts; in Canada, Alaska, Greenland and Siberia they drag sledges over the snow. In the exploration of the Polar regions the dog has played a not inconspicuous part. Without his 246 sledge-dogs Robert Peary could not have reached the North Pole in 1909.

HIGH SPEED IN ARCTIC WASTES

The dogs used for sledge-hauling in the frozen wastes of North America are capable of covering long distances at a remarkably high average speed. For a team to cover 100 miles in under twelve hours is not at all unusual; and good animals can average about fifty miles a day for weeks at a time.

The animals used by the Eskimos have an extraordinary capacity for doing hard work on a very meagre allowance of food. Silver-grey in colour, with a bushy tail and a sharp muzzle, the Eskimo sledge-dog weighs about 6½ stone. Faithful to its master and extremely courageous, it is also inclined to be bad-tempered and for ever on the look-out for a fight.

HORSE AND HIS RELATIONS

Like that of the dog, the date of the horse's enslavement is lost in the mists of antiquity. The horse probably originated in Siberia, but even at the dawn of history it had moved far from its first home, and now it and its relations—the mule, the pony and the donkey—are to be found in almost every part of the globe.

The mule, a cross between the horse and the donkey, was used by the Greeks of the 9th century B.C.; and it is thought to have been first bred in Asia Minor. The mule is less highly strung than the horse, has more stamina and can go for longer periods without food.

The donkey is not nearly so stupid as is generally supposed by those who have never had occasion to make use of it. Patient and good-tempered to a degree unequalled by any other domestic animal, it is also capable of long-sustained hard work. A beast of burden in the East from time immemorial, it was not much used in Britain before the 16th century.

CAMEL STURDIER THAN THE HORSE

One hundred and fifty pounds is a good load for a pack-horse, but a camel can carry four times this amount with ease. This bad-tempered, ugly-looking animal played a valuable part in the development of the various ancient civilizations in the Near East, including the earliest, that of Sumeria (before 3500 B.C.). It is today used extensively as a pack-animal in Asia, Africa and Australia. The camel was introduced into the United States of America in 1856 for use in the Wild West.

There are two species: the one-humped Arabian camel, or

dromedary; and the two-humped Bactrian camel of the Far East. As a pack-animal the former is much more valuable than the latter, which is mainly used for riding. The dromedary can go without water for six days, or just twice as long as the Bactrian.

Novelists and others sometimes endow camels with a capacity for speed that they certainly do not possess. Two and a half to three miles an hour is a respectable speed for a pack camel, and even the fastest animals are not normally capable of anything in excess of nine miles per hour; but they can plod on for more than fifteen hours without any sign of fatigue.

ELEPHANT'S STRENGTH AND WEAKNESS

The largest, strongest and probably the most intelligent of the animals that help to carry the burdens of men (both white and coloured) is the elephant. Of the two species, African and Asiatic, the latter is the more easily tameable. It was, indeed, for long supposed that the African elephant was quite untameable; but Hannibal used African elephants in his struggle against Rome (end of 3rd century B.C.), and numbers have been tamed in the Belgian Congo in the present century. The most obvious difference between the two species is in the size of the ears, those of the African elephant being extraordinarily large.

In India elephants are much used for transporting and piling logs. In work of this nature they display at once their great strength and remarkable intelligence. The use of the elephant as a pack-animal is limited by the fact that the skin of its back, tough-looking as it is, chafes very easily under burdens. Another factor that limits its usefulness is the ease with which it develops sore feet.

LAPLANDER'S PACK-ANIMALS

That the reindeer is a valuable pack-animal is known to every child, for is it not Santa Claus's means of transport? Reindeers are used not only at Christmas but all the year round in Lapland, that bleak but fascinating area in the Far North of Europe. They have been introduced into North America, there to meet their cousins the caribous; and there are large numbers in Siberia.

The reindeer can carry a pack weighing 130 lb., or just about 20 lb. less than the horse. It can haul a sledge weighing 200 lb. 100 miles a day; and its speed, laden, is about nine miles an hour.

To the Laplander the reindeer is horse, cow and sheep rolled into one; for in addition to its uses in carrying and hauling, it supplies its hardy owners with milk, meat and clothing.

The yak, a member of the ox family, has a unique capacity for carrying and hauling in rarefied atmospheres. Hence it is the only transport animal in use in many parts of Tibet and Mongolia, 20,000 ft. above sea-level. Other members of the ox family do transport work all over the world: in Germany and in South Africa, in Madeira and in the Philippines.

ROADS OF THE ANCIENT WORLD

THE greatest advance in the history of transport was the invention of the wheel, though strictly speaking the wheel was not invented but evolved.

The first big loads moved by man were carried on his shoulders and back. Later he discovered that it was often easier to drag a load along the ground than to lift it. This dragging process was facilitated by placing the load on a smooth-bottomed board—the first sledge. Later still, when heavier loads were to be transported, it was discovered that the labour of dragging the sledge was greatly lessened if logs were placed under it.

FROM LOG ROLLING TO WHEELED TRANSPORT

No one knows what period separated the first sledge-rolling logs from the first real wheel. It may have been a matter of hundreds—perhaps thousands—of years, but on the other hand it may have been a comparatively short period. The first pair of wheels was probably fashioned out of a log by the simple expedient of whittling away to the core the greater part of the log, leaving six inches, let us say, untouched at each extremity.

Fixing the crude axle of this apparatus to the underneath part of a sledge must have been the occasion of a good deal of mental activity on the part of the primitive carpenters. It had to be held in one place, but it had also to revolve because the wheels were fixed to the axle. No doubt the problem was solved by the cutting of a groove in the under surface of the sledge and the placing of blocks on either side of the groove.

The next step in the evolution of wheeled transport was probably the making of unfixed wheels by cutting off disks from the end of a log. Holes would be bored in the centres of the disks and then thin logs would be whittled down so as to fit into the holes and serve as axles. All this is, of course, theoretical reconstruction. How the wheel actually came into being will never be known.

CIVILIZATION'S DEBT TO THE WHEEL

Without the wheel, not only would transport still be in its infancy, but the great majority of the mechanical devices now in use would still be in the womb of time. The civilization we know could never have come into being without the wheel.

The wheel was known to the Sumerians of 3500 B.C., and before 1500 B.C., as we know from paintings, the Egyptians were using chariots with finely-wrought spoked wheels.

The Romans modelled their chariots on those of the Egyptians. They were also taught something about wheeled vehicles by the ancient Britons. On his return from the invasion of Britain in 54 B.C., Julius Cæsar brought with him specimens of the large-wheeled British war chariot. This vehicle, which is supposed to have been introduced into England about 700 B.C., was called the *essedum* by the Romans.

TRADE-ROUTES OF ANTIQUITY

Before the coming of the wheel there were no roads in the ordinary sense of the term. Footpaths and rude tracks along which to drag sledges existed in plenty, but there were no highways with metalled surfaces.

The wheel necessitated the construction of roads because its narrow rim dug deep into tracks that had served well enough for foot and sledge. Logs and stones were laid down upon the previously plain surface, and so the first roads came into being.

One of the earliest international trade-routes was that along which amber, the first precious stone to be used extensively for personal adornment, was transported from the shores of the North Sea to those of the Adriatic Sea. There are no historical records of this trade until about 300 B.C., but that it took place at a very much earlier date is known from two significant facts. Amber has been found in graves of the Newer Stone Age in Crete and the Iberian Peninsula, and the routes along which it was borne have been traced by the discovery along almost their whole length of pieces of amber and metal ornaments dropped by the traders.

The earliest amber-route was in use about 2000 B.C. It ran from the western coast of Denmark, up the valley of the River Elbe, past Hamburg, Magdeburg and Dresden, through Bohemia and Slovakia, along the course of the River Moldau, then along the River Inn through Innsbruck, over the Brenner Pass into Italy to the shore of Lake Garda, and then down the River Po to the Adriatic.

Another amber-route, first used about 1000 B.C., ran from Danzig on the Baltic, up the Vistula, then, roughly south-east, by Posen and Breslau, across the Carpathian Mountains by the Glatz Pass, thence across the Danube near Pressburg, by Waatsch and St. Marein to Trieste on the Adriatic.

ROYAL ROAD OF HERODOTUS

The historian Herodotus (about 484-425 B.C.), tells us of the ancient Royal Road, which ran from the eastern shores of the Ægean Sea to Persia, and which was already of extreme antiquity when he wrote of it. His account is not as clear as it might be, and there is considerable doubt as to the course this road took.

From Herodotus it would seem that it started at Ephesus, on the Ægean Sea, ran thence northward to Sardis, thence across the River Halys, thence, turning sharply southward, through the Taurus Mountains by the famous pass of the Cilician Gates, thence to Tarsus, which is situated not far from the most easterly point of the Mediterranean. From Tarsus it ran eastwards again to cross the Euphrates at its westernmost bend. Thence, south-east, across the Tigris to Baghdad, and south-east again to Susa (of old an important city) and the Persian Gulf.

Herodotus tells us that where the Royal Road crosses the Halys there are " gates through which you have to pass before you can cross the stream. A strong guard protects this post." He adds that the whole distance from Sardis to the Palace of Memnon at Susa was 13,500 furlongs : " travelling then at the rate of 150 furlongs a day, you would take exactly 90 days to accomplish the journey."

ROUTE OF THE BLUE GEM

The ancient Royal Road that ran through Asia Minor and Persia was connected up with great roads that ran to Afghanistan, India and even to north-eastern China, whence came silk for the grand ladies of Mesopotamia, Egypt and Greece.

Along the Afghanistan-Mesopotamia Road were transported quantities of lapis lazuli, the blue gem which the peoples of the eastern Mediterranean so much admired. The Sumerians of Mesopotamia used it for ornamental purposes, while the Persians ground it into a powder from which they made paint. The road did not end in Afghanistan, but was continued on through the Khyber Pass into northern India, where existed a civilization almost as ancient as that of Sumeria. A flourishing trade was carried on between Mesopotamia and the Indus Valley thousands of years before the Christian era.

SILK ROAD FROM FAR CATHAY

It is generally supposed that the Chinese were engaged in the production of silk as early as 2600 B.C. They guarded the secrets of its origin and manufacture so carefully that these were not known in Japan and India until approximately 3,000 years later. But the Persians had apparently founded a silk industry of their own about 300 B.C. It is said that the Chinese secrets were betrayed to them by a princess of China who married a Persian prince. Be that as it may, it seems certain that from a very early date silk was being transported from the north-east of China, across Central Asia to Persia.

The route along which the silk was conveyed must surely be the most romantic in the history of man. It passed through Persia and Kashgar to the Tarim Basin in Chinese Turkestan, thence north of the Kun-Lun Mountains, across southern Mongolia to the banks of the Hwang-Ho and beyond to the far north of China.

The first stone-paved road of which we have record was that constructed by Cheops (29th century B.C.), King of Egypt, for the transport of the millions of blocks of stone, each weighing about two and a half tons, used in the building of the Great Pyramid. Herodotus tells us that vast numbers of slaves toiled for ten years to make this road, which he considered as impressive as the pyramid itself.

He gives the road's dimensions as " five furlongs long, ten fathoms wide, and in height at the highest part, eight fathoms." It was " made of polished stone and covered with carvings of animals."

ROADS OF THE ROMAN EMPIRE

It was not from the Egyptians but from their greatest enemies, the Carthaginians, that the Romans learnt the art of road-making. We are told that Carthage possessed an elaborate system of paved roads in the 5th century B.C.

The Carthaginians were " the first that contrived to strengthen, to secure, and to consolidate the Roads with Stones and Flints knit together with Sand, and as it were fasten'd by Masonry on the Surface of the Earth, which we in one word call Paving; and . . . in Imitation of them, the Romans fell to paving the Highways almost throughout all the then known World."

One of the most valuable parts of the legacy of Rome is the system of roads with which she covered the Mediterranean countries and Western Europe. So successful were the Roman efforts to establish an efficient communications system, that in the time of Marcus Aurelius it could be said: "A man can now go wheresoever he pleases without fear. The harbours of the Empire are busily engaged in commerce; and even the mountains are as safe for travellers as are the cities for those who dwell within them."

Edward Gibbon, the great English historian of the Roman Empire, tells us that the roads " united the subjects of the most distant provinces by an easy and familiar intercourse; but their primary object had been to facilitate the march of the legions; nor was any country considered as completely subdued, till it had been rendered, in all its parts, pervious to the arms and authority of the conqueror."

CONQUERING THE WORLD BY ROAD

The first of the great highways along which the Roman legions marched to conquer the world was the Appian Way, which was called after Appius Claudius, the man who started to build it in 312 B.C. The first section joined Rome to Capua, in the south of Italy. At Capua it forked, one branch going eastwards across the Italian peninsula to Brundusium (Brindisi), where east-bound travellers took ship across the Adriatic to Apollonia (in Macedonia), the terminus of the great road which stretched thence to Byzantium (Constantinople).

The other branch of the Appian Way ran south to Reggio, at the extremity of the Italian mainland, where travellers boarded ferries for Messina, in the island of Sicily. Africa-bound travellers took ship from the south coast of Sicily, some going by sea to Alexandria, others going straight across to North Africa and then travelling by road, either east to Alexandria or west to Algiers.

ANTICIPATING THE SUEZ CANAL

The most important commercial centre of the Roman Empire was Alexandria, in Egypt. It owed its supremacy partly to its geographical position; partly to its excellent harbours. It was the common meeting-ground of Europe, Africa and Asia. In its streets were seen Italians,

Egyptians and Arabs, Greeks, Indians, and Jews. Alongside its wharves were ships from Spain, Rome and Asia Minor, from India, Ethiopia (Abyssinia) and Arabia. In their holds were spices and drugs, silk and cotton, ivory and hides, amber and tortoise-shell, tin and steel.

Through Alexandria passed a large proportion of the west-bound products of the East, but Egypt herself was one of the wealthiest of the Mediterranean countries and not a little of the merchandise Alexandria handled was produced on the banks of the Nile. The great river was —as it still is—the source of all Egypt's wealth. It was also the highway for the transport of goods and men. Its navigability rendered a great system of roads unnecessary.

Numerous canals branching off the Nile further supplemented the water-transport facilities of the country. One of these canals joined Alexandria to the Red Sea, anticipating the Suez Canal by 2,000 years.

LINKING EGYPT WITH CHINA

Egypt was not entirely without roads. The city of Alexandria, as befitted the greatest centre of commerce in the world—the London of antiquity—possessed magnificent thoroughfares which extended far out into the country. Moreover, several roads ran from the east bank of the Nile through the passes in the long range of mountains which juts up between the Nile and the Red Sea. Along these roads were borne the manifold products of Arabia, Persia, Afghanistan, India and China. These Egyptian trade-routes were not paved like the Roman roads in Europe. They did not need to be, because wheels rarely touched their surfaces, most of their loads being camel-borne.

At the head of the Gulf of Suez, where now stands Suez and Port Tewfik, was the city of Arsinoe, where three great overland trade-routes centred. The shortest ran northwards to Pelusium (near Port Said) on the Mediterranean; another ran north-east to link up with the roads of Palestine and Syria; the third ran east to the Persian Gulf.

A JOURNEY OF FOUR WEEKS

Arsinoe was in constant communication with Damascus in Syria, another great focal-point of trade-routes. The main port for Damascus was Sidon—with which the name of Tyre is linked in the Bible. Goods from the Far East were landed at the head of the Persian Gulf, transported overland to Damascus, and thence sent on to Sidon for re-shipment to Alexandria.

Sidon also lay on the great road which, beginning at Alexandria, ran along the south-east coast of the Mediterranean past Gaza and Jaffa to Tyre and northwards through Antioch, the capital of Syria, and on through Asia Minor to Byzantium. The whole journey from Alexandria to Byzantium could be accomplished in just over four weeks.

There had been roads in Syria long before the Romans came, but they extended the system and paved and straightened many of the existing routes.

ROME'S HIGHWAY TO THE EAST

The first section of Rome's overland route to the east (the continuation of the Appian Way) ran straight across the Greek province of Macedonia from Apollonia, on the Adriatic, to Thessalonica, on the Ægean Sea. This section was paved about 150 B.C. The Roman, wishing to travel to the Near East, went by the Appian Way to Brundusium (modern Brindisi); and took ship there for Apollonia, which was only about thirty miles away by sea. Having crossed Macedonia to Thessalonica, he would travel along the northern shores of the Ægean to Byzantium, on the Bosphorus. The overland journey from Rome to Byzantium took about twenty-five days.

Less romantic than the roads in the East were those the Romans built in many parts of North Africa, in Spain, in Gaul (France), in Central Europe and in Britain. Edward Gibbon, the historian, estimated that when the road-system of the Romans was complete there were 3,740 English miles of first-class roads connecting Antonine's Wall in Scotland with Jerusalem—broken only by the Straits of Dover and the Bosphorus.

In the itinerary of Antonine, probably compiled in the reign of Diocletian (245-313), are listed 372 Roman roads with a total length of 52,964 miles.

ROAD HOUSES ARE VERY OLD

Gibbon tells us that "along the main (Roman) roads houses were everywhere erected at the distance of only five or six miles; each of them was constantly provided with forty horses, and by the help of these relays, it was easy to travel one hundred miles a day along the Roman roads."

It is said that the Emperor Tiberius (born 42 B.C.) covered 200 miles a day when he was hurrying through Germany on his way to Lyons, where his brother was dying. A more ordinary rate of travel for horse-drawn vehicles was about forty to fifty miles a day. Pedestrians rarely covered more than twenty miles a day. These speeds were not improved upon until the coming of the steam-driven locomotive in the 19th century.

The Roman roads were built partly by soldiers, partly by trained artisans, partly by the natives of the countries through which they ran, and partly by criminals. It was with the assistance of the Legions that the Emperor Hadrian built that "famous wall in Great Britain, fourscore Italian miles in length, to part the Roman Dominions from the Barbarians."

It has been suggested, with a certain degree of plausibility, that the main object of the Romans in building many of their roads was to keep both the soldiers and the natives out of mischief: "that the Multitude of every Province might have no Opportunity to mutiny, they were employed on the Work of the Highways by way of personal Service."

Sometimes the hard labour on the roads gave rise to the very trouble it was designed to prevent. Not infrequently the soldiers broke out into mutinies and open rebellion against their commanders. They demanded that they should be employed to fight with men and not with " rapid rivers, thick forests, rocky mountains, and undrainable marshes : declaring loudly that they were no giants to oppose nature, and oblige her against her will to obey the Emperor and his Lieutenants."

LABOURING FOR POSTERITY

The natives of the subdued provinces did not like the work of road-making any better than the soldiers. It is recorded that Galgacus, Prince of the Caledonians or Scots, exhorted his men to fight vigorously against the Romans under Julius Agricola, because of the " miserable condition of other Provinces already subdu'd in Great Britain, whose Goods and Fortunes the Romans had taken away for tribute, and consum'd their hands and bodies, in making ways through woods and marshes, amidst stripes and reproaches."

They were obliged " to cleave the rocks, to dig in quarries, and take out the stones; others to carry them ten, twenty, or thirty leagues in length, to those places where there were none; others to fetch up from the bottom of rivers the gravel and sand; others to burn lime, and others to hew down forests to furnish the kilns with wood; and in fine, others to compose one work of all these materials, to settle each of them orderly in its place, to ram, and consolidate them, and in all respects to give them their due form and perfection to render them lasting to posterity."

SENTENCED TO WORK ON THE HIGHWAYS

We are told that many criminals who would otherwise have been sentenced to death were condemned " to work all their life-time upon the highways." The Romans apparently derived this custom from Anisis, a blind king of Egypt, who during the fifty years of his reign would not permit any criminals to be put to death, sentencing them instead to build a certain length of rampart about the towns in which they were born. The " length of rampart " depended upon the gravity of the crime.

Before Caligula's time only " mean persons " were employed upon the making of roads, but Suetonius, the Latin author, informs us that: " He (Caligula) condemn'd many well born, after branding them, to the mines, or to work at the highways, or to be devour'd by wild beasts." They were branded on the forehead with the " ignominious mark used upon criminal slaves."

The most striking example of the use of criminal labour in ancient times occurred in the reign of Nero (A.D. 37-68). He ordered that a canal should be cut from Lake Avernus to the port of Ostia, and he directed that prisoners and criminals should be sent from all parts of the Roman Empire to take part in the work.

ALL THE WORLD MADE ROADS

A 17th-century writer points out that all the tremendous sums which were expended on the construction of such mighty works as the Pharos Lighthouse, the Pyramids of Egypt and Vespasian's Temple of Peace, are dwarfed into insignificance by the amounts spent upon the highways of the empire. "Only one town, one province, or one kingdom, contributed to any other work, tho' never so great; but as for the highways we treat of, there was no People, Nation, Province or Country, but gave something to it, besides what the City of Rome contributed on its own."

The same writer refuses even to hazard a guess at the amount spent or the number of men employed upon the Roman highways, for, as he says, "the greatest part of the inhabitants of the then known world did actually labour at them with their hands for above 400 years in the Provinces, and above 600 years in Italy. And as for those who did not work in person, they contributed towards it with their purses, without any exception from the highest to the lowest; the work of the highways being the only one in the world which can boast that all persons contributed to it either by their labour or purses."

ROMAN ROADS OF BRITAIN

Although Britain was invaded by Julius Cæsar in 55 B.C., it was not until near the end of the first century of the Christian era that the country was thoroughly subdued; and it was not until about a hundred years later that the Romans completed their British road system.

Their first trips to Britain were very disappointing to the Romans. They had heard many far-fetched tales about the great wealth of the country but, after a preliminary exploration, Cicero penned the bitter words: "It would seem that there is practically nothing worth removing from Britain except the chariots."

There were many roads in Britain before the Roman engineers set to work, but they were of a comparatively primitive type, very few having stone surfaces. Stonehenge was the commercial centre of the island in the pre-Roman days, but the Romans made London the focal point of their roads.

One road ran south-west from London to Old Sarum (Salisbury), Dorchester and Exeter. The Midlands were served by the famous Watling Street, which ran north-west to St. Albans and then on to Wroxeter and Chester. The road through the eastern counties to the North ran by Lincoln, Eboracum (York) and Newcastle, to the Great Wall. Among the other important roads were those joining London to Colchester, and London to the Channel ports.

North of a line drawn between the mouths of the Mersey and the Humber the Roman roads were not much used except for military purposes and therefore comparatively little trouble was expended upon them, but some of the roads south of this line were as good as any in the empire.

ROADS BUILT BY GIANTS AND SORCERERS

William Camden, the 17th-century antiquary, author of a celebrated guide-book to England known as the *Britannia*, tells us that in his time few people knew the origin of the Roman roads.

"Our common sort," he writes, "say the Roman works were made by giants. . . . But Geofrey of Monmouth says, those ways were the work of a king descended from Brutus, and call'd Malmutius, who liv'd long before the Birth of Christ; and adds, that this Malmutius being a great sorcerer, perform'd that by the assistance of his Art, and of Devils, which it was impossible for men to do; for that in a few days England was furnished with highways of a beautiful and admirable structure, from one end to the other, which were still entire in many places in his days, to the amazement of all that beheld them."

At various times China has had magnificent road systems, meriting comparison with that of the Romans, not only because of their great extent but also because of the high quality of the surfaces, many of which were paved with huge blocks of stone. But the main arteries of commerce in China have always been the rivers and canals, though in modern times road-making has again been vigorously developed. The "good roads movement" founded in Shanghai in 1921, the increasing use of motor transport, and the exigencies of the Sino-Japanese war have contributed to this development.

WHY CHINA'S ROADS ARE CROOKED

One of the most remarkable features of the Chinese road is its bridges, which are everywhere numerous and nearly always beautiful. The smaller rivers and gorges are crossed by the stone-arched type; the larger ones by suspension and cantilever type structures. Some of the bridges are covered in and are used as club houses for the villagers, who forgather there to gossip and drink tea.

Unlike their Roman counterparts, many of the Chinese roads are extremely crooked. It is said that the reason for their crookedness is that it enables the traveller to give evil spirits the slip. These spirits are only capable of travelling in a straight line and the curves in the road make them lose their way. A less romantic explanation of the roads' crookedness is that it makes travelling easier on hills.

There are teashops at frequent intervals along the Chinese roads where the weary traveller may obtain refreshment at a very low cost.

AMERICAN ROAD 1,000 YEARS OLD

One of the greatest man-made wonders of the American continent was the 4,000-mile-long road which stretched from Quito in Ecuador to Tucuman in Argentina. No modern phenomenon was this, for it was in use 500 years before Columbus re-discovered the New World. Nor was there anything primitive about it. It was twenty-five feet wide, and part of its surface was paved with stone, part with asphalt.

In covering a distance approximately equal to one-sixth of the distance round the equator, it traversed every imaginable variety of country. The engineers who laid it down cared as little for 15,000-feet-high mountain ranges as they did for canyons thousands of feet deep. Trackless deserts, treacherous swamps, madly-rushing rivers were tackled and conquered with the same matchless skill. Zigzag highways were hewn out of the mountain-side; canyons were either filled in or bridged; dykes were thrown across swamps and lakes; paved tracks were laid in the burning desert; rivers were bridged by mammoth cables of wool and fibre.

The road was the work of the Incas of Peru, who in the days before the Spanish conquest dominated the north-west portion of South America, where they built up a remarkable civilization. It was the main artery of a magnificent system of roads. Parallel to it for half its length was another great road only five feet narrower, and many minor roads ran across country to join them. "Throughout the whole of Christendom, no such roads are to be seen as those which we here admire." So said a brother of Francisco Pizarro, the conqueror of Peru, in reference to the Inca highways system.

MESSAGES AT TEN MILES A MINUTE

At frequent intervals along the main Inca road, sentries, equipped with signalling apparatus, were stationed. By this device messages could be conveyed from one point to another with extraordinary rapidity. It is said that it used to be possible to send a message along the whole 4,000 miles of the road in six hours.

Equally amazing was the speed with which goods could be transported along the Inca roads by runners, each of whom covered about fifteen miles. It was customary, so we are told, to dispatch fish from the Pacific to Cuzco, 300 miles away, in thirty hours. This is very remarkable in view of the fact that the journey entailed the crossing of a 15,000-feet-high mountain range.

ROADS AND VEHICLES IN BRITAIN

About the year 900, King Alfred laid down that, "If a far-coming man or a stranger journey through a wood out of the highway, and neither shout nor blow his horn, he is to be held for a thief and either slain or redeemed." This was probably the first English royal ordinance dealing with highways.

The first Act of Parliament on the subject of roads was the Statute of Winchester, passed in the reign of Edward I. The Act, among many other things, laid down that shrubbery should be cut away from the sides of the highways "so that there be neither dyke nor bush, whereby a man may lurk to do hurt, within two hundred foot of the one side and two hundred foot of the other side of the way."

No roads worthy of the name were built in Britain between the time the Romans left the country and the 18th century, by which time the highways were in a truly appalling state. Ironically enough, it needed a rebellion to convince the English Government that something ought to be done about it.

The first good post-Roman roads were those begun in Scotland under the direction of General George Wade in 1726. They were a direct result of the Jacobite Rebellion of 1715, when the English efforts to drive the Jacobites out of their hiding-places in Scotland were largely frustrated by the absence of good roads. Determined to remedy this state of affairs the Government ordered General Wade, Commander-in-Chief in Scotland, to provide Caledonia with a system of military roads.

Five hundred soldiers were employed upon the work, and were given sixpence a day for their pains. Wade laid down 250 miles of road, but his system was subsequently extended to more than three times this length. In the second half of the 18th century £7,000 a year was being spent on their maintenance.

One of the roads built by Wade, that between Fort Augustus and Dalwhinnie, is the highest surfaced road in the British Isles. It reaches a height of 2,519 ft.

BLIND JACK THE ROAD-MAKER

The roads that Wade built, though efficiently constructed, represented little advance on the methods used by the Romans. The first native of Britain to approach road-making with an open mind and a willingness to adopt unconventional methods was John Metcalf (1717-1810), otherwise known as Blind Jack of Knaresborough.

The son of poor parents, he went totally blind at the age of six; but this disability did not prevent him from wandering about the country alone, first on foot, and later, when he had saved enough money, on horseback. Nor did it prevent him from taking part in the ordinary business of life. He became, in turn, fiddler, soldier, chapman, fish-dealer, horse-dealer and general carrier. He fought in the '45 rebellion. Finally, in 1765, he applied for, and was given, the contract to build three miles of road between Minskip and Fearnsby.

So successfully did Metcalf complete this project that he was immediately offered more work of a similar kind. He was particularly successful in bridge-building and in the carrying of roads over marshy ground and swamps. He did not give up road-making until he was seventy-five.

WORK OF THOMAS TELFORD

Thomas Telford, born forty years after Metcalf, took up the task of improving the roads of Britain where the latter left it. He also constructed bridges, canals, docks and harbours. Among his major achievements were the construction of 1,070 miles of road and a very large number of bridges in Scotland, and the making of 123 miles of the London-Holyhead Road. In this latter connexion he was responsible for the Menai Suspension Bridge and Conway Bridge.

The feature in road-construction on which Telford laid most stress was efficient drainage, since he realized that nothing was more calculated to harm road surfaces than the percolation of water through the upper layer on to the lower one.

The lower layer of a Telford road consisted of pieces of stone measuring between four and seven inches, carefully laid in position with their broadest sides downwards. On top of these he placed a layer of small stones and gravel. At 100-yard intervals he laid drains across the road between the two layers of material. He endeavoured to obviate the necessity for steep gradients on his roads by cutting his way through hills whenever possible.

ROAD-MAKER WHOSE NAME ENRICHED THE DICTIONARY

John Loudon McAdam (1756-1836) was of the opinion that roads were " perhaps the most important branch of our domestic economy," and this belief induced him to spend the greater part of his life studying the principles of road-construction and inducing the authorities to put the results of his researches and experiments into practice.

Briefly stated, the most important discovery that McAdam made was that the best way to prevent water from percolating through the road was to surface it with small, broken stones to a depth of about nine inches. Under the pressure of traffic, the stones, having irregular edges, would adhere together in a well-nigh solid mass upon which neither the weather nor the weight of heavy vehicles would have much effect. This principle, which became universally known as " macadamization," proved even more effective after the invention of the steam-roller.

WAGONS FOR PASSENGERS

Prior to the 16th century the traveller in England was given the following choice of transport facilities : he could walk; he could ride on horseback; he could have himself carried in a litter; or he could travel in a springless wagon. Riding on horseback was, of course, the quickest means of progression, and very often the next quickest was walking.

The 16th century saw the introduction of the coach, which was at first hardly more than a glorified covered-in wagon, but which was gradually made more comfortable by elaborate padding of the seats and more skilful hanging of the body.

Fynes Morryson, writing in 1617, says that ". . . carriers have long covered wagons in which they carry passengers to and fro; but this kind of journeying is very tedious; so that none but women and people of inferior condition travel in this sort. Coaches are not to be hired anywhere but in London. For a day's journey a coach with two horses is let for about 10s. a day or 15s. with three horses, the coachman finding the horses' feed."

Stage-coaches, that is large coaches for the use of the public, began to be used about the middle of the 17th century. For about 100 years after their introduction they were too expensive for the poorer classes, who had to be content with the extremely uncomfortable wagons.

A writer of 1649 refers to the recent introduction of stage-coaches, " wherein any one may be transported to any place sheltered from foul weather and foul ways, free from endamaging of one's health and one's body by hard jogging or over-violent motion on horseback." Thirteen years later (1662) there were apparently only half a dozen stage-coaches in the whole of Britain, but their numbers increased steadily thereafter. By 1673 there were coach services between London and Exeter, Chester and York; and many between London and places within a day's journey. The time taken to travel from London to Exeter was eight days in summer and ten in winter; and the fare was about £2.

LONDON TO MANCHESTER IN FOUR AND A HALF DAYS

The art of stage-coach building did not appreciably improve for more than 100 years after its introduction, but by the middle of the 18th century travelling by stage-coach was a much faster business than it had been in its early days. In 1754 a coach service between London and Manchester was advertised in the following terms: ". . . however incredible it may appear, this coach will actually arrive in London in four days and a half after leaving Manchester."

The coach of that period was " usually drawn by three horses, on the first of which a postilion rode with a cocked hat and a long green and gold coat. The machine groaned and creaked as it went along with every tug the horses gave, and the speed was frequently but four miles an hour."

Fast mail coaches, capable of six miles per hour and more were introduced in 1786, mainly owing to the efforts of John Palmer. A few years before that date a letter posted in London on Monday would not arrive in Bath until Wednesday morning. Palmer's efforts led to the placing of eighty fast mail-coaches on the road. Their number was gradually increased until in 1835 there were 700 in the United Kingdom.

TAXATION OF HORSE-DRAWN VEHICLES

The outcry which is frequently heard today against taxes on motor vehicles was paralleled 150 years ago by a similar protest against the taxation of horse-drawn vehicles. In the last decade of the 18th century the tax upon two-wheel vehicles in general was £3 17s. od.; while that on four-wheel carriages was £8 16s. od. for the first, and £9 18s. od. for the second, but if three or more carriages were kept it was necessary to pay £11 tax on each vehicle.

A 19th-century writer on the history of coaches remarks that, after considering the subject of the taxation of carriages, " we can have no hesitation in saying that sufficient attention has never been given to the remonstrances of coach builders and hackney carriage owners at the offices of the Inland Revenue, and that consequently the owners and users of carriages have suffered an amount of annoyance that might and should have been avoided." How like a statement from a section of the motor car industry today!

In the second decade of the 19th century there were approximately 70,000 carriages in Great Britain upon which tax was being paid. Of these, 23,400 were four-wheelers; 27,300 were large two-wheelers, and 18,500 were small two-wheelers. At the same period the coach-building industry was producing over 3,600 vehicles every year.

Ten years later (1824), partly owing to the reduction of the duty payable on them, but mainly owing to the introduction of elliptical springing, the number of carriages in use had increased to 90,000. The number continued to grow until by 1874 there were 285,000 two-wheeled and 125,000 four-wheeled carriages, making a total of 410,000, or nearly six times as many as in 1814.

HACKNEY CARRIAGES AND CABS

Four-wheeled hackney carriages were used for the first time in London in 1625. They immediately became very popular but, owing to opposition on the part of the Thames watermen, whose trade they took away, and of those who feared that if they became too numerous they would wear away the streets, measures were taken to limit their numbers.

In 1635 the number of hackney carriages was restricted to fifty, but fifteen years later, despite regulations, there were 300 on the streets; and in 1694, about 700.

The first two-wheeled cabriolet, commonly called a " cab," made its appearance on the London streets in 1823, in honour, so we are told, of George IV's birthday. " They are built," says a contemporary newspaper, " to hold two persons inside besides the driver (who is partitioned off from his company), and are furnished with a book of fares for the use of the public, to prevent the possibility of imposition. . . . The fares are one-third less than hackney coaches." Seven years after their introduction there were 165 cabs in London.

Some years later four-wheel cabs were introduced, and then came the Hansom patent safety cab, which was called after its inventor, Joseph Aloysius Hansom, the architect of the Birmingham Town Hall.

LONDON'S FIRST BUS

The omnibus, that is, the carriage " for all," was introduced into London in 1829 by George Shillibeer. Drawn by three horses, it had accommodation for about twenty-two people. The horse-drawn bus was gradually enlarged and improved until in 1877 it carried twenty-eight passengers at up to eight miles per hour.

The London General Omnibus Company, the parent body of the present-day London Passenger Transport Board, was founded in 1855. Within a year it was running about 600 omnibuses.

STEAM ON THE ROADS

The first person in Britain to suggest the application of steam power to road transport was probably Dr. John Robinson, subsequently

Professor of Natural Philosophy in the University of Edinburgh. This he did in 1759. Ten years later a Frenchman, Nicolas Joseph Cugnot, built a steam carriage for use on the roads.

In 1782, Oliver Evans, an American wheelwright, began to consider the subject. He made such good progress in his experiments that by 1786 he was in a position " to petition the legislature of Pennsylvania for the exclusive right to use his improvements in flour-mills, and his steam wagons, in that State. The committee . . . heard him very patiently while he described the mill improvements, but his representations concerning steam wagons made them think him insane."

Evans made a good high-pressure fixed engine, which he designed for use on the road. His faith in steam locomotion remained unshaken, as is proved by these words of his: " I verily believe that the time will come when carriages propelled by steam will be in general use, as well for the transportation of passengers as goods, travelling at the rate of fifteen miles an hour, or 300 miles a day on good turnpike roads."

MAN WHO TRAINED THE STEAM ENGINE

In 1784 James Watt, " whose wonderful genius broke in and trained the steam engine," took out a patent for a method of applying steam power to wheel carriages.

Eighteen years later (1802), Richard Trevithick took up the project, and in 1804 succeeded in producing a steam-propelled carriage. After many experiments he abandoned the attempt to make a satisfactory road vehicle and turned his attention to railways. This is not to be wondered at in view of the shocking state of the highways at the beginning of the 19th century.

STEPHENSON'S RAILWAY LOCOMOTIVES

In 1814-1815 George Stephenson produced a " travelling engine " for use on the tramroads at Killingworth colliery. It represented a very great advance on anything hitherto made. Stephenson, like Trevithick, turned his attention to the possibilities of railways, with results that are known to everyone. In 1825 the first public passenger train the world had ever known was hauled by a Stephenson locomotive. In 1829 his famous *Rocket* appeared, and in November, 1830, a sensation was created when Stephenson's engine, the *Planet,* covered the distance between Manchester and Liverpool (thirty-one miles) in sixty minutes.

PIONEER STEAM CARRIAGES

Among the first steam carriages to be used as an " established and regular conveyance for the public " were those put into operation between Gloucester and Cheltenham in 1831 by Sir Charles Dance. These steam carriages—three in number—were the work of Goldsworthy Gurney, a brilliant inventor whose first successful locomotive had appeared six years earlier (1825).

The Gloucester-Cheltenham service was suspended after four

months, not because the carriages proved in any way unsatisfactory, but on account of opposition from various quarters. Bills laying prohibitory tolls on steam carriages were rushed through Parliament. These bills originated, so we are told, " partly in the stable habits of some country gentlemen, who love no change." The said gentry were apparently backed by " the old ladies of Cheltenham," who always offered a " formidable opposition to any innovation."

DEFEATED BY PEERS AND VESTED INTERESTS

Gurney was interrogated before a Committee of the House of Commons in 1831, and much interesting information about steam carriages was then brought to light. The Committee stated in their report that the steam carriage " is one of the most important improvements in the means of internal communication ever introduced," and they accordingly advocated the repeal of the bills by which extortionate tolls had been placed upon it. But in vain. A repeal bill passed the Commons, but the Lords threw it out.

Gurney, who had spent £30,000 in cash and five or six years in time in his attempt to put steam on the roads, still fought on desperately against the Lords and the coaching interests. In the end he was beaten; and not only he, but many others who, like him, saw the great benefits that steam carriages would confer upon the community. Within ten years of the Gloucester-Cheltenham venture the steam carriage industry which had shown such promise of vigorous life was dead. Between 1840 and 1860 various attempts were made to revive it, but without success. By then the antagonistic influence of the railway industry was united to that of the coaching concerns.

It was not until near the end of the century that another rival to the horse and the railroad carriage appeared. Desperate attempts were made to prevent the motor car from coming on to the road; but this time mechanical road transport won.

COMING OF THE MOTOR CAR

THE year 1865 saw the passage of an Act of Parliament which for thirty years thereafter regulated the use of mechanically propelled vehicles on the roads of Britain. The measure became known as the " Red Flag Act " because one of its provisions was that a mechanically propelled vehicle should be preceded along the highway by a person carrying a red flag. It also laid down that the locomotive should be accompanied by at least three persons, and that its speed should not exceed four miles per hour on the open road or two miles per hour through " built-up " areas.

It is to be suspected that the Act came into being not so much because there was a general suspicion of mechanically propelled road vehicles, but because various bodies were determined, out of regard for their own interests, to suppress such vehicles. However that may be, the Act was certainly instrumental in turning the attention of English inventors away from road locomotion, with the result that when the first motor cars appeared on the roads of Germany and France, the roads of England boasted nothing more advanced than traction engines and bicycles.

The Act of 1865 was followed thirteen years later by an equally repressive measure, under which it was made compulsory for owners of road locomotives to pay up to £10 to every county council in the territory of which the vehicle was used.

EMANCIPATION DAY

By 1895 there were a considerable number of automobiles in free use in France and Germany, and there was consequently a growing demand in England for the repeal of the penal laws against the use of motor cars. This resulted in the passing of the Locomotives on Highways Act (1896), the first measure in which a distinction was made between motor cars and traction engines.

The Act did away with the old restrictive regulations in regard to vehicles with an unladen weight of three tons. This weight-limit was imposed to prevent the production of public service vehicles and large lorries which would compete with the railways and the canals. All motor vehicles above three tons were subject to the original restrictions. But even the vehicles under three tons were not to travel at a speed in excess of twelve miles per hour. Regarded in the light of the present day, this Act does not appear over-generous in its concessions, but its importance in the history of transport cannot be over-estimated because it made the motor car legal. It came into law on November 14, which day has ever since been celebrated by motorists as Emancipation Day.

COMING OF COMMERCIAL VEHICLES

As the motor-car industry developed the discontent with what was virtually a prohibition of commercial vehicles increased to such an extent that in 1905 the weight-limit was raised to five tons without a trailer, and six and a half tons with a trailer. Not till then did the commercial vehicle as we know it today come into being. In 1911 there were approximately 3,500 commercial motor vehicles in the London area. In the same year the London General Omnibus Company withdrew the last of their horse omnibuses from service to replace them with motor-driven vehicles. In 1902 the ratio of horse to motor omnibuses in London was 3,736 to 10; in 1905 it was 3,551 to 31; by 1906 it was 3,484 to 241; and in 1910 it was 1,771 to 1,180. And, whereas in 1906 the ratio of horse to motor cabs was 10,492 to 96, by 1911 it was 4,386 to 7,165.

By 1933 there were 11,430 public service passenger transport vehicles in service in the London area. Of these 5,350 were omnibuses, 420 were motor coaches, 60 were trolley buses, 2,600 were tramcars and 3,000 underground railway cars.

The coming of the motor car made it necessary to spend enormous sums on highway construction and repair. Whereas in 1908-1909 only £5,000,000 was spent on roads by the county and rural district councils, in 1920-1921, £43,000,000 was paid out for the same purpose by various bodies; and ten years later the corresponding figure was £65,750,000, showing a thirteen-fold increase within about twenty years. In 1932 there were 1,926,600 motor vehicles in service in Great Britain, or a million more than in 1922. By 1938 the figure had risen to over three millions.

BRITISH MOTOR INDUSTRY TODAY

By September 30, 1938, there were 1,944,394 private cars alone on British roads. In 1937, 326,000 new cars were sold. Of the new private cars sold fifty-eight per cent were of 10 h.p. and under, and over ninety-four per cent were British. The number of motor vehicles per 1,000 of the population was 51.2. During the year the motor car industry paid the Exchequer £50,000,000, mainly in duty on fuel. One-fifth of the new vehicles produced were exported, the British Empire taking eighty-five per cent of these.

In the year October, 1937 to September, 1938, the British motor car industry produced 342,000 new vehicles, or about 60,000 less than in the previous year.

MODERN ROADS

IN Great Britain the approximate total mileage of roads is 178,100 miles; 152,400 in England and Wales, 25,700 in Scotland. Some 27,000 miles are first class and 16,800 miles second class, according to the Ministry of Transport. In the United States there are 271,614 miles of surfaced State highways, out of 324,312 miles of State highways, while rural roads total about three million miles, these for the most part being very rough.

In recent years the cost of maintenance alone of British roads has been £32,000,000 annually, or £100,000 every weekday. The total cost, including new construction and widening, was over £60,000,000 in 1934-1935.

ROAD ACCIDENTS

In the ten years ended December, 1936, 66,000 people were killed and 2,000,000 injured in road accidents in Great Britain. On an average there are twenty people killed and 600 injured every day on British roads. In the year June, 1936 to June, 1937, December was the most fatal month, with 694 road deaths, and February the least with 461.

During 1937 there were 1,057 people killed and 56,327 injured in the London Metropolitan Police District; but in the same year there were only seventeen killed and 422 injured in the narrow streets of the City of London.

During 1936 there were 5,188 people killed on the roads of Britain; 8,381 on those of Germany; and 4,415 people killed in motor accidents in France.

The most frequent cause of accidents attributable to drivers of vehicles is emerging or turning from one road into another without due care.

LONGEST AND HIGHEST ROADS

The two longest motor roads in the world are the Pacific Highway, which runs from Vancouver on the west coast of Canada to the Mexican frontier, a distance of some 1,500 miles; and the road from Atlantic City, via Philadelphia, St. Louis, Denver, Salt Lake City, Sacramento, and Oakland, to the Pacific Ocean. This is 3,219 miles long, passes through fourteen States, reaches a height of 6,500 ft. above sea-level, and can be traversed in eighty-one hours by vehicles averaging forty miles per hour. When completed, the motor road from Alaska to Tierra del Fuego will be the greatest modern road.

The longest continuous footpath in the world is the Appalachian Way, U.S.A. It is 2,183 miles long, and runs from the State of Georgia to that of Maine; it is rarely crossed by any other track. The John Muir Trail, opened in 1937, 1,683 miles long, runs from the Canadian frontier to Mexico, and passes through magnificent scenery. In Europe, a new footpath opened in 1937 runs from the Saar to Silesia; it is 625 miles long and is intended solely for recreation.

The highest motor road in the world was opened in Peru in 1936. It runs from Lima to Oroya, and its highest point is the Anticona Col (about 15,820 ft. high). Previously, the highest motor road was that which crosses Pike's Peak in Colorado at a height of 13,000 ft. What is probably Europe's highest road crosses the Pic de Veleta in the Sierra Nevada in Spain (11,090 ft.); but the highest practicable motor road is that over the Col de L'Iseran in France (9,002 ft.), opened in 1937.

ON THE GREAT IRON ROAD

Railways of a sort were being used in 1670 at Newcastle-upon-Tyne for the transport of coal from the pit-heads to the quays on the River Tyne. The rails were of beechwood, and were held in position by sleepers like those on present-day railways.

These early railways were nearly always placed on an incline so that much of the haulage work was done by that cheap labourer, gravity. The wagons were "sufficiently large to contain many tons of coals; the wheels were exceedingly low; an ordinary horse would, without difficulty, draw three tons of coals on these roads from the pits to the river."

Wooden rails were introduced into the collieries of Whitehaven in 1738, but they were quickly abandoned in favour of iron ones. The first attempt to form a railway of iron was by fixing flat bars of iron on the top of wooden rails; "but after a great variety of unsuccessful attempts, the wood was totally laid aside, and the rails themselves wholly composed of cast-iron bars, in short lengths, and united at their extremities, and resting on sleepers composed of square blocks of stone placed at short distances on each side of the road." By about the middle of the 18th century nearly all the collieries in England were equipped with iron railways, both under and over ground. Rails were also introduced on canals, where they were "employed in the place of locks, for the purpose of raising barges on an inclined plane, from a lower to a higher level, and even in several instances, fully adopted in preference to the canal itself."

FIRST PUBLIC RAILWAY

The first railway built in England for the use of the public, as distinct from one built to serve a colliery, for example, was the Surrey Iron Railway. An Act of Parliament authorizing its construction was passed in 1801. With a total length of 9½ miles, it ran from the town of Croydon to the Thames at Wandsworth.

According to Frederick Clifford, the builders of this railway only contemplated the use of horse power. "The tracks, when laid down, were meant, like canals, for general use by carriers and freighters. The companies did not provide rolling stock; any person might construct carriages adapted to run upon the rails. . . . Passenger traffic was not expected or provided for." It was the ambitious hope of those who sponsored the Surrey Iron Railway that the line would ultimately be continued as far as Portsmouth. It was actually extended a further sixteen miles to Reigate, but it ended there. The railway remained in operation for nearly forty-five years.

STEAM OUSTS HORSES

The first man to apply steam to railway wagons was Richard Trevithick, of Cornwall. This he did with the aid of a Mr. Vivian, at Merthyr Tydfil, Wales, in 1804. His locomotive "drew as many carriages or wagons as contained about ten tons and a half of iron, travelling at the rate of five miles and a half an hour, for a distance of nine miles." His principles were adopted by John Blenkinsop and Charles Brandling, who were jointly instrumental in running a steam-driven goods train on a four-mile-long railway line between Leeds and the Middleton Collieries. This locomotive was known as "Blenkinsop's Patent Steam Carriage." Described as an "ingenious and extraordinary piece of mechanism," it could draw thirty wagons, weighing 105 tons, at 3 m.p.h., along a level railway.

So rapidly did the use of steam engines progress that by the year 1824 there were about 10,000 in use in Great Britain.

The next public line opened was the Stockton and Darlington. Constructed with the aim of "facilitating the conveyance of coal, iron, lime, corn and other commodities from the interior of the county of

Durham to the town of Darlington and the town and port of Stockton," it was opened for traffic in September, 1825, its chief engineer being George Stephenson. A locomotive of Stephenson's design, the *Locomotion*, was immediately put into service on the line; but it shared the iron road with horse-drawn vehicles. Any one who complied with the by-laws of the company could run a carriage on the railway. The *Locomotion*, which weighed seven tons, had a normal speed of about 5 m.p.h. and a maximum speed of 8 m.p.h. It was apparently supplanted in 1827 by the *Royal George*, a much more efficient locomotive, designed by Timothy Hackworth.

In 1834 all horse-drawn vehicles were withdrawn from the line and it was thoroughly established as a fully-fledged steam railway, carrying both passengers and goods. "This date," says E. A. Pratt, the historian of inland transport, "probably marks the final disappearance of the horse as a means of traction for passenger traffic on public railways in England." The Stockton and Darlington line was extended from time to time, ultimately to become part of the North-Eastern Railway.

BORN BEFORE HIS TIME

The history of mechanical progress presents few more striking instances of a man born before his time than Thomas Gray (1787-1848) who, in 1820, published *Observations on a General Rail-way, with Plates and Map illustrative of the Plan; showing its great superiority . . . over all the present methods of conveyance.* He advocated the systematic laying-down of a network of railways all over the British Isles. According to his plan, there were to be six main lines radiating from London to the great centres of population, with subsidiary lines branching off these. Had his proposals been put into operation, Britain would have had a magnificent transport system in a very short time. But his suggestions were contemptuously rejected, despite his fervent advocacy of them, and the country was forced to wait until men with smaller minds than he had muddled their way through to a less efficient system at great expense of time and money.

A friend of the dreamer tells us that: "With Thomas Gray, begin where you would, on whatever subject, it would not be many minutes before you would be enveloped in steam, and listening to a harangue on the practicability and the advantages to the nation of a general iron railway." He died in poverty, a disappointed and embittered man

LIVERPOOL AND MANCHESTER RAILWAY

It was Gray who suggested the making of a railway between Liverpool and Manchester, and this suggestion at least was accepted, though he does not appear to have got much credit for it. The suggestion was accepted because of the exorbitant charges that had to be paid in canal dues for goods between Liverpool and Manchester. Despite the merchants' repeated requests for reductions in the charges the canal owners remained adamant.

Finally, in desperation, the merchants prepared plans for the construction of a railway. The canal owners replied by using all their wealth and influence " to oppose, by a united effort, the establishment of railroads wherever contemplated." The Bill for the construction of the Liverpool and Manchester Railway was rejected in 1825 and passed the following year only after a section of the canal owners had been heavily bribed to give way. The laying down of the line was then begun under the direction of George Stephenson.

TRIUMPH OF THE "ROCKET"

Two years after the commencement of building operations the owners of the Liverpool and Manchester Railway were still undecided as to what motive power they should use. It was in this uncertain frame of mind that a number of the directors visited Killingworth Colliery, to see Stephenson's locomotives in action, and then went on to Darlington to see the new steam trains on the Stockton and Darlington line. So impressed were they that their doubts were immediately resolved: they would have steam.

The company then offered a prize of £500 for the most suitable locomotive. The premium was won by George Stephenson, whose *Rocket*, carrying a load of seventeen tons, put up the amazing speed of 29 m.p.h. during its trials. The directors had not dared to hope for more than about 10 m.p.h.

The ceremonial opening of this railway in September 1830 was marred by a tragic accident. Mr. William Huskisson, M.P. for Liverpool, was knocked down and fatally injured by the *Rocket* just after he had exchanged greetings with the Duke of Wellington. Distressing as was this accident, it had an immediate sequel which proved in dramatic fashion the value of railways. Huskisson was carried to Eccles, fifteen miles away, by the locomotive *Northumbrian* in twenty-five minutes; that is, at an average speed of 36 m.p.h. Few people had even imagined that such a speed was possible for a locomotive. Its achievement did much to make England railway-conscious.

The Liverpool and Manchester Railway was an immediate success. In little more than three months from the time of its opening about 72,000 passengers had used it and over 4,000 tons of coal and other commodities had been transported along it. In the year 1831 no fewer than 440,000 people booked seats in its trains.

DIFFICULT BIRTH OF THE L.M.S.

The first railway to link London with the provinces was that from London to Birmingham. Opened in sections, it was completed in September 1838, the engineers being George and Robert Stephenson. One hundred years later the London, Midland and Scottish Railway, of which the line now forms a part, chose this date to celebrate its centenary.

Before the railway came the only practicable means of transporting heavy goods from Birmingham to London was by canal. At least three

days were spent in transit; sometimes much longer. And since Birming
ham, which had already a population of over 110,000 in 1830, was
rapidly increasing in industrial importance, it was imperative that she
should acquire a speedier means of transport to the sea. Despite this
obvious fact, the sponsors of the London-Birmingham Railway had to
fight a desperate battle against powerful interests that opposed its
coming into being.

The Bill for its construction was passed by the Commons but was
thrown out by the Lords. Their Lordships' objections were overcome
by judicious bribery and the paying of extravagant sums to compensate
them for the "damage" the railway would do to their lands. But they
were not alone in their opposition.

The authorities of Northampton, through which it was proposed
to lay the line, flatly refused to permit their town to be contaminated
by iron monsters, and Robert Stephenson was forced to lay his line
some distance from the town. To do this it was necessary to drive
a tunnel at Kilsby. The contract for the tunnel was let out at £90,000,
but the contractor threw up the project in despair when he came upon
quicksand. Robert Stephenson himself then took over control of the
boring operations.

According to E. A. Pratt, "he had to have 1,250 men, 200 horses
and thirteen steam engines at work raising 1,800 gallons of water per
minute night and day for the greater part of eight months before the
difficulty was overcome. By the time the tunnel was completed the
cost of construction had risen from the original estimate of £90,000
to over £300,000, this enormous expenditure having been incurred, not
because it was necessary for the line, as first designed, but to meet the
opposition and to spare the feelings of the then short-sighted dwellers in
the town of Northampton."

The London terminus was at Euston, where a magnificent station
with an imposing Doric arch (still standing) was erected; but at first the
locomotives only drew the trains as far as the Camden Depot, since
the gradient between Euston and Camden was regarded as too steep
for them. Between Euston and Camden the trains were operated by
stationary engines. Euston station cost the comparatively small sum of
£81,532, while the Camden Depot cost nearly £30,000 more.

COST OF OVERCOMING OPPOSITION

The London and Birmingham Railway Company were forced to
pay £6,300 a mile for the land on which they laid their line. The
corresponding figure for the Great Western was £6,696; for the London
and South Western, £4,000; and for the Brighton Railway £8,000. A
striking contrast is offered by the procedure in certain European countries, where landowners, instead of being encouraged by the State to
extort exorbitant sums from the railway companies, were forced
to sell land at a reasonable price whenever it was needed for railway
construction.

John Francis, an early historian of the railways, tells of a certain nobleman who expressed great resentment when it was proposed to lay down a railway in his grounds. "In vain was it proved that the new road would not come within six miles of his house, that the highway lay between, that a tunnel would hide the inelegance. He resisted all overtures on the plea of his feelings, until £30,000 was offered. The route was, however, afterwards changed. A new line was marked out which would not even approach his domain; and, enraged at the prospect of losing the £30,000, he resisted it as strenuously as the other."

WORLD'S MOST EXPENSIVE RAILWAYS

Another great source of expense to the companies was the Parliamentary proceedings that had to be gone through before permission to lay the line could be gained. The most startling instance is the £75,673 that the Blackwall Railway Company had to pay for permission to lay down 5¼ miles of line—£14,414 a mile. The Great Western paid £89,197 on this score; the London and Birmingham, £72,868; the South-Eastern, £82,292. Within fifteen years of the opening of the Liverpool and Manchester Railway, sixteen British companies had collectively paid away over £680,000 in Parliamentary costs alone.

One company, not included in the above-mentioned, spent nearly half a million before it was granted the required powers. Another company paid £146,000, but was never granted its Bill.

In the early years of the present century there were 22,843 miles of railway in the British Isles. The cost of their construction was estimated at £1,272,600,000 or £55,712 per mile. It is interesting to note that the cost per mile of the Danish railways was only £10,884; of the Canadian £12,022; of the American £15,071. The British were by far the most expensive railways in the world, the next in that respect being the Belgian, which cost £37,088 per mile.

FOUR MILLION PASSENGERS A DAY

In 1847, seventeen years after the opening of the Liverpool and Manchester Railway, British railways carried over fifty million passengers who paid £5,148,000 in fares; and the freightage on the goods they transported was over £3,360,000. Thirteen years later (1860) they were carrying more than three times as many passengers, and receiving a gross income of £27,000,000.

Twenty years later (1880) the number of passengers carried (exclusive of season-ticket holders) was about 604 millions. In the same year 235 million tons of freight were transported. But profits had not increased in the same proportion: the net receipts in 1860 were £14,000,000: in 1880 they were only £32,000,000.

The total length of the British Railways was 18,000 miles in 1880. It had increased to 20,000 by 1890; to 22,843 in 1905; and to 23,718 in 1913. Since then there has been little expansion.

In 1913—perhaps the most prosperous year the railways ever had, since after the World War they were faced with the competition of the motor car—the number of passengers (exclusive of season-ticket holders) stood at 1,455 millions, or just under four million a day. In the same year 568 million tons of freight were carried, and the net receipts were £52,000,000, an increase of £20,000,000 on the figure for 1880.

BRIDGES OF RENOWN

PRIMITIVE man had many problems to face which are unknown to civilization. One of them was how to get across a stream that was too broad to jump and too deep to wade. It was not an insuperable problem; there were several solutions. A man might swim across; he could use a boat; he could walk along the bank until he found a fordable spot, or he could build a bridge.

Each of these methods had its limitations, but the last, where practicable, offered many advantages. Once built, a bridge reduced the labour of crossing almost to nothing. It was safer than either swimming or going by boat, and it could be thrown across water passable by neither of these methods. It could be used in almost any weather, and at any hour of the day or night.

NATURE POINTS THE WAY

So primitive man set himself to build bridges, learning, as usual, from Nature, who, if necessity be the mother of invention, might reasonably be called the father thereof. Man's first bridge was for certain the tree trunk which by great good luck had fallen athwart a stream. It was not a great step forward from observation of that to the use of two tree trunks, one projecting from each bank and supported by piles driven into the mud.

At least as early as the New Stone Age man had learned that two tree trunks or two slabs of rock placed on end and inclined together would carry far greater weight than single supports at intervals.

In the tropics he saw and used tracks in the tree-tops made by parasite plants which in their growth leaped from tree to tree and crossed streams and narrow ravines with ease. In stony lands he came across natural bridges cut out of the solid rock.

So that he had before his eyes examples of almost every type of bridge that is known today, from the single-span to the suspension bridge.

The oldest bridges were built on piers. Such a one spanned the Euphrates at Babylon in the days when that city was the head of a mighty empire. The bridge was made of cypress, palm and cedar wood, and supported by more than 100 stone pillars. During its construction the river was diverted from its normal course.

Among the greatest bridging feats of antiquity must be reckoned that of Xerxes, King of Persia, who in 480 B.C., on his way to invade Greece, flung two bridges of boats across the wide and swiftly flowing current of the Hellespont (modern Dardanelles) and marched over them an army which may well have numbered half a million men.

ROME THE MASTER BUILDER

But bridge-building remained in a comparatively rudimentary state until the rise to power of Rome, when was initiated a period of construction such as has never been excelled for magnificence of conception and excellence of execution.

The Romans built in stone. Their work was immensely durable, so that traces of it remain to this day. At Rimini, in Italy, there stands a bridge built by the Emperors Augustus and Tiberius in the 1st century A.D. At Narni, on the Tiber, fifty miles from Rome, can be seen the ruin of a lovely single-arch bridge probably nearly 2,000 years old.

The name of the town of Alcantara in western Spain means in Arabic "The Bridge." Here the River Tagus is spanned by one of the finest bridges the Romans ever built. Erected about A.D. 105, its granite blocks were cut to form a solid mass, and neither cement nor mortar was used in its construction.

Four bridges in the Eternal City claim to date from the Imperial Age, but, as with all these ancient structures, it is unlikely that much of the original material now remains. Water below and traffic above take a heavy toll of the stone bridge, even when constructed with Roman solidity. To see certain evidence of the excellence of Roman work it is necessary to turn to their aqueducts, the finest examples of which are to be found at Tarragona and Segovia, in Spain, and Nîmes, in France.

A curious fate befell the remains of the wooden Drusus Bridge built by the Romans at Mainz in Germany. Two thousand years after its erection a number of oak piles were dug up from the river bed. From the sound wood at the core of these, four pianos were made in Berlin, to produce a tone which delighted all ears.

The English carried on the Roman tradition of bridge-building, so that today English-built bridges are to be found all over the world. The most memorable achievement of medieval England was the famous old London Bridge, begun in the last years of the 12th century and still standing in the early years of the 19th. But all over the British Isles are to be seen exquisite examples of the medieval stonemason's art.

WORLD'S GREATEST BRIDGES

San Francisco, the second sea-port of the United States, possesses the two greatest bridges in the world: the San Francisco-Oakland Bridge and the Golden Gate Bridge. The longer of these is the San Francisco-Oakland. This spans Oakland Bay to link the cities from which it derives its name. The sections of the bridge that are over deep water are no less than 4½ miles long; the total length is 8¼ miles.

The structure is in fact a system of bridges, being divided into two main sections by Yerba Buena Island in Oakland Bay. The section joining San Francisco to the island is known as the West Crossing. It consists of two main suspension spans, both of which are anchored to an immense concrete pier in the middle of the fairway, and four side spans. The main spans are each 2,310 ft. long and the side spans 1,160 ft.

The East Crossing, the section joining the island to Oakland, is 19,400 ft. long. It consists of a cantilever bridge, a number of girder spans and a mile-long mole. The cantilever bridge has a central span of 1,400 ft., and two side spans each 512 ft. long. There are nineteen girder spans: five with an average length of 507 ft., and fourteen smaller ones each 291 ft. long. The bridge has two decks, the upper one accommodating six lines of motor traffic and the lower three lines of lorries and two lines of electric trams. Construction was completed in November 1936, by which time about £16,000,000 had been expended.

SPANNING THE GOLDEN GATE

The Golden Gate structure, which bridges the channel through which the waters of the Pacific pass into and out of Oakland Bay, is only a quarter the length of the San Francisco-Oakland Bridge, but all its parts are on a much grander scale. It is a suspension bridge with a main span of 4,200 ft. and two approach spans of 1,125 ft. The main span is by far the longest in the world. The two steel towers supporting the suspension cables are each 746 ft. high. Construction was begun in 1930 and completed seven years later.

Ranking next to the Golden Gate Bridge in point of suspension-span length is the George Washington, over the Hudson River, New York. Completed in 1931, it has a clear span of 3,500 ft. Following the San Francisco-Oakland bridge as regards length and complexity is the Triborough system of bridges which unites the three New York boroughs of Bronx, Manhattan and Queen's across Hell Gate and adjacent waters. It consists of four distinct bridges, which together with approaches have a length of twenty-five miles. £12,000,000 had been expended on the system when it was opened in July 1936.

BRIDGES OF THE EMPIRE

Outside the United States of America, the most spectacular bridge is that over Sydney Harbour, Australia. It has a span of 1,650 ft., or two feet less than that of the Bayonne Bridge, which spans the Kill van Kull Channel between Port Richmond, Staten Island, and Bayonne, New Jersey. Canada possesses in the Quebec Bridge, completed in 1917, the longest cantilever span in the world—1,800 ft. The next longest cantilever span, 1,710 ft., is that of the Forth Bridge, in Scotland.

The Hardinge Bridge over the River Ganges, at Sara, is one of the greatest structures of its kind in India. It has fifteen main spans, each of 345 ft., and three land spans, each 75 ft. long. The bridge proper is 1⅛ miles long, but including approaches it has a length of fifteen miles. Before construction could begin the banks of the river in the neighbourhood of the bridge had to be reinforced with 38,600,000 cubic feet of earth and 23,370,000 cubic feet of stone to keep the river to its proper course. The whole structure took six years to complete and at one time there were 24,400 men on the contractors' pay-roll.

The Ava railway bridge over the Irrawaddy, nine miles from Mandalay, Burma, has sixteen spans, nine of which are 360 ft. long. Ten thousand tons of steel were put into the structure and the total outlay on it was over £1,000,000.

TUNNELS OF YESTERDAY AND TODAY

IN the eighteenth chapter of the Second Book of Kings there is a reference to "the conduit of the upper pool which is in the highway of the fuller's field." This conduit, one of the oldest tunnels of antiquity, is still in good condition. It connected the two pools of Siloah (or Siloam, or Bethesda). "The pool of Siloam," says Edward Robinson, "is a small deep reservoir, into which the water flows from under the rocks out of a smaller basin hewn in the solid rock a few feet farther up. . . . This is wholly an artificial work; and the water comes to it through a subterraneous channel under the hill Ophel, from another fountain higher up in the valley of Jehoshaphat." It was made by Hezekiah, one of the greatest of the kings of Judah, at about the end of the 8th century B.C. Its length is about 1,640 ft., and work was begun on it from both ends at once. Its vaulting is constructed in the solid rock, 100 ft. below the surface.

Tunnelling, however, goes back much farther than that. The fact that early man was cave-dwelling for perhaps thousands of years probably accounts for the readiness with which early civilized men began boring into rock, as well as for the delight taken by children in exploring caves.

TUNNELLING FOR TOMBS

The kings of Thebes in Egypt invariably began tunnelling when they came to the throne. The object was to make an extensive approach to their future burial chambers. King Mineptah's shaft is driven 350 ft. into a hill; after sinking a shaft, the delvers then continued for another 300 ft. In Nubia, India, and in the American Aztec country, similar tunnels are found.

The Egyptians were as great tunnellers as they were builders. According to Sir Flinders Petrie, the method employed was to drive several galleries about 20 ft. square, and then cross-cut, making a single gallery several hundred feet wide, with pillars 20 ft. square. Egyptian tube drills leave a track just like the modern diamond drill.

Under the Palace of Nimrûd in Assyria is a vaulted drain; and a tunnel 12 ft. high and 15 ft. wide, arched with bricks, has been found under the Euphrates. Another ancient tunnel still in existence is the water-conduit, 3,250 ft. long, built on the island of Samos by the Greek tyrant Polycrates about 530 B.C.

The Romans left tunnels nearly everywhere they went in Europe, especially in Switzerland. They were used for water-pipes, drains and roadways. One of the most remarkable of their achievements was the construction of a tunnel through Monte Salviano, in the Apennine range, for draining Lake Fucino. Completed about A.D. 52, it was over 3½ miles long, 10 ft. high and 6 ft. deep. It is recorded that 30,000 workmen toiled upon this task for eleven years.

PIERCING THE MOUNTAINS FOR RAILWAYS

Perhaps 4,000 tunnels for railways alone have been cut. Through the hearts of mountains run tunnels of relatively immense length, each of which represented in its day a triumph of engineering.

The Mont Cenis tunnel (eight miles long) was finished in 1870; the St. Gotthard Tunnel (9⅓ miles) ten years later. The construction of the Simplon Tunnel, the longest main-line railway tunnel in the world, necessitated the explosion of 1,350 tons of dynamite to remove about a million cubic yards of stone; 12⅓ miles long, it was finished in 1906. The Lötschberg, between Kandersteg and Gopperstein in Switzerland, is over 9 miles long and was finished in 1911. An unfortunate accident occurred while the Lötschberg was being constructed: the tunnellers broke through unexpectedly into the subterranean gorge of the Kander River and twenty-five men were killed by the inrush of water. The tunnel through the Apennines between Bologna and Florence is 11½ miles long.

Among the other great main-line railway tunnels of the world are the New Cascade, at Washington, U.S.A. (7.8 miles); the Moffat, Colorado, U.S.A. (6.2 miles); the Shimizu, Japan (6.1 miles); the Otira, New Zealand (5.3 miles); the Rogers Pass, British Columbia (5 miles). England's longest main-line railway tunnel, that under the Severn, is 4 miles 624 yards long. About half the length is under water.

The greatest passenger subway in Europe is the white-tiled tunnel running beneath the Quirinal in Rome, while the most substantial river tunnel is the Holland Tunnel which connects New York with New Jersey. It consists of twin thoroughfares, each for two traffic lines, 1.61 miles long, some 85 ft. below the Hudson River. Over 46,000 vehicles use the tunnel daily.

LONDON'S SEVENTY-THREE MILES OF UNDERGROUND

The London Underground system is by far the most extensive series of tunnels in the world, with some seventy-three miles of iron-lined tunnelling and thirteen miles more in immediate contemplation. James Greathead (1844-1896) built the first true "tube," the Tower Subway, in 1869, though Marc Isambard Brunel, by studying the shipworm's methods, had earlier evolved the modern method of tunnelling.

The first section of the modern system, the Monument-Stockwell section of the old City and South London line, was completed in 1890. This is now part of the Northern line. The Waterloo and City line was opened in 1898, the Central London in 1900, the Great Northern and City in 1904, the Bakerloo also in 1904, and the Piccadilly in 1906.

The Greathead shield, which evolved from the Brunel shield, and the rotary excavator, used in clay, are the two types of shield used for the work at the earth-face. Work proceeds so accurately that the maximum deviation reckoned permissible in half a mile is 1¼ in., although work may be begun at both ends of a section 6,000 ft. apart.

PROPOSED TUNNEL UNDER ENGLISH CHANNEL

The first person to make any serious proposals for the construction of a tunnel connecting France to England was a French engineer named Mathieu, who suggested it in 1802. "That is one of the great things we could do if we could work together," C. J. Fox told Napoleon I, but war broke out and the project came to naught. It was revived by J. A. Thomé de Gamond (1807-75), who in 1856 placed a detailed plan before Napoleon III. The idea aroused great enthusiasm on both sides of the English Channel. In Great Britain, Queen Victoria said that, " If it can be done you may say that I will give my blessing." The Prince Consort, Isambard Brunel, and Gladstone were among its principal supporters. Count von Moltke expressed the opinion that, "A foreign army could no more enter England through the Channel Tunnel than through my library door." In France all the people who mattered supported it, and when the plans were shown at the Universal Exhibition held in 1867 they aroused much interest. In 1875 an Anglo-French convention was drawn up to regulate it.

Digging began in 1880, and the French Channel Company sank a shaft at Sangatte and bored a mile under the Channel. Similar work was begun near Shakespeare Cliff, Dover. A shaft lined with cast-iron segments was sunk 160 ft. and extended for 2,015 yards. Two other shafts were begun at Abbots Cliff and connected by a gallery 880 yards in length. Over 7,600 soundings were made and some 3,000 samples were taken from the bottom of the Channel. In 1882 the British War Office offered objections, and the plan was held up. Among those who raised their voices against the tunnel at various times were Lord Wolseley, Joseph Chamberlain, and Lord Randolph Churchill. Swinburne ridiculed it in a poem. In later days Prince Louis of Battenberg and Sir John French (later Earl of Ypres) were in favour of the undertaking. Bills were promoted in the British Parliament again and again, but all to no purpose.

The project was again officially considered in England in 1924, when Ramsay MacDonald, the Premier, held a conference on the subject with the four ex-Premiers, Stanley Baldwin, Bonar Law, D. Lloyd George, and Henry Asquith. After a discussion which lasted no more than forty minutes they decided against it, apparently on the ground that

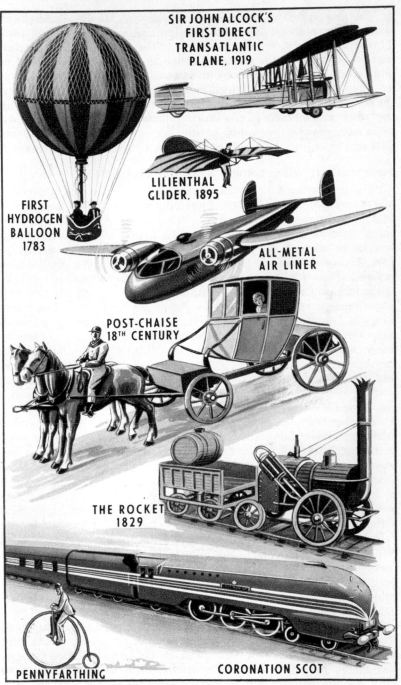

SIR JOHN ALCOCK'S
FIRST DIRECT
TRANSATLANTIC
PLANE, 1919

LILIENTHAL
GLIDER, 1895

FIRST
HYDROGEN
BALLOON
1783

ALL-METAL
AIR LINER

POST-CHAISE
18TH CENTURY

THE ROCKET
1829

PENNYFARTHING

CORONATION SCOT

Lines of Development on Land and in the Air

NORMAN SHIP

13TH CENTURY SHIP

SHIP OF THE TIME OF HENRY VIII

ARAB SHIP

BIRCH BARK CANOE

HONG KONG HARBOUR SAMPAN

EAST COAST COBLE

EMPRESS OF BRITAIN

Ships Ancient and Modern

it would be a danger in time of war. On this point it is interesting to note the opinion of Marshal Foch, who said, in 1922: "If the Channel Tunnel had been built it might have prevented the War, and in any event it would have shortened its duration by one-half." In 1924 there was a two to one majority in favour of it in the House of Commons. The matter was brought up again in 1930, but the proposals were once more rejected.

The proposal is briefly this: the tunnel would have a length of thirty-one miles, two-thirds of it being 260 ft. below sea-level and 95 ft. below the bed of the Channel. It would consist of two tubes lined with reinforced concrete 50 ft. apart and each 20 ft. in diameter. Its English portal would be between Dover and Folkestone, and its French one between Boulogne and Calais. It would take about five years to construct and cost from £25,000,000 to £30,000,000.

BRUNEL, GREATEST TUNNEL ENGINEER

Sir Marc Isambard Brunel (1769-1849) is generally regarded as the greatest of all tunnel engineers. He took out a patent in 1818 for a tunnelling process which used a shield and surrounding cast-iron wall, thus anticipating the modern supporting shield. Between 1825-1843 he completed the Rotherhithe-Wapping, the first tunnel under the Thames. From 1833, as engineer of the projected Great Western Railway, he had to battle with many tunnelling problems, especially difficult being the tunnels through the soft red cliffs of south Devon.

His son, Isambard Kingdom Brunel (1806-1859), assisted in the construction of the Thames Tunnel. He also designed the Clifton Suspension Bridge and several big ships, including the *Great Eastern*.

POSTAL SYSTEMS

XENOPHON tells us that Cyrus, King of Persia (6th century B.C.), set up a post system operated by horsemen during the Scythian War. We read that Cyrus "caused it to be tried how far a horse could go in a day without baiting (eating), and, at that distance, appointed stages and men whose business it was to have horses always in readiness." This, according to William Lewins, the historian of posts, is the first recorded instance of a riding post. Cyrus's postal service was operated along the Ancient Royal Road of which an account is given in another part of this book. The Royal Road had 111 postal stages, "a day's journey distant from one another, between Susa (near the northern extremity of the Persian Gulf) and the Ægean Sea. . . . At each stage a large and beautiful structure was erected, with every convenience for the purpose designed."

A postal service similar to that of Cyrus existed in China from a very early date, as we know from Marco Polo, the Venetian traveller who lived there in the 14th century. According to Polo there were 10,000 postal stations at twenty-five-mile intervals along the roads of China.

At some of these posts 300 horses were kept, there being 200,000 horses altogether engaged in the service.

This service, like that operated by the Romans along their trunk roads was mainly, if not solely, for official use.

FIRST LETTER-POST IN EUROPE

The Emperor Charlemagne instituted a postal service in the early years of the 9th century, but it did not remain in operation for very long. Four centuries later the first regular letter-post was established by the Hanseatic merchants in northern Europe. The next was that established by the princes of the House of Thurn and Taxis between Austria and Lombardy, in the reign of the Emperor Maximilian. In the 15th century the French King, Louis XI, revived Charlemagne's postal system by establishing a corps of long-distance messengers, numbering 230. A similar corps of official couriers existed in England as early as King John's reign.

A POSTMASTER-GENERAL'S SALARY

The first English Postmaster-General of whom any account survives was Sir Brian Tuke (died in 1545), who flourished on a salary of £66 13s. 4d. in the early years of the 16th century. His duties included the appointment and supervision of the postmen; and the provision of horses for the transport of letters. The wages of his postmen ranged between one and two shillings a day.

" FOREIGN OR STRANGERS' " POST

Until near the end of the 16th century the Royal Posts did not handle private letters to and from foreign parts. Their only concern was official letters. There were several means by which private persons could correspond with people on the continent of Europe. Conspicuous among them was the " Foreign or Strangers' Post " which was run by foreigners—Italians, Spanish and Dutch—resident in London. This post was suppressed in 1591 on the ground that it facilitated the passage of treasonable correspondence and also that it did not handle the letters of Englishmen as expeditiously as those of foreigners. Nevertheless, not long afterwards a foreigner, De Quester by name, was appointed one of the Royal Posts " beyond seas "; and in 1619 he became Postmaster-General for " foreign parts." He was granted the sole right to deal with foreign mail.

FIRST MAN TO MAKE POSTS PAY

De Quester was succeeded in this position by Thomas Witherings, who was described by his enemies as a " home-bred shopkeeper, without languages, tainted of delinquency and in dislike with the foreign correspondents." " He was," said they, " no fit person to carry a trust of such secrecy and importance." But despite this condemnation he carried out his duties so satisfactorily that he was, in 1635, given control of the

Inland Posts as well. He established a central Post Office in London and thoroughly overhauled the whole postal system, inland and foreign. He was the first man to make the posts pay. They paid handsomely, and by the year 1685 they were producing a clear profit of £65,000. Charles II instituted the practice of granting pensions out of the Post Office profits. One of the first persons to receive such a pension was Barbara Palmer, Duchess of Cleveland, an intimate friend of the Merry Monarch. She was given £4,700 a year; and the right to receive this sum was vested in her successors, the Dukes of Grafton. It was not until 1856 that the State redeemed the grant by paying the holder of the title the sum of £91,181 17s. 7d.

PENNY POST IN LONDON

By the middle of the 17th century there was a fairly efficient postal service in operation between London and a large number of the principal towns of Britain, but no means existed of sending letters from one part of London to another. The merchants of the capital made many un-successful attempts to induce the government to establish such a service. Then, in 1683, an enterprising upholsterer named Robert Murray established a penny post for London and its suburbs. "All letters and parcels not exceeding a pound weight, or any sum of money not above £10 in value, or parcel worth not more than £10 might be conveyed at a charge of *one penny* in the city and suburbs, and of twopence to any distance within a given ten-mile circuit." Offices for the reception of letters and parcels were opened in all the main streets. Hanging at the doors of these offices were placards bearing the words: "Penny post letters taken in here."

COLLECTIONS EVERY HOUR

Stow, the historian of London, tells us that: "Letter carriers gather them (the letters) every hour, and take them to the grand office in their respective districts. After the said letters and parcels are duly entered in the books, they are delivered at stated periods by other carriers." In the heart of the City there were half a dozen or more deliveries daily, and as many as four in the outlying districts. This, in the 17th century. Originated by Robert Murray, the London penny post was taken over soon after its inception by William Dockwra.

Immediately it began to appear that this post was a money-making proposition the long-somnolent authorities began to wake up. The Duke of York had, in 1675, been granted the profits of the Royal Post Office, and in virtue of this grant he sought, and was given, authority to appropriate the penny-post system that had been built up by the expenditure of much money and labour on the part of Murray and Dockwra.

To operate the system, the duke opened a London district office at the General Post Office, and this district office was continued as a separate department until 1854.

When Dutch William came to the throne, Dockwra was appointed Controller of the District Post, and shortly afterwards he was granted a pension of £500 a year for seven years, " in consideration of the good services performed to the Crown in inventing and settling the business of the penny Post-office." What reward, if any, Murray got, we do not know.

PENSIONS FROM POST OFFICE FUNDS

Dockwra's pension was paid out of the profits of the Post Office, the prosperous condition of which is proved by the fact that in 1694 six other persons, including the beautiful Barbara, were receiving pensions from it. The total amount being paid away in this fashion was £21,200 per annum.

One of the pensioners was Maynard, Duke of Schomberg, whose heirs were still receiving £4,000 a year from the Post Office funds in the middle of the 19th century. Maynard's claim to benefit thus from the public purse was based on the fact that he was related to a gentleman who helped to win the Battle of the Boyne. In 1707 a grant of £5,000 a year was made to the Duke of Marlborough and his heirs for ever from the Post Office funds. In view of these and subsequent grants it seems extraordinary that the Post Office should ever have survived.

POST OFFICE ACT OF 1710

In 1710 there was passed "An Act for establishing a General Post-Office in all Her Majesty's dominions, and for settling a weekly sum out of the revenue thereof for the service of the war, and other of Her Majesty's occasions." By far the most important Post Office Act hitherto passed, it remained in force until 1837, the year of Queen Victoria's accession. It provided, among many other things, for the establishment of " chief offices " in Edinburgh, in Dublin, in New York and other convenient places in the American colonies, and in " the islands of the West Indies, called the Leeward Islands." All these offices were placed under the control of Her Majesty's Postmaster-General.

The amount to be paid out of the postal revenues towards the cost of the war was to be no less than £700 a week, i.e., £36,400 a year, a staggering sum for a struggling institution to have to bear in addition to the pensions already mentioned.

SHOULD M.P.'S LETTERS GO FREE?

The story of the introduction of the franking system, by which the letters of Members of Parliament were sent free of charge, makes amusing reading. The proposal that " Members' letters should come and go free during the time of their sittings " was put forward by the sponsors of the Post Office Act of 1660 as a bait to induce members to support the Bill. A number of members were, however, indignant at the suggestion, seeing in it an insult to their dignity. "It is," said

one, " a poor mendicant proviso, and below the honour of the House."
The Speaker of the House at first refused to have anything to do with
the proposed clause, saying he " felt ashamed of it." Finally, after much
high-sounding talk, the House got down to business and approved the
clause by a large majority. The Post Office Bill was then sent to the
Upper House, which immediately deleted the clause, not, as it pretended,
because of its " shameful " nature, but because it did not allow for the
letters of the noble Lords themselves to be sent free. The farce came
to an end some years later, when a clause providing for the extension of
the privilege to the Lords was put forward.

The privilege was very greatly abused by members of both Houses,
who allowed their franks to be used by others; and also by non-members,
who by various wiles succeeded in passing off their correspondence as
that of members. Whereas in 1716 the Post Office lost £27,000 by reason
of the franking system, in 1763 it lost more than six times this amount.

TWO GUINEAS A WEEK FOR VINEGAR

Before the Great Fire (1666), the General Post Office was " at " the
" Black Swan " in Bishopsgate Street. After the fire it was moved first
to Covent Garden and then to Lombard Street, where it remained until
1829. The Lombard Street premises were described in 1814 as " so close
and confined as to be injurious to the health of those concerned "; and
it was said that " two guineas were expended weekly for vinegar to
fumigate the rooms, and prevent infectious fevers."

The present site, St. Martin's-le-Grand, was chosen in 1825; and
the new building, " one of the handsomest public structures in London,"
was opened in 1829.

As soon as the Liverpool and Manchester Railway was opened in
1830, the mails of the district were handed over to it; and in 1838 Acts
were passed " to provide for the conveyance of mails by railways."
The Post Office authorities would appear to have been reluctant to
entrust their precious burdens to the new fangled steam engines; but,
as a Board of Trade official said in 1838, " the Post Office was obliged
to have recourse to railways, or suspend operations; the iron roads had
already put a stop to most of the stage-coach traffic on the principal
roads."

TOO COSTLY TO WRITE LETTERS

When Queen Victoria ascended the throne in 1837 the average letter
cost 9½d. to send, or about twice as much as at the beginning of the
18th century. This exorbitant rate damaged the Post Office as much
as the general public, although it took the postal authorities a long time
to realize the fact. In 1815 Post Office revenue amounted to £1,500,000;
but twenty years later, despite large increases in population and in
trade and vast improvements in methods of transport, the revenue
had increased by not more than a few thousand pounds.

The reason was that the high postage rates discouraged private persons from letter writing and forced business people to look for alternative ways of sending letters, in contravention of the law which had granted a monopoly to the Post Office. So great was the number of contraband letters, that several carriers were said to be doing as much business as the Post Office itself, and at one time officialdom despaired of ever being able to prevent the illicit trade. Obviously nothing could be done until the Post Office had been thoroughly reformed.

ROWLAND HILL'S PREPOSTEROUS PLAN

Needless to say, there were not a few people who dared to criticize the postal authorities and to demand reform; but little or nothing was done until a certain Mr. Rowland Hill (1795-1879) began to interest himself in the problem. After having made an exhaustive study of every aspect of the postal system, Hill published, in January 1837, a pamphlet called *Post Office Reform: its Importance and Practicability*. This pamphlet was a masterpiece of accurate statement, clear thinking and originality.

Having demonstrated that the apparent average cost of *conveying* each letter was less than one-tenth of a penny, and that it cost little more to *send* a letter 200 miles than to send it twenty—the main expenses being those of collection and delivery—he suggested that there should be a uniform rate, regardless of distance, for every letter weighing less than half an ounce. (Hitherto it had been customary to vary the charges according to the distance the letter had to cover.)

Hill further suggested " a large diminution in the rates of postage, say even to one penny per letter "; a general speeding-up of the services; and a simplification, leading to economy, in the operation of the whole postal system.

Few pamphlets can have been received with such enthusiasm on the part of the general public and such horror and indignation on the part of authority. The Postmaster-General was moved to declare that " of all the wild and visionary schemes which I have ever heard of, it is the most extravagant." An outraged colonel bluntly described it as " a most preposterous plan, utterly unsupported by facts, resting entirely on assumptions." But, unfortunately for the highly-placed opponents of the scheme, Hill had written his pamphlet so ably that practically all the merchants and tradesmen in Britain were convinced of the practicability of his plan, and so great a clamour was raised that in January 1840, exactly three years after the pamphlet's appearance, a minute was issued ordering the adoption of a uniform penny rate.

FIRST ENGLISH POSTAGE-STAMP

The first English penny postage-stamp was designed by Messrs. Bacon and Petch—their design having been chosen from more than 1,000 others—and was engraved on a steel die, costing sixty guineas, by Charles Heath. Issued in 1840, it was first printed in black, but the colour was changed to brown after two years because it soon appeared that it was too easy to use black stamps more than once. To make the post-mark more obvious still the colour was shortly afterwards changed again, this time to red.

Stamp collecting as a hobby appears not to have enjoyed much popularity until after the year 1860. A writer of the mid-19th century refers to "the *timbromanie,* or stamp mania." He goes on: "The scenes in Birchin Lane in 1862, where crowds nightly congregated, to the exceeding annoyance and wonder of the uninitiated—where ladies and gentlemen of all ages and ranks, from Cabinet-ministers to crossing-sweepers, were busy, with album or portfolio in hand, buying, selling, or exchanging, are now known to have been the beginnings of what may almost be termed a new trade."

In 1864 there were "dozens of regular dealers (in stamps) in the metropolis, who were doing a profitable trade." The practice of collecting stamps originated in France. Stamp collectors were at first the object of much good-natured ridicule, but, to quote the patronizing remarks of Mr. William Lewins: "The gathering of a complete set of postage-stamps, and a proper arrangement of them, is at least a harmless and innocent amusement."

IMPERIAL PENNY POST

In 1874 the Post Office introduced a uniform rate of 2½d. for all European letters, and in 1892 this rate was applied to the whole world. The postal order was introduced in 1881; the parcel post in 1883; the sixpenny telegram in 1885. The introduction of a penny post between every part of the Empire was hailed with great enthusiasm after the celebration of Queen Victoria's Diamond Jubilee in 1897.

The World War of 1914-1918 caused an increase in Post Office rates. In 1915 the sixpenny telegram disappeared, to be followed three years later by the penny post. In 1919 the letter-rate was 1½d.; in 1920 it was 2d.; in 1922 it was again reduced to 1½d., at which level it has since remained.

Some 22,000,000 letters are posted in Great Britain every day; the Post Office runs regularly four special trains, seventy sorting carriages attached to main-line trains, and 15,000 motor vehicles. It has twenty-one radio stations, 5,600 telephone exchanges, and 24,500 post offices.

In a recent year it sold 8,000 million stamps, 2,000 million telephone calls were made, 52 million ordinary telegrams were despatched, three million greetings telegrams sent, 25,600,000 letters and circulars were delivered daily, and 550,000 parcels posted every week-day. The annual turnover was £960,000,000; the wages bill £45,500,000, and the number of people employed 275,000.

POST OFFICE TELEGRAPHS

The first British telegraph company came into being in 1846. By 1863, when the question of making the telegraphs a State monopoly first came to the fore, the original company had three or four competitors. Five years later a Bill giving the State power to buy up competing companies was passed through Parliament, and in 1869 the Post Office was granted a monopoly of inland telegraph systems. About £7,200,000 had to be paid to the private companies in compensation and £800,000 to the railways.

Sir Evelyn Murray tells us that: " Financially the telegraph service is not, and never has been, a success. Before the War the deficit . . . had risen to about £1,250,000; it now (he was writing in 1927) stands at a slightly higher figure."

TELEPHONE SERVICES

In the year 1880 it was laid down by the High Court that "a telephone is a telegraph within the meaning of the Telegraph Acts and that telephonic communications are therefore within the Postmaster-General's monopoly." This judgment was given only four years after Lord Kelvin had brought the first telephone to England from America. The intervening period had seen the invention of the microphone (1878), by which a practical means of transmitting speech was introduced; and, immediately afterwards, the establishment of two private telephone companies.

Had the Post Office been controlled by vigorous and far-seeing men it would no doubt, in consequence of this judgment, have taken steps to gain absolute control of the telephone system. Instead of doing this, it compromised, allowing a number of private companies to operate lines in certain areas, but placing numberless restrictions upon their activities. The result was chaos and thoroughly inefficient services. It was not until 1912, after thirty years of muddle, that all the public telephone systems of the country came under Post Office control. Since then steady progress has been made in the provision of cheap and efficient services.

BRITISH WIRELESS COMMUNICATIONS

The first recorded use of wireless by the British Post Office was in 1895, when, after a cable had broken down, wireless communication was set up between the Island of Mull and the mainland. Three years later (1898) a ship-to-shore station was established at the Needles; in 1899 wireless communication across the English Channel was set up. Even then wireless was not taken very seriously by the public. But when, in 1901, Marconi succeeded in transmitting signals across the Atlantic between England and Newfoundland, the doubting Thomases ceased to doubt.

It soon became obvious that it would be necessary to exercise a large measure of State control over wireless, and in 1904 the Wireless Telegraphy Act came into force. By this measure it was made illegal for anyone in the British Isles or in British ships to install any kind of wireless apparatus whatever without a licence from the Postmaster-General. Later an International Radio-Telegraph Convention, regulating the international use of wireless, was signed by all the principal nations. The main concern of the signatories was to ensure international co-operation in the matter of ship-to-shore wireless communication. Since then the original convention has been greatly revised and expanded to meet modern conditions.

FOUR THOUSAND YEARS OF SHIPS

THE earliest known representation of a sea-going ship is a carving on the wall of the temple of King Sahure of Egypt, who lived in the 28th century B.C. The vessel had a large double mast and twenty oars, ten on each side. The hull looks like that of a modern sea-going yacht. Egyptian river boats made of bundles of papyrus reeds lashed together were in use at least as early as 3000 B.C., and probably many centuries before that time. Boats of exactly similar construction are still used on Lake Tana in Abyssinia. They probably represent the oldest type of boat still in use.

On the other side of the Red Sea, in Iraq, the Assyrian *kalek,* a raft supported by inflated sheepskins, is still in use at least 3,000 years after it was first introduced. Another very ancient craft used by Iraqi boatmen on the Tigris and the Euphrates is the *gufa.* Circular in shape, it has a wooden framework covered with skins made watertight with bitumen.

ANCIENT MEN-O'-WAR

Ships similar to those of King Sahure were still being built in Egypt more than a thousand years after his death. A relief in the temple of Deir el Bahari (1480 B.C.) gives us detailed representations of the ships sent by Queen Hatshepset to a country near the southern end of the Red Sea about 1500 B.C. The vessels were probably about 70 ft. long and 17 ft. wide. Each carried thirty rowers and was also fitted with elaborate sails. Phœnician ships of that date were of similar general design.

The earliest known representation of a naval battle, engraved on the wall of an Egyptian temple, shows the fleet of Rameses III (about 1200 B.C.) defeating that of a northern Mediterranean confederation. Nine ships are shown and four are Egyptian. It was the Egyptian practice in naval warfare to discharge arrows at long range and then to close in upon the enemy vessels and grapple with them. The grappling instrument had four iron hooks which were thrown into the enemy craft.

SHIPS OF THE GREEKS

By about 700 B.C. *biremes,* or ships of war equipped with two banks of oars on different levels, were in common use in the Mediterranean. The *bireme* was invented by either the Egyptians or the Phœnicians. The Greeks adopted the *bireme,* and it was probably they who first improved on it by adding a third tier of oars, thus making it a *trireme*. Between 500 B.C. and 300 B.C., the *trireme* was the largest warship in the Mediterranean. After that period ships with four, five, six, and even more banks of oars were built.

A typical Greek *trireme* carried a crew of 200, of whom 170 were oarsmen. It had an overall length of about 150 ft., a beam of 16 ft., and a depth from deck to keel of about 8 ft. The rowers could maintain a speed of from seven to nine miles an hour for twenty-four-hour periods.

The Romans did not take up naval warfare until the end of the 3rd century B.C. It was then that they built their first fleet of five-banked ships that were slavish imitations of a Carthaginian vessel.

VIKING SHIPS

The first great seafaring people of northern Europe were the Vikings who flourished between the 8th and the 10th centuries. In the Museum of Archæology at Oslo is preserved a Viking ship of the 9th century which was found almost intact at Gokstad, near Oslo, in 1880. Built of oak, it is 79 ft. long, 17 ft. broad and 7 ft. deep. It was manned by thirty-two oarsmen and also carried sails. An exact copy of this ship was fitted with an auxiliary engine and navigated across the Atlantic in 1892. The original Gokstad ship may have crossed the Atlantic, because we know that the Vikings travelled to Greenland and Labrador.

SPEEDS OF SHIPS IN ANCIENT TIMES

Herodotus informs us that the passenger ships of antiquity travelled at rates ranging from $5\frac{1}{2}$ to $9\frac{1}{2}$ miles per hour. Generally speaking the speed of a merchantman was about the same as that of a modern Mediterranean coaster. Five days were required for the voyage from Ostia, the seaport of Rome, to Tarragona, on the east coast of Spain. Later, the ships of the Hanseatic League took two days and two nights to go from Jutland to Flanders, and often as long again to go from Cornwall to Brittany. Cervantes (1547-1616), the author of *Don Quixote,* was twelve days at sea when travelling from Naples to Barcelona.

The first warship of which a description survives is the *Argo,* which was built in Greece about the year 1350 B.C., and was propelled by fifty rowers. It is said to have been built of oak wood and afterwards to have been preserved in the grove of the sea-god Poseidon on the Isthmus of Corinth. The legendary ship in which Ulysses wandered round the Mediterranean after the fall of Troy is shown, transformed into a cliff, on the island of Corfu; and that other vessel which, after the destruction of his native city, Troy, bore Æneas through the Greek lines to Italy, was preserved by the Romans (just as the British have preserved Nelson's flagship, the *Victory,* at Portsmouth) in the docks on the Tiber, where it was seen by the Greek historian Procopius in the 6th century A.D.

EUROPE'S OLDEST VESSELS

The oldest surviving ship in Europe is the " Hjörtspring " boat which was found in the island of Alsen in 1921; it was built for sacrifice to the gods and dates from the time of the birth of Christ; in construction it represents the transition from the dug-out to the Viking ship. In 1935 another boat of this kind, 65 ½ ft. long, was found on the Danish island of Fünen. Since 1926 the museum at Zürich has possessed a dug-out, made of pitch-pine, which dates from the 2nd century B.C., and was discovered in the Lake of Bienne. In 1936 two Frenchmen accomplished a 7,500-mile voyage in the Pacific in a dug-out.

The oldest vessels still in service are two ex-pirate ships built in 1723 and 1749 respectively, which now ply along the Swedish coast. A still older vessel, the *Santa Barbara,* which was built in 1637, foundered off the Balearics in 1936. The life of most modern passenger steamers and battleships is only twenty to thirty years, but the *Thelholm,* a single-masted Danish vessel built in 1776, was still in service off the west coast of the Danish island of Laaland in 1936, and a White Star liner which was put in service in 1876 was still plying between England and New York in the same year.

MAMMOTH SHIPS

Abnormally large vessels were not unknown in the late classical period. The three-masted *Alexandria,* which is said to have been built to the order of King Hiero II of Syracuse and to have been presented by him to the King of Egypt in 230 B.C., was too big to be accommodated in any Sicilian harbour. Its displacement was 4,200 tons, its length 408 ft., and it carried 80,000 bushels of corn and 10,000 earthenware vessels filled with salted fish. It had sixty rooms and saloons, kitchens, a garden, bathrooms, and a library. The motive power was provided by 4,500 rowers.

The ship which in A.D. 40, at the command of the Emperor Caligula, brought an ancient Egyptian obelisk to Rome, where it now stands in the Piazza of St. Peter's, was of 2,500 tons capacity. Another mammoth vessel had room for 600 sailors and 300 soldiers and was fitted with towers, missile-throwing engines, saloons and bathrooms. A transport built in the reign of the Roman emperor Augustus had a crew of 200 and passenger accommodation for 1,200; it was also capable of carrying 93,500 bushels of grain. It was this vessel which brought to Rome the obelisk which stands to this day in the Piazza del Popolo. The galley that conveyed the Egyptian queen Cleopatra to Asia Minor was furnished with the utmost luxury.

Small in comparison with these were the ships of the Hanseatic League, such as the *Koggen,* of only 150 tons burden, and which, in contrast with the long Viking ships and the Mediterranean galleys, were short and broad and rose well above the water-line. The Lübeck warship *Adler,* built in 1565, was considered a huge vessel with its burden of 1,400 tons. Modern battleships, with displacements of over

40,000 tons, are manned by as many as 1,400 men and travel at a speed of thirty knots and upwards.

The " blue riband " of the Atlantic was won in 1930 by the German liner *Bremen,* in 1935 by the French liner *Normandie,* and in 1936 by the British liner *Queen Mary.* The *Normandie* recaptured the record in August, 1937, but a year later the *Queen Mary* again claimed it after having made an east-bound crossing in 3 days, 20 hours, 42 minutes, with an average speed of 31.69 knots. The *Queen Mary* has a gross tonnage of 80,773, her engines produce 200,000 h.p., and she carries over 3,000 passengers and crew. The blue riband trophy is of silver, the gift of Mr. Harold K. Hales, and was presented for competition in 1935.

"NEW" IDEA THAT IS 300 YEARS OLD

In the summer of 1931 Sir Hubert Wilkins, the distinguished explorer, attempted to reach the North Pole in a submarine. The *Nautilus,* as he had christened the obsolete undersea craft he had bought from the United States Navy, passed three weeks under the ice of the Arctic Ocean. During this time much useful information was gained about the forms of life to be found in these far-northern waters, and also about their temperatures and tides, but unfortunately it was not possible to reach the Pole.

At the time when Sir Hubert first suggested this expedition his idea was regarded as extremely novel; but, in point of fact, the germ of it had been suggested almost 300 years earlier by Sir Hubert's lineal ancestor, John Wilkins (1614-1672), Bishop of Chester. In the year 1648 this right reverend gentleman published a book called *Mathematicall Magick,* chapter five of which is devoted to " the possibility of framing an ark for submarine Navigations. The difficulties and conveniences of such a contrivance." Among the conveniences he reckoned the fact that " such a contrivance " is " safe . . . from ice and great frosts, which doe much to endanger the passages towards the Poles."

Another of the bishop's suggestions was that the submarine might " be of a very great advantage against a Navy of enemies, who by this means may be undermined in the water and blown up."

SUBMARINE PROPELLED BY OARS

He thought that such a contrivance was " feasible and might be effected " since it had already been experimented with " here in England by Cornelius Dreble." Dreble, a Hollander, was in the employment of the English king, James I. In 1620 a submarine constructed by him was tried out in the Thames, where it was navigated under water for several hours by twelve rowers.

In 1776, during the American War of Independence, an unsuccessful attempt was made by an undersea vessel in the service of the colonists to sink an English warship off New York. The first vessel to be sunk by a submarine was the *Housatonic,* which went down with all hands off Charleston, in the United States, on February 17, 1864, after it had been torpedoed. This was during the American Civil War.

IRON AND STEAM

An iron boat was built in England as early as 1777, but forty years were allowed to elapse before British shipbuilders began seriously to tackle the problems of iron-constructed vessels. In 1853 the *Lord of the Isles,* an early English clipper ship, was constructed of iron. Iron frigates were built for the British Navy in 1845 but it was not until 1859 that the first British iron warship appeared. The first engagement in which iron-clad ships took part was that between the American vessels *Merrimac* and *Monitor,* in March, 1862.

In the year 1736, Jonathan Hulls took out a patent " for a machine or boat for carrying vessels out of, or into port, against wind and tide, or in a calm." Here, most probably, we have the first steam tug. Hulls was the first to discover how to convert the alternate rectilineal motion of a piston-rod into a continuous rotary one by means of a crank.

In 1807 Robert Fulton, an American, produced the paddle steamer *Clermont* which carried passengers between New York and Albany. The paddle ship *Savannah* was the first steamship to cross the Atlantic. This she did in 1819, taking 35 days. Her paddles were not a success, and she would probably never have been able to finish the voyage without her sails. The first Atlantic crossing made under steam power alone was that of the Dutch *Curaçao,* in 1827.

A ship of distinction was the City of Dublin Steam-Packet Company's *Royal William.* She was the first passenger steamer to cross the Atlantic; the first steamer to leave Liverpool; and the first to be fitted with iron bulkheads dividing her into watertight compartments. Her tonnage was 817; she was 145 ft. long and capable of a speed of ten knots.

ARTIFICIAL WATERWAYS

IN Iraq (Mesopotamia) are traces of the canal which ran in a dead-straight line between the rivers Euphrates and Tigris. Known as the River of the Kings, it was built about 1000 B.C. by the Assyrian monarchs and was in use until the early Christian era. It was lined throughout with bricks from Babylon and could carry fleets considered large in those days.

Two thousand years ago the Nile was connected with the Red Sea by means of a canal which was completed in the reign of the Egyptian monarch Ptolemy II (309-246 B.C.). It was thirty-seven miles long, 100 ft. wide and 40 ft. deep. Traffic did not take kindly to the waterway, though the Emperor Trajan (died A.D. 117) enlarged it. It ran from a point on the Nile north of Cairo to the Red Sea, its purpose being to carry grain ships to Arabia. It was not until A.D. 768 that it was filled in by the invading Arabs.

PEOPLE WHO LIVE ON CANALS

Canals have played an important part in Indian transport from an early date. About the year 1355 the Emperor Ferose III made a 100-mile-long canal joining the River Sutlej to the River Jumna. The same monarch subsequently constructed five other canals, all of which were of equal utility for irrigation and the transport of goods.

The Chinese system of artificial waterways is likewise of very great antiquity. Among the most remarkable of the engineering feats of the ancient Chinese was the construction of the Royal Canal, completed in A.D. 980 (some authorities say 1289). It is said to have given occupation to 30,000 men for forty-three years. From the main waterway, which terminates at Canton and is 825 miles long, innumerable smaller canals branched off.

A writer of the early 19th century states that: "Upon the surface of this canal and its subsidiaries many thousand families live in vessels, which form their travelling habitations, and which they seldom quit from their birth till their decease. And some idea may be formed of the traffic upon it, when it is stated that the Emperor alone has ten thousand vessels constantly employed upon the different parts of its line."

The first canal on which tunnels were used was the Languedoc, in France. Begun in 1661, and completed fifteen years later, it joined the Mediterranean to the Atlantic. A tunnel of considerable length was driven through a mountain in the neighbourhood of Belgiers to allow this canal to pass.

PROPOSED CANAL ACROSS EUROPE

Among the more ambitious projects of Peter the Great, Tsar of Russia, was that of constructing a canal from the Caspian Sea to St. Petersburg (Leningrad), "whereby he proposed to open a mercantile communication between that place and Persia." He was not successful in this; but his zeal for the extension of inland navigation was inherited by his successors, so that by the end of the 18th century, Russia was as well equipped with canals as any other country in the world. It is interesting to note that Catherine the Great in her efforts to extend the canal system "offered a large sum of money and many local advantages to our countryman, Mr. Smeaton, on condition of his accepting the office of chief engineer in her dominions." John Smeaton (1724-1792) was responsible for the construction of the Forth and Clyde Canal.

In the early years of the 19th century it was possible to transport goods by water practically all the way from the frontiers of China to St. Petersburg, a distance of 4,472 miles: land transport was only necessary for sixty miles. It was possible, also, to transport goods by water all the way from St. Petersburg to Astrakhan, on the Black Sea. Within recent years the Soviet Government has vastly extended the canal system of Russia.

One of the first canals in England was the Caerdike, constructed by the Romans to afford communication between the rivers Nene and Witham. One extremity joined the Nene near Peterborough; the other opened into the Witham three miles below Lincoln. The total length was forty miles.

LEONARDO DA VINCI AS CANAL ENGINEER

Among the seemingly innumerable activities of which Leonardo da Vinci was master was that of canal cutting. He is credited with having constructed a 200-mile-long canal from the River Adda to the city of Milan about the year 1488. The Mortesana, as it was called, supplied Milan with water, and was navigable throughout its whole length. An 18th-century account states that Leonardo "happily achieved what some may think miraculous, rendering hills and valleys navigable with security." This statement strongly suggests that the great artist-engineer knew how to construct locks. He was, indeed, probably the inventor of locks.

The first canal-locks in England were constructed on the Exeter-Topsham artificial waterway by a certain John Trew, of Glamorganshire, in 1563.

DUKE SPENDS FORTUNE ON CANALS

The first modern-type canal in England was the Bridgewater, the first part of which, from Worsley to Manchester, was completed in 1761. It derives its name from Francis Egerton, the third and last Duke of Bridgewater (1736-1803), who conceived the project. The duke, who spent £200,000 on artificial waterways, was the first Englishman in modern times fully to appreciate the value of inland water transport. He entrusted the construction of the Bridgewater Canal to James Brindley (1716-1772) "an uneducated but heaven-taught engineer."

An old account states that "the inequalities of the ground, and the interventions of rivers and public roads, were surmounted by stupendous mounds of earth, by a tunnel cut through a hill fifty feet under the surface, and in some places hewn out of the solid rock; by aqueduct bridges over the public roads; and by what even professional men then pronounced impossible, an aqueduct bridge over the navigable River Irwell at the height of 38 ft. above its surface, which presented to the wondering spectators the new and surprising sight of vessels sailing aloft in the air, high above other vessels sailing below in the river."

MANCHESTER SHIP CANAL

The canal was subsequently extended to Liverpool. It was purchased by the Manchester Ship Canal Co., for £1,786,313 in August 1887, three months before the first sod of the Ship Canal was cut. The Ship Canal, opened for traffic on New Year's Day, 1894, converted Manchester, an inland city, into a seaport. With a length of 35½ miles, it involved a capital expenditure of £15,173,402 and the excavation of 53,000,000 cubic yards of material.

ROMAN CANALS

The Romans were not only great architects but also accomplished engineers. In the time of Nero a plan was mooted for cutting through the Isthmus of Corinth and connecting the Gulf of Corinth and the Gulf of Ægina, but it was only partially carried out and the waterway was not completed until 1893. The Romans did succeed, however, in building the Rhine-Meuse Canal and, in the reign of the Emperor Drusus, the Rhine-North Sea Canal.

Their most ambitious project, the joining of the Mediterranean to the North Sea by means of a Moselle-Sâone canal, was frustrated only by the obstruction of a governor of an area in what is now Belgium, who in the reign of the Emperor Claudius forbade the entry of the Rhenish legions into what he called "his" province.

In Europe, Roman canals quickly fell into decay. With the advent of the modern era the value of artificial waterways for commercial transport was soon recognized. The first of these, the Hansa Canal, known also as the Great Ditch, was constructed in 1390 as a link between the rivers Trave and Elbe, and was used for carrying salt from Lüneburg. Then Charles V built the Aragon Canal, forty-one miles long, joining Saragossa to the River Tudela. The Trave-Alster Canal, opened in 1550, was soon abandoned owing to the difficulty of keeping it supplied with water.

CANAL TUNNEL FIVE MILES LONG

The great French canals, built in the reign of Louis XIV, were models of their kind. Many more have been constructed since that time, so that now France shares with Holland the distinction of having more canals per square mile than any other country. The largest subterranean canal tunnel in Europe connects Marseilles with the Rhône Canal. It passes under the Rove hills, is five miles long, and cost £12,500,0000. Begun in 1911 and completed in 1926, some 3,000 men were employed on a project that enables sea-borne commerce to be sent direct to the interior of France and also to reach Germany and Switzerland. Some sixty million cubic feet of rock and earth were removed.

The Amsterdam Canal (18½ miles) was cut in 1876. The Princess Juliana, finished in 1935, is twenty miles long and cost £11,000,000. The Albert Canal, which runs from Antwerp to Maastricht and was opened in 1935, is notable because of two difficulties of a totally different nature which were successfully overcome. In one part solid rock had to be blasted to a width of 130 ft. and a depth of 210 ft. for nearly a mile, and in another a cutting 100 ft. deep had to be made through fine sand, necessitating extensive drainage. In 1938 the Rhine and the Baltic were joined by a waterway known as the Midland Canal, which had been forty-six years in the making and cost over £50,000,000. The largest lock in the world is at Ymuiden, Holland, at the entrance of the North Sea Canal, connecting the North Sea with Amsterdam. Its dimensions are 1,312 ft. by 164 ft.

A hundred years ago Germany had no canals except in the Mark of Brandenburg and its eastern dependencies. Transport was confined almost entirely to roads, but this method was so costly that in 1832 even such a wealthy city as Leipzig was unable to afford the expense of bringing stone to the city for the paving of its streets.

RHINE-MAIN-DANUBE WATERWAY

At the end of the 8th century the Emperor Charlemagne prepared a plan for linking the North Sea with the Black Sea, thus providing a cheap means of transport through the heart of Europe. His plan necessitated the cutting of a canal to join the Rhine, through its tributary the River Main, with the Danube. Work was started during Charlemagne's reign but was soon abandoned and nothing further was done until 1836, when King Ludwig of Bavaria sanctioned a plan for linking the Main and the Danube, between Bamberg on the former and Kelheim on the latter river. The Ludwig Canal, as this connexion is called, was completed in 1848.

In 1921 a Government-subsidized company undertook the work of making a Rhine-Main-Danube connexion that would meet modern requirements. This called not only for the construction of new canals but for the canalization of long stretches of the Main and Danube. By 1938 the Main had been made fully navigable between Mainz (where it joins the Rhine) and Würzburg, by the construction of a series of 300-yard-long locks. When the work is completed in 1945 there will be a continuous waterway 7–8 ft. deep and capable of taking vessels of 1,500 tons. The cost is estimated at about 750,000,000 marks or nearly £40,000,000.

The industrial importance of the Rhine-Main-Danube connexion can hardly be over-estimated, since it will link up the heart of Germany with Yugoslavia, Hungary, Rumania, Bulgaria and Greece, enabling the Third Reich quickly and cheaply to obtain food, oil and industrial raw materials from those countries in return for manufactured goods. It will make an effective blockade of Germany virtually impossible.

GERMAN MIDLAND CANAL

October, 1938, saw the completion of a great German canal system, work on which was begun six years before the outbreak of the World War. The Mittelland (Midland) Canal, as it is called, affords water transport facilities right across the north of Germany from near the Dutch border to Königsberg, capital of East Prussia, and has a total length of 300 miles. It links the rivers Rhine and Ems, in the west of Germany, to the River Elbe, in Central Germany, and rivers Oder and Vistula in the east; and thus, incidentally, affords inland water communication between the North Sea and the Baltic. The first canal to link these two seas was the Kiel, opened in 1895. It is fifty-three nautical miles long and 37 ft. deep. It runs from Holtenau, the harbour of Kiel, to the mouth of the Elbe.

CONNECTING MOSCOW WITH FIVE SEAS

Shortly after the World War the Soviet Government began to plan the complete reconstruction of the canals of Russia. They aimed at linking up all the seas of European Russia with ship-carrying waterways, and at turning Moscow into a port connected with five seas. The first great project was the construction of a canal linking the Baltic with the White Sea. The idea was not new, but all the engineers who had previously considered the project had declared it impracticable. Work was begun in 1931, and two years later the 140-mile-long waterway, the greatest of its kind, was completed. Ten thousand convicts, "enemies of the State," had worked upon it, thereby earning remission of their sentences.

With its twelve giant locks, nineteen sluices and fifteen major dams, the White Sea-Baltic Canal enables ships to go direct between Leningrad and Archangel instead of voyaging round northern Scandinavia.

The second of the great Soviet waterway projects, the Moscow-Volga Canal, was begun in 1933 and completed four years later. It connects the Volga and Moskva rivers and raises the level of the latter, thereby increasing its navigability. About 40,000 buildings in 203 villages were moved to make way for the canal. Eighty miles long, it links together seven lakes and reservoirs, the largest of which has an area of 123 square miles. Along its course are eleven locks, twelve dams, eight hydro-electric stations, nine bridges and two tunnels.

The third, and final, part of the scheme is the Volga-Don Canal, which will link the Volga with the Azov and Black Seas. To make a navigable channel up to 20 ft. deep between the Volga and the Sea of Azov, six hydro-centres, each consisting of a dam, a sluice and a hydro-electric station, will be constructed on the Don. To enable large ships to come up to Rostov, at the mouth of the Don, a sea-canal with a depth of 20 ft. will be constructed in the Sea of Azov.

From Rostov, on the Sea of Azov, to Stalingrad, on the Volga, the canal will be nearly 800 miles long. It will have a width of between 330 and 623 ft. and a depth of between 26 and 65 ft. The hydro-electric stations on the Don will produce 2,200 million kilowatt-hours of energy, which will be consumed by the industrial plants in the neighbourhood. The cost of the scheme is estimated at 3,500 million roubles, and the time allowed for construction is 5½ years.

THE SUEZ CANAL

Towards the end of the 15th century the Venetians suggested to the Egyptians that a canal should be cut through the Isthmus of Suez. This would have more than neutralized the advantage gained over the Venetians by Portugal when her mariners discovered the sea-route to India round Africa. Venetian engineers, who had had experience in their lagoons, could have carried out the plan, and there was no lack of money, but Turkey intervened to prevent the project being carried out.

Nothing was done till 1854, when the Frenchman, Ferdinand de Lesseps, was granted his first territorial concession by Mahommet Said, the Viceroy. The first sod was cut five years later. Napoleon Bonaparte had ordered a survey of what is now the Suez Canal Zone in 1798, but the engineers gave him a pessimistic report, which, although largely erroneous, induced the First Consul to abandon the project.

De Lesseps's interest in the project was aroused by reading this adverse criticism. His plan was frowned upon by British statesmen, including Lord Palmerston, who maintained that it was impossible of realization; that it would end British maritime supremacy; and that it was simply a French trick to get power in the East. Not only did Britain disapprove: she actively worked to prevent de Lesseps from succeeding. She took no shares in the company formed to make the canal.

Despite her opposition, the canal was successfully completed and opened in 1869. Six years later, Disraeli (later Lord Beaconsfield), the British Prime Minister, atoned for the stupidity of his predecessors in office by quietly buying 176,602 shares from the Khedive of Egypt for £4,000,000. It was thus that Britain acquired an important voice in the control of the affairs of the canal. The company is nominally Egyptian, but of its thirty-two directors, twenty-one are French, ten are British, and one is Dutch.

The canal, which connects Port Said on the Mediterranean to Suez on the Red Sea, is 101 miles long and cost 884,196,095 francs to construct and enlarge. It is nominally neutral territory in war-time, but its control is obviously in the hands of the Power that dominates the Mediterranean.

LINKING ATLANTIC AND PACIFIC

Connecting the Atlantic and Pacific oceans across the Isthmus of Panama, the Panama Canal is 50¾ miles in total length, of which the Gatun Lake channel accounts for twenty-four miles. It was projected centuries ago in the reign of Philip II of Spain (1527-1598), but the notion did not receive the approval of the Church. "What God hath joined together," said the Archbishop of Madrid, "let no man tear asunder," and so North and South America were not severed. In 1881 Ferdinand de Lesseps, who had already built the Suez Canal, began to cut a way through, but in 1889 the company which financed the undertaking was bankrupt, after an expenditure of about £50,000,000. The company was reconstructed in 1894, and work was again started. Malaria and yellow fever played havoc with the workers, of whom it is estimated 20,000 perished. Defeated by lack of sanitation and the prevalence of mosquitoes, which carried the dread diseases, the great ditch was abandoned. What remained of the wreck was sold to the United States Government in 1903, the purchase price being some £8,000,000.

The microscope as well as the steam shovel helped to build the great waterway. De Lesseps, who died a broken man, did not know that it was the prevalence of noxious insects that warred against him rather than what was regarded as a deadly climate. He was fighting nature in two ways, one of which could have been partially eliminated had he known the means. One of the preliminary appointments made by President Theodore Roosevelt when his country determined to proceed with the undertaking was that of Dr. W. C. Gorgas as head of the health department. In 1898 Sir Ronald Ross found that the *Anopheles* mosquito was the carrier of malaria, sucking the blood of a malaria patient and transferring the germs to others when it pierced their flesh. Two years later, Dr. Walter Reed discovered that yellow fever—the dreaded "yellow jack" of sailors—was similarly spread by the *Stegomyia* mosquito. With this valuable information, Dr. Gorgas tackled the problem and spent £70,000 yearly on keeping the workers healthy. The disease was not stamped out, but it was kept under control. On one occasion General G. W. Goethals, the chief engineer, remonstrated with the medical man. "Do you know," he said, "that every mosquito you kill costs the United States Government ten dollars (£2)?" "Yes," replied Gorgas, "but just think, one of those ten-dollar mosquitoes might bite you, and what a loss that would be to the country."

Vessels do not navigate the waterway under their own steam, but are towed by electric cog-track locomotives, the passage taking from ten to twelve hours. The cost of what may be regarded as the new Panama Canal was over £75,000,000. The first ocean steamer passed through on the day before Great Britain's entry into the World War, August 3, 1914.

MAN'S FIGHT FOR MASTERY OF THE AIR

THE earliest account of the construction of a flying machine is probably that to be found in the pages of the historian Aulus Gellius, who lived in the 2nd century A.D. He tells us that Archytas, a mathematician of the 4th century B.C., "constructed a wooden pigeon which could fly by means of mechanical powers and an *Aura Spirit.*"

No precise account of either the mechanical powers or the spirit is given, but the old historian assures us that the pigeon was "not less marvellous, though it appears less absurd than other alleged inventions of the same kind; for many men of eminence among the Greeks . . . have, in a most positive manner, assured us that the model of a Dove or Pigeon formed in wood by Archytas, was so contrived, as by a certain mechanical art and power to fly; so nicely was it balanced by weights, and put in motion by hidden and enclosed air."

Despite this warm assurance, it is doubtful whether the marvellous pigeon ever made a mechanical flight. This is not to say that the "eminent" Greeks were lying, but that they were deluded by a magical trick, the magicians of that time being extremely skilful in the production of illusions.

There are records of a man who flew high in the air over Rome during the reign of Nero (died A.D. 68). The story goes that this enterprising individual was killed in his descent, not through any mechanical failure, but because his evil genius or spirit had become displeased with him when aloft, and had consequently "suffered him to fall down."

"FILLED WITH ETHEREAL AIR"

The first man to make a scientific study of the principles of flight and to leave a record of his work was Roger Bacon, the great English philosopher of the 13th century, whom his contemporaries called the "Wonderful Doctor." John Wise, the American historian of flight, says that "the art of sailing, or, at least, the principle by which it is accomplished, seems to have been so well understood by him (Bacon) that we may safely ascribe to him the discovery of its main principle," that is, atmospheric buoyancy.

Bacon discussed the possibility of constructing large and powerful engines which could convey passengers and goods at great speed over both land and water. From that he goes on to speak of transport through the air. The flying machine which he envisaged "must be a *large hollow globe* of copper, or other suitable material, wrought extremely thin, in order to have it as light as possible. It must then be filled with ethereal air or liquid fire, and then launched from some elevated point, into the atmosphere, where it will float like a vessel on the water."

It will be seen from this quotation that Bacon had in mind a flying *ship*. It does not appear that the doctor ever succeeded in constructing a flying machine, but he concludes his dissertation with the following enigmatic statement: "There is certainly a flying instrument, not that I ever knew a man that had it, but I am particularly acquainted with the ingenious person who contrived it."

In another place, deserting the idea of a flying ship, he states that "there may be made some flying instrument, so that a man sitting in the middle of the instrument, and turning some mechanism, may put in motion some artificial wings which may beat the air like a bird flying."

CHILDREN TRAINED TO FLY

Bacon's speculative mind was looked upon with considerable distrust by the ecclesiastical authorities of his time. He was accused of being in communication with the devil; his works were put on the banned list by Nicholas IV, and he himself was placed under restraint.

John Wise tells us that " soon after Bacon's time, projects were instituted to train up children from their infancy in the exercise of flying with artificial wings, which seemed to have been the favourite plan of the flying philosophers and artists of that day." The wings enabled their users, by a combination of running and flying, to sail over the ground rapidly and with little exertion. Wise goes on to tell how he himself used to do something similar with the aid of a balloon which was about 18 ft. in diameter, or just large enough to raise him off the surface of the earth. Suspended from this balloon, he would beat against the air with his artificial wings and "bound against the earth with his feet, so as to make at least a hundred yards at each bound." On one occasion, Wise tells us, he traversed a pine forest several miles wide "by bounding against the tops of the trees."

John Wise was the first important American aeronaut. He started experiments with balloons in 1835 and remained actively interested in aeronautics until his death by drowning, while attempting a long flight in 1879.

A VERY TALL STORY

Fifteenth-century chroniclers tell of a certain Johann Müller (1436-1476), also called Regiomontanus, who constructed an artificial eagle at Nürnberg. One account states that this mechanical eagle was flown out from the city to welcome the Emperor Charles V and that it flew back again with him. Unfortunately the emperor in question was not born until a quarter of a century after the death of Müller, which rather discredits the story; but the mechanical eagle of Nürnberg deserves to be remembered as the first successor to the Pigeon of Archytas.

"THE MAN WHO KNEW EVERYTHING"

Roger Bacon's first successor in the line of scientific students of aeronautical problems was Leonardo da Vinci (1452-1519), who has been called, with pardonable exaggeration, "the man who knew everything." He certainly seems at least to have studied everything, and to have brought an extraordinary intensity of thought to bear on every problem.

Two extremely important inventions—the first ever made in aeronautics—stand to the credit of Leonardo. They are: the helicopter, a machine that has the power to raise itself straight up into the air by means of a horizontal propeller; and the propeller itself. It is curious to reflect that the helicopter is still in its infancy, although there is today an acute realization of its potentialities in enabling an aeroplane to rise perpendicularly or to hover in the air like a hawk. Equally curious is the fact that the propeller, first thought of by Leonardo as an aeronautical device, should have been used for steamships many years before it enabled a flying machine to cleave the air.

WHERE LEONARDO WENT ASTRAY

Leonardo succeeded in constructing several small model helicopters which actually flew. That he could not make a large helicopter—though his notebooks contain plans for one ninety-six feet in diameter—was due to the fact that, the internal combustion engine being still in the womb of time, he was unable to devise an engine powerful enough to work it.

On this subject of motive power Leonardo made a grievous error, in that he assumed it possible for a human being, provided with wings, to fly by the strength of his own muscles, like a bird. Belief in this error persisted for hundreds of years after da Vinci's death. It is lucidly refuted in these words of Octave Chanute (1832-1910), the French-American aeronautical expert: "The strength of a pigeon is such that if it weighed 57 lb. and its muscularity increased in the same ratio, it could exert a horsepower; if a sparrow weighed 49 lb. it could do likewise; yet a man of average strength, weighing 150 lb., can exert as much as a horsepower for only a few seconds at a time and on continuous exertion can exert only one-twelfth to one-tenth of that amount."

THE MAN IN THE MOON

In the year 1638 there was published in London a little book called *The Man in the Moone or A Discourse of a Voyage Thither*. It relates in graphic and entertaining language how a man had himself carried to the moon on a platform borne by twenty-five swan-like birds of a species whose habit it was to migrate to the moon every year. The adventurous traveller found the moon to be inhabited by a race of long-lived giants who had a knowledge of the earth. He was hospitably received by the lunar men and he remained with them for many months before returning to earth by the same means as he had used to escape from it. This lunar visit is alleged to have taken place in 1601. The outward journey occupied eleven days and the return journey nine.

EARLY ACCOUNT OF THE ATMOSPHERE

The most remarkable feature of the book is its curiously modern accounts of the atmosphere, which are reminiscent of those given us by 20th-century stratosphere balloonists. Here is a typical passage: "After the time I was quite free from the attractive beames of that tyrranous loadstone the earth, I found the ayre (air) of one and the selfsame temper, without winds, without raine, without mists, without clouds, neither hot nor cold, but continually after one and the same tenor, most pleasant, milde, and comfortable, till my arrivall in that new World of the Moone."

The Man in the Moone was written by Francis Godwin (1562-1633), successively Bishop of Llandaff and Hereford, under the Spanish-sounding pseudonym Domingo Gonsales. It is generally believed that it was a perusal of this work that caused John Wilkins (1614-1672), Bishop of Chester and principal founder of the Royal Society, to compose his *Discovery of a New World or A Discourse Tending to prove, that 'tis Probable there may be another Habitable World in the Moon. With a Discourse Concerning the Probability of a Passage thither*. It is amusing to find two 17th-century bishops making romantic speculations about matters which one would imagine to be strictly outside their province.

TIME, THE FATHER OF NEW TRUTHS

The lunar reflections of Wilkins are a good deal more scientific, but hardly less picturesque than those of Godwin. Wilkins was apparently convinced that one day man would devise a means of reaching the moon. He says in a magnificently prophetic passage, that "Time, who hath always been the Father of new Truths, and hath Revealed unto us many things which our Ancestors were Ignorant of, will also Manifest to our Posterity that which we now desire, but cannot know. . . . As we now wonder at the Blindness of our Ancestors, who were not able to discern such things as seem plain and obvious unto us, so will our Posterity Admire our ignorance in as Perspicuous matters."

TO COLONIZE THE MOON

Wilkins quotes the great German astronomer Kepler (1571-1630) as having said that "as soon as the art of flying was found out, some of their Nation (the German) will make one of the first Colonies" on the moon. A humorist might say that this was the 17th-century equivalent of the Kaiser's "place in the sun," and surely the first record of German colonial aspirations!

Wilkins tartly remarks that he supposes "his (Kepler's) appropriating this pre-eminence to his own Countrymen, may arise from an Over partial Affection to them. But yet," he says, "thus far I Agree with him, That whenever that Art is Invented . . . whereby a Man may be conveyed some Twenty Miles high, or thereabouts, then, 'tis not altogether Improbable that some or other may be Successful in this Attempt."

Wilkins discusses the great difficulties confronting the would-be moon-voyager. "I believe," he says humorously, "he shall scarce find any lodgings by the way. No inns to entertain passengers, nor any castles in the air (unless they be enchanted ones) to receive poor pilgrims or errant knights."

He bases his belief in the possibility of reaching the moon on the fact that, as he supposed, at some distance above the earth's surface a flying machine would be released from the pull of the earth's gravity. He was right in that supposition, but he gravely underestimated the distance, and he had no conception of the power that would be needed to raise a flying machine to the desired point.

"CONCERNING THE NATURE OF GRAVITY"

How like a paragraph from a 20th-century work on rocket flight are these words of the old bishop: "From that which hath been said concerning the nature of gravity, it will follow that if a man were above the sphere of this magnetical vertue which proceeds from the earth, he might there stand as firmly as in the open air, as he can now upon the ground: And not only so, but he may also move with a far greater swiftness than any living creature here below, because then he is without all gravity, being not attracted any way, and so consequently will not be liable to such impediments as may in the least manner resist that kind of motion which he shall apply himself unto."

FLYING CHARIOT

Wilkins suggested several alternatives to "ascending beyond the sphere of earth's magnetical vigor." First, with wings fastened to the body: second, with the help of birds, such as those described in *The Man in the Moone*: third, "I do seriously, and upon good grounds, affirm it possible to make a flying chariot." In another work, *Mathematicall Magick*, Wilkins points out that besides its usefulness for transporting people to the moon, a flying chariot "would be serviceable also for the conveyance of a man to any remote place of this earth: as suppose to the Indies and Antipodes."

He complains that "Amongst other impediments of any strange invention or attempts, it is none of the meanest discouragements, that they are so generally derided by common opinion, being esteemed only as the dreams of a melancholy and distempered fancy." A sentiment with which almost every inventor would doubtless agree.

Wilkins's writings on flying make fascinating reading, but his proposals are for the most part extremely vague. It may be that the bishop had definite plans which he kept secret, partly through fear of ridicule and partly lest any one should steal a march on him, for he was acutely conscious of the glory that the invention of a flying machine would confer upon a man.

JESUIT FORESEES AERIAL BOMBING

The first definite practical proposals for the construction of a lighter-than-air machine were those made by the Jesuit scientist, Francesco de Lana (1631-1687), in 1670. His idea was to suspend a wicker-work gondola from four vacuum balloons, that is, balloons from which the air had been exhausted. The balloons were to have copper shells 1/225th of an inch thick, and they were to have a diameter of 20 ft. De Lana was the first aeronautical writer to attempt to verify his theories mathematically, but being ignorant of the tremendous pressure exerted by the atmosphere, he was unaware that it would crush his frail balloons. He never attempted to construct his flying-ship because he was afraid that it would be used for military purposes! There may be many now who wish that his ingenious successors had been possessed of a like solicitude for the welfare of mankind, in view of the terror that aerial warfare has brought into the world.

The following quotation from de Lana's writings is interesting as being the first definite recorded prediction of the military use of aircraft: "God would not suffer such an invention to take effect, by reason of the disturbance it would cause to the civil government of men. For who sees not that no City can be secure against attack, since our

Ship may at any time be placed directly over it, and descending down may discharge soldiers; that the same it would happen to private Houses, and Ships on the Sea : for our Ship descending out of the air to the Sails of Sea-Ships . . . may over-set them, kill their men, burn their ships by artificial Fire-works and Fire-balls. And this they may do not only to ships, but to great Buildings, Castles, Cities, with such security that they which cast these things down from a height out of Gun-shot, cannot on the other side be offended by those from below."

FLYING AS AN AID TO COURTSHIP

It was on very different grounds that Addison, the English essayist, objected to attempts at flight. The invention of a method of flight would, he says, "fill the world with innumerable immoralities, and give such occasion for intrigues as people cannot meet with who have nothing but legs to carry them. You should have a couple of lovers make a midnight assignation upon the top of the monument, and see the cupola of St. Paul's covered with both sexes like the outside of a pigeon-house. Nothing would be more frequent than to see a beau flying in at a garret window, or a gallant giving chase to his mistress, like a hawk after a lark."

MAN RISES INTO THE AIR

The words quoted above were written in 1713, exactly seventy years before the first flight was achieved by the Montgolfier brothers, the sons of a French papermaker. In 1783 the first balloon rose into the air, twenty-two centuries after the first recorded aeronautical experiments. The men who achieved the first flight did so almost by accident within twelve months of their first experiments in aerostation, or flight by craft lighter than air.

SMOKE USED TO INFLATE BALLOON

Etienne Montgolfier, the younger of the two brothers, had noticed that smoke always rose straight up into the air unless driven sideways by the wind. It was as a result of this simple observation that in November 1782, he and his brother Joseph made the experiment, in the privacy of their home, of filling a small paper bag with smoke. As they had hoped, it immediately rose upwards to the ceiling, where it remained for a few moments before descending. A similar experiment was made in the open air, with encouraging results. The brothers then constructed a spherical-shaped envelope with a capacity of 600 cubic feet. When this had been inflated with smoke it broke its mooring strings and ascended to a height of about 700 ft.

A much larger balloon, one thirty-five feet in diameter, and with a capacity of 23,000 cubic feet, was sent up to about 1,000 feet in April, 1783. All these experiments had been conducted in private, but now convinced that they had made a great discovery, the brothers arranged a public demonstration, which took place in June, 1783. It proved a great success, the balloon rising to a height of about 7,000 feet and travelling a mile and a half from its point of release. A contemporary newspaper describes the balloon as " an immense bag of linen lined with paper. . . . When filled with vapour proper for the experiment, it would have lifted up about 490 lb., besides its own weight, which . . . was equal to 500 lb. . . . The bag was composed of several parts, which were joined together by means of buttons and holes, and it is said that two men were sufficient to prepare and fill it, though eight men were required to prevent its ascension when filled."

"SAFETY FIRST" TEST OF BALLOON

The fire that created the " vapour " with which the Montgolfier balloon was filled in order to make it ascend was of chopped wool and straw. It was thought by many that the burning wool and straw gave off a peculiar gas that could not be obtained by any other means. The Montgolfier brothers themselves at first thought that it was *smoke* that enabled their aerostatic machines to rise. In point of fact it was neither a peculiar gas nor smoke, but simply hot air, which, as everybody now knows, is lighter than cold air and therefore rises. Experiments showed that the hot air with which the balloons were filled was only about half as heavy as the surrounding atmosphere.

The first living creatures to ascend in an aerostatic machine were a sheep, a cock and a duck. These animals went up in a wicker-work basket attached to a Montgolfier balloon, at Versailles, in the presence of the King and Queen of France, in September, 1783. They reached an altitude of 1,500 ft. and descended alive, 10,000 ft. from the place of ascent.

FIRST HUMAN BEING TO FLY

On the successful conclusion of this first " passenger " flight, Pilâtre de Rozier volunteered to make an aerial voyage. A new balloon, 74 ft. high and 48 ft. in diameter, was constructed. At its bottom end it had an aperture with a diameter of 15 ft., suspended underneath which was an iron brazier containing a fire to supply hot air. De Rozier made several preliminary ascensions to a height of two or three hundred feet and with the balloon anchored to the ground with ropes, before attempting a flight.

On his first real flight, made on November 21, 1783, de Rozier was accompanied by the Marquis d'Arlandes. This flight was a magnificent success. The balloon, which weighed 1,600 lb., remained in the air for twenty-five minutes, during which time it attained a height of 3,000 ft. and travelled a distance of five miles. The flight was carried out above Paris, much to the amazement of the inhabitants.

We are told that the marquis lost his nerve and demanded that a precipitate descent should be made when the balloon caught fire from the brazier, but the stout de Rozier resolutely refused the nobleman's request. He had thoughtfully provided himself with a sponge and water, and armed with these he extinguished the fire, and the flight was continued. Later on, when the machine threatened to descend on some houses, de Rozier stoked up the fire, thus forcing the balloon to rise out of danger.

It soon became obvious that before aerostatic machines could be put to any practical use it would be necessary to discover a less hazardous method of making them rise than suspending fires underneath them. The Académie des Sciences in Paris, having discovered that it was the comparatively light hot air that made the Montgolfier balloons rise, remembered that the English scientist, Henry Cavendish, had shown that hydrogen gas might be only 1/14th as heavy as air. Hydrogen was obviously the thing, and the Académie set about constructing a hydrogen balloon.

Cavendish discovered the properties of hydrogen gas in 1766. Soon afterwards it occurred to Dr. Black, of Edinburgh, "as an obvious consequence of Mr. Cavendish's discovery, that, if a sufficiently thin and light bladder were filled with inflammable air, the bladder, and the air in it, would necessarily form a mass lighter than the same bulk of atmospheric air, and which would rise in it." The doctor intended to make the experiment, but the pressure of work prevented him from doing so at once and he finally dropped the idea because of the difficulty of obtaining the necessary apparatus. Had he persevered with the idea he would have gone down to history as the inventor of aerostation.

FIRST HYDROGEN BALLOON

The intense interest created in scientific circles by the flights carried out in the Montgolfier balloons spurred on the Académie des Sciences in their preparations for the construction of a hydrogen-filled balloon. The Académie entrusted the Robert brothers with the actual work of construction, and they delegated J. A. C. Charles, a chemist, to fill it with gas. The balloon, thirteen feet in diameter and weighing twenty-five pounds, was made of silk which had been rendered gas-proof by the application of gum elastic dissolved in turpentine.

ESCORTED BY SOLDIERS

The process of filling the balloon, with primitive apparatus, proved extremely difficult and tiresome, but it was finally completed in time for an ascent on August 27, 1783. The balloon was carried, in the early hours of the morning, to the Champ de Mars, Paris, on a cart escorted by a strong military guard to prevent its destruction at the hands of the over-enthusiastic mob. "Torches, flambeaux, musical instruments, guns, and everything that the lively imagination of the people could suggest, were brought into requisition, to render the procession grand and animating . . . and as the strange and novel machine passed along . . . reflecting the light of the numerous torches, giving it the appearance, at a distance, of a bright star, the air fairly rang with the shouts of the assembled and pleased multitude."

By five o'clock, when the ascent began, there were 100,000 people assembled in drenching rain to watch the first gas-filled balloon rise from the ground. Within two minutes it was lost in the clouds, at a height of 3,123 ft. It remained in the air for three-quarters of an hour, descending in a field near the village of Gouesse, fifteen miles from the point of ascent.

PEASANTS' FEAR OF AERIAL MONSTER

The people who had watched it rise were filled with joyful enthusiasm: the poor ignorant peasants who saw it fall were terror-stricken. The scene at its descent was thus described:

"A small crowd gains courage from numbers, and for an hour approaches by gradual steps, hoping meanwhile the monster will take flight. At length one bolder than the rest takes his gun, stalks carefully to within shot, fires, witnesses the monster shrink, gives a shout of triumph, and the crowd rushes in with flails and pitchforks. One tears what he thinks to be the skin, and causes a poisonous stench; again all retire. Shame, no doubt, now urges them on, and they tie the cause of alarm to a horse's tail, who gallops across the country, tearing it to shreds."

Extravagant stories were spread through the countryside about the monster. These caused so much general alarm that the Government had to issue a proclamation stating that: "Any one who shall see in the sky a globe which resembles the moon in an eclipse should be aware that . . . it is only a machine . . . that cannot possibly harm any one, and which will some day prove of service to society."

LONE AERONAUT TAKEN ILL

The first voyage in a hydrogen balloon was made by J. A. C. Charles and one of the Robert brothers on December 17, 1783. They ascended from Paris; attained an altitude of 6,000 ft., and after travelling for an hour and three-quarters landed twenty-seven miles away. After the balloon had come to earth, Robert got out of the gondola, thus considerably lightening the balloon and enabling his companion Charles to reascend to a height of 10,506 ft.

This second ascent is of considerable scientific interest in that it appears to be the first during which the aeronaut suffered extreme discomfort from the coldness and rarefication of the atmosphere. When Charles began his lone ascent the temperature was 47° Fahrenheit, but ten minutes later he was experiencing 21°. The sudden drop in temperature produced immediate unpleasant effects. Charles was benumbed and he experienced an agonizing pain in the right side of his head. As the air gradually grew thinner the balloon expanded and the aeronaut was forced to release a quantity of gas to prevent the fabric from bursting. These experiences taught the air-minded that flight at high altitudes was not going to be as pleasant or as easy as some had imagined after the first few successful flights.

In April of the following year Messieurs Morveau and Bertrand ascended to 13,000 ft., "where they enjoyed one of the most sublime and magnificent prospects that the imagination could conceive. The mass of clouds that floated in silent disorder through the regions below them, presented the appearance of a serene and boundless ocean, while a beautiful parhelion of concentric circles, that began to form as the sun went down, heightened the grandeur of the scene."

FIRST WOMAN TO FLY

The first woman to make an ascent was a Madame Thible, who, on June 4, 1784, ascended from Lyon in the presence of King Gustave of Sweden. She was accompanied by a man named Flerand. The balloon remained in the air for forty-five minutes and covered a distance of two miles.

The first English aeronaut was James Sadler (1751-1828) who, in February, 1784, sent up a passenger-less Montgolfier balloon at Oxford. On October 4 of the same year he himself made an ascent from Oxford in a Montgolfière. He remained in the air for half an hour and descended six miles from his starting point, between Islip and Wood Eaton.

In 1812, when he was sixty-one years of age, Sadler made a courageous attempt to cross the Irish Sea in a balloon which had a diameter of fifty-five feet. He set out from Dublin shortly after midday and succeeded in reaching a point over Anglesey, off the Welsh coast, about five o'clock the same day. But just when success seemed within his grasp the direction of the wind changed, and he was driven out to sea again. He then released a quantity of gas and came down on the water in the hope of being picked up by a passing ship. When his strength was almost exhausted he was rescued by a fishing boat forty miles north of Great Orme's Head.

In 1817, James Sadler's son William (1796-1824) achieved the feat his father had attempted in vain. He landed near Holyhead six hours after leaving Dublin, and the next day he repeated the voyage in the opposite direction.

ENGLISH CHANNEL CROSSED BY AIR

The English Channel was crossed by air for the first time on January 7, 1785, by Jean-Pierre F. Blanchard (1753-1809), a Frenchman, and Dr. Jefferies, an American physician. This flight is doubly memorable, in that it was also the first ever made across the sea. It was financed by Jefferies, who paid £700 for general expenses and £100 as the price of his seat in the balloon, which was navigated by Blanchard.

The balloon was the same one in which Blanchard had made several flights in 1784. Twenty-seven feet in diameter, it had a boat-shaped gondola suspended from it. It rose from Dover at one o'clock in the afternoon and descended near Calais three hours later.

From the beginning of the flight the balloon threatened to crash into the sea. To prevent this the aeronauts were forced to throw overboard every movable article in the gondola. When only two-thirds of the way across they had expended the whole of their ballast. Jefferies tells us that Blanchard "threw away his great coat. On this I was compelled to follow his example. Then he stript and cast away his trousers. We put on our cork jackets, and were, God knows how, but as merry as grigs, to think how we should splatter in the water."

Having thrown away all their landing-gear they had considerable difficulty in bringing the balloon to rest when over French soil. They came down over a forest and Jefferies succeeded in catching hold of a tree-top. "You would have laughed to see us," says Jefferies. "Each without a coat of any sort; Mr. Blanchard assisting at the valve, and I holding the top of a lofty tree, and the balloon playing to and fro over us, holding almost too severe a contest for my arms." After half an hour's struggling they succeeded in landing, and were flatteringly received by the inhabitants of Calais. A contemporary newspaper stated in a leading article that: "This is the sixth voyage performed by Mr. Blanchard in this balloon, and one of the most singular and bold attempts ever made by man; Mr. Blanchard and Dr. Jefferies have the honour of being the first aerial mariners."

FIRST FATAL ACCIDENT

Pilâtre de Rozier, the first human being to make a balloon ascent, met his death in attempting to emulate the feat of Blanchard and Jefferies. He and a companion attempted the Channel crossing in a compound balloon, consisting of a large hydrogen balloon with a small hot-air balloon suspended underneath it. The composite craft burst into flames at a height of 3,000 ft. and both aeronauts crashed to their deaths. The conflagration was caused by a spark from the brazier under the hot-air balloon coming in contact with the highly inflammable hydrogen. This was the first fatal accident in the air.

EARLY PARACHUTES

A form of parachute, differing but little from an ordinary umbrella or parasol, was in use in the Far East at an early date, as a means of enabling people to jump from great heights in safety. In 1793 a French general named Bournonville was treacherously seized by the Prince of Saxe-Coburg and imprisoned in the fortress of Olmutz. He made a valiant attempt to escape by jumping from a lofty window with an open umbrella in his hand. Unfortunately, he being a corpulent man, the umbrella failed to operate in the desired manner. His leg was broken, and he was recaptured.

The first person to study parachutes from the point of view of aeronautics was Leonardo da Vinci. Leonardo's ideas were expanded by Fausto Veranzio who, in 1617, published a detailed plan for the construction of a parachute.

Joseph Montgolfier was experimenting with parachutes some four years before he and his brother produced the first balloon. These experiments were carried out mainly to test the sustaining power of air.

DOG TO TEST PARACHUTE

The first person to construct a parachute for use with a balloon was probably Blanchard. In August, 1785, during the course of a 300-mile voyage, he threw out a parachute from which was suspended a basket containing a dog. The animal reached the ground unhurt.

Conspicuous among the first human users of the parachute was a Frenchman named André-Jacques Garnerin (1770-1825) "who has dared repeatedly to descend from the region of the clouds with that very slender machine." In the year 1802 Garnerin visited London to give an exhibition of his parachuting prowess. "He rose majestically from an enclosure near North Audley Street at six o'clock in the evening." About ten minutes later he attempted to descend from his balloon by parachute, but there was a strong wind blowing and he was carried, suspended from the parachute, over Marylebone, Somerstown and St. Pancras. He finally came to earth in a field beyond St. Pancras.

"The shock was so violent as to throw poor Garnerin on his face, by which accident he received some cuts, and bled considerably. He seemed to be much agitated, and trembled exceedingly at the moment he was released from the car."

FIRST MILITARY USE OF AIRCRAFT

The French were the first to make balloons, and it is not, therefore, surprising that they were the first to put them to military use. In 1793 Capt. J. Coutelle, of the French Army, was entrusted with the task of establishing a flying corps at Meudon, near Paris. In the following year the same officer, accompanied by two colleagues, made a balloon ascent for reconnaissance purposes behind the French lines at the Battle of Fleurus, in Belgium. When the Austrians caught sight of the balloon they were terror-stricken, but they quickly recovered their nerve and opened up a brisk cannonade on the craft. The occupants of the balloon immediately rose higher until they were out of range of the guns. They remained in the air for two spells of four hours each, and it was mainly owing to the valuable information that the aeronauts communicated that the French won the battle.

TRAGIC END TO POLAR FLIGHT

The first attempt to reach the North Pole by air was made in a balloon by Solomon Auguste Andrée (1845-1897) and two companions. They set off from Virgo, Spitzbergen, in July, 1897, and were never seen again. Eleven days after their departure a carrier pigeon sent out from the balloon was picked up near Spitzbergen. The message it bore was: ". . . All goes well on board. This message is the third sent by pigeon."

Nothing further was heard of the three explorers until 1930, thirty-three years later. In August of that year their bodies were discovered by a Norwegian Expedition on White Island between Spitzbergen and Franz Josef Land. The full story of the ill-fated assault on the Pole was then fully divulged because the log of the expedition and the diaries of Andrée and Nils Strindberg, one of his companions, were recovered in good condition. The adventurous trio had quickly succumbed to cold and hunger after their balloon had been forced down.

GREAT BALLOON OF NASSAU

The progress that ballooning had made by the beginning of the Victorian era is shown by the exploits carried out in the Great Balloon of Nassau, which was launched in 1836. The balloon had a circumference of 150 ft., and its height, when inflated and with gondola attached, was about 80 ft. It was filled not with hydrogen but with ordinary coal gas supplied by the London Gas Company. It is said that the company, fully appreciating the publicity value of the use of coal gas, sometimes gave the gas free of charge. The balloon held 70,000 cubic feet of gas, of which the cost was about £70, and which gave a lifting power of nearly 5,000 lb.

After several trial flights the balloon was prepared for a long voyage over the Continent by Charles Green (1785-1870), one of the most distinguished of early British aeronauts, and two companions. One of the passengers tells us that: " The appearance which the balloon exhibited previous to the ascent, was no less interesting than strange. Provisions, which had been calculated for a fortnight's consumption in case of emergency; ballast to the amount of upwards of a ton in weight, disposed in bags of different sizes . . . together with an unusual supply of cordage, implements, and other accessories to an aerial excursion occupied the bottom of the car; while all around . . . hung cloaks, carpet-bags, barrels of wood and copper, coffee-warmer, barometers, telescopes, lamps, wine jars and spirit flasks, with many other articles designed to serve the purposes of a voyage to regions, where once forgotten nothing could be again supplied." The aeronauts were also equipped with " passports directed to all parts of the Continent."

500 MILES IN EIGHTEEN HOURS

The balloon left London at 1.30 p.m. on November 7, 1836; was over France at 5.30 p.m. the same day; and landed in a valley in the Duchy of Nassau, six miles from Weilberg, at 7.30 a.m. the next day, having covered 500 miles in eighteen hours. It was from the circumstance of having landed in the Duchy of that name that the balloon became known as the Great Balloon of Nassau.

The daring aeronauts were accorded an extraordinarily warm welcome by the German peasants, after the latter had recovered from the initial shock of the sudden descent in their midst. "A few words in German . . . served to dissipate their fears and . . . as if eager by present assiduity to make amends for former backwardness, they absolutely seemed to contend with each other in their exertions to afford us assistance and execute our several behests."

This voyage created a distance-record for balloons that was not broken until 1859, when the American, John Wise, covered 1,150 miles in under twenty hours, an average of nearly sixty miles per hour.

PROJECTED ATLANTIC FLIGHTS

Charles Green, to whom the credit for the Nassau flight is due, was something of an aerial showman. On one occasion he attached a pony to a balloon by bands passed under its belly and made an ascent on the animal's back. His intention of making an ascent with a tiger as passenger was frustrated by the authorities.

In 1840, four years after the voyage from London to Nassau, Green announced that he was making plans for a crossing of the Atlantic. He proposed to fly from west to east at a height of 10,000 feet, at which level he would have had the benefit of a following wind all the way across. Lack of support forced him to abandon this ambitious project.

In 1843 John Wise announced his intention of making a trip across the Atlantic in the following summer. Wise felt confident that because of the "regular current of air blowing at all times from west to east, with a velocity of from twenty to forty, and even sixty miles per hour," his proposed trip would not be "attended by as much real danger as by the common mode of transition." Wise was an extremely sane and practical man whose proposals were far from hare-brained, but thirty years passed before he was able to find backers for his enterprise. He constructed a balloon with a capacity of 400,000 cubic feet, and planned to fly from New York to London. Just before the flight was due to begin, Wise quarrelled with his backers. Three other men took off in the balloon, which crashed forty miles from its starting point.

DID THE CHINESE INVENT BALLOONS?

Father Vassou, who during the second half of the 17th century lived as a missionary in Canton, China, tells us that the Chinese have records of the ascent of a balloon from Pekin in 1306, to celebrate the accession to the throne of the Emperor Fo-kien. If this be true, the Chinese were practising aerostation nearly 500 years before Europeans. Vassou's account of this Chinese balloon is contained in a letter dated September 5, 1694, or nearly a century before the first ascent in Europe.

The authenticity of the account is vouched for by a French author, Delaville Dedreux, who in 1863 published a highly imaginative work on *Aerial Navigation in China*. M. Dedreux claimed to have travelled far into the interior of China and to have made an aerial voyage there in 1860. He relates how that he expressed surprise to a mandarin when he saw an airship in China, whereupon the mandarin sarcastically inquired : " Are you not so advanced as to have these things in Europe?" "Oh, yes," answered the European, "but they are of smaller dimensions. Our engineers devote their attention chiefly to the study of methods of destruction."

CHINESE AERIAL EXPLORATION

In answer to a query as to whether the Chinese could guide balloons at will, the mandarin said: "Not altogether; but it is seldom that the captain does not follow his proposed route, and return within a given period. This is effected chiefly by a knowledge of the atmospheric currents, and of the meteorological circumstances that change their direction. The knowledge of the winds is a science that is enriched by daily observations. The Celestial Empire possesses a great number of observatories, which send their reports of the currents at the various heights to the captains of aerostats, who are guided accordingly."

The mandarin went on to tell of the State aerial flotilla, the main object of which was scientific research. "There is not," he says, "one of our mountains that has not been explored by Chinese savants by means of these aerostats. There are many narratives of voyages far to the south, but their progress has been stopped by the excessive heat. An excursion has even been projected to the Pole."

When asked why Chinese aeronauts had never visited Europe, he replied:

"Your little country is hardly worth the trouble. Barbarians . . . are not esteemed by our Government, who are certain the Chinese would only import pernicious ideas from Europe. Aeronauts are forbidden . . . to visit that small agglomeration of evil-disposed and fighting men."

ARRIVAL OF THE DIRIGIBLE

The first balloon that was completely navigable, that is, the first "airship" in the modern sense, was produced by a French engineer, Henri Giffard (1825-1882), in 1852. Fitted with a three-horse-power steam engine, it was 144 ft. long and had a maximum diameter of 40 ft. The first flight of this airship was from Paris to Trappes.

Giffard constructed a longer and narrower airship a few years later. It crashed on its trial trip, but neither the inventor nor his companion was seriously injured. After this accident Giffard's airship plans, though displaying great ingenuity, became over-ambitious. He designed a craft that was to be 1,970 ft. long, to have a diameter of 98 ft., and to contain 7,800,000 cubic feet of gas. It was to have an engine weighing thirty tons and capable of driving it at forty miles per hour. Needless to say, this scheme came to nothing.

During the second half of the 19th century many navigable airships were produced but none was really successful, mainly because the steam engine was too cumbersome as a source of power. When, in the closing years of the century, fairly reliable internal combustion engines began to be produced, it became possible to construct useful airships.

In the summer of 1900, Count F. von Zeppelin produced the first of the series of airships that bore his name. With a length of 420 ft. and a diameter of 38 ft., it had a capacity of 400,000 cubic feet, and was fitted with two sixteen-horse-power engines. It had a framework of aluminium covered with linen and silk, being the first lighter-than-air machine to be built on these lines. The envelopes which supported all the earlier airships had no framework, being merely gas-filled bags.

FIRST COMMERCIAL AIRCRAFT

The first Zeppelin having proved itself by flying at twenty miles per hour, its inventor proceeded to construct a second rigid airship. A number of unfortunate accidents prevented the latter from accomplishing the feats for which it had been designed, but in 1906 the count produced a third airship the performances of which were so spectacular that they won him the patronage of the Kaiser and put an end to all his financial difficulties.

The production of airships was taken up with great enthusiasm in Germany, and in the four years immediately preceding the World War these craft carried 17,000 passengers and covered 100,000 miles. They were thus the first flying machines to achieve commercial importance. During the World War the airship proved its military importance. After the War it pioneered the aerial crossing of the Atlantic, and was being commercially used on the Atlantic routes long before it was thought possible to operate aeroplane services between the Old and the New Worlds.

HAS THE AIRSHIP A FUTURE?

After the wreck of the *Hindenburg* Zeppelin, 129th of her line, in the early summer of 1937, there was a widespread belief that airship production would never again be resumed, even in Germany. This belief was based on the assumption that the airship could not be made as safe as the aeroplane.

Nevertheless, there are still many aeronautical experts who believe that the airship has a great future before it; that it will become the great merchandise-carrying craft of the air. They say that the *Hindenburg* disaster would not have occurred had that craft's envelope been filled with non-inflammable helium gas instead of hydrogen, which is highly inflammable.

Unfortunately for the German airship enthusiasts the United States Government, which has a virtual monopoly of helium, will not allow the precious gas to be exported in large quantities, since it fears that it may be used for military craft. But modern chemists may find a means of producing an adequate substitute for helium, in which case the believers in airships may realize their ambitions.

In 1938, LZ 130, or *Graf Zeppelin II,* as it has been christened, was completed on the shore of Lake Constance, where the first of its line made its appearance thirty-eight years earlier. It was originally designed for service on the transatlantic routes.

MODERN EXPLORATION

IN these days of rapid communication, of fast aeroplanes and wireless, with our meteorological and medical knowledge enabling us to combat fever, malaria, scurvy, frost-bite and other diseases, it seems strange to speak of portions of the globe as being unexplored. Yet such is the case. An atlas will reveal that there are still large areas of the world's surface very sketchily filled in. We have better maps of some portions of the moon than we have of some areas around the Polar regions. Until these blanks are filled in and their secrets laid bare the spirit of adventure will continue to lure men and women from the comforts of civilization, in an effort to learn the mysteries of these unknown places of the earth.

LIVING ON PEMMICAN IN LONDON

While the explorer of today is far better equipped than were his companions of earlier days, it must not be thought that his task is an easy or a pleasant one. True, he has the experience of previous travellers to guide him and is materially assisted in his task by practical advice from scientific institutions interested in his quest, such as the Royal Geographical Society. The aim of this body is to render aid to British explorers by furnishing them with all possible information—route, transport, food, and what equipment should be carried.

Before Gino Watkins set out to cross the Greenland Ice Cap he and one of the officials of the society spent a week in London living on pemmican. This is meat cut into thin slices, divested of fat and dried in the sun. It is then pounded into a paste, mixed with melted fat and dried fruit and pressed tightly into cakes. It will keep for a long time, and contains all the vitamins necessary to sustain energy under the most rigorous conditions.

EXPLORERS' MANY AIDS

Explorers today carry cameras and moving-picture machines to show the world what they have seen. The theodolite puts it in their power to add something definite to the map of the world. Their vision is extended by the telescope. Arms of precision defend them better against man and beast. Neatly packed drugs aid them to fight disease. Preserved and essential foods provide a handy staff of life. In short, the latest discoveries of science are at their service.

Though in some details modern exploration is less laborious than when Marco Polo and Columbus travelled, there are nevertheless difficulties enough remaining to leave the romance of exploration untouched. Every explorer carries his life in his hand, however fine may be his outfit. Like St. Paul, he suffers perils of waters and of robbers; perils of the wilderness and of the seas. Like him, he suffers from weariness and pain, from hunger and thirst, from watchings and cold. Like him, he carries a burden of care—the care of a man who toils scientifically in the face of adverse circumstances.

At the beginning of the 20th century there were still large areas of Africa that were unknown, despite the daring journeys of explorers such as Livingstone, Stanley, Park, Grant, Baker, Burton and Speke. The interior of the Sahara was largely a closed book. The boundaries of many of the more important African states had not been surveyed. There were huge blanks on the map in Central Asia. The sources of such great rivers as the Indus and the Brahmaputra were veiled in misty legends. Beyond the Himalayas were towering ranges as virgin as the mountains of the moon.

Virtually nothing was known of the great Takla-Makan Desert in eastern Turkestan, and our knowledge of Tibet, Mongolia and the Gobi Desert was scanty. There was still much to be learned about the interior of Australia, while that intriguing island of mysterious tropical forests and native races, New Guinea, had hardly been tapped. Neither had explorers succeeded in reaching the North or South Pole. Even today the world's highest peak, Mount Everest (29,002 ft.) remains unconquered despite several serious attempts to scale it.

LIGHT ON DARKEST AFRICA

THE source of the Nile was discovered only seventy-odd years ago by Speke; the world-famed Victoria Falls were first seen by Livingstone when he descended the Zambezi in 1855; it was Stanley who first circumnavigated the great lakes of Central Africa and traced the course of the Congo.

It was not till the opening of the 20th century that Sir Henry Trotter, as the British representative of an Anglo-French Boundary Commission, was able to establish the exact position of the source of the Niger, in an attempt to ascend which Mungo Park lost his life.

Sir Henry penetrated to the source of this great waterway through a malarial jungle. The natives declined to point it out, "assuring me that it was the seat of the devil. . . . They believe that any one who looks on the Niger source will die within the year, and they regard the water as poisonous."

MYSTERIOUS MOUNTAINS OF THE MOON

In many respects the strangest piece of country in Central Africa is the Ruwenzori Range, or Mountains of the Moon. Though first seen by Stanley so far back as 1888, their peaks remained unscaled until 1906. "My eyes were directed by a boy to a mountain said to be covered with salt," wrote the explorer at the time. "I saw a peculiar-shaped cloud of a most beautiful silver colour, which assumed the proportions and appearance of a vast mountain covered with snow. Following its form downward . . . I became first conscious that what I gazed upon was not the image or semblance of a vast mountain, but the solid substance of a real one, with its summit covered with snow."

Ruwenzori is in reality a clump of peaks, the range having a length of sixty-five miles and a breadth of a little over thirty miles. The peaks reach a height of over 16,000 ft. They lie close to the Equator between Lakes Albert and Edward, and have an enormous rainfall, as much as 180 in. yearly. This combination of heat and moisture causes the peaks to be constantly shrouded in mist, so that it is only on rare occasions they are visible from below. Explorers who went to look for them after Stanley's discovery actually passed them by without seeing them, and accused Stanley of having invented them.

The mist is only a minor phenomenon compared with the freakish vegetation of these mountains. Mr. Patrick M. Synge, who recently visited Ruwenzori for the purpose of collecting plants, says: "A grey mist made a fitting background for the most monstrous and unearthly landscape that I have ever seen. Vague outlines of peaks and precipices towered around us. Here were plants which seemed more like ghosts of past ages than ordinary trees and herbs. They appeared as a weird and terrible dream to me, a botanist and hunter of strange plants. It all seemed unreal, like some imaginary reconstruction of life in a long-past geological age, or even upon another planet. Our familiar common herbs seemed to have gone mad. We saw groundsels, swollen, distorted, with woody trunks twenty feet high, lobelias like giant blue and green obelisks, heathers mighty as great trees. . . . On the ground grew a thick carpet of mosses. Some were brilliant yellow, others deep crimson in colour. Every shade of green was represented. The tree trunks were also clothed in thick moss, often tussocked into the semblance of faces, while from their branches dangled long streamers of a pale, sulphurous yellow lichen, the old man's beard."

DUKE OF ABRUZZI'S QUEST

Stanley's amazing discovery of Ruwenzori prompted many mountaineers to attempt the exploration of the range, but the barriers of forested foothills, clouds of fog and, higher up, of glaciers, defeated them all. A few years before his death, the veteran explorer begged that some lover of mountains should choose Ruwenzori as his goal and explore its wild valleys and hidden gorges. The challenge was accepted by the Duke of Abruzzi, an Italian, and one of the greatest explorers of this century. As a young man of twenty he had been the first to climb the 18,000-foot peak of St. Elias, in Alaska; two years later he had spent a winter in Franz Josef Land, when his ship the *Stella Polare* was crushed in the ice; and subsequently he sledged nearer to the North Pole than any of his predecessors.

It was in April, 1906, that the duke set out on his quest to map and scale the Ruwenzori heights. No fewer than 194 porters were gathered to carry the loads, and the whole caravan had a strength of about 300. The expedition started from Fort Portal, and worked up the Mobuku Valley. Crossing the turbulent Mobuku River, the actual climb began up a steep and narrow path through thorny bushes. The ground, soaking wet, was so slippery that the porters could scarcely keep their feet. As the height increased, great tree-ferns gave place to bamboo and giant heather. The Baganda porters—people of the plain—kept dropping out, and had to be replaced by Bakongo hill-men. The latter were tall, robust fellows, with shaven heads and rough, sun-tanned skins. Some wore leopard skins over their shoulders, or cloaks made of rabbit pelts, with fur pouches suspended from their necks for pipes and tobacco.

STRANGE VEGETATION

The route lay up the Mobuku Valley, but the going was very bad. The path was all water and mud in which the travellers sank to their knees. It took all day to climb 1,300 ft., and camp was made under a vast rock wall, in a morass of mud where it was necessary to build a platform of branches before a tent could be pitched. There was little firewood, and the weather was miserably cold and wet.

Rock terraces led to a plateau where the trees were thick with leprous moss and the ground hidden by piled-up masses of dead trunks. The porters had to jump from trunk to trunk, to crawl under overhanging branches and to perform miracles of equilibrium on sloping trunks. But they bravely carried on. The vegetation was a strange mixture. There were thickets of blackberry brambles, violets, ranunculus, geraniums, epilobium, and thistles. Above the heath-forest, the ground was carpeted with a deep layer of sopping moss dotted with large clumps of everlasting flowers—pink, yellow, and silver-white. There were giant lobelias and huge groundsel.

Eventually a base camp was set up at a height of 12,461 ft. Here there was a heap of blocks surrounded by tree heaths and overhung by a high rock which served as a canopy. On this eyrie, where there was hardly any flat ground, were pitched six tents, and the porters burrowed under the pile of boulders to find caverns which would serve as shelters. Because of the cold warm flannels and blankets were distributed to the porters. The woollen vests puzzled them somewhat and some tried to put their legs through the sleeves.

DUKE'S LEOPARD VISITOR

The amenities of the base camp were not improved by the nearby presence of a leopard's lair. The leopard was first seen devouring two sheep belonging to the expedition, and on the following night the duke was sitting at the opening of his tent quietly writing when he looked up to find the leopard only a few paces off. When the duke stood up the animal fled; but for many days afterwards the natives were very scared. Eventually the cook arranged a cunning snare with a piece of meat, and the terror of the camp was trapped and shot.

From the base camp systematic expeditions were made to all parts of the range. In design the range resembles the letter G. There are six main mountains—Gessi, Emin, Speke, Stanley, Baker and Luigi di Savoia. Mount Stanley, which lies in the centre of the group, is crowned by two peaks which are the highest in the range. To scale these peaks the duke had brought along two guides and two European porters from the Alps.

Crossing the glacier they at last gained the lower peak (16,749 ft.), which they named Alexandra. The higher peak called for all the daring and skill of the Alpine guides before it was conquered. To gain it they had to cross a narrow strip of ice bounded on either side by wide, unbridged crevasses. Negotiating this they found their path blocked by a wall of ice up which they had to cut steps. Climbing this wall they reached the bottom of a cornice, where ice stalactites and stalagmites stood as thick as trees in a forest. Upon these columns rested a heavy snow dome extending upwards to the peak.

THE SUMMIT REACHED

Like so many squirrels they scrambled round this fairyland colonnade until they came to a cleft in the cornice. Here, there was a vertical gully some six feet high. One of the guides planted himself firmly in a wide ice-step and thus served as a ladder for the second guide, who climbed first on his shoulders, and then on his head (in his heavy nailed boots), and stuck his ice-axe firmly in the snow above the cornice. In this way he hauled himself up, and soon the whole party stood on the highest peak of Ruwenzori. Here, at a height of 16,815 ft., the little tricolour flag with its embroidered motto *Ardisci e Spere* (Dare and Hope), was unfurled, and the spot was named Margherita, after the Queen of Italy. Subsequently all the other peaks in the Ruwenzori Range were climbed by members of the expedition. A careful map of the range was also made.

The final secrets of the Mountains of the Moon were unveiled during the expeditions of Dr. Noel Humphreys in 1926, 1931, and 1932. He made several flights across the range and discovered a number of lakes.

CONQUERING THE SAHARA BY MOTOR CAR

THE latest region of Africa to be explored is the Sahara, an area almost as large as Australia, stretching from the Atlantic to the Nile, and from the southern confines of Morocco, Algeria, Tunis and Libya southwards to the vicinity of the Niger and Lake Chad. The idea that the whole of this region is a sandy waste is wrong. There are great stretches of sand, but there are also fertile spots (oases), some of them large enough to have towns and villages, groves of date palms, and fields of millet and maize. There are also mountain ranges reaching to a height of several thousand feet. In this vast area dwell many strange tribes—Berbers, Tuaregs, Tebus, Zouias, Senussi and other races, many very warlike and fanatical.

The ordinary camel caravans from Tugart, in southern Algeria, to Timbuktu, on the Niger, take from four to five months. Today the same journey can be performed by motor car in seven to ten days.

The first attempt to cross the Sahara by motor car was made in 1916 by two cars. One had to give up, and the second reached In Salah, half-way across the desert, in twenty days, "with the help of lifting jack, shovel, traction-camel, and elbow-grease." In 1920 a fleet of thirty-two cars set out to reach the wireless station at Tamanrasset. This lies about two-thirds of the distance over the desert. Only nine of the cars got through. Then M. Citroën, a French motor car manufacturer, designed a special car with caterpillar wheels for desert travelling. Five of these cars reached Timbuktu, 2,200 miles from their starting point, early in 1923 after a journey of some thirty days.

COVERING THE CONTINENT

This success led to the organization of the greatest motor car expedition Africa has yet seen. The expedition was under the direction of Georges Haardt and Louis Audouin-Dubrieuil, both of whom had already earned fame for their travels in the Sahara and other parts of Africa. The route selected extended over 15,000 miles of desert, bush, savanna, marsh, and forest, necessitating the sending out of preliminary supply expeditions, whose duty it was to provide petrol, food, and other supplies at selected posts stretching across the continent from Algeria, through the Belgian Congo, to the Indian Ocean.

On October 28, 1924, the cars, eight in number, slipped into gear and pulled out of Algiers, crossed the Sahara to Burem, when they struck eastward towards Lake Chad. As far as Burem they had traversed desert, but now the country changed to bush, with great hollow basins hidden beneath tall grass and covered with dense vegetation. It proved a severe test for the cars. Slipping down into these natural craters was a simple matter, but climbing out on the other side was severe work. The endless belts of the cars answered every demand upon them, and after many anxious moments Lake Chad was reached on December 14, 1924. It was the first motor car journey from the Mediterranean to the lake entirely through French territory.

WINGED PESTS OF LAKE CHAD

Millions of mosquitoes awaited the explorers at Lake Chad. The naturalists in the party were enthusiastic about the many varieties, but the others could not share their interest. The only method discovered by which they could eat in comfort when darkness came was to turn the headlights of the cars towards the sky, over the tables, which were then left at peace. Despite mosquito nets, two members of the expedition were so badly bitten that their faces were hardly recognizable.

Hastily pushing on to escape from the winged pests, they reached a watercourse which had to be crossed. The only craft with which to ferry the heavily laden cars over the stream was a pontoon made of two hollow tree trunks. As the first car left the bank, causing the pontoon to sink until the water was but half an inch off the engines, the explorers knew real anxiety. An hour later all the cars were safely across and, worn out, the members of the party slept until dawn before pushing on to Fort Lamy, which was entered on Christmas Eve, 1924.

Soon the expedition was moving southward towards the Belgian Congo. They had not travelled far before they ran into an advance guard of an army of tsetse flies—carriers of sleeping sickness. The flies assailed the adventurers with such fury that, having bitten into the skin, they would allow themselves to be crushed rather than release their hold. The travellers were advised not to drink from the stagnant pools since the water contained little parasitic worms which lodge in the veins and bring on severe sickness.

THROUGH THE GREAT EQUATORIAL FOREST

Crossing the frontier into the Belgian Congo the expedition entered the great equatorial forest. Here a rough roadway had been made for a distance of 500 miles. Some 40,000 natives had been engaged in this task for several months. They had willingly performed this feat because the authorities had told them that envoys of Boula-Matari were about to come from a distant country, riding on animals made by him, in order to bring them a special message. Such was the prestige of the name Boula-Matari that whole villages went to meet the expedition.

Boula-Matari means "the man who blew up the rocks." It is the name given to Sir Henry M. Stanley, who blasted a passage for his canoes through the rapids of the Congo, a feat which greatly impressed the natives.

At Kampala, in Uganda, the expedition split up into four sections of two cars each, and continued the journey to the coast by different routes, to Mombasa, Dar-es-Salaam, Mozambique and Capetown respectively. Madagascar was also traversed from north to south. This proved no small feat. Extensive swamps and marshes and much difficult country had to be negotiated. Madagascar is as large as France, Belgium and Holland combined, and has a population of three and a half million.

WHERE MEN LIVE IN VEILS

A particularly interesting piece of exploration work in the central Sahara was that undertaken by F. R. Rodd in 1922, and again in 1927, among the wandering Tuareg tribes which inhabit the Mountains of Air. The men of this tribe wear veils while their womenfolk go unveiled. Not that the men are effeminate. They are hardy, great hunters and fearless fighters, and in the past gave the French considerable trouble.

The veil is a long slip of indigo cloth, woven and dyed in the Sudan. The best quality is made of six narrow strips, about one inch wide, sewn together. It is so worn as to form a hood over the eyes and a covering over the mouth and nostrils. Only a narrow slit is left open for the eyes, and no other part of the face is visible.

In this veil the men live and sleep. They lift up the *imawal*—as the lower part of the veil is called—to eat, but in doing so hold the hand before the mouth. When the veil requires re-fixing, a man will disappear behind a bush to conceal his features, even from his own family. When the French induced some Tuaregs to visit Paris, they declined to allow themselves to be photographed unveiled. The men do not don the veil until the mature age of twenty-five. The ceremony of putting it on for the first time is accompanied by much rejoicing in the family and feasting and dancing. Why the Tuaregs should have donned the veil no one knows. All that they will tell you is that a man is not a proper man until he has put on the veil.

WOMAN EXPLORER'S DARING TRAVELS

It was left to an Englishwoman, Mrs. Rosita Forbes, who has rightly earned fame for her daring travels in many parts of the world, to unravel the mysteries of the oasis of Kufara, the headquarters of the Senussi, a fanatical Mohammedan sect rather than a tribe, to which for years has been attributed every raid and every murder in the eastern Sahara. The community was founded many years ago by a fanatic Moslem of decidedly puritanical views. He forbade the use of gold and jewels and any form of luxury. Smoking was punished by the loss of a hand, and it was regarded as a meritorious deed to kill any infidels attempting to approach the cities of the Senussi. They accepted only the primitive Koranic law administered by the brothers of the order known as *Ekhwan*.

Kufara lies far out in the Libyan Desert. Various explorers had attempted to reach it, only to pay for their daring with their lives. Gerhard Rohlfs, the German explorer, who had travelled extensively in the Sahara, succeeded in 1879 in reaching the outskirts of Kufara, where his followers were murdered and he narrowly escaped a like fate. It was only the timely interference of an old sheikh who knew him that saved him. He managed to reach civilization again, but brought back no information or details of this strange religious resort in the desert.

SURROUNDED BY SPIES

Mrs. Rosita Forbes argued that where a male explorer failed she might succeed. She would go veiled, disguised as Sitt (Lady) Khadija, an Egyptian lady of good family, making a pilgrimage to the sacred villages. She was fortunate in her choice of a companion, Hassanein Bey, the son of an Egyptian nobleman. At Benghazi, in Cyrenaica, from which a start was made in the autumn of 1920, they enlisted the help of Sidi Mohammed, Emir of the Senussi. Partly on account of an old friendship with his co-religionist, Hassanein Bey, and partly because of the well-known pro-Arab sympathies of Mrs. Rosita Forbes, he gave the travellers a letter of welcome, without which they would never have reached their goal.

Kufara lies about 580 miles to the south of Benghazi, and although it is a trading centre of the eastern Sahara, the journey from the sea is so difficult that none but the best-equipped caravans attempt it. South of the oasis of Jalo, a journey of seven hard, waterless days, brings the caravan to Zeighen. Here there is water but no fodder. Another five weary, waterless marches across the dunes leads to Hawari, on the outskirts of the Kufara group of oases; and there is a chain of mountains to be crossed before the secret cities are reached.

"From the outset," says Mrs. Rosita Forbes, "we found ourselves surrounded by spies who watched every movement and drank in carefully inaccurate conversation planned for their benefit. A section of the older brethren were strongly opposed to our journey, and, as they could not openly oppose the wishes of their emir, they decided on that simplest of all desert remedies—to have us murdered as soon as we left the town! Warned of this amiable project, we decided on a midnight flight, and, announcing our departure a week ahead, secretly made preparations for instant action. The last day was almost intolerable, with its atmosphere of plot and counterplot. The Italians were determined that no English traveller should make a journey which they felt should first be done by their own countrymen, and we knew that our lingering in the tiny frontier town had already made them suspicious."

ALL PROVISIONS EXHAUSTED

The travellers made good their escape at night with considerable difficulty and started south in real earnest. The emir's brother, Sayed Rida, had promised a guide who knew the route to Kufara, and an escort of soldiers. The plan was for the two travellers, accompanied by two servants of the emir's brother, Yusuf and Mohammed, and a small escort, to proceed across the desert to Wadi Farig and there await the caravan which Sayed Rida had promised to send after them. Wadi Farig, or "empty valley," was safely reached, but as the promised supporting caravan had not arrived it was decided to push on to Aujela. The decision was taken because of the presence at Farig of spies, who might inflame the tribesmen against the travellers. They made friends with a certain She-ib, a merchant whose caravan was going southwards, and joined his train and set off.

Aujela was reached a week later after a trying march, during which they suffered from hunger. They got very little sleep, for their companions travelled by night or day, or both, as the mood struck them, wasted hours in consuming quantities of green mint-scented tea, and camped wherever there was a little grass for the camels. Their reception at Aujela was none too pleasant. Stones were thrown at them whenever they ventured into the little settlement. On the second day of their arrival the long-delayed caravan arrived—twelve camels and a dozen men and the guide, Abdullah.

Without delay a start was made for Jalo, the party consisting of seventeen people, with twenty camels, including ten black soldier slaves (one of whom ran away to get married), and Abdullah and Yusuf, who acted as guides. At Jalo the travellers were given a royal welcome as accredited friends of the emir.

The next stage of the journey, from Jalo to Buseima, was a seven days' march across over 250 miles of waterless desert. No sooner had they started than they ran into a severe sandstorm. But Buttafil, the last well, was reached on Christmas Eve. Here the camels were given their first meal of dates. Next day, while on the march, they were found to be suffering from a severe attack of indigestion due to their unusual meal of the previous night. Christmas Day was spent massaging the animals. "On the fifth day of the march, by which time most of the party were suffering from swollen, blistered feet, or fever, Abdullah announced that he had lost the way, and that Allah meant us to die! The soldiers began to quarrel and threatened to beat the guide. Three days later when they were without fuel, and had only a few drops of water, and but two feeds left for the camels, Mohammed, the bravest of the Arabs, suggested that we had better ' die comfortably beside our baggage.' "

That evening a faint line of dunes revived their hopes. Two days later Buseima was reached. Here is a lovely blue lake, fringed by green rushes and palms. To the famished and weary travellers it seemed like a veritable Garden of Eden. The people of Buseima, however, were not satisfied with the travellers' letters of credence. "Had we but a force equal to yours," said one, "you should not now depart."

GUIDE TURNS TRAITOR

It took four days to cross the great belt of dunes by which Kufara is surrounded. On the last day of the journey the travellers came upon a whole caravan which had died of thirst. It must have been a recent tragedy, for the bodies were still intact, with their white woollen robes wound round them. Thus Hawari, which is on the outskirts of Kufara, was reached.

The tribesmen of Hawari refused to allow the caravan to proceed. When they attempted to move on, a wild, threatening group of Zouias surrounded them, shouting: "You shall not move from here till orders come from Jof! No strangers shall come into our country!"

Apparently the discredited guide, Abdullah, had turned traitor. Probably he hoped to be avenged on the soldiers, who had been so insulting when he had lost his way. He had secretly gone ahead to Jof—one of the villages of Kufara—and had promised to send news to the tribesmen of Hawari. When he reached Jof he spread wild rumours about the travellers declaring they were two Christian spies from Italy. "They have cheated the emir," he told the governor. "Ever since they left they have been secretly making maps, and the Sitt held a watch (compass) in her hand all the time." He drew lurid pictures of the barometer which hung in the tent and the field-glasses " which made the country look big while it was far away." As a result the governor ordered him to tell Yusuf and Mohammed to turn back.

When Mohammed and Yusuf heard the governor's orders they were furious. They at once recognized the plot, which was that the party should be left to the mercy of the tribesmen of Hawari—and that meant death. Abdullah would eventually return and tell how the explorers had lost their way in the desert and succumbed to thirst.

Mohammed swore he would discover the truth, and post-haste he hurried way to Jof to explain the true state of affairs. He came back at sunset, triumphant. He had exposed Abdullah's plot and brought with him a letter of welcome to the friends of the emir.

So at last the caravan mounted the hills, coming abruptly upon a wonderful scene. On the edge of the cliff, 150 ft. high, stood the mud-walled village of Taj, with its government building, massive *zawai*, or holy place of the Senussi, colleges, and mosque.

RACE WITH DEATH

Here Mrs. Rosita Forbes spent nine days as the guest of the *Ekhwan*. She was permitted to see the holy places and the house of the governor. The latter was a large building of many courts and passages. The walls of the room in which she was received, she tells us, " seemed to be entirely hung with clocks, barometers, thermometers and other such objects. I counted fifteen clocks, most of them going." While in Taj the travellers were safe, but when they set out to explore the valley they met with the usual suspicion and hostility.

Now came the question of the return journey. Abdullah had turned into their most bitter enemy and they were uncertain of the loyalty of their other followers. So they decided to take a new route, then unknown to Europeans, by way of Jaghabub, another holy place of the Senussi, to the Egyptian border. It meant a new guide and the party was reduced to six. " This route," says Mrs. Rosita Forbes, " entailed a seventeen days' march from the outskirts of Kufara, with only one well on the fifth day out. Consequently our already overstrained camels had to do twelve days without water, and this, I believe, is a record for desert travelling. Once started, nothing must stop the march, for the traveller has neither time nor provisions in hand. If he does not arrive at Jaghabub on the twelfth day his camels will give out, and that spells death."

On the second day out the party had a narrow escape from a band of marauders, who had followed them from Kufara. They were evidently spies sent out by the guide Abdullah. Eventually, however, the Egyptian frontier was reached, and the travellers stumbled across a patrol of the Egyptian Camel Corps. The appearance of the corps was most opportune. Both camels and travellers were exhausted, while Hassanein Bey had broken his collar bone.

Two years later, in 1928, Hassanein Bey made another and longer expedition across the Libyan Desert. While he was at Kufara with

Mrs. Rosita Forbes he was told strange stories of two " lost " oases away to the south-east, which no white man and few natives had seen. It was eight years since a caravan had gone from Kufara in that direction, and it had been wiped out on the frontier of Darfur in the Sudan. He decided to visit these oases and travel on to Darfur.

Six days' hard travelling from Kufara brought him to Arkenu, the first of the two mysterious oases. There were no inhabitants to be seen, but there was herbage for the camels among the rocky hills. They could find no wells, but rain-water had collected in hollows of the rocks. The expedition stayed here for four days in order to recuperate, and then pushed on to the second oasis, named Uweinat. Here they found a small village, built among the rocks; there were 150 inhabitants, and their nearest neighbours were 200 miles away. While exploring the district Hassanein Bey found rock engravings depicting processions of giraffes, lions, gazelles, ostriches, and other animals. One significant omission was the camel, and Hassanein was driven to the conclusion that once upon a time Uweinat had been a fertile district where wild animals were plentiful but camels did not exist.

Beyond Uweinat stretched the desert, where for 270 miles there was no well. It was so scorching hot by day that the party travelled at night time. At last they reached the hills of Erdi and Ennedi, where they met the first human beings they had seen since leaving Uweinat. They were very suspicious about the strangers who had sprung like jinns out of the desert, but did not attack them. Forty-five days after leaving Kufara the first village in Darfur was reached. They were short of food and their clothes were in rags, but they had accomplished a wonderful journey from one end of the Libyan Desert to the other. Hundreds of miles of unknown country had been explored, and the total distance travelled was about 2,200 miles.

EXPLORATION WORK IN CENTRAL ASIA

AT the dawn of the present century Central Asia was still largely a closed book to Europeans. The daring Swedish explorer, Dr. Sven Hedin, filled in a lot of the blank spaces on the maps of this part of the Asiatic continent. In the spring of 1895 he left Merket, a town on the westerly edge of the great Takla-Makan Desert and after a terrible ordeal which nearly cost the lives of the whole of his party, succeeded in crossing the desert from west to east. This was the first time a crossing had been made by Europeans.

TERRORS OF THE TAKLA-MAKAN DESERT

The terror of the Takla-Makan Desert, which has an area equal to that of Great Britain, is its sand dunes, which rise to the extraordinary height of 350 ft. and cross one another at an angle so as to form the meshes of a gigantic network. It was not long before tragedy overtook the footsteps of the little caravan. The weary men toiled up sand dune after sand dune until their water supplies were exhausted. Even some of the camels gave up the struggle.

" We were so tormented with thirst that the men drank the camels' rancid oil," records Hedin, " and I drank some Chinese brandy, which otherwise was used for a lamp-stove. . . . We slaughtered the last sheep, in order to drink its blood, but it was so thick and sickening that no one would taste it."

LIVING ON GRASS AND TADPOLES

One by one the men fell exhausted, and Hedin, with his faithful servant, Kasim, dragged themselves along with the ebbing strength of dying men. Kasim was dreadfully giddy and confused. At last they reached the wooded banks of Khotan Daria, only to find the bed of the river bone dry. Undaunted, Hedin pushed on alone. It took him five hours to go scarcely two miles. Suddenly he came across a pool of fresh water. Having satisfied his own needs Hedin carried some of the precious liquid back to his companion in one of his top boots, and so rescued him from the very jaws of death. He then left him to go in search of food, and after living on grass and tadpoles for three days and two nights, fell in with some shepherds. Kasim followed up his tracks, and Islam, another member of the party, who had been found by some merchants, also rejoined him, leading the camel that bore the explorer's notes, instruments and Chinese money. The other seven camels and two men had perished.

Some two years later Hedin against crossed the Takla-Makan, but this time in a different direction. On this occasion he found the remains of what must once have been a great and populous city. There had been legends of the existence of such a place. As far as the eye could reach were the weather-worn frames of houses, covering an area two and a half miles in diameter. Excavations revealed images of Buddha, tastefully painted walls, pillars, and evidences of various kinds of industry. Basing his calculation on the the rate at which the sand dunes travel, Hedin concludes that this " second Sodom in the desert," as he calls it, was overwhelmed some 1,500 years ago.

Later, in 1906, Sir Aurel Stein, during one of his many travels in the wastes of Asia, visited this lost city and carried out extensive excavations. He found written records on both wood and paper proving that this ancient city was called Loulan and was a frontier town on the great " silk road " between China and the Roman Empire. Bales of yellow silk, bronze mirrors, rings, bells, stone seals, and remains of ancient woven fabrics were found. Eventually four camel-loads of " finds " were brought away.

It was in Tibet that Hedin made some of his most important explorations. On two occasions he tried hard to reach the forbidden city of Lhasa and on both occasions was turned back. That was in 1901. He had entered Tibet with the largest caravan he had led up to that time into unknown regions. It comprised thirty-five men, including a Mongolian lama, or priest, who was to act as interpreter, and over 200 animals.

When nearing their goal, Hedin left his caravan and, accompanied by the lama and a Cossack, set out on a wild ride towards the forbidden city. The three travellers wore Tibetan clothes and all their accoutrements and utensils were of Tibetan pattern. Hedin had his head shaved and his face darkened with grease to a brown hue. He got to within fifty miles of the city when his road was blocked by a force of Tibetan soldiers, and the disappointed explorer was reluctantly forced to turn back.

TEA FOR 4,000 MONKS

In the autumn of 1905 Hedin once again set out to explore the vast ranges of mountains which were supposed to exist north of the Tsangpo, or Upper Brahmaputra. The expedition suffered terribly from cold. Horses and sheep were frozen to death, and the puppies had to be provided with felt sleeping-jackets. Once the leader had a narrow escape from death when he was charged by an infuriated yak bull.

When nearing the Tashi-lhünpo, their objective, the expedition was met by the governor of the province, who ordered the travellers to go back. "I started out on this journey," replied Hedin, "with one hundred and fifty beasts of burden. I have only eight horses and one mule left. How can I return until I have replenished my caravan with new supplies?" In the end he was permitted to proceed.

At Tashi-lhünpo, Hedin watched the New Year celebrations, and to his surprise and delight was allowed to inspect the strange temple-town. He saw a mighty kitchen where, in six enormous cauldrons, tea was brewed for 4,000 monks. In another gloomy hall were the 108 volumes of the Holy Scriptures of the Lamas.

SOURCE OF THE BRAHMAPUTRA

On this journey Hedin found the glacier source of the Brahmaputra River. The holy Lake of Manasarowar was also visited and explored. The Hindus believe that bathing in the waters of this lake, which lies over 15,000 ft. above sea-level, ensures passage to the paradise of Brahma. Hedin rounded off this trip by seeking the source of the River Indus, and in September, 1907, he reached a place where a spring gushes forth from a flat shelf at about 17,000 ft. above sea-level. Thus he was able to claim that he was the first white man to penetrate to the sources of two of the greatest rivers of Asia.

In 1904 a British military expedition fought its way to Lhasa and forced the delegates of the Dalai Lama to sign a treaty providing for increased trading facilities between Tibet and India and for the payment of an indemnity of £166,000. Thereafter, four British officers—Rawling, Ryder, Bailey and Wood—all of them famous explorers in Tibet, were appointed to survey a route to Gartok, the capital of western Tibet, along the Valley of the Brahmaputra.

ARABIA'S EMPTY QUARTER

THE last area of Asia to give up its secrets was the Rub'al Khali, referred to as the "empty quarter" of Arabia. It is an immense desert in extent equal to the combined areas of France and Spain. Over long distances there are no wells, and the few Arabs who venture to cross it have to exist almost exclusively on camels' milk. Two other difficulties face the would-be explorer: the hostility of the Bedouins who live on the fringes of the desert, and the problem of obtaining an escort willing to venture into this " abode of death."

EXPELLED BY AN EMIR

In the years 1930-1932 the inhospitable Rub'al Khali was first crossed by Europeans, two British explorers, Bertram Thomas and H. St. John Philby, the former traversing it from south to north and the latter from east to west. Other travellers, however, had penetrated into Arabia, and associated with exploration work in this particular quarter of the globe are such names as W. Scawen Blunt, C. M. Doughty, Gertrude Bell, W. H. Shakespear, R. E. Cheesman, T. E. Lawrence, Rosita Forbes and Freya Stark.

Doughty made many trips into Arabia, and he certainly took his life in his hands. Joining a pilgrim caravan, he managed to reach Hail. The emir was suspicious, and to test the explorer, he was given an historical work, and asked to read a certain line chosen at random. The passage happened to run: " The king slew all his brethren and kindred." Doughty was expelled from Hail with such intense hostility that he feared the worst. However, his *rafiq*, or guide, proved trustworthy and he escaped. Later he made a memorable journey from Berida right across Arabia to Jeddah. The story of this journey is told in his great work *Travels in Arabia Deserta*.

EXPLORER WHO HELPED TO WIN THE WORLD WAR

In 1913, Gertrude Bell, then already an experienced traveller, also made a journey to Hail, travelling from Damascus. It was a particularly dangerous feat for a woman. It meant travelling in a land where raids were the order of the day. Fortunately, owing to the abundance of rain-water, she was able to avoid the wells. At one point of the journey, however, she was held up by tribesmen who demanded her revolver and binoculars. They tried to induce her *rafiq* to desert her and share the spoils. Unlike Doughty, she not only reached Hail but was permitted to inspect the fortress and town. The knowledge of the country and tribes which she gained on this and previous journeys was of immense help to the British in the World War.

Colonel T. E. Lawrence, whose name is so closely associated with Arabia, also traversed much unknown country. Although his military exploits throw his geographical discoveries into the shade, the latter were, nevertheless, considerable.

FABLED LAND OF PUNT

Many legends had sprung up concerning the vast uninhabited wilderness of the Rub'al Khali. Some declared it was the fabled land of Punt, whence Queen Hatshepsut of Egypt procured her frankincense, aromatic woods and "green gold"; and here also was Ophir, from which King Solomon obtained his gold.

In 1930, Bertram Thomas succeeded in crossing the Rub'al Khali from south to north, being the first European to do so. The journey was made from Dhufar on the coast of Doba, a distance of some 700 miles. Thomas had seen a dozen years of post-War service in Arabia, had made many journeys in the country, knew the various tribes and could speak their dialect. The route at first lay through known country, where frankincense trees flourished in desolate wadi-beds. Here, as from time immemorial, the natives still make incisions in the trunks of the trees, and collect the fragrant green transparent oil.

The journey proved trying. Water-holes were often five or six days' march apart. All the time a sharp look-out had to be kept against raiding parties. The explorer was anxious to make notes and to take astronomical bearings. In order not to arouse suspicion he had his own tent set up some thirty yards away from the main camp, for the Arab of the desert is inclined to associate astronomical instruments with witchcraft.

One day, quite suddenly, the Arabs pointed to the ground, and cried, "There is the road to Ubar!" They went on to relate the story of the great and fabled city of wicked King Ad, which had been destroyed by heavenly fire and which was inhabited by jinns. It was a city rich in treasure, with date gardens and a fort of red silver. Now, they said, it lies buried beneath the sands. Thomas thought Ubar might turn out to be the Arabian Ophir, but he failed to locate it.

SOLVING THE RIDDLE OF SINGING SANDS

The Arabs of Arabia had often spoken of "singing sands," but no one knew exactly what they meant. On this journey the mystery was solved. The men were struggling over steep dunes when the silence was suddenly broken by a loud droning on a musical note. It continued for about two minutes and then ceased. This strange phenomenon was due to the cooling of the sands in the evening. This causes a landslide, or rather a trickle, and so a musical note is produced.

Thomas's memorable crossing of the Rub'al Khali occupied sixty days. Philby also crossed the great desert in 1932, but on this occasion from east to west. Like Thomas, he knew Arabia well and was lucky enough to travel under the patronage of the King of the Hedjaz. His party consisted of nineteen persons and thirty-two specially selected camels. The total distance covered was 1,800 miles and the journey occupied ninety days. The expedition had to cross a tract of territory where, according to the Arabs, no rain had fallen for twenty years. At one time the party was without water for ten days.

CITY DESTROYED BY A METEORITE

It was on this journey that the mystery of the fabled city of Ubar was solved. Philby told his men that he would pay for any treasure found, and give in addition a pound sterling for every building that might be discovered. One day one of the Arabs wandered off on his own in the hope of getting a rich reward. Some hours later he re-appeared with the news that he had come across the ruined city, and produced from under his cloak as evidence a large brick pitted with numerous air bubbles.

"We marched on, all terribly excited, till the ruins came into sight, a long, black wall, as it seemed, riding on the sand. Hastening forward, I found myself looking down on the ruins of what appeared to be a volcano!"

There were altogether five craters, which varied in diameter from fifty to a hundred yards. Most of them were filled with sand, but they were marked by fringes of blackened slag. The craters had been caused by a gigantic meteorite striking the earth in the distant past.

HUTS LIKE MUSHROOMS

After her success in reaching Kufara in the Libyan Desert, the home of the fanatical Senussi, Rosita Forbes decided to visit Sabya, the capital and holy city of the Idrisi, in western Arabia. It entailed an exciting journey from Jeizan, on the coast, through Asir and North Yemen Tehama. The route lay through thickly populated valleys, the thatched huts of the Arabs having the appearance of monstrous mushrooms. The valleys are so fertile that three crops a year can be obtained, and livestock is so plentiful that a sheep costs only six shillings.

The Idrisi tribesmen are fanatical and invariably shoot first and think afterwards. On one occasion, the plucky woman explorer tells us, " in a town harem, the women had been talking of the fate of any Christian who ventured into their land. ' We should just tear him to pieces,' said a crone whose hands were like claws. When someone else added, ' Had I your grey eyes, I should not travel far in this country,' I was hot and embarrassed enough to accept gladly a slave's suggestion of a bath. Only when I found a row of coal-black Abyssinians waiting to wash me did I realize that my beautiful brown complexion, bought out of a bottle of Clarkson's, only came down to my shoulder-blades! I saved all explanation by simulating a fit, most realistic foam being produced by sucking a fragment of soap which was providentially in my pocket. The slaves thought I was possessed by jinns and fled!"

Mrs. Rosita Forbes found that the same puritanical ideals of Kufara were followed even more rigorously in Asir. Life was divided into work, prayer and sleep; luxury was unknown. Five times a day every adult male prayed in the open. A curfew drum ordered every citizen indoors at sunset. There was no festive music; there were no sand-walled cafés where the sheikhs could suck their long-stemmed water-pipes, no dancers, and hardly any feasts.

Freya Stark, who has many interesting journeys to her credit in little-known parts of northern Iran (Persia), has carried out valuable exploratory and archæological work in the Hadhramaut, a great valley a hundred miles long and almost as wide, lying between the Rub'al Khali and the south coast of Arabia. In ancient times this region was noted for its frankincense and myrrh, and the former commodity is still exported thence. Old quarries found in the mountains are held by scholars to be ancient gold diggings and may be the Biblical Ophir.

It is only during recent years that the Hadhramaut has been opened up. The ruling families of this Arabian province live in huge castles which, in their construction, resemble children's castles of toy bricks. They are sometimes seven stories high and cover as much as an acre of ground. They are built of mud bricks and generally whitewashed, so that the principal town, Shibam, has been likened to "a large round cake with sugar on it."

IN THE HEART OF AUSTRALIA

ALTHOUGH Australia was first crossed by Robert O'Hara, Burke and Wills so far back as 1861, much of its interior was still unknown at the beginning of the present century. In 1908-1909, S. Weston explored a large tract between Sturt's Creek and the mountains of Central Australia, and reported that although there was a complete absence of surface water, yet the country was covered with timber and bush, afforded "excellent sustenance for the camel," and there was plenty of good grass. Similarly, D. Mackay, in 1926, filled in a blank that remained in the south-western corner of the map of the Northern Territory. The country examined lay between Oodnadatta and the Patermann Range.

IN SEARCH OF MINERALS

Among the modern explorers of the interior of Australia, Michael Terry ranks high. Over a period of eleven years (1923-1934) he led no less than twelve expeditions, mainly in search of mineral deposits, but incidentally making accurate maps. On his first expedition he crossed, with a single companion, from Winton, in Queensland, to Broome, in Western Australia, in an old Ford car. It proved an adventurous journey of 2,700 miles, much of it through unexplored territory. Negotiating the roadless bush, the dried-up gullies, creeks and river beds proved an arduous task.

In his subsequent expeditions Terry used motor transport of various kinds; combinations of trucks and camel parties and, for exploration in sand-dune country, camel strings alone. As a result, a reconnaissance survey of a huge area bounded by the deserted gold-field of Tanami on the north, by Alice Springs on the east, and by Lake Amadeus on the south, has been accomplished.

Terry discovered that many of the blacks are definitely hostile to white settlement. During his 1928 tour, for example, when he pioneered a route from Tanami to Alice Springs on six-wheeler Morris cars, he found that the " Wallmullas " were on the warpath. Lonely settlers in the neighbourhood of Alice Springs had been attacked and killed. When the expedition went " off the map " at Tanami there was ample evidence of nomadic " jackies." Every day smoke signals and hunting fires were seen. Even in regions where there were apparently no water supplies of any sort thin columns of smoke would rise up at intervals of about a mile.

AMONG NEW GUINEA'S HEAD HUNTERS

NEW GUINEA, a great island lying to the north of Australia, is 1,500 miles long and over 400 miles wide. There are snow-capped mountain ranges, dense jungles, deadly swamps, roaring mountain torrents, poisonous snakes, deep rocky chasms and head-hunting natives.

The head hunters of New Guinea are among the most primitive peoples in the world. Very often they go naked except for a grass kilt. They wear the black plumes of the cassowary or the feathers of a cockatoo for head-dresses and plaster their hair into fantastic rolls with beeswax and honey. They are very superstitious and carefully destroy all remnants of cooked food lest an enemy should seize them and work a spell on those who had partaken.

Tribal warfare is often carried on, and explorers frequently meet bands of natives in full war regalia, carrying arrows and gruesome battle-clubs. On such occasions their very appearance is enough to alarm the traveller, for it is their habit to paint themselves with yellow or red clay, stick pencils of bone or cane through their noses, and hang skulls or human jaw-bones round their necks.

TRAVELLING THREE MILES A DAY

During the present century many discoveries have been made in New Guinea. In 1907, C. A. Moncton travelled from the Waria River to the Gulf of Papua, and a year later D. Mackay and W. S. Little explored the Upper Purari River. In 1910-1911, Staniforth Smith made a pioneer journey across a large area north-west of the Gulf of Papua and east of the Fly River basin.

He set out with four other white men, twenty-five native police and fifty native carriers. His first objective was Mount Murray, which rises to a height of 7,000 ft., and when this had been climbed he sent back most of his party. Then he turned westward into the unknown, accompanied by two white men, Bell and Pratt, eleven police and seventeen native carriers. The way led along a high limestone plateau. They soon came to a fertile valley and had not travelled far before they stumbled upon a tribe of natives, few of whom had seen a white man before. Fortunately they proved friendly and offered the explorers some sweet potatoes.

The route now lay along a tributary of the Kikor, and here the expedition was soon in difficulties. The limestone was cut up into a series of precipitous ridges and deep gorges. The travellers were constantly scrambling up or down mountain-sides clothed with thick jungle. For days on end they could see no more than a few yards ahead, and they had to hack their way through the impenetrable undergrowth, like moles burrowing underground. The compass was their only guide, and on an average they advanced about three miles a day. They suffered from thirst and from hunger. The rock was so porous that rain-water sank immediately into the ground, and they often travelled for twenty-four hours without a drink. Their provisions ran out and they had to subsist on the pith of the wild sago-tree.

TRIBES WHO LIVE IN PILE HOUSES

At last they struck the Mobi River. Upon its banks dwelt many savage tribes. They lived in long thatched houses perched on steep rocky ridges and raised on wooden piles some ten to twelve feet above the ground. A whole tribe, sometimes numbering seventy or more, lived in the one building. Sometimes the native villages were further protected by rickety wooden drawbridges which spanned deep ravines.

At one village the natives, who had never seen a white man before, were hostile. They armed themselves with bows and arrows and began to shout their blood-curdling war cries. Smith ordered his men to sit down on the ground before the huts, not to touch anything nor to display their firearms, but to hold up pieces of red cloth. The savages did not quite know what to make of their strange visitors. They simply hid in the surrounding jungle ready for any emergency. Leaving some presents before the huts, the explorers continued on their way. They had not travelled far before the headman of the village came after them and made them presents of food. Moreover, in that mysterious fashion which has often puzzled westerners, the news of the peaceful intentions of the expedition were spread ahead, and on several occasions the natives came to the rescue when food supplies were at a low ebb.

PERILOUS VOYAGE ON AN UPTURNED RAFT

After many days of arduous travel along first one river and then another, the explorers reached the crest of a range of mountains, and away in the distance they could see a large waterway. Smith thought that once this river was reached their troubles would be over, for it would be possible to build a raft and float down the river to the coast. Reaching the river, however, proved a prodigious task. When they did so they found themselves at the foot of a steep cliff on a small piece of flat ground. They had descended the cliff by means of ropes manufactured out of strong creepers. Though they had managed to get down, it was impossible to get up again with all their provisions. The little plain on which they had landed was bounded by a roaring torrent, which flowed away through gorges so narrow that there was no possibility of walking along the banks of the stream. They had no option but to build rafts from the trees growing on the little plain and trust to luck in shooting the rapids which they knew from the roar of the waters lay ahead.

Smith embarked on the first craft with three police and two carriers. For two hundred yards they pitched and tossed along the boiling waters, and then they came to a sudden sharp bend. The raft turned turtle, and the passengers were all thrown into the swirling torrent. By good luck they managed to cling to the upturned raft, and so they dashed along, swept by great waves and dazed in rapid whirlpools. Suddenly the river divided into two branches. The raft went careering down one of the channels, and then, to their horror, they saw a huge timber-barrage which stretched across the stream. The raft charged the obstruction like a mad buffalo and was dashed to pieces. The battered crew managed to scramble ashore, but they were in a desperate plight. One of the carriers was so badly injured that he died the next morning. They had lost all their food, clothing, and baggage, and had nothing left but three rifles, a revolver, some ammunition and their sheath knives.

They started back along the bank of the stream in an attempt to rejoin their companions. The undergrowth along the river was so thick they had literally to hack their way through, foot by foot. Imagine their horror to discover that they were on an island. They had now to find a place where the stream could be forded. They were without food and continually drenched by torrential rains. On the fifth day they detected a group of natives on the opposite bank holding up baked sago. Faint with starvation, the men hastily built a crude raft and reached the other side of the river in the last stages of exhaustion.

LIFE ON SOUP POWDER AND COCOA

While they were eating the food given them by the natives, they had another surprise, for they heard a shout, and looking up saw Bell and Pratt and some of the police and carriers emerging from the jungle. Seven of their carriers had lost their lives.

The explorers continued their journey down-stream. They had no means of making a fire and no food other than that which they could beg from the few natives they met. For the next hundred miles they passed rapid after rapid, and for twenty-nine days they had to exist on a few handfuls of soup powder and a few tins of cocoa saved from the capsized rafts. They slept in caves and under palm-leaves, and since they had no matches they had to keep a fire burning day and night. At last the river became smooth enough to enable them to embark in two frail dug-out canoes, in which the voyage down the river was successfully completed. This daring journey resulted in the opening up of the largest area previously unexplored in British New Guinea.

Since the World War the task of filling in the remaining blank spaces on the map of British New Guinea has been carried on by administrative officers in the course of their official duties. In 1915 F. Macdonnell crossed from Tufi, near Cape Nelson, to Port Moresby; in 1917, W. R. Humphries travelled south-eastward from Nepa, near the old German boundary, and ultimately reached the coast at Marobe, while E. W. P. Chinnery explored the Kunimaipa Valley and proved its identity with the Lakekamu.

FINDING PYGMIES AND GOLD

In 1922, L. A. Flint and H. M. Saunders explored the Samberigi Valley and L. Austen the Alice River district; in 1924, Austen and W. H. H. Thompson completed the examination of the north-west corner of Papua, between the Palmer and the Alice rivers, the former reaching the Fly River 600 miles above its mouth; and in 1927 C. H. Karius and J. F. Champion succeeded in crossing the island by the Fly and Sepik rivers, thus virtually completing the map so far as British New Guinea is concerned.

In 1910, Captain C. G. Rawling discovered a race of pygmies in Dutch New Guinea. The men were about 4 ft. 6 in. in height. The finding of gold in many parts of New Guinea attracted many prospectors. Quite a number of them paid for their daring with their lives, falling victims to hostile natives. One of the most intrepid of these prospectors, who is entitled also to be regarded as a daring explorer, is Michael Leahy. During 1930-1934 he made ten journeys into the unknown plateaux and ranges and made many important discoveries.

"BIG PIGS" FOR RIDING

He made a special study of the Purari River and its confluents. The Purari rises in a high plateau, is difficult of access, and the natives dwelling here are cannibals. Although a father will reverently bury his son's intestines, he does not hold any malice against his fellow villagers for eating the flesh of his offspring. Most of the villages are surrounded by a barricade of timber twelve feet high and protected with outworks. Fighting between the villages is so common that a man will never venture forth without his bow and arrow.

Whilst Leahy and his brother were travelling in the Mount-Hagen district a native begged that he might be allowed to accompany the explorers to the coast so that he might see the wonders of the white man. Leahy agreed, but he had much difficulty in protecting the native from the over-zealous attentions of his friends, who were quite convinced that the white men were taking him away to eat him. When Leahy reached the temporary aerodrome on the Ramu River, this native was sent on a trip by plane to the coast. He came back the next day with two bottles of salt water, a collection of ironware, and a handful of hairs out of a horse's tail—this last item to prove to his friends that the white man "has big pigs on which to ride!"

STIRRING ADVENTURES ON THE MIGHTY AMAZON

THERE have been many instances of famous explorers venturing into the unknown and never being heard of again. There is the case of Colonel P. H. Fawcett, who disappeared with his party into the wilds of the vast Amazon forest, never to be seen again. In 1907 Fawcett was called upon to delimit the boundary between Bolivia and Brazil. At that time much of the country was still unexplored. The swamp lands to the south had hardly been traversed by white men, much less surveyed or mapped. Fawcett was fully aware of the difficulties and the dangers. But the prospect did not alarm him, for he had spent much time in exploring the jungles and ruins of Ceylon, and was one of those fortunate folk who are almost immune to malaria. He was also a man of fine physique and great muscular strength, a good shot, a clever fisherman, and well versed in woodcraft and camp lore. He had an unusual gift for understanding Indian languages. He used to say that, given a fortnight with any tribe, he was able to converse with them.

EXPLORER WHO NEVER RETURNED

In his work in Bolivia, Fawcett crossed the great mountain chain which divides Bolivia from Chile and Peru no fewer than six times; explored amazing Lake Titicaca, which is 120 miles long, 120 fathoms deep, and lies more than 12,000 ft. above sea-level; ascended the rivers La Plata and Paraguay nearly to their sources, forcing his way through jungle so thick that sometimes no more than 500 yards was accomplished in a whole day's journey.

Fawcett was fearless and never fired except in the last extremity. While he and his party were travelling up a small, unnamed creek in the Amazon basin, inhabited by the warlike Parecis, an arrow, shot from the bank, struck his boat, penetrating the solid timber to the depth of an inch. Fawcett, instead of retaliating, stood up and called out that he was not hostile, but the Indians refused to show themselves. His own men were terrified; they said they would be killed if they went on. Fawcett then landed on a sand-bank and, unarmed and with hands held high, walked slowly toward the trees behind which the Indians were hiding. It was a terrible risk, but it succeeded. The Indian chief, squat, ugly, and powerfully built, stepped out and greeted the brave intruder. Within a short time he and Fawcett were fast friends, and after that there was no more trouble.

ROOSEVELT AS EXPLORER AND NATURALIST

When the 20th century dawned the vast Amazon basin still concealed a number of major secrets. The course of the main river was known, but lying both to the north and south of it were tributary streams, some of them 1,000 miles in length, down which no one had

yet sailed.   Between these tributaries were immense stretches of forest
territory of which nothing whatever was known.   Here and there
adventurous seekers after rubber had penetrated a few miles along
subsidiary streams, only to find further progress barred by dangerous
rapids and hostile Indians.

Many of the great tributaries in the southern basin of the Amazon
were explored during the early years of the present century by that
famous Brazilian traveller, Colonel Rondon.   Not only did he survey
them, but managed to make friends with the Indians.   In 1913 he
accompanied Theodore Roosevelt, ex-President of the United States, on
a particularly daring journey in the hinterland of Brazil.

On the Paraguay River they were brought in contact with that remarkable fish, the piranha, found in certain of the Amazon streams.   Though
only eighteen inches long it is armed with formidable teeth and is very
ferocious.   These fishes go about in shoals, and woe betide cattle and
even human beings venturing into the water.   Blood excites them to
madness.   Believing there were no piranhas about, Rondon went for
a swim.   It cost him a toe and severe bites on his thighs and hands.

ANIMAL TERRORS OF THE AMAZON

One of the terrors of travelling in the region of the Amazon is its
wild life.   It seems to be imbued with a peculiar and terrifying ferocity.
The numerous rivers, marshes, and lagoons are the haunt of that dreaded
monster of the night, the anaconda.   Colonel Fawcett records how he
killed one of these snakes on the Abuna River.   It was coiled round
a tree with its tail in the water.   It measured 48 ft. out of the water, and
he estimated there were another 17 ft. immersed.   An anaconda killed
near Corumba measured 85 ft. in length.

Apart from the man-eating piranha there are the stinging-ray and the
electric eel.   So powerful is the sting of the ray that it will pierce thick
leather, and natives and animals often die from the shock, while many
men who do not succumb are rendered lame for months.   The electric
fish is capable of giving a shock, when touched, equivalent to 400 volts,
sufficient to incapacitate any man.

In the virgin forest poisonous snakes are as common as rats in a
disused warehouse.   The forest is also the home of the savage jaguar,
puma and peccary.   The latter is a small, hog-like creature, with tusks
like a wild boar.   Peccaries hunt in packs and do not know what fear
is.   Worse still are the insects.   One, called piums, will attack in thousands and cover the victim with tiny blood-blisters.   There are
mosquitoes so small that they will penetrate any net; moths and flies that
lay their eggs under the skin, which becomes infested with maggots;
jiggers, which penetrate beneath the toe-nails; and ticks which burrow
and die under the skin.   Then there are the ants.   They are of all sizes,
and each variety has a different bite.   The sting of the fire ant is worse
than a prick from a red-hot needle.

Crossing the Matto Grosso, the Roosevelt expedition reached the scene of Rondon's former exploration, of which Roosevelt wrote that it " was as remarkable as, and in its results even more important than, any similar work undertaken elsewhere on the globe at or about the same time." From Tapirapoan, on the river of that name, the expedition started northwards across the Plan Alto, or "Highland Wilderness," of Brazil. The route lay through the land inhabited by Nhambiqueras, natives of the most primitive type. Both sexes were naked, and "the men had holes pierced through the septum of the nose and through the upper lip, and wore a straw through each hole."

DISCOVERING THE RIVER OF DOUBT

Some weeks later they struck an entirely unknown river, some 900 miles in length, which they named the River of Doubt. Using seven dug-outs, they started down-stream. The rapids and whirlpools proved particularly trying, necessitating exhausting portages, some of considerable length. Roosevelt's son Kermit had a narrow escape. His small canoe was caught in a whirlpool and carried over some dangerous rapids. The canoe filled and turned turtle. One of the two paddlers was pummelled to death on the boulders, but Kermit, breathless and half-drowned, managed to clutch an overhanging branch and, with the help of the second paddler, scrambled ashore.

They followed the river for forty-seven days, meeting with all kinds of adventures, here and there penetrating into the forest to collect specimens of its wild life. They had trouble with Indians while their own carriers suffered severely from festering sores set up by insect bites. Sometimes their rate of progress did not exceed two miles a day. At last they arrived at the mouth of the stream, utterly exhausted, Roosevelt and his son suffering from the effects of fever and Rondon laid up with an inflamed bruise. To their surprise and delight they found the river flowed into the Madeira, one of the main tributaries of the Amazon.

PERISHED AT THE HANDS OF HOSTILE TRIBES

In 1925 Colonel Fawcett, accompanied by his son Jack and another Englishman, Raleigh Rimell, started out from Cuyaha, and disappeared into the then unknown territory of the Xingu. He was led to undertake this trip because of the rumours and legends concerning a strange race of Indians who inhabited the depths of the primeval forest. Their skin was said to be white; they had red hair and blue eyes. They travelled and hunted by night and hid by day. There were also rumours of wonderful old ruins and strange animals, of tracks huge and unrecognized. Fables gather, of course, around unexplored places, but we must not forget that the African pygmy and the okapi were for long discredited.

Fawcett was last heard of from Bakairi, situated some distance to the north of Cuyaha, in May, 1925. "Our journey has been no bed of roses," he wrote. "We have cut our way through miles of *cerraba,* a forest of low, dry scrub; we have crossed innumerable small streams by swimming and fording; we have climbed rocky hills of forbidding aspect, we have been eaten by bugs. . . . The primitive Indians here have the unpleasant habit of carrying their victims threaded on bamboos or slung to them by the tendons of arms and feet, feeding on them in a state of decomposition. . . . Our two guides go back from here. They are more and more nervous as we push farther into the Indian country."

A year passed, and then two, when every one became anxious as to what had happened to the little band of travellers. At last, in 1928, Commander Dyott, who had already travelled far and wide in the Amazon basin, raised a relief expedition. It was a trip that involved considerable hardship and danger. Dyott crossed the country from Cuyaha to the Kulisehu River, reached the Xingu, and followed that river to its mouth. He experienced considerable hostility from the Indians, and on more than one occasion found it necessary to alter his route or beat a hasty retreat.

Dyott records how during this remarkable journey through an unexplored wilderness he saw isolated sheer-sided hills such as those described in the " lost world " legend. He saw escarpments crowned by eminences worn by wind and rain into peculiar shapes which at a distance might be mistaken for houses, towers, or even ruined cities. He also noted that the slanting rays of the sun reflected from some of the polished rocks might well have given rise to the stories of flashing lights seen in the windows of ancient stone buildings.

Dyott traced Fawcett's route as far as the Kulisehu, where he discovered relics of the explorer, including an air-tight case. That Colonel Fawcett and his companions perished at the hands of hostile tribes seems to him and to all his party beyond dispute. Thus perished a splendid pioneer whose name is inscribed for all time in the list of great explorers of South America.

TRACING THE COURSE OF THE RIVER UAUPES

While explorers were busy in the southern basin of the Amazon, Dr. Hamilton Rice, an American, was toiling in the north-west section of the basin, particularly in regard to the Rio Negro and its mighty confluents. In 1907 he crossed the Andes from Bogota in an effort to trace the course of the River Uaupes, which is one of the main tributaries of the Rio Negro. While paddling down a stream, the ariare, a large macarel (a member of the rattlesnake family) cut across the bows of the boat in mid-stream. One of the paddlers struck the snake a heavy blow with a paddle. In a moment all was confusion. The furious snake leaped aboard the canoe, and there was a mad scramble for guns and cutlasses before a lucky blow killed the invader.

A few days later Rice and a companion disembarked, intending to procure monkeys for breakfast. They became separated, and both spent a miserable day floundering in a big swamp from which they could find no exit. To add to their difficulties, a violent storm arose.

and then they had the bad luck to stumble across a small herd of peccaries. They were forced to take shelter up a tree and wait for the peccaries to retire. At last they reached the Uaupes River and sailed down it for 400 miles, where it emptied itself into the Rio Negro.

Five years later, in 1912-1913, Rice returned to the same region and explored the Inirida, one of the main tributaries of the Orinoco. Then he went across country to the Icana River, another great tributary of the Rio Negro. On these trips the exploring party suffered hunger and were tormented by myriads of insects. One of the carriers, while fishing in a stream, was stung by a ray. For two days he crawled along through the undergrowth to the base camp shadowed all the way by a pair of pumas. When he reached camp he was in a state of utter collapse. In 1919, Rice surveyed the Rio Negro up to the Cassiquiare River and the Orinoco, while on a fifth expedition, in 1924-1925, he did similar work on the Rio Branco and the Uraricoera. On his later trips Rice made use of aeroplanes.

EXPLORING ARCTIC CANADA

IT was the Canadian explorer Vilhjalmur Stefansson who first exploded the idea, held by many people, that the Arctic regions of Canada are all ice and snow, entirely devoid of any form of life, and of little value to anyone. During the brief Arctic summer these lands in the far north of the Dominion enjoy considerable sunshine. The mosses and coarse grass support herds of caribou and musk-oxen, numbering sometimes hundreds of thousands in a single band. Banks Island, for example, which lies far to the north in the neighbourhood of the Pole, is, in the summer, white with millions of geese and resplendent with beautiful Arctic flowers.

TRIBE OF BLONDE ESKIMOS

Stefansson learnt the secret of how to live happily in the Arctic during the many exploratory journeys which he made in the northlands of the Dominion between the years 1908-1912. Briefly, it consists of a knowledge of the Eskimo language and being prepared to live as they do off the land. Not only did he bring back valuable information concerning the flora and fauna of the Arctic, but discovered, among other interesting things, a tribe of blonde Eskimos. Then followed his memorable expedition of 1913-1918, when he was away from civilization for five and a half years, during which time he found and explored a great Arctic continent lying between the North Pole and the far northern coasts of Canada.

The expedition was financed by the Canadian Government, and its object was to ascertain whether land existed to the north-west of Banks Island, and also to explore and chart the unvisited northern coasts of Victoria and Prince Patrick Islands, as well as the coasts to the east of the Mackenzie Delta. There were three ships—the steam-whaler *Karluk*, of 275 tons, and two small motor-driven schooners of fifty tons, the *Mary Sachs* and the *Alaska*.

Rounding Point Barrow the three vessels steamed eastward through the loose ice until they became frozen in near Camden Bay, the *Karluk* at a distance of some fourteen miles from the shore and some fifty miles west of the two smaller vessels.

SHIP THAT DISAPPEARED

Stefansson naturally imagined that his ships were now held up for the winter, so went ashore on a hunting trip, accompanied by two white companions and two Eskimos. He calculated that he could obtain all the meat he required and be back again within ten days. The little party never saw their ship again.

They had not travelled far before they were overtaken by a fierce blizzard, compelling them to take shelter on a neighbouring island. For four days the wind blew continuously, accompanied by heavy snow and fog. Then imagine their horror to discover that the ice had broken up and they were surrounded by " leads " of open water. For several days longer they remained on the island, living as best they could. By that time the ice had formed again, and they hastened back to their ship for further supplies. But she was not there, nor anywhere in sight.

Stefannson concluded that the *Karluk* had been carried with the ice back towards Point Barrow. Anxious for the safety of his flagship, the explorer abandoned his hunting trip and started for Point Barrow, where he arrived eight days later, only to learn from some Eskimos that a ship had been seen a week previously drifting westward far out on the ice. To continue the pursuit was now useless.

With his biggest ship gone, his force largely diminished, and his main supplies lost, Stefansson faced conditions which would have seemed hopeless to a man of weaker fibre. But his courage never failed, nor was his purpose shaken. What he had planned to do by ship and sledge had now to be done by sledge alone. He turned about once more and made for Martin Point, 325 miles distant to the east, to join Dr. Anderson and the two smaller schooners.

STEFANSSON'S DARING SLEDGE JOURNEY

It was in many respects a daring sledge journey. Stefansson's companions record how even their two Eskimos marvelled at the leader's extraordinary skill as an ice traveller. " He taught us how to pitch camp in a blizzard and how to find our way without the aid of a compass by referring to the snowdrifts made by prevailing winds. On one occasion, after a south-west blizzard, with wind blowing at the rate of sixty miles an hour, and in a blinding snowstorm, Stefansson led us without a trail or a landmark of any sort for twenty miles, and at the end of the journey was only a hundred yards out of the way. On several occasions that day, the last few hours of which we travelled in darkness, we entirely lost sight of him, although at no time did he ever go more than twenty feet ahead of the dogs."

Here it is necessary to digress somewhat to learn the fate of the *Karluk*. Caught in the swirling vortex of the main Arctic drift, she was carried westward, absolutely helpless and at the mercy of the current, sometimes drifting stern first and at other times moving swiftly broadside on. Thus she was carried westward for 110 days, when she sank, her sides crushed in by the ice.

Before the vessel went down all the stores and instruments were removed to two houses, one built of wood and the other of snow, which had been erected on the ice close by. Captain Bartlett, in charge of the vessel, reckoned he was about seventy miles from Wrangell Island, the nearest land, and determined to reach it as speedily as possible. Four men were sent on ahead to pick out a way, but were lost in a blizzard; while a like fate overtook a second party, also consisting of four brave souls, including three of the scientific staff. It was not until a month later that the remainder of the party, consisting of twelve white men and six Eskimos, succeeded in getting to the island.

Here they were at once put on short rations, while Captain Bartlett, with only one companion—an Eskimo—started for the Siberian shore, 120 miles to the south, in search of help. After months of weary travelling, during which he suffered great hardships, he managed to hail a whaler in the Bering Sea, and at last got to Nome. Immediately a relief expedition was organized, and three ships went north to rescue the castaways. The survivors were found in a desperate condition, on the verge of starvation. Two of the party had died, and a third had accidentally shot himself since Bartlett had left them.

SURVEYING AN UNKNOWN COAST

Meanwhile, Stefansson, who was unaware of the fate of his flagship, had ventured north into the unknown, aiming for Banks Island over the Beaufort Sea, accompanied by two companions—Anderson and Stokensen—six dogs, 360 rounds of ammunition, and food for about forty days. They were considerably hindered by violent gales and enormous ice ridges, 20 ft. and more in height. One severe blizzard lasted twelve whole days and nights. They ran short of food and the dogs were so hungry that they ate pieces of fur clothing discarded by the men. Just as things began to look black the party killed a couple of polar bears, and were thus able to replenish their scanty stock of provisions. They were destined to spend ninety days on the moving ice before the island was reached.

The summer and ensuing winter were spent surveying and mapping Banks Island. In the following spring, despite the fact that his dogs were nearly done for, the intrepid explorer went north again and surveyed and charted the unknown coast of Prince Patrick Island. Then they again turned their faces north over the ice-covered ocean. Often they had to fit up their sledge as a boat to negotiate open water.

One morning, from the top of a forty-foot ice hummock, they sighted mountain tops indicating new land to the north. The discovery put new life into them. They reached the new territory next day and found two islands, now known as Borden and Brock Islands. Stefansson took possession of them in the name of the king. Even so far north as this caribou and musk-oxen were found.

GIVEN UP AS LOST

On returning to Herschel Island the party discovered that they had long been given up as lost. The following year Stefansson ventured again into the unknown north. On this trip he discovered another unknown island now known as Meighen, lying beyond the Ringnes Islands. It was the nearest approach to a barren land which he had so far seen. Even here, however, there were great flocks of geese. Other islands and land were also discovered.

In the course of his work in the Arctic, Stefansson surveyed over 100,000 square miles of unknown seas and lands. These surveys covered 65,000 square miles of Beaufort Sea, 10,000 square miles of the Arctic Ocean west of Prince Patrick Island; and nearly 20,000 square miles to the east and north-east of Prince Patrick. In addition to verifying previous discoveries, and filling in unknown coastlines, three large and many smaller islands were discovered.

CONQUEST OF THE NORTH POLE

OF the two Poles the North was the first to be conquered. The honour of this daring feat belongs to that gallant American Arctic explorer, Rear-Admiral Robert Peary (1856-1920), who succeeded in reaching it, after a stirring sledge journey, on April 6, 1909.

PEOPLE WHO HAD NEVER SEEN A TREE

"For more than a score of years that mathematical point of the earth's surface had been the object of my every effort," wrote Peary, shortly after his return from the North Pole. "To attain it I had dedicated my whole being, physical, mental, and moral; had risked my life a hundred times, and the lives of those who had been glad to take the chances with me. This last journey was my eighth into the Arctic. I had spent in these regions nearly twelve years out of the twenty-three between my thirtieth and my fifty-third year, and the intervening time which I had spent in civilization during that period had been mainly occupied with preparations for the Arctic journeys." It was virtually, therefore, a twenty-three years' hard battle against terrible odds. Over and over again Peary returned from his Arctic journeys with the proud record of "farthest north."

Although Peary's primary object on his many expeditions was to reach the Pole, he also carried out extensive exploration schemes, mapping out many thousands of miles of unknown Arctic territory.

He was the first explorer to discover that Greenland was an island—a great island continent, in fact, boasting an area of about 827,000 square miles. He traversed its treacherous coasts, fighting storms, blizzards, fogs, ice floes, and dodging icebergs, for thousands of miles, and made two daring sledge journeys right across its vast interior. In its northern latitudes, at a distance of only some 1,200 miles from the North Pole itself, he stumbled across a splendid race of Eskimos, the most northerly people on the face of the earth. They had never seen a tree growing and lived entirely by fishing and hunting.

Peary's indomitable courage is evidenced by his refusal to alter his plans when he broke his leg. He was standing by the wheelhouse of his ship when the rudder struck a heavy piece of ice and forcibly jerked over the tiller as it swung, catching the explorer by the leg and pinning him against the wall of the house. There was no escape from the position, and the pressure of the tiller gradually increased until the bone of the leg snapped. The doctor of the party immediately set the limb; but the sufferer refused to return home, and some days later was carried ashore at Melville Bay, in Smith Sound, strapped to a plank. Then he sent his ship back and settled down for the winter among the Eskimos.

ACROSS THE GREENLAND ICE-CAP

As soon as he was able to get about, Peary went hunting, and he vividly describes a narrow escape he had from the ferocious walrus. Noting a herd of them asleep on the ice, the Eskimo in the boat harpooned one. Immediately the rest slid off the ice and surrounded the little craft. Others from the neighbouring ice patches also charged rapidly on to the scene, and the situation of the boat and its occupants was dangerous in the extreme. As the infuriated animals came up to the boat they tried to get their powerful tusks over the sides, and had any succeeded in doing so there would have been slight hopes of any one escaping. Had the boat been capsized no one could possibly have survived, and to keep the angry crowd off was no easy matter.

All around they swarmed, and not less than 250 were estimated to be engaged in the attack. Peary, with his injured leg, sat in the stern of the boat firing at them, and the other white men kept up a fusillade. The walrus came on in bunches to the attack, and immediately they were fired at all those nearest to the boat leaped out of the water and then plunged out of sight. Whereupon another batch hastened forward, and so the battle continued until the shore was reached.

As soon as spring came Peary started with a single companion—a young Norwegian—on his journey across the Greenland ice-cap, which up to that time had never been crossed, not even by the Eskimos. After fifty-seven days of hard travelling the explorers were nearly on the verge of starvation; their provisions had almost run out, and they were hastening on to the opposite coast with the hope of securing some seals. Suddenly they came to the limits of the ice-cap and stood, silent and

amazed, looking down from the summit of the snow desert across
a wide and open plain, covered with vegetation, with here and there
a snowdrift showing white, and with herds of musk-oxen contentedly
grazing over it.

Here, right in the north of Greenland, surrounded by the great
ice-cap and monster glaciers, was a fertile valley, unknown even to the
Eskimos, where the Arctic poppy and the dandelion were in bloom, and
where the drone of the bumble-bee was to be heard.

Explorations to the north revealed the fact that Greenland was an
island, and that between it and the Pole lay an ice-covered ocean.

STARTING FOR THE POLE

It was in July, 1908, that Peary sailed north in the steamer *Roosevelt*
to make what proved to be his successful journey to the Pole. The
winter was spent at Cape Sheridan. "Imagine us," says Peary, "in
our winter home 450 miles from the Pole, the ship held tight in her icy
berth 150 yards from the shore, ship and the surrounding world
covered with snow, the wind whirling in the rigging and shrieking
around the corners of the deck-houses, the temperature ranging from
zero to sixty below, the ice-pack in the channel outside us groaning
and complaining with the movement of the tides."

Early in the following spring a base was established at Cape
Columbia some ninety miles away. Here were gathered seven of Peary's
men, fifty-nine Eskimos, 140 dogs, and twenty-eight sledges. Each
sledge was complete in itself; each had its cooking utensils, its four men,
its dogs, and provisions for fifty or sixty days.

On March 1 the cavalcade started in a freezing east wind, and soon
men and dogs became invisible amid drifting snow. Day by day they
went forward undaunted by the difficulties and hardships of the way,
now sending back small parties to the depot at Cape Columbia as well
as those who became incapacitated through frost-bite. On and on they
went till they had broken all records and passed the eighty-seventh
parallel into the region where it is daylight for half the year. Thus
they marched for a month; party after party had been sent back, till the
last supporting party had gone and Peary was left with his negro
servant Henson, and four Eskimos. He had five sledges, forty picked
dogs, and supplies for forty days when he started off to dash the last
133 miles to the Pole itself. Every event in the next week is of thrilling
interest.

After a few hours of sleep the little party started off shortly after
midnight on April 2. Peary was leading. "I felt the keenest exhilara-
tion," he says, "as I climbed over the ridge and breasted the keen air
sweeping over the mighty ice, pure and straight from the Pole itself."
On the following day they were delayed for some time by open water.
Two days later they had a narrow escape. It was necessary to cross
a hundred yards of newly-formed ice over more open water. Just
as the last sledge left it there was a report like that of a cannon, as the

ice split in every direction. If the ice had broken a minute or so earlier, men, dogs, and sledges would have been precipitated into the icy ocean. Still they went on, covering twenty or twenty-five miles a day.

STARS AND STRIPES AT THE POLE

On April 6, 1909, Peary and his little party stood at the Pole, that historic spot in the northern hemisphere "which knows no north, nor west, nor east." Through all his perilous expeditions to the Arctic regions Peary had worn a silken flag, worked by his wife, wrapped round his body. This he removed and proudly planted on a great hummock of ice which represented the Pole.

Peary remained for thirty hours in the neighbourhood of the Pole. At a distance of five miles from it he found a crack in the ice, and boring a hole there with a pick-axe he took a sounding of 9,000 ft. and found no bottom. Thus, after four centuries, during which it is computed that 755 brave men had sacrificed their lives in attempting to gain this end, was the North Pole conquered by this daring American explorer.

TO THE POLE BY AEROPLANE

The first to reach the North Pole by aeroplane was Commander R. E. Byrd, who, flying from Spitzbergen on May 9, 1926, reached the Pole and returned in fifteen hours. Two days later Roald Amundsen, Umberto Nobile and Lincoln Ellsworth left Spitzbergen in the Italian airship *Norge* and reached the Pole in sixteen hours, making Point Barrow in Alaska some thirty hours later.

Sir Hubert Wilkins, who had covered much unexplored country in Alaska, while making preliminary flights in 1928, flew from Alaska to Spitzbergen in twenty hours—a distance of 1,200 miles. In this year the airship *Italia* under General Nobile flew to the Pole via Cape Bridgeman, the northernmost point of Greenland, traversing a large unexplored area. The Pole was safely reached, but on the return journey a disaster occurred, Roald Amundsen losing his life while flying to the rescue.

FROM LONDON TO CANADA VIA GREENLAND

Owing to the development of flying, it was decided in 1930 by Henry George (Gino) Watkins, then a Cambridge undergraduate, to examine the possibility of organizing an air route from London to Canada via Iceland and Greenland. It was essential to learn something about the meteorological conditions in Greenland and to survey an unexplored portion of the great ice-cap. This latter called for extensive sledging trips. Angmagssalik, an Eskimo settlement on the east coast, was selected as the base of the expedition, and a camp to study meteorological conditions was established about 140 miles inland on the ice-cap, where observations were taken throughout a whole year.

Relieving the men at the station during the long Arctic winter proved a particularly arduous task on account of blizzards which lasted days with wind gusts of over 100 miles an hour.   At one period only one man, Courtauld, was left at the station because of the shortage of supplies.   When, some time later, an aeroplane was sent with food to the station (it was a bell-shaped tent) it could not be located.   Two attempts to find the station by dog-team also failed.   Watkins thereupon organized another relief party and went himself as leader.   The course was plotted with as much care as if they were navigating a ship.

When they knew they must be near, each man took a dog and began a diligent search.   After hours of searching they stumbled across an inch or two of a brass ventilating pipe sticking up above a snow-drift. It marked the site of the station, now buried deep in snow.   Watkins knelt over the tiny shaft and shouted, and was greatly relieved to hear Courtauld's voice.   The snow was dug away until the apex of the dome-tent appeared.   Then Watkins slit a hole in the canvas and gazed down at a very dirty, bearded hermit in the midst of a squalid, frozen ice-cave, some nine feet in diameter.

In order to hunt alone with reasonable safety, Watkins and his companions learned to roll right round with the *kayak,* the Eskimo one-manned boat, and come up on the other side, an accomplishment rare among Europeans.   Alas, while out hunting, Watkins lost his life. Exactly what happened no one knows.   His *kayak* was found drifting low in the water, but the throwing-stick and gun were missing. Watkins's trousers and *kayak* belt were found, soaking wet, on a nearby ice-floe.   "Thus perished in his youth," says Sir Percy Sykes, "the greatest of the younger generation of Arctic explorers."

THE SOUTH POLE AND THE ANTARCTIC

AFTER Peary's success in reaching the North Pole the zest to conquer the corresponding point in the southern hemisphere became somewhat intense.   Valuable work, particularly by British explorers, had already been done in surveying the outer fringe of the vast Antarctic continent.

SOUTH POLE REACHED BY RIVAL EXPEDITIONS

In 1901 Captain R. F. Scott's expedition set sail in the *Discovery,* specially built to cope with ice conditions in all circumstances, spent two seasons in the Antarctic, discovered King Edward VII Land, and made sledge journeys of nearly 400 miles from their winter quarters.   The expedition revealed the existence of a great plateau rising to nearly 10,000 ft. beyond the coast mountains.   Then came a German expedition under Professor von Dryalski and two more by the French explorer, Jean Baptiste Charcot.

In 1907 Sir Ernest Shackleton reached the Antarctic in the *Nimrod* and established winter quarters at Cape Royds on Ross Island.   He scaled the active volcano of Mount Erebus to a height of 13,700 ft., to find himself on the "brink of a precipice of black rock forming the inner edge of the old crater." He made a dash for the Pole, using Siberian ponies for transport, and reached the very high latitude of 88° 23′ S., within about 120 miles or so of the coveted goal, when scarcity of provisions and continuous blizzards forced him to return. The great journey into the unknown proved that the attainment of the Pole was practicable with good organization.

The South Pole, however, was destined to be reached by two rival expeditions within thirty-three days of each other. The Norwegian explorer, Roald Amundsen, gained it on December 14, 1911, and the English explorer, Captain R. F. Scott, on January 16, 1912.

HALTED BY A FIVE-DAY BLIZZARD

Amundsen was well aware of Scott's plan to reach the Pole, and had also made a close study of the previous expeditions of Shackleton and others. He came to the conclusion that the most favoured point of attack was from the Bay of Whales, an inlet on the Ross Barrier. This was 100 miles nearer his objective than the point which Shackleton had chosen. The risk Amundsen ran was that his base might "calve" off the barrier and float away as an iceberg. Scott, like Shackleton, had decided upon Manchurian ponies as draught animals, while Amundsen, impressed with Peary's success with dogs, decided that they were preferable to ponies.

He sailed south in Fridtjof Nansen's old ship the *Fram* in August, 1910. When the vessel left Norway not even the crew knew her real destination and were not informed until Madeira was passed. The Bay of Whales was reached in the following January and depots with supplies were laid out over the ice for the forthcoming dash to the Pole. The great enterprise started on October 19, 1911, Amundsen being accompanied by four companions on four sledges, each drawn by thirteen dogs. Their progress was greatly hindered by crevasse ice, and on one occasion a blizzard forced them to halt for five days. One sledge fell into a crevasse and it was only prompt action on the part of its leader that saved both dogs and sledge. Shackleton's "farthest south" was passed. By this time the explorers were suffering from frost-bitten faces, and as they neared the Pole they were in a fever of anxiety to learn their fate. "Shall we be first?" At three o'clock in the afternoon of December 14, 1911, a simultaneous "Halt!" rang out from the sledge drivers. The South Pole had been reached.

"WITHOUT THE REWARD OF PRIORITY"

In the June of 1910, two months before the *Fram* had started from Norway, Captain Scott had already sailed south in the *Terra Nova*. After weathering a dangerous storm and forcing her way through 370 miles of ice, Cape Evans, on Ross Island, was reached and winter quarters established.

Scott had undertaken to carry out considerable scientific work, and it was not until November 1, 1911, after supplies depots had been established, that he started on the great journey to the Pole. On November 15, One Ton Camp was reached, situated 130 miles from Cape Evans, and a day's halt was decided upon. As the journey progressed, the ponies were killed to feed the explorers and the dog teams, but Scott wrote: "Our luck in the weather is preposterous." On December 5 a blizzard necessitated a halt of four days. When the journey was resumed, the deep, soft snow made the situation serious. The remainder of the ponies were slaughtered on December 9 near the Beardmore Glacier.

The ascent of the glacier proved terribly difficult, as Shackleton had found it, the crevasses constituting a real danger. On Christmas Day an alpine rope had to be requisitioned to pull a member of the party out of a crevasse fifty feet deep and eight feet across. The plateau gained, the supporting party turned back.

The expedition now consisted of Captain Scott, Dr. E. A. Wilson, Lieut. H. G. Bowers, Captain L. E. E. Oates and Petty-Officer Evans. On January 9, 1912, Shackleton's "farthest south" was passed and seven days later, on January 16, the Pole was reached. Imagine their surprise and disappointment to discover a black flag tied to a sledge bearer, showing that the Norwegians had forestalled them. Small wonder that Scott wrote: "Great God! this is an awful place, and terrible enough for us to have laboured to it without the reward of priority."

END OF AN ENGLISH GENTLEMAN

The return journey of 800 miles of solid dragging now began. Both Evans and Oates were suffering from frost-bite. Still they made fair progress until the Beardmore Glacier was reached. Negotiating the maze of crevasses and confused ice taxed the endurance of the explorers to the uttermost. So much so that Evans collapsed and died. Eighteen days later the already exhausted explorers reached the Middle Barrier depot to discover there was a shortage of oil. This was serious, for Oates was suffering badly from frost-bitten feet. Now came one of the most heroic episodes in the whole history of exploration. Oates realized that he was desperately ill and therefore a serious handicap, since he had to delay the march every morning while he struggled into his foot-gear. Incidentally, he knew that these delays would mean that the supporting party of dogs, which were waiting at One Ton Camp, would have to return to the base owing to shortage of food.

Here Scott's diary reads: "Oates slept through the night before last, hoping not to wake, but he woke in the morning—yesterday. It was blowing a blizzard. He said, 'I am just going outside and may be some time.' He went out into the blizzard, and we have not seen him since. . . . We knew that poor Oates was walking to his death, but though we tried to dissuade him, we knew that it was the act of a brave man and an English gentleman. We all hope to meet the end with a similar spirit, and assuredly the end is not far."

The three stricken survivors struggled painfully on until, on March 19, when only eleven miles from One Ton Camp, there came a fearful blizzard. They had no fuel and only food for one or two days. In the last hours Scott still kept his diary. The last entry was dated Thursday, March 29, and records that for the last eight days the gale had been so ferocious that they had not been able to leave the tent. Eight months later their bodies were found and Scott's famous message to the public, one of the most moving ever penned by a dying explorer: " Had we lived, I should have had a tale to tell of the hardihood, endurance and courage of my companions which would have stirred the heart of every Englishman. These rough notes and our dead bodies must tell the tale."

FILLING IN THE BLANK SPACES

Although the South Pole had been reached, the vast Antarctic continent that surrounded it was still a great blank upon the map. In 1911 Sir Douglas Mawson filled in some of this blank space. He explored and surveyed a large area of unknown territory lying between Victoria Land and Kaiser Wilhelm II Land, known today as George V and Queen Mary Land.

In 1911 came Shackleton's ambitious attempt to cross the entire Antarctic, a distance of 1,800 miles. He reached unexplored land, which he named Caird Coast. His ship, the *Endurance*, was then caught in the ice in the Weddell Sea and was lost, the exploring party having to camp on an ice-floe. When the floe broke up they managed to escape to Elephant Island, in the South Shetlands.

Realizing it was impossible to spend the coming winter here, Shackleton took one of their three small open boats, decked her over with canvas, and with a few picked companions navigated her 750 miles across the stormiest seas known to South Georgia. They were forced by bad weather to land on the south side of the island, whereas their intention was to sail round to the whaling stations on the northern side. With two companions Shackleton set out to cross the island, a feat which had never been attempted before. It was a continuous march of thirty-six hours across unknown glaciers, ice-fields, and mountain ridges 4,000 ft. in height.

EXPLORERS' TERRIFYING APPEARANCE

A journey of thirty miles brought them to the outskirts of Stromness Whaling Station. Approaching the station they met two boys who, on seeing them, turned and bolted for their lives. Farther on they met an old man and he also fled. " Our uncivilized appearance frightened them. Our beards were long and our hair was matted. We were unwashed and the garments which we had worn for nearly a year without a change were tattered and stained." Even the manager of the station, who knew Shackleton well, failed to recognize him until he spoke. He took the travellers in, fed and reclothed them, while arrangements were made for the rescue of the castaways on Elephant Island.

Shackleton started south again in the *Quest* in 1921, but died of heart failure following influenza on board ship off South Georgia in January, 1922. The gallant explorer lies buried on the island.

EXPLORATION MARCHES ON

Since then the mapping and charting of the Antarctic has continued, the explorers being helped in their work by aeroplanes. Four expeditions working in the Far South in 1928 and 1929 all used machines of one type or another, and most important discoveries have been made. Admiral Byrd, from a base near the Bay of Whales, has examined Marie Byrd Land, behind King Edward VII Land, and has also flown to the South Pole and back. Sir Hubert Wilkins has added Hearst Land, south of Graham Land, to the map. Sir Douglas Mawson, in the *Discovery,* has added McRobertson Land to the continent east of Hemp Land.

Thus the coastline of the Antarctic continent, which is almost as large as Australia, is gradually taking shape, and the features of the surface are appearing on the map.

LAW AND JUSTICE

THE oldest surviving code of laws is that drawn up by Hammurabi, King of Babylon, about 2050 B.C. This great and wise monarch had his code engraved upon a shaft of stone eight feet high, which was placed in the temple of the god Marduk in Babylon. The shaft survives to this day. The code occupies 3,600 lines, which extend all round the shaft, and the upper part of the stone is engraved with a relief of Hammurabi receiving the laws from the Sun-god. The code was not in fact of divine origin: it was an orderly and concise statement of a large number of laws, some of great antiquity, which had not up till then been collected together, with the addition of certain laws laid down by Hammurabi himself.

"MODERN" MATRIMONIAL LAWS 4,000 YEARS OLD

One of the most interesting features of this 4,000-year-old Babylonian code is the enlightened attitude to women that it reveals. Matrimonial laws resembled, in many respects, those in force in civilized European countries today. Women appear to have enjoyed practically all the rights of male citizens, and they engaged freely in commerce and the learned professions.

The code included laws designed to protect the widow, the fatherless and the poor; but many of its clauses would be offensive to jurists of our day. The principle of " an eye for an eye and a tooth for a tooth " was rigorously applied, and its application often caused greater injustices than those it was supposed to punish.

The Egyptians of 5,000 years ago had an elaborate code of laws, as we know from scattered inscriptions, but unfortunately no copy of it has yet been found. Such evidence as we have tends to indicate that many of the legal concepts of the Egyptians were both wise and just by modern European standards.

Markedly different from ours were their ideas on marriage and the kindred subject of property. As in ancient Babylon, women occupied a high position in social life and property was inherited mainly through the mother.

Marriage between brother and sister was permissible, even laudable, as is proved by the fact that it was extensively practised in royal circles. It was permissible, too, for a man to keep concubines, who were known as sisters.

MOSES AND THE TEN COMMANDMENTS

It was at one time popularly supposed that Moses, the " lawgiver," as he is called, was responsible for framing practically all the laws of the Israelites, but this is now regarded as highly improbable. Even the Ten Commandments can hardly be ascribed to Moses in the forms in which they are found in the Old Testament, although they probably summarize the ethical ideas of the man who brought his people out of the land of Egypt and gave them both their nationhood and their religion.

The oldest code of Hebrew law, that given in the Book of the Covenant (Exodus xx-xxiii), is original only in details, being simply a Hebrew version of the codes of Babylon and Assyria. The Israelites were nomads (wanderers of the desert) under Moses, while the Book of the Covenant contains a code suited only to an agricultural people. It is therefore reasonable to suppose that this first Hebrew code was drawn up after the Israelites were settled in Canaan (Palestine); that is, after the death of Moses. No doubt much of the code was borrowed from the despised Canaanites, who enjoyed a high degree of civilization at the time when the comparatively barbarous Israelites invaded their territory.

The second code of laws in the Bible, that given in a series of addresses in Deuteronomy, includes the greater part of the first code; but it is in much greater detail than, and shows a cultural advance upon, the first.

SLAVERY IN ANCIENT PALESTINE

The first code laid down the principle of " eye for eye, tooth for tooth, foot for foot," etc., but it is noteworthy that this only applied among freemen. If a free Israelite knocked out the eye, or cut off the limb of his servant (i.e., slave), the servant was given his freedom, but the freeman went unpunished. An employer might even inflict mortal injury on his servant, but so long as the injured person did not expire before the day was out the murder went unpunished.

The principle of " eye for eye " was still maintained in Palestine in the time of Jesus, who cast it aside to replace it with the dictum " Resist not evil." There is no record that Jesus condemned slavery, but the whole spirit of His teaching is fundamentally opposed to it.

Paul tacitly approved the institution of slavery. In this he had the backing of the heathen philosophers Aristotle and Plato, the former of whom regarded it as wholly beneficial to masters and slaves alike.

LEGISLATION IN ANCIENT GREECE

Neither the *Iliad* nor the *Odyssey*, the great Greek epic poems which are usually attributed to Homer and are supposed to have been written in the 9th century before Christ, gives us much information on the laws and judicial system of ancient Greece. It was not, indeed, until the 7th century B.C. that the customary law of the early Greek communities was first written down.

The earliest Greek legal code is supposed to have been that drawn up by Zaleucus about the middle of the 7th century B.C. (663). Prior to Zaleucus judges were apparently permitted to impose whatever penalties seemed best to them, but the code of Zaleucus defined the punishment for each crime.

FIRST LAWGIVER OF ATHENS

The first great Athenian legislator was Draco, who in 621 B.C. arranged all the existing laws of Athens in an orderly form, and considerably modified many of them. The decision to codify the laws was forced upon the ruling class in Athens by the mass of the people, who had for a considerable period been agitating against the unjust class-distinctions of the legal system. Draco's code was very far from representing perfect justice, but it did at least take the administration of the law out of private hands and place it in the hands of tribunals, which were, to some extent, under popular control. Aristotle tells us that Draco laid down that all who bore arms should have the right to vote, but this is probably erroneous.

The whole of Draco's code, except the part dealing with murder, was scrapped by Solon, the greatest of the Greek lawgivers, when he introduced a new constitution in 594 B.C. Solon made great changes in the laws relating to mortgages on land and to debt. As a final court of appeal, he set up a body known as the *Heliæa*, in which, theoretically at least, all classes of the people were represented; he endowed every adult male in Athens with a seat in the popular assembly, the *Ecclesia*, and he reformed the Senate. Although Solon was regarded by his countrymen as the founder of the legal system of Athens, his constitution was discarded before his death.

TWELVE TABLES OF GORTYN

On the site of Gortyn, an ancient city of Crete, there has been found a number of archaic inscriptions which tell us a good deal about the laws of that city. There are two distinct sets of inscriptions; those of the first period, dating from between 650 and 600 B.C., and those of the second period, probably dating from about 450 B.C. In the second set are included what are loosely known as the " Twelve Tables of Gortyn."

The most striking feature of Gortynian law is that it maintains the most advanced principles alongside many primitive ideas. As an illustration of the latter we may take the case of rape, which was not regarded as a crime, but could be atoned for merely by the payment of compensation to the injured party or her representatives. The imposition of fines was regarded as sufficient punishment for many other offences which, according to modern ideas, should be dealt with by imprisonment. Cases were not tried, as was usual in other Greek states, by bodies resembling our juries, but by a single judge.

The most advanced parts of Gortynian law were those dealing with marriage, property and the family. The property rights of married women were very carefully protected against unscrupulous husbands, and daughters could inherit property just like sons. In general, it may be said that the legal position of Gortynian women was very enviable except by the most enlightened standards.

A ROMAN "TWELVE TABLES"

The first legal code of ancient Rome was the Twelve Tables, which was drawn up by ten jurists in 451-450 B.C. Like the code of Draco the Athenian, it was prepared in consequence of the long-standing discontent of the lower classes with the administration of justice. The Roman code shows obvious signs of the influence of the legal ideas of the Greeks, and it has even been said that Rome sent emissaries to Greece to collect information on the legal system in operation there. The Twelve Tables were models of clarity, and they were still being quoted with respect more than 500 years after their compilation.

With the spread of the Roman Empire, Roman law was gradually diffused over a large part of Europe and the non-European Mediterranean countries. Often when the Romans conquered an area they allowed the inhabitants to retain their own laws and customs, but only to a limited degree: the native laws were gradually made to conform with those of Rome.

FINAL FORM OF ROMAN LAW

In the early part of the 4th century A.D., when Constantine the Great made Constantinople (formerly Byzantium) the centre of government of the Roman Empire, Roman law underwent considerable modification from contact with powerful Christian and Hellenistic (Greek) influences.

In A.D. 438 was issued the Theodosian Code. Compiled by the Emperor Theodosius II, it was a collection of the "imperial constitutions" (by which Roman law was modified) published since the time of Constantine.

Roman law was given its final form in the Corpus Juris (body of law) of Justinian, Emperor at Constantinople between the years A.D. 527 and 565. The law had then been in existence in a codified form for about a thousand years.

BASIS OF MODERN LEGAL SYSTEMS

The Corpus Juris is divided into four main sections: (i) the "Institutes," (ii) the "Digest" or "Pandects," (iii) the "Code," and (iv) the "Novels." The "Institutes," published in 533, gave a short summary, in simple language, of the whole body of Roman law. It was based, with modifications and additions, on the manual of the same name which was first published in A.D. 161 by Gaius, a legal authority who lived during the reign of Marcus Aurelius.

The "Digest," which appeared in the same year as the "Institutes," is a much larger work than the latter, consisting of extracts from the great Roman jurists. The "Code," first published in 529, is a collection of the enactments of the emperors, and of their "rescripts," or opinions on disputed points of law. The "Novels" (new things) was a supplement to the other three parts, consisting of the laws made after the compilation of the "Code."

More than 500 years after its publication the *Corpus Juris* of Justinian came into use as a legal textbook in the University of Bologna, Italy. As time passed other European universities took up the study of Roman law, with the result that its influence was powerfully felt all over Europe.

Among the present-day countries whose legal system is largely based on Roman law are: Italy, Spain, Portugal, France, Belgium, Holland, Scotland, Greece, the Dutch East Indies, Ceylon (once under Dutch control), Quebec (formerly French), the American State of Louisiana, and the Union of South Africa. Roman law has also influenced the German and the English legal systems.

PECULIARITIES OF ROMAN LAW

The outstanding feature of the civil law of the Romans was its organization of the family, in which the father was all-powerful. In early times the father was given power of life and death over the members of the family. He could also sell members of his family, and his control of their property was at one time absolute.

In the early days of Rome an unmarried woman was under the absolute control of her father during his lifetime, and of her nearest male relative after the father's death. On marriage she came under the absolute control of her husband.

As the Romans became more civilized the laws and regulations governing women were gradually relaxed, or allowed to fall into abeyance, with the result that by the beginning of the Christian era Roman women enjoyed a large measure of independence, both in respect to their persons and to their property.

USES OF TORTURE

Torture has played an important part in judicial processes from the earliest times. It was practised by the ancient inhabitants of Mesopotamia, by the Egyptians, by the Greeks and by the Romans. It had two uses: as a punishment and as a means of extracting confessions.

Torture was extensively practised in ancient Greece, mainly as a means of obtaining evidence from slaves and persons who did not enjoy Greek citizenship. Among the methods used were those of the rack and the wheel. The Greeks regarded torture as necessary and natural, and such great men as Aristotle and Demosthenes upheld it.

WHEN CRUCIFIXION WAS COMMON

The Romans practised torture even more than the Greeks, and, in their usual systematic manner, drew up careful regulations concerning its application. Among the methods they used were those of the rack, barbed hooks, leaden balls, the hot plate, mutilation, exposure to wild beasts and crucifixion, which was quite common. As in Greece, torture was much less frequently used upon free citizens than upon slaves and freedmen (slaves who had been granted their freedom).

TORTURE IN THE CHRISTIAN CHURCH

Despite that the whole of Christ's teaching is opposed to cruelty in any shape or form, many sections of organized Christianity in an excess of mistaken zeal attempted to spread the faith and to correct the wrong-doer by means of torture. In the 5th and 11th centuries heretics were vigorously persecuted by the Church. In the latter period large numbers of the unorthodox were done to death at the stake and by strangling, and in 1252 a papal bull gave instructions that heretics should be tortured.

At that time it was not wrong, according to the law of the Church, for Christians to inflict torture. Under the Inquisition (Enquiry) for the detection and punishment of heretics, a very large number of people were tortured in the most barbarous fashion. One of the most infamous directors of the Inquisition was Thomas Torquemada (1420-1498), Inquisitor-General of Spain for a period of eighteen years, during which time he is said to have burnt 10,220 people.

Torquemada worked on the principle that a person should be tortured if there existed a strong probability that he was guilty; and that if a confession made under torture was withdrawn the accused should be made to undergo yet more terrible brutalities. Various codes of regulations governed the administration of torture in the name of the Church, but they were more honoured in the breach than the observance. Torture was not officially abolished by the Roman Church until 1816, the year after the battle of Waterloo.

TORTURE IN VARIOUS COUNTRIES

More laws governing the use of torture have been passed in Germany and Austria than in any other countries. Among the commoner tortures in use in the German States were breaking on the wheel, burial alive, impaling on pointed stakes and tearing with red-hot pincers. All these forms were in frequent judicial use for about 200 years after the beginning of the 16th century, and they were far from unknown before that period. The last German State to abolish torture was Baden (1831). Its use practically ceased in Prussia about 1740, during the reign of Frederick the Great, but it was not formally abolished there until the year of Trafalgar (1805).

Torture played a prominent part in the judicial processes of the Italians until near the end of the 18th century, and it was occasionally used in Naples until 1859. Torture regulations very similar to those of Italy were in force in Spain. France appears to have a comparatively good record in respect to torture. Its use seems not to have been officially recognized there until about the middle of the 13th century, and it was altogether abolished in 1789. The French did not, apparently, indulge much in torture for its own sake, unlike the inhabitants of several European and Asiatic countries.

The native inhabitants of the Netherlands never had any great liking for torture, but their various foreign conquerors indulged in it fairly freely. Torture was in official use in Russia until near the middle of the 19th century, despite that it had been formally abolished fifty years earlier. Catherine II (1729-1796), acting under the influence of Voltaire, the great French writer, had done much to restrict its use.

The Swedes never officially recognized torture as part of their judicial processes, but they occasionally resorted to it secretly. A similar state of affairs existed in England, where torture was only inflicted in comparatively rare instances. It was more extensively practised in Scotland, but hardly at all in Ireland. There are few records of its judicial use in the British possessions overseas.

In almost every part of Asia torture was in constant use, from a very early date until comparatively modern times. The shocking severity of Japanese and the terrible ingenuity of Chinese tortures are well known. The Japanese shared with the earlier Romans a taste both for crucifixion and for the torture of Christians.

BEGINNING OF THE PRISON SYSTEM

The practice of sentencing offenders to terms of imprisonment is a comparatively recent innovation. In ancient Rome those convicted of crimes were only confined until such time as punishment—chastisement, torture or execution—could be meted out.

The idea that attempts should be made to cure enemies of society of their anti-social tendencies by confining them for a period regulated by the seriousness of their offences did not begin to be held until a thousand years after Christ, and even then five or six hundred years were allowed to elapse before any considerable efforts were made in that direction. One of the first institutions for the reform of offenders was that built for women in 1593 by the Protestants of Amsterdam. Forty years earlier a prison for vagabonds and loose women had been established in Bridewell, London, but it was a "house of correction," its object being punishment rather than reform.

FIRST GREAT ENGLISH PRISON REFORMER

John Howard (1726-1790) was the first great Englishman to make prison reform his life's work. His interest in the subject was aroused when in 1773, as High Sheriff of Bedford, he paid visits to Bedford jail. Terrible abuses were rampant there, as in practically every other prison in Britain.

The chief jailer and his assistants were paid no salaries, being dependent on fees received from prisoners, who were kept in confinement until the payment of the same. The result was that many perfectly innocent persons, and many whose guilt had not been proved, were unjustly detained. Moreover, the conditions under which they were forced to exist—they cannot, without exaggeration, be said to have lived—were horrible beyond words.

Howard was galvanized into action by the horrors which a tour of county jails revealed to him, and in 1774 he gave an account of his investigations to a sympathetic House of Commons. Very soon afterwards Acts were passed providing for the payment of jailers, the liberation of prisoners against whom no cases could be made out, and the improvement of the sanitary and medical conditions of the prisons.

In 1775-1776 Howard visited many prisons in France, Germany, the Low Countries and Switzerland. He discovered that those of Holland were far in advance of all others. Those of Germany, on the other hand, were very bad.

After the publication, in 1777, of his *State of the Prisons in England and Wales . . . and an Account of some Foreign Prisons*, a Bill was drawn up providing for the establishment of prisons, one object of which was to turn the criminal into a useful member of society. This Act may be regarded as the foundation on which the English prison system was built. Its aims were enunciated in these words: ". . . by sobriety, cleanliness and medical assistance, by a regular series of labour, by solitary confinement during the intervals of work and by due religious instruction to preserve and amend the health of the unhappy offenders, to inure them to habits of industry, to guard them from pernicious company, to accustom them to serious reflection and to teach them both the principles and practice of every Christian and moral duty."

Needless to say, these lofty sentiments were regarded more as indicating ideals to be aimed at in the distant future than as a practical rule of conduct for dealing with immediate needs. The horrors of the system introduced by the Act of 1778 were very great, but a beginning had at least been made.

From the time of the passing of the Bill until his death from camp fever, contracted while inspecting a Russian hospital, Howard worked ceaselessly for the amelioration of the prisoner's lot. He travelled widely on the Continent, wrote books and articles, drew up plans for prisons, and did research work on the means of preventing contagious distempers. Howard brought light, humaneness and knowledge into an age of darkness, brutality and ignorance, and he will always be remembered with grateful affection by those who are struggling to lessen the sum total of man's inhumanity to man.

WORK OF BECCARIA, VOLTAIRE AND MIRABEAU

It was not only in England that crime and punishment were attracting the attention of great men. Italy produced Cesare Beccaria (1738-1794), mathematician, economist and social reformer. His book on *Crimes and Punishments,* published in 1764, was translated into more than a score of European languages. Howard's Italian counterpart believed in the abolition, not only of torture, but of capital punishment. He felt that more energy should be devoted to the prevention of crime and less to its savage punishment; and that where punishment was deemed to be necessary it should follow the crime as quickly as possible.

The French edition of Beccaria's book had a preface by Voltaire, who was in almost complete agreement with the ideas expressed in it, and who played a noteworthy part in inducing a more humane attitude towards criminals.

In 1791 the leaders of the Revolution in France decreed that reformatory imprisonment should be substituted for the less humane punishments in the penal code. The man chiefly responsible for this notable advance in the treatment of criminals was the Comte de Mirabeau (1749-1791), one of the great intellectual leaders of the Revolution.

TRANSPORTED FOR LIFE

The first British Prisons Act, to which reference has been made above, was introduced in 1777. The year is important. It was the year following that in which the American colonies achieved their independence. But what have American colonies to do with English prisons? A great deal.

Before the colonies won their freedom they were a dumping-ground for undesirable natives of Britain. The power to transport convicts across the seas was given to justices in the reign of Elizabeth. In that of James I " dissolute persons " were sent to Virginia. Thereafter large numbers of convicts were sent to New England. But when, in 1776, the colonies broke away from the mother country, transportation to them ceased and English justices were forced to look round for other means of dealing with convicts.

This explains why John Howard's efforts to reform the English jails were so sympathetically considered by the Government. For a short time a good deal of attention was devoted to the new prison system, but soon a substitute for New England presented itself to the anxious gaze of the transportationists. In 1770 Captain James Cook had sighted Botany Bay, Australia. Seventeen years later the first Australian convict fleet left England. It consisted of nine transport vessels and two men-of-war.

Transportation on a scale America had never known was inflicted on Australia. For more than half a century convicts—many of whom were guilty of no serious crime, and others who were of the scum of Britain—continued to pour into the newly re-found continent. The system was bad for the convicts, bad for England, and bad for Australia. It was abandoned because of growing discontent in Australia three years after Queen Victoria's accession (1840).

But for the re-discovery of Australia and its use as an easy way out of the convict problem, the British penal system might have been the envy of the civilized world by the end of the 18th century. As it was, it lagged far behind France, Holland and the United States, and, in the words of Lecky, the historian, was " shamefully below the average of the Continent." So bad was it that in 1817 Sir Samuel Romilly (1757-1818), the law-reformer, was able truthfully to say : " The laws of England are written in blood."

"GREATEST HAPPINESS OF THE GREATEST NUMBER"

Sir Samuel Romilly was a disciple of Jeremy Bentham (1748-1832), a hard-headed, commonsensical, but very advanced gentleman, who fought determinedly against the evils of the penal system, and who, in the words of his friend J. S. Mill, "found the philosophy of law a chaos and left it a science."

One of his earliest works was the *Rationale of Rewards and Punishments,* which, although written in 1775 (when John Howard was beginning his inquiries) was not published until 1811, and then not in English but in a French translation by Etienne Dumont, an associate of Mirabeau. As this fact suggests, Bentham was more honoured on the European continent and in the United States than in his own country.

He was made a citizen of the French Republic in 1792, mainly in recognition of his *Introduction to Principles of Morals and Legislation* (1789). In this work he put forward the then novel suggestion that all punishment is of itself evil and ought therefore only to be allowed in so far as it "promises to exclude some greater evil." He saw the proper aim of government and law as "the greatest happiness of the greatest number." This phrase he got from Beccaria.

He was not content merely to formulate theories. For about twenty-five years he laboured on the working out of a plan for a model prison system, which he vainly hoped would be accepted by the Government. He pressed hard to induce those in authority to spend more time and money in efforts to discover the causes of crime and then to eradicate them.

Although the Government did not accept Bentham's scheme, it was largely as the result of his agitation that a convict prison was built at Millbank, London, on the site now occupied by the National Gallery of Modern Art (the Tate Gallery). The prison cost, so it is said, £500,000 and took ten years to build (1813-1823). Covering an area of sixteen acres, it had accommodation for 1,120 prisoners. It was shut down in 1890 and demolished in 1903.

SAINT VISITS THE PRISONS

In the year that saw the laying of the foundation stone of Millbank penitentiary a young Quakeress named Elizabeth Fry (1780-1845) paid her first visit to Newgate Prison, in the City of London.

Newgate was so terrible a place that, according to a good authority, even the governor was afraid to venture into its cells. Elizabeth Fry was there confronted by a "swarm of drunken, mad, half-naked, starving women, living more like beasts than humans." Such an experience should, one would think, have been enough to cure a gently-nurtured, well-off woman of any desire to pursue her investigations further, but it only increased Mrs. Fry's compassion and strengthened her determination to spend herself and her fortune in doing away with such places.

Nothing about this wonderful woman was more remarkable than the almost magical power she was able to exercise over the most hardened and depraved members of society. A word in her quiet voice, or a glance from her gentle eyes could make the toughest convict her devoted slave. By the sheer force of her goodness she accomplished what all the rigours of an unspeakably barbarous penal system were powerless to effect. " To see," said Sidney Smith, " that holy woman in the midst of the wretched prisoners . . . clinging to the hem of her garment, and worshipping her as the only being who has ever loved them, or taught them, or noticed them, or spoken to them of God! This is the sight which breaks down the pageant of life."

Gathering round her a group of devoted helpers, she threw herself into the struggle and achieved miracles of reform. She was wealthy when she began her crusade, but even when, seventeen years before her death, her husband went bankrupt, she still continued to spend herself—a gift more precious than gold—for humanity. It is further noteworthy that in her Herculean prison labours she did not neglect her own large family.

Her reforming zeal knew no national frontiers : like her forerunner, John Howard, she travelled extensively—in France, Switzerland and Germany, in Belgium, Holland and Denmark. Everywhere she went she was eagerly received, nor were the lessons she taught quickly forgotten. All over Europe unhappy prisoners who never knew her name were indebted to this woman whose Christianity belonged to every day of the week and every minute of the day.

CAPITAL PUNISHMENT FOR PETTY CRIMES

Whereas capital punishment had been abolished under the influence of Beccaria—and during his lifetime—by Peter Leopold, Grand Duke of Tuscany, it was within the power of English justices to inflict it for no fewer than 200 offences at the beginning of the 19th century. The great majority of these offences were trifling in the extreme, and since it would have been quite impossible to execute every one who committed one of them, administration of the law was chaotic. Sentence of death was often pronounced, but seldom—and then usually capriciously— carried out.

Sir Samuel Romilly (1757-1818) probably did more than any other Englishman to bring about a comprehensive reform of the English law with regard to capital punishment. Romilly was greatly influenced by Beccaria and the great French writers and reformers of the 18th century, including J. J. Rousseau, Voltaire and Mirabeau. He was on intimate terms with the last-named, and supplied him with information on the English parliamentary system for use in devising a similar system for France.

Romilly became Solicitor-General in 1806 and immediately commenced a vigorous attack on the more barbarous features of the penal system. Two years later he made a great breach in the strongly defended walls of the citadel of barbarity by bringing about the repeal of the law under which it was a capital offence to steal from the person. Thereupon the defenders of reaction, headed by Lord Ellenborough, rallied all their forces to repel further attacks.

For ten years the House of Lords prevented Bill after Bill introduced by Romilly from reaching the statute book. Only once, in 1812, did they give way, to permit the passage of a minor Bill. In October, 1818, when the great-hearted Sir Samuel was bowed under the burden of his repeated defeats, his wife, whom he dearly loved, died. This last blow was too much for him. Four days after she had passed away he too died, and by his own hand.

Only a very thoughtless person would say that Sir Samuel Romilly's struggles ended in failure. The Lords, backed by a corrupt ruling class, had had their little day, but all the thinking people of England had been won over by Romilly, and it was not long before his dreams became realities.

For more than a hundred years now the capital sentence has only been carried out in normal circumstances in England in cases of murder. Moreover, the statute-book mentions only four crimes for which it is possible to execute an Englishman. They are high treason, murder, piracy with violence, and destruction of dockyards.

WHERE CAPITAL PUNISHMENT HAS BEEN ABOLISHED

Today there are about twenty countries in which capital punishment has been completely abolished except during war time, and a number of others in which, though still the law of the land, it is very rarely inflicted. In the first category are included Holland, in which it was abolished as early as 1870; Sweden, Norway, Denmark, Latvia, Spain, a number of Central and South American countries; and about eight States of the American Union.

In Finland sentence of death has not been carried out except under martial law since 1826, in Belgium not since 1863. At the other extreme is Germany, where in the five years 1933-1938 there were 200 executions for high treason alone.

DEATH PENALTY IN ENGLAND

A House of Commons Select Committee on Capital Punishment declared in 1930 that: " Our prolonged examination of the situation in foreign countries has increasingly confirmed us in the assurance that capital punishment may be abolished in this country (Great Britain) without endangering life or property or impairing the security of society." In view of so strong a declaration by a Select Committee, and of the fact that in November, 1938, Mr. Vyvyan Adams's motion in the House of Commons in favour of the abolition of the death penalty was carried by 114 votes to 89, there is good reason to suppose that capital punishment will soon be abolished in Britain.

Those who oppose its abolition say, in the first place, that the general public is so much in favour of its retention that were capital punishment to be abolished there would be an outbreak of lynch law, i.e., the mob would forcibly seize and kill those suspected, or convicted, of atrocious crimes. In the second place, say the anti-abolitionists, burglars would be more likely to carry lethal weapons if the fear of the death penalty were to be removed. Thirdly, according to them, reprieved murderers are likely to commit further crimes on their release.

HOW THE DEATH PENALTY IS INFLICTED

Many and various are the means that have been employed to carry out the sentence of death. In Great Britain the condemned person is " hanged by the neck until he is dead." He is allowed to drop 6–8 ft. with a noose around his neck, and at the end of the drop his neck breaks.

Hanging has been practised in England from a very early date, and by the middle of the 12th century it was the normal means of killing murderers. At that time the power to hang offenders was vested in a variety of persons and bodies, including lords of manors, heads of abbeys and municipal authorities.

After hanging, the corpse was often hung in chains near the place where the crime was committed. Gibbeting, as this practice was called, was not officially recognized until 1752, when also it was enacted that, instead of being hung in chains, the corpse might be given to the surgeons to be dissected. Gibbeting was abolished in 1834; dissection two years earlier.

Until 1790 it was customary in England to burn those convicted of certain forms of treason; and the beheading of traitors was permissible for nearly a quarter of a century thereafter.

DRAWING AND QUARTERING

Until 1870 the barbarous punishment of drawing and quartering could still be inflicted in England. Two Irish patriots were sentenced to undergo it in 1867, but the sentence was not carried out. The first person to be hanged, drawn and quartered was the Welsh prince David (1284).

The sentence was carried out as follows : the unfortunate victim was first hanged by the neck; but before death claimed him, his entrails were cut out and burned before his eyes. He was then beheaded; after which his corpse was cut into four parts.

Sentence of death was carried out in public as late as the seventh decade of the 19th century. The last person to be executed in public was Michael Barrett, an Irishman, who in 1868 was found guilty of blowing up a wall of Clerkenwell Prison in an endeavour to set at liberty two of his comrades who were serving a sentence there.

The guillotine, a machine by which the prisoner's head is severed from his body, deserves to be considered a very humane instrument, despite its horrible reputation. It was, indeed, upon humane grounds that Dr. J. I. Guillotin recommended its use to the Constituent Assembly of France in 1789. In the guillotine a heavily-weighted knife descends upon the victim's neck, severing the head instantly. Such a method is obviously more humane than beheading with an axe, in which the painlessness or otherwise of the execution depends upon the headsman's nerves and skill.

The guillotine was not, as is frequently supposed, invented by the doctor whose name it now bears. It was in use hundreds of years before the French Revolution, not only on the continent of Europe, but also in Scotland and England. It was last used in Scotland in 1685, and in England some thirty or forty years earlier. It was in use in Italy from the 13th century, and in Germany from about the same time.

AXE AND BLOCK

Of other methods of execution beheading with an axe was until recent times by far the most widely practised. It is frequently used under the Nazi regime in Germany as a punishment for treason, a word which has a wider meaning in the Third Reich than in the majority of modern States.

Beheading was practised by both the Greeks and Romans, among whom it was regarded as the least disgraceful form of execution. Likewise in England, where this method was introduced by William the Conqueror, beheading was looked upon as an honourable means of death. It was used there from the 12th till the 18th century, mainly on noblemen and for the crime of treason.

HURLED FROM A ROCK

The ancient Israelites, among whom a large number of crimes were punishable by death, practised principally stoning to death and burning. Drowning was the humanest of several Babylonian methods. Impaling upon sharpened stakes was a common punishment among the Assyrians, but they, too, had several alternatives.

In ancient Rome sentence was frequently carried out by hurling the condemned from the top of the Tarpeian Rock, on the Capitoline Hill. Crucifixion was, as a rule, only inflicted on those who were not Roman citizens. The Romans practised flogging extensively, and to be condemned to receive more than a certain number of lashes was equivalent to sentence of death, because this punishment was administered with little regard to the health of the victim.

Under Roman law a man convicted of the killing of his father was sewn up in a sack with an ape, a dog, a cock and a viper, and then thrown into deep water. A somewhat similar method was to throw the victim into a pond full of large eels.

Years before the Declaration of American Independence was adopted by the united colonies in 1776, the New England States made such reforms in the criminal code they had inherited from Great Britain that it was in many respects among the most humane in the world. One of the changes they made was to abolish the death penalty for all except the most serious crimes. In this respect they were very many years ahead of most European countries, including England.

Of those States of the American Union which have not abolished the death penalty, some practise hanging, some electrocution; one, Nevada, executes by lethal gas; and in another, Utah, the condemned is allowed to choose between hanging and shooting.

In electrocution the condemned is strapped into a specially constructed chair, where a number of powerful currents of electricity pass through him. Death is said to be painless and instantaneous, but there are those who contest this statement. Electrocution was first practised in the State of New York in 1890. It has since been adopted by about twenty-five States.

LYNCH LAW

Lynch law is a term used to denote the principles, or rather absence of principles, which guide a mob intent on administering what it imagines to be justice without considering the forms of law.

The name is most probably derived from Charles Lynch (1736-1796), an American justice of the peace, who, in 1780, illegally imprisoned a number of men who had formed a conspiracy. His action was loudly acclaimed, and it inspired others to go and do likewise, often with the most tragic results. The term lynch law is also supposed to have been derived from James Lynch Fitzstephen, one-time mayor of Galway, Ireland, whose sense of justice led him to disregard a strict interpretation of the law.

Lynch law has operated in many parts of the world even in recent times, but the term is now usually reserved for outbreaks of mob " justice " in the less law-abiding States of the American Union. There lynching is usually only practised on black people. During the forty years immediately preceding 1926 there were about 4,250 people lynched in the United States. Of these more than 3,200 were black, and the great majority took place in the backward Southern States. Since 1926 there has been a slow but fairly steady decrease in the numbers of lynchings, and there is good reason to hope that before many years have passed lynch law will no longer obtain.

FLOGGING

In recent times flogging has been abolished as a punishment in many civilized countries, including most States of the American Union. Until 1938 it was used in Britain as a punishment for robbery with violence and certain other offences, and as a means of maintaining discipline in prisons. It is now used there only for the last-named purpose. One instrument in use in Britain is the " cat-o'-nine-tails," consisting of an eighteen-inch handle, to which are attached nine knotted raw-hide thongs. It is difficult to exaggerate the severity of punishment with this instrument.

More barbarous than the "cat" is the Russian "knout," which was in frequent use under the tsars. It has raw-hide thongs to which hooked wires are attached. Each stroke of the knout tears pieces of flesh from the body of the victim; and not infrequently death results.

Flogging is still practised in schools, even in the more civilized countries, but the instruments used are very different from the criminal lash. Fifty years ago it was generally supposed that thrashing was "good" for a child, but this belief has now been largely discarded.

SEPARATE BEDS FOR PRISONERS

The first important English Prison Act in the 19th century was that passed in 1824. It contained no very revolutionary provisions, but it is important as an indication that the work of the reformers of the 18th century was beginning to take effect.

The Act laid down, among numerous other regulations, that where possible each prisoner should have a separate cell; but where this was out of the question—it very often was because of limited accommodation —each prisoner should at least have a separate bed.

Some thirty-five years prior to the passing of this Act the Pennsylvanians, under the influence of the Quakers, had introduced the principle of solitary confinement in the Walnut Street jail in Philadelphia.

This action was prompted by the belief that to permit the prisoners to associate made it possible for the more degraded to corrupt those who were not yet hardened, and that solitary confinement would give the prisoner ample opportunity to reflect upon his misdeeds and to commence the work of mental reformation.

The Pennsylvania principle, as it came to be called, was introduced into the Cherry Hill jail, Philadelphia, in 1829. Meanwhile, a rival system had been introduced in Auburn jail, New York. Under the Auburn system, established between 1816 and 1824, the prisoners spent their nights in separate cells, but during the day they worked and fed together—in silence.

Both systems had ardent supporters among prison reformers, and both were thoroughly experimented with. In the end the Auburn system prevailed over the Pennsylvania system in the American Union. But before this happened the controversy had attracted the attention of prison authorities in Europe.

ORIGIN OF PENTONVILLE PRISON

A delegation representing England, France, Belgium and Germany was sent to America to examine the workings of the rival systems. On their return they reported in favour of the Pennsylvania system of solitary confinement both by day and by night, with the result that work was begun on the construction in Pentonville, London, of a prison on the Pennsylvania plan.

Completed in 1842, Pentonville prison was set aside for first offenders, aged 18-35, who would otherwise have been transported. In 1847, after a very favourable report on the workings of the plan had been received by the Home Office, it was definitely decided to adopt it everywhere in Britain.

INTRODUCTION OF PENAL SERVITUDE

Penal servitude was introduced in 1855-1857 after the cessation of transportation. The convicts were kept in " public-work prisons," and they spent the first nine months of their sentence in solitary confinement, after which they associated for labour on public works. Convicts who would formerly have been sentenced to transportation for seven years, received a four-year sentence under penal servitude. The minimum penal-servitude sentence was three years.

But three years after the passing of the Second Penal Servitude Act (1857), by which the system was firmly established, prison reform on humanitarian lines received a serious set-back. In 1862 a sudden outbreak of violent hooliganism occurred in many large English towns, and in order to suppress it the Garrotting Act of 1863, which provided for an extended use of flogging, was passed. In the following year a very severe Penal Servitude Bill was introduced on the ground that the existing regulations were too lenient. In the new Bill it was proposed to make seven years the minimum sentence and to re-introduce transportation in a modified form, i.e., the convict was to undergo part of his sentence in West Australia. The part of the Bill providing for transportation was never put into force because of determined opposition from the Antipodes. Moreover, the minimum sentence was ultimately reduced to five years.

The unfortunate events of 1862-1864 showed first that the authorities were still regretting the abolition of transportation; and second that there were still many who believed, in spite of abundant evidence to the contrary, that humanity in the administration of the penal code encouraged crimes of violence.

On the other hand, the events of those years had the good effect of awakening public interest in the treatment of criminals. Public opinion forced the Government to take over all the prisons in the country in 1878 and at the same time to establish a central authority to control them.

CURTAILING CORPORAL PUNISHMENT

From about the middle of the 19th century onwards much attention was devoted on the European continent—particularly in France, Italy and Germany—to scientific study of crime and the criminal. The theories of the European criminologists did not escape attention in England, and in 1894 the British Government instituted an inquiry into the prison methods then in use.

The first result of this inquiry was the passing of the Prison Act of 1898, by which, among other things, the use of corporal punishment was curtailed, certain cruel and unnecessary forms of hard labour were abolished, and prisoners were divided into three categories according to the nature of their offence.

THE BORSTAL SYSTEM

Much more revolutionary was the Prevention of Crime Act of 1908, which established the Borstal system and introduced the principle of preventive detention for habitual criminals.

Under the Borstal system, an adolescent offender—between the ages of sixteen and twenty-one—in the case of whom " criminal habit or tendency " had been established, could be detained for a period not exceeding three years in special reformatory schools. These schools are known as Borstal institutions, from the village of Borstal, Kent, where the system was first tried out. On leaving Borstal the adolescent offenders are watched over by members of the Borstal Association. The importance of this reform may be gauged from the fact that when it was introduced about 20,000 young criminals were being sent to prison every year. Now two out of every three Borstal inmates so benefit from their detention that they commit no further crimes on their release.

Under the preventive detention plan, those adults whose repeated offences made it necessary to class them as habitual criminals were first sentenced to a term of penal servitude, and then " detained " for a period of between five and ten years. During this period of preventive detention the prisoner was to be treated much more leniently than during penal servitude, and to be given every possible encouragement to re-adjust himself to normal life.

Here at last in these two systems—the Borstal and the preventive detention—we see the emergence of a really humane and scientific outlook on the part of the English prison authorities.

REFORMATORY SCHOOLS

Borstal institutions were not the first of their kind, despite that their establishment represented a revolutionary advance. So long ago as 1756 a school for the reform of young criminals was established by the Marine Society; and about thirty years later a reformatory school was instituted by the City of London. This latter developed into a farm-school at Redhill, Surrey. Then, in the year after Queen Victoria's accession (1838), a prison specially for juvenile offenders was established at Parkhurst.

The first Reformatory School Act, passed in 1854, provided that child offenders between the ages of twelve and sixteen should be sent to reformatory schools, but only after they had served a short sentence in prison. The insistence on the principle of imprisonment before reformation constituted a serious evil, since it rendered the work of reformation doubly difficult. It was abandoned under the Prison Act of 1898.

In the year (1908) that the Borstal system was established a very important Children's Act, which came to be known as the Children's Charter, was passed into law. It forbade the imprisonment of any person under the age of sixteen, except in the rarest cases. It also divided juvenile offenders into two categories : " children " under fourteen, and " young persons " between fourteen and sixteen. Special courts, known as juvenile courts, were established for the trial of persons in these two categories, and provision was made for their " detention " for periods of less than a month.

One of the most astonishing facts disclosed by criminal statistics is that thirteen is the most lawless age in Britain. Further, one out of every hundred English boys and girls come into a police court.

CRIMINAL JUSTICE BILL OF 1938

In November, 1938, Sir Samuel Hoare, the Home Secretary, introduced a new Criminal Justice Bill in the House of Commons. This Bill was, to quote Mr. Leo Page, " born of the union of humanity and understanding," and it represented " an attempt to induce the courts to treat each case as the problem of an individual offender and not as a mere unit in a calendar of crimes."

Containing no fewer than eighty clauses, it is a sweeping measure of penal reform. That it should have been introduced by Sir Samuel Hoare was appropriate, since he claims kinship with the great Elizabeth Fry.

TREATMENT OF THE YOUNG OFFENDER

The most revolutionary clauses are those dealing with the treatment of the young offender. The Bill aims at the ultimate doing away with the imprisonment of all persons under the age of twenty-one except in the gravest cases. Meanwhile, it provides for the establishment of " Remand Centres," where young offenders between the ages of seventeen and twenty-three, remanded or committed for trial, are to be sent instead of to prison.

" Regional remand homes " are to be established for " problem " children, and for those under the age of seventeen who require medical observation.

An interesting experiment will be the establishment of institutions to be known as Howard Homes, in honour of the great reformer. These are for offenders of between sixteen and twenty-one years of age whose records, though not bad enough to justify their being sent to Borstal, indicate that they should be removed from their former environments and placed under official control. The inmates of Howard Homes will continue in their normal employments in office, shop or factory, but will be under control outside working hours.

It is also proposed to establish " Compulsory Attendance Centres " where young people who come before the courts, and who would, under the existing regulations, be either fined or imprisoned, will be made to attend in the evenings and on half-holidays.

ABOLITION OF FLOGGING

The Bill's proposals with regard to corporal punishment represent a great step forward. In accordance with the recommendations of a recent committee (the Cadogan), all the powers which the courts hitherto possessed to pass sentences of corporal punishment are to be swept away.

Corporal punishment does not entirely disappear from the penal code, but it is retained only as a punishment for offences committed in prison. The maximum sentence permissible is eighteen strokes of the cat-o'-nine-tails for those over twenty-one years old, and twelve strokes of the birch-rod for those under twenty-one.

It is proposed to frame new regulations regarding preventive detention for habitual offenders. Whereas formerly sentences of preventive detention could only be given in addition to terms of penal servitude, under the new Act it will be possible to pass sentences of preventive detention alone. These sentences will normally be from two to four years for persons over thirty, but in exceptional cases it will be possible to raise them to between four and ten years. In cases of habitual offenders of between twenty-one and thirty years, it will be customary to pass sentences of from two to four years' corrective training, instead of penal servitude.

SING SING, A GREAT AMERICAN EXPERIMENT

In 1913, Thomas Mott Osborne, an American reformer, voluntarily underwent a period of imprisonment in Auburn jail, New York, so that he might be able to look at penal problems from the criminal's point of view. His experiences there confirmed him in the conviction that far from helping to fit the prisoner to make an honest living on his release, the American system then in operation made the criminal more anti-social than ever. Determined to remedy this deplorable state of affairs, he introduced at Sing Sing prison a system of convict self-government calculated to bring out the best in every prisoner. He entirely abolished punishment and devoted all his energies to improvement. His experiments were greeted with derision from various die-hard quarters, but they proved eminently successful, not only in Sing Sing but in the naval prison at Portsmouth, New Hampshire.

Sing Sing is still one of the most advanced prisons in the world. Its population of 3,000 includes murderers, kidnappers, gangsters, embezzlers and felons, whose average age is twenty-three and who are serving sentences which average out at six years. Correction instead of punishment remains the rule of the " house."

The prisoners are graded, but not degraded. They work, play, study and are entertained. They talk freely among themselves and to their warders, whom they are taught to regard as friends. The illiterate are educated by the learned among the prisoners in school-rooms well-stocked with books. As reward for a long term of good behaviour a prisoner is given a large room with a view out to trees and the sky.

WAR'S TERRIBLE COST

IN the period from 1469 B.C. to A.D. 1930 only 287 years were blessed with peace as against the 3112 that were cursed with war. According to Professor Pella, of the University of Bucharest, some 8,000 treaties, meant "to last for all time," were signed between the years 1500 B.C. and A.D. 1860, but the average life of these "inviolable" agreements was two years.

Since the outbreak of the Thirty Years War in 1618, 1,700 major campaigns have been fought, in which France appears as the most frequent participant, followed by Austria-Hungary, Great Britain, and since 1740, Prussia. During this period France was at war with Great Britain for seventy-three years, with Prussia and the German Empire for eighty years, and with Spain for sixty-two years. The longest war of modern history is the Hundred Years War between England and France, which began in 1337; the shortest is the six days' war between Sardinia and Austria in 1849.

CIVILIZATION DOES NOT END WAR

Professor P. A. Sorokin and Lieut.-General N. N. Golovin have approached the problem from another angle. As a result of their researches they find that from 500 B.C. to A.D. 1925, Greece, Rome, Central Europe, Germany, Italy, France, Great Britain, the Netherlands, Spain and Russia have taken part in 902 regular wars. In the 12th and 13th centuries Russia was the Power most heavily involved in conflict, in the 14th century England, in the 15th, 16th, 17th and 18th centuries Austria (Holy Roman Empire), and in the 19th century France. According to the eminent authorities cited, war does not tend to disappear with the progress of civilization. Further proof of this is furnished by the World War of 1914-1918 and the succession of wars involving various countries since the conclusion of the "war to end war."

ORIGIN OF CHEMICAL WARFARE

Whereas in antiquity comparatively large armies and naval units faced each other in battle, the average strength of the armies engaged in the battles that were fought in the period between the Barbarian Invasions (A.D. 375) and the Thirty Years War (1618-1648) was only 15,000 men. In the 18th century it rose to 40,000, to double this number in the Napoleonic Wars, and in the Russo-Japanese War to 100,000 men.

Half a million men took part in the battle of Leipzig (1813), 320,000 in the battle of Sedan (1870). In the World War the 4,840 guns distributed along the forty-mile long Italian front at Vittorio Veneto fired over 3,000,000 rounds in sixteen days, at a cost of over £30,000,000.

Smoke and flame throwers as a means of warfare were used as early as the 11th century in China. The Mongols used them for the first time in the 13th century, in their incursion into Europe. With the aid of primitive machines "stink pots" were flung into the enemy lines and by their overpowering smell forced him to retreat. This was the real origin of chemical warfare.

The effectiveness of modern chemicals was put to a practical test in the World War. About 3,000 kinds were tried out, but only twelve were regarded as successful. Although gas warfare was unanimously rejected at the Washington Congress in 1921, this humane decision has received no official ratification in international law, and since then every nation has been feverishly engaged in producing poison gases. Poison gas was used by the Italians in the Italo-Abyssinian War of 1935-1937, and by the Japanese in China in 1938-1939.

INVENTION OF GUNPOWDER AND CANNON

Gunpowder is said to have been discovered in China in the 6th century of our era, but to have been used at first only for fireworks. The first hand-grenades containing gunpowder were made by the great Mongol leader Kubla Khan in 1230. Details regarding the composition of gunpowder had already been set down in the 9th century by a Byzantine of the name of Græcus. In the 13th century the English Franciscan friar and scholar, Roger Bacon, succeeded in producing it, and in 1313 it was re-invented by Berthold Schwarz, a monk of Freiburg. "Greek fire" was similar to modern gunpowder.

The first use of gunpowder in Europe was in 1247 at the siege of Seville. By the invention of gunpowder and the construction of the first cannon chivalrous methods of fighting were seriously restricted. The first occasion on which gunpowder was used in open warfare was the battle of Crecy, in 1346; the second was the defence of Einbeck, in Germany, in 1365. It was not till 1882 that smokeless powder was invented.

Cannon were first used as naval weapons (bombards) in 1338. The first naval engagement in which both sides were equipped with cannon was that of Brest (1512); both vessels, English and French, were set on fire, and 900 Frenchmen and 500 Englishmen lost their lives. Mohammed II, Sultan of Turkey from 1451 to 1481, had an enormous cannon cast during the siege of Adrianople; black stone balls 300 lb. in weight were inserted in it, and the noise of the discharge is said to have been heard within the radius of thirteen miles. After being drawn by oxen to Constantinople, this giant cannon burst and killed its inventor.

The first description of breech-loading guns was published by the Italian Lorini in 1597. Krupp made his first cast-steel gun in 1856, and by 1901 the range of the field gun had reached six miles, the maximum height of its trajectory three miles. During the World War the German long-distance gun (Big Bertha) fired 300 rounds to a height of twenty-five miles and a distance of eighty miles. It fired a 330-lb. shell which left the muzzle of the gun at 5,000 ft. per second. The explosive effect of a 16-in. shell is equal to the impact of four railway coaches running against a concrete wall at a speed of sixty miles per hour. The biggest gun is probably one in the possession of the U.S.A. It has a range of thirty miles.

In the World War the consumption of materials and munitions was enormous. From January 1, 1917 onwards the French factories alone produced 175,000 light and 40,000 heavy shells per day. About 300,000,000 hand-grenades were delivered to the German front, and 1,300,000 tons of steel were rained down on Verdun in thirty days.

FIRST MILITARY BOOTS AND SADDLES

The first mention of military boots is found in an Egyptian papyrus of 2000 B.C. Horseshoes that were permanently attached to the hoofs were not known until A.D. 300. Until then only temporary coverings that could be taken off when not required were used. Horseshoes were not necessary on the grass-covered steppes of Asia and on the loose soil that prevailed elsewhere. The Japanese bound their horses' hoofs with straw. It was long before the ancient Romans realized that their paved streets were harmful to the horses' hoofs; the first Roman horseshoes were made of leather.

To the ancient Greeks and Romans stirrups were unknown; they were introduced into Europe by the Sarmatians, whose descendants are now settled in Russia. Saddles, on the other hand, were in use from the earliest times and in the most varied forms. Even the early Assyrian cavalry were equipped with saddles, and the Romans covered their horses' backs with cloths, hides, and furs.

BLUE JACKETS AND RED BREECHES

The blue and white of the uniforms worn by the navies of every modern nation originated in a whim of King George II of England, who introduced them into his navy on being pleasantly impressed by that colour combination in the wardrobe of the Duchess of Bedford.

Red breeches were introduced into the French Army by Napoleon III to encourage the cultivation of the madder plant, from the roots of which a red dye of this shade is obtained. Epaulets are said to owe their origin to the Dutch rebels who, when the Spanish Duke of Alva threatened them with death by hanging, fought against him with cords round their necks as a sign of their contempt.

FLAGS AND BANNERS

Even the ancient Egyptians went into battle with flags flying; on them were painted pictures of the Apis bull and the sacred crocodile. Assyrian standards bore the symbol of their Queen Semiramis—a dove —while the Persians carried a golden eagle on their lance heads. The Spartan flag displayed the figure of Heracles; the Athenian flag a red owl. The emblems on the Roman standards were eagles, wolves, boars and horses, but from the time of Marius onwards (about 100 B.C.) they were restricted to the legionary eagle.

Under Constantine the Great (about 288-337) the battle standard consisted of the Roman *labarum* with the Sign of the Cross and the Greek initial letters of the name of Christ. Lions, dragons, and eagles figured on the banners of the Saxons led by Widekind. As we see from the Antonine Column in Rome, the dragon, symbol of sagacity, was the battle standard of nearly all the Teutonic peoples. Under Otho the Great (912-973) the Archangel Michael appeared on the banner as the protector of the Holy Roman Empire.

UNION JACK IS THREE FLAGS IN ONE

The Union Jack is three flags in one, for it includes the English flag of St. George, the Scottish flag of St. Andrew and the Irish flag of St. Patrick. Each is a cross, and the Union Jack may therefore be said to have both a national and a religious significance. The word " Union " was first applied in 1603, when James VI of Scotland became James I of Great Britain, and the flag of Scotland was incorporated with that of England; Ireland was not united to Great Britain until 1801.

The term " Jack " is said by some authorities to be derived from the leather tunics emblazoned with the cross of St. George which were worn by soldiers who served on warships during the reign of Edward III. Others point out that the jack was a small St. George's flag carried on a jackstaff at the bows of men-of-war long before the Union Flag was created. It gave place to the new design in 1605.

The cross of St. George is the broad, red, upright cross in the centre on a white field, that of St. Andrew the white x-shaped cross on a blue field, and that of St. Patrick the red cross of the same shape. The correct way to hang the Union Jack is to place the broader edge of the white strip on top nearest the head of the pole. To invert it is a signal of distress. After many changes the present Royal Standard was first hoisted on the Tower of London on January 1, 1801.

STARS AND STRIPES

The first American flag consisted of the Union Jack in the top left-hand corner and thirteen horizontal stripes, alternately red and white, representing the thirteen British colonies. Thirteen white stars in a blue field were substituted for the Union Jack in 1777.

The house on which it was first displayed, once the headquarters of Washington and later of Lieut.-General Sir Henry Clinton, commanding the British Army in America, still stands in Roger Morris Park, New York. Today the flag bears forty-eight white stars, each representing a State, on a blue field, arranged in six rows of eight stars each.

Under the Carolingians the national colours of the Holy Roman Empire were white and red, under the Franks red, under the Saxon emperors black, under the Swabians a golden yellow, under the Hapsburgs black and yellow.

When going into battle the emperor was preceded by the St. George's banner of the Swabian-Frankish nobility. In 1219 King Waldemar II of Denmark, on the eve of a crusade against Estonia, was presented by Pope Honorius III with a consecrated banner known as the Dannebrog, or strength of Denmark. Legend has it that the origin of this banner was a cross seen in the sky by the king. The Teutonic Order, like the Order of Templars which preceded it, had a black and white flag, which subsequently became the flag of Prussia. Before the French Revolution, which brought with it the tricolour, the national ensign of France was the white banner of the Bourbons with its three lilies.

The ensign of the all-conquering Mongols consisted of from one to four horses' tails, according to the size of the horde; that of the Chinese was a blue dragon on a yellow ground. The flag of the Mohammedan peoples was green. The double-headed German eagle, looking towards the east and west, was brought from the Eastern Roman Empire to Russia, and thence introduced into Germany by the Hapsburgs.

ORIGIN OF THE IMPERIAL EAGLE

In the same way as the lion is the symbol of the majesty of the State expressed in physical power, the eagle symbolizes the urge to accomplish noble deeds and the flight of thought.

For the early Indians the sun was the eagle Garuda which repeated every day its victorious flight across the sky; the Teutonic peoples saw the eagle as a petrel perched on Yggdrasil's Ash, the "world tree." The Sumerians of 5,000 years ago used the eagle as the symbol of their power. Wrought of gold and fixed to their lance heads, it flew before the Persians as they went into battle; under the Ptolemies it was the emblem and national device of the Egyptians; the Romans took the seated eagle from the sceptres of the Etruscan kings; and as a military device in wood, silver, or gold it led the Roman legions as they marched forth to conquer the world.

Charlemagne brought it back with him from Rome after his coronation there in A.D. 800, and introduced it into medieval heraldry, where it appeared first as a single-headed eagle, then, in 1433, as the double-headed eagle of the Holy Roman Empire. Emperor Frederick II of Hohenstaufen bestowed this imperial symbol on the Knights of the Teutonic Order for their campaign against the Slavs, and through them the black eagle became the heraldic device of Prussia. In 1701 the Hohenzollerns gave it a crown, and in 1870 it became the imperial eagle of the German Empire. Ivan the Great, who ruled Russia from 1462 to 1505, used double-headed black eagles. The spread eagle symbolizes the United States of America.

The Prussian eagle was black; that of Brandenburg was red, and that of Poland white; the Napoleonic eagles, like those of the Romans, were golden. The eagle figures in banners and orders and is embroidered in the coronation robes of the king and queen of England.

WAR-CRIES

The war-cry of the Greeks was *Alala, Alala!* a cry adopted by the Italian Fascists in 1922. The Romans shouted *Feri, Feri!* (Strike hard! Strike hard!), the Christian East Romans *Christe boethei!* (Christ to our aid!), the Crusaders *Adjuva Deus!* (God be our help!). The Russians used the war-cry of the Tartars. *Hurra, Hurra!* which means roughly Kill! Kill!

The cry of the English was "St. George for England!" That of the French was *Montjoie et St. Denis!* It is now *En avant!* (Forward!). The Spaniards' cry was *San Iago!* the Turks' *Allah Esmid!*

FROM PEASANT MILITIA TO CONSCRIPTION

In Egypt, about the year 3000 B.C., each district had its militia, which in time of war united with the others to form an army. There were only two arms of the service: spearmen and bowmen. Helmets, armour and swords were unknown. About 1,500 years later there were two standing armies, the nucleus and the officers of which were Egyptians, while the rank and file were hired troops of every nationality. By this date axes, short swords, and chariots were in use; instead of batons the marshals carried fans.

The Babylonians, Medes, and Assyrians had excellent infantry, cavalry and charioteers. The Persian Empire was the first to have a standing army—the royal troops, who took an oath of allegiance to the King of Kings alone. Annual reviews of the king's bodyguard, the " 10,000 immortals," were held.

The Parthians, whose country was south-east of the Caspian Sea, had the best cavalry in those days and were the first to be provided with armour; they were afterwards incorporated in the Roman forces. When at the height of their power, the Carthaginians had a picked body composed of the best men of their own nation; the remainder of their armed forces were mercenaries.

The Greek forces were composed of a civil militia, which was unpaid; the slaves were armed only in an emergency. There was no cavalry. Sparta, on the other hand, had a standing army, but it was never reinforced. The Spartans, and after 146 B.C. the Cretans, were quite willing to hire themselves out as mercenaries. Macedonia also possessed a standing force and, in addition, hired troops. Until well into the 2nd century (B.C.) the Romans were the best unmounted fighters in the world. From the time of Augustus (63 B.C.-A.D. 14) Rome maintained a standing army of 450,000 men.

Among the early Germans, the call to arms was issued originally by the district assembly, later by the king. From the time of Charlemagne (742-814) able-bodied men rallied to the standards of seven different leaders: the king, ecclesiastical and temporal princes, counts, bannerets, knights, and all free vassals of knightly rank. These armed bands were succeeded by the armies of the feudal lords, and the latter by the mercenary armies of the various princes. Frederick William, the Great Elector of Brandenburg (1620-1688) organized the first regular corps of officers, the French Revolution saw the first general levy, and G. J. D. von Scharnhorst (1755-1813) introduced universal military service into Prussia in 1808.

WAR CHARIOTS AND TANKS

The war chariots of early antiquity, two-wheeled cars flanked with sickles, an invention of the Assyrians which enabled the nomadic people known as the Hyksos to subjugate the Egyptians, have been resurrected in the form of tanks and are now integral parts of a modern army. The armoured car built by Cores in 1885 was unsuccessful because of the amount of fuel it had to carry. Daimler's armoured car equipped with a quick-firing gun appeared in 1904, and in 1914 armoured cars were used in action for the first time by the French.

At the beginning of 1937, Russia possessed from 6,000 to 10,000 modern tanks, France 4,500, Great Britain and Poland 600 each, Czechoslovakia 350, Italy 320, Yugoslavia 120, Rumania 90.

LIFE-GUARDS AND BODYGUARDS

The first company of grenadiers was formed in Sweden in 1634. They took their name from the hand-grenades which they threw and which looked like pomegranates. In France in 1667 they were provided also with bayonets. The Great Elector of Brandenburg raised six battalions of grenadiers as life-guards. Archers were so called after the Italian *arciero* (archer); the Royal Company of Archers is the King of England's bodyguard in Scotland.

Our word " hussar " is the Hungarian *huszar* (meaning " twenty "), which was used of a troop of these soldiers because King Matthias Corvinus (1443-1490) used to enlist one horseman from every twenty houses. Later, the hussars formed the contribution to the national forces of the pure Hungarian nobility and were converted into light cavalry. In 1721 the Wuthenow Hussars were formed in Prussia, and in 1741 the Brown Hussars, so called because they had donned Capuchin cowls at the taking of a convent in Silesia.

The musketeers, when first formed in 1521, carried muskets, the firearm of the foot soldiers; they were gradually replaced towards the end of the 17th century by the fusiliers. The uhlans (from the Tartar word for " brave ") were originally the national troops of Poland; in 1790 the name was adopted by Austria, and in 1808 by Prussia also. Foot soldiers have always been the basis of every army. Charles V (1500-1558) was the creator of the Spanish Army. His " royal troop " of infantry, the so-called *tercios*, were the noblest and bravest men of the nation. In this body of troops the private soldier was esteemed as highly as his officer.

As long as there have been armies there have been bodyguards to which the king and his government have looked for support, but which, when things were going badly, have often taken power into their own hands and formed a military dictatorship. Whereas when a country was flourishing the cream of the army, both officers and men, was drawn from the native population, the situation often changed in times of decay.

The Jewish kings had a bodyguard of Philistines. The Byzantine emperors were guarded by a body of Scandinavian adventurers who were also the last defenders of Constantinople against the Turks (1453). The Turkish sultans in their turn were guarded by the janizaries, who were young Christian captives. In 1826 they rebelled against their masters, their barracks were burned to the ground, and 8,000 of them perished in the flames.

YEOMEN OF THE GUARD

The sultans of Egypt were guarded by Nubians, the caliphs of Baghdad by Turks. The tsars surrounded themselves with the Strelitz (a word meaning " guards "), then with Cossacks; the doges of Venice were protected by Croats, the kings of Spain by Flemings, the popes by Swiss, the kings of France by Scots and Lorrainese, the kings of Denmark by Holsteiners, the Grand Duke of Tuscany by German mercenaries. The Hohenstaufen rulers of the Holy Roman Empire built up a bodyguard of 20,000 Saracens. Regiments of Hungarian life-guards saw to the protection of the emperors of Austria. The bodyguard of the Prussian kings came from what is now the Swiss canton of Neuchâtel. The oldest existing bodyguard is the Yeomen of the Guard, founded in 1485.

POLITENESS IN WARFARE

An incident typical of military etiquette in the 18th century took place at the battle of Fontenoy in Belgium, which was fought between the British and French in 1745. Of the two commanders of the opposing regiments of guards neither was willing to deprive the other of the honour of firing the first shot. Finally the Frenchman, being more eloquent, had his way, but his courtesy cost him dear, for he fell at the first British salvo.

The same high standard of politeness was maintained when the forces were encamped, it being customary to send champagne and other delicacies to the commander of a beleaguered fortress. With the advent of the unkempt generals of the French Revolution, however, all such refinements gave way to more rough-and-ready methods.

HAVOC OF CONFLICT

DULL as statistics usually are, they strike home when they tell us in plain figures of the havoc wrought both to the victors and to the vanquished by wars. In the Thirty Years War (1618-1648) Germany lost 12,000,000 inhabitants—Saxony alone 900,000—while the population of Württemberg was reduced from 900,000 to 50,000.

The French Revolutionary and Napoleonic Wars dealt a deadly blow at the population of France, for no less than 10,000,000 Frenchmen were left dead on Napoleon's battlefields. Of the *Grand Armée* of 600,000 men which set out to conquer Russia in 1812, only 20,000 returned to France. According to Mulhall the cost in treasure was £1,250,000,000.

In the American Civil War (1861-1865), in which 4,000,000 troops were involved, the North lost roughly 300,000 men, the South 500,000. The cost of the war—a contributory cause of which was the question of slavery—was in the neighbourhood of £740,000,000, a sum sufficient to have bought the freedom of every slave in the world, without entailing the loss of a single human life.

The Crimean War (1854-1856) cost £305,000,000. Of the 150,000 British soldiers who fought 20,000 were killed. The Indian Mutiny (1857) and the Chinese War of 1860 caused the loss of 52,000 lives. In the Franco-Italian War of 1859 there were 55,000 victims, in the Austro-Prussian War (1866) 400,000 killed and wounded, and 1,250,000 lives were lost in the Russo-Turkish War of 1859. The Franco-Prussian War of 1870-1871 cost France £506,000,000, including the indemnity; the loss of life was 290,000 men. The Spanish-American War (1898) cost the United States £50,000,000, and Spain £35,000 a day.

COST OF THE WORLD WAR

The World War of 1914-1918 cost approximately £80,000,000,000, according to the calculations of Dr. Nicholas Murray Butler, the distinguished American propagandist for peace. This sum would have been sufficient to buy up the whole of France and Belgium and everything they contained five times over. More than 10,000,000 people were killed outright in this war; 20,000,000 were wounded; and a further 10,000,000 died in the influenza epidemic that followed and was a consequence of the conflict. The number of people directly engaged was about 70,000,000.

The loss in production during the war years is incalculable; for the period 1919-1927 the loss is estimated to have amounted to £42,500,000,000. In Germany during the war years the number of births decreased by 3,000,000. Five years after the signing of the armistice nearly 7,000,000 war pensions were being paid by the impoverished Central Powers.

When the World War ended, British Government departments sold surplus stores and properties. The disposal of over 350,000 patterns and descriptions of stores in all parts of the world involved more than 3,000,000 transactions and realized the sum of £665,000,000.

Metals obtained £70,000,000; textiles £32,250,000; various kinds of plant and machinery, £24,000,000; huts, buildings, furniture, timber and building materials, £14,500,000; horses and other animals, £21,000,000; mechanical transport and road plant, £17,500,000. Thousands of miles of railways and a fleet of craft lying in various harbours were included in this colossal sale.

FOR THE CONQUEST OF ABYSSINIA

In 1935 and 1936, Italy transported to Abyssinia 350,000 men, 53 million feet of tent canvas, 62 million feet of assorted cloth, 87,000 horses and mules, 13,500 motor vehicles, 11,500 machine-guns, 450,000 rifles, 800 guns and 300 tanks. No less than 215 bake-ovens, 5,500 telephones (with 2,000 miles of wire), 1,081 wireless sets, 54 aerodromes and 10,995 water and fuel containers were used.

Over 1,000 tons of bombs were dropped from 637 aeroplanes, and 155,000 rounds of ammunition were fired by machine-guns. Over 46 tons of food were brought to advance posts by aeroplane.

ARMED FORCES OF THE GREAT POWERS

ON January 1, 1938, the British Army had an effective strength of just over 500,000 officers and men, and a total strength, including all reserves, of 621,000. On the same date the British Army in India had an effective strength of just over 210,000. Of these about 155,000 were Indians.

At the beginning of 1938 the Royal Air Force had between 1,500 and 1,750 aircraft. The construction programme for 1938-1939 called for the establishment of a first-line strength of 2,860 machines, of which 490 were to be stationed at home. In 1938 the Royal Air Force personnel numbered 62,900.

The number of officers and men serving with the Royal Navy in 1938 was about 120,000, of whom 11,600 were Marines. The number of the naval reserves was about 60,000. In the same year the total of vessels in service was 280, of which fifteen were capital ships or battle cruisers, six were aircraft carriers, fifty-four were cruisers, 153 were flotilla leaders or destroyers, and fifty-two were submarines. The total tonnage was 1,211,420; the number of guns, 1,725; and the number of torpedo tubes 1,809. There were seventy-five vessels with a tonnage of 477,265 under construction.

The British budget expenditure on the armed forces was £93,500,000 in 1933-1934: it rose to £172,333,000 in 1936-1937. The estimated figure for 1937-1938 is £262,000,000, and for 1938-1939 £327,000,000. The sums paid away in pensions are not included in the above figures: they amounted to £60,000,000 in 1936-1937, and the estimate for 1938-1939 is about £58,000,000. In 1937 the Treasury was authorized to borrow an additional sum of £400,000,000, to be spent on the defence services during the five financial years 1937-1938 to 1941-1942.

FRANCE DEVELOPS HER NAVY

The French Army has a normal strength (1937) of 692,860 men, of whom 486,000 are stationed in France; 85,000 in Algeria and Tunisia; 48,000 in Morocco; 12,000 in the Levant; and 60,000 in the colonies and China. The Air Force had about 63,000 officers and men in 1938: the number of aeroplanes was not made public. The Air Estimates for

1939 totalled £60,000,000, an increase of £20,000,000 on those for 1938. The average cost of a French military aeroplane was £17,000 in 1938. The Air Ministry proposed to build 500 a month during 1939.

The naval effectives numbered 70,157 in 1936, and two years later there were 174 vessels with a tonnage of 552,000 in the Navy. In 1939 the naval dockyards were building 130 vessels totalling 340,000 tons. This programme was described by the Minister of Marine as the most ambitious ever carried out by France.

GERMANY'S STRENGTH

In 1913 Germany had a standing army of 800,000, and a fleet with a tonnage of 1,000,000. On these she spent £70,000,000 a year. In 1928 she had a standing army of only 100,000 and a fleet with a tonnage of 150,000, on which she spent £30,500,000. Since then conscription —forbidden under the Versailles Treaty—has been re-introduced, and Hitler's Government has been spending immense sums on rearmament. No accurate figures of the strength of Germany's armed forces are available; but it is generally agreed that she has a stronger air force and a larger army than any other country, with the exception of Russia.

In 1938 the German Navy had thirty-seven surface vessels in service and was building twenty-nine more, to bring the tonnage up to 342,000. She had also seventy-two submarines with a tonnage up to 31,532. In December, 1938, the German Government announced its intention of increasing the numbers of its submarines and cruisers.

VAST LEGIONS OF SOVIET RUSSIA

The Soviet Union, which has a population of at least 180,000,000, could put a larger army into the field than any other Power. In 1936 her effectives, not including the reserves and the non-permanent territorial force, numbered 1,300,000. Since then they have been greatly increased. Between 1935 and 1938 no fewer than 5,360,000 men were called up for training.

The Russian Air Force had 750 planes in 1931: five years later, more than four times this number. The Navy has 186 vessels, with a tonnage of 290,589 built and in the course of construction, but many are of obsolete design. In 1938 it was announced that the Soviet Navy was to be modernized and expanded.

ARMED FORCES OF THE UNITED STATES

In 1937 the Regular Army of the United States numbered just over 180,000, including the members of the air component of the land forces. The total of the Air Armed Forces—the Army and Navy air components together—was 18,742. In addition to the Regular Army, the United States have a National Guard about 190,000 strong and Reserve forces totalling 112,000, which brings the total strength of the combined land and air forces to about 485,000. At the end of 1938 the combined American Air Arms were aiming at an establishment of at least 5,320 planes, but it was being suggested that only with twice this number would America be secure against potential aggressors. An air force of this size would place America far ahead of all her competitors in the air arms race.

The United States boasts the second largest navy in the world. The latest available figures show 334 vessels in service and eighty-three in course of construction, giving a total tonnage of 1,427,135. The vessels are equipped with about 2,000 guns and 2,350 torpedo tubes. Twenty-four of the guns are 16-inch, and 124 are 12-inch. Of the 417 vessels built or in course of construction, seventeen are battleships, 251 are destroyers, 106 are submarines, thirty-seven are cruisers, and six are aircraft-carriers.

The naval air arm had 584 heavier-than-air craft (aeroplanes) in service in January, 1936. On the same date it had five lighter-than-air craft in service. Of these latter, two were rigid, two non-rigid, and one was metal-clad. The largest, the airship *Macon,* was 785 ft. long and had a capacity of 6,500,000 cubic feet. At the end of 1938 the personnel of the United States Navy numbered 115,000 exclusive of the Marine Corps.

The budget expenditure on national defence was in excess of £200,000,000 in 1937-1938. In 1938 an enormous increase in armed strength was planned. The United States has a population of about 140,000,000, and is capable of building up a more powerful army than any other country with the exception of Soviet Russia.

JAPAN AND CHINA

In 1937 Japan launched a large-scale war of aggression against China. No reliable figures are available concerning the strength of her arms after the beginning of the war. In 1936 she had a standing army of only 250,000, but in the same year 630,802 conscripts were called up for examination. In July, 1938, she had an army 1,000,000 strong in China. At that date her casualties amounted to about 90,000 killed and 100,000 wounded. The Chinese armies then totalled about 2,500,000.

In 1935 the Japanese Air Force had 1,025 aeroplanes; three years later it may have had 4,000. In 1937 the Imperial Navy had 242 vessels in service and 11 in course of construction, giving a total tonnage of 906,430. There were ten battleships fitted with sixteen 16-inch guns and seventy-eight 14-inch. Cruisers numbered 42, destroyers 133, and submarines 62.

ITALY'S SWOLLEN FORCES

The Italian land army has a normal effective strength of just over 500,000, but since these figures were given Italy has been engaged in two wars—the Abyssinian War of 1935-1937, and the Spanish Civil War of 1936-1939. As a result of these the number of men serving with the colours has been enormously increased.

In 1934 the Italian Air Force had 1,860 aeroplanes and a personnel of 25,860. This force was actively engaged in the two wars mentioned above, so that by 1939 its strength had vastly increased.

In 1938 the Italian Navy had a total of 272 vessels, 226 of which were in service. It was made up of six battleships, twenty-two cruisers, one aircraft-carrier, 138 destroyers and 105 submarines. The total tonnage was in excess of 560,000.

EXPENDITURE ON ARMAMENTS

Here are some interesting statistics showing fluctuations in the world's arms bill. In 1932 armaments expenditure increased in fifteen countries, remained stationary in six, and decreased in thirty-seven. In 1935 it increased in forty-one countries, remained stationary in two, and decreased in fifteen. In the same year it increased by fifty per cent or more in seven countries. In 1937 it increased in forty-nine countries, remained stationary in one, and decreased in eight.

In the year 1932, Great Britain was supplying one-third of the world's armaments requirements, according to the *World Export Trade in Arms Statistical Year Book*. The world's armaments bill increased from 4,300,000,000 gold dollars (approximately £1,454,000,000) in 1932 to 7,100,000 gold dollars (approximately £2,400,000,000) in 1937. It was three times as great in 1937 as in 1913.

Whereas in 1932 European armaments expenditure only represented thirty per cent of the total, it had risen to sixty-three and two-fifths per cent five years later. Between 1932 and 1937 British expenditure trebled itself. In Soviet Russia it rose from 1,412,300,000 roubles to 20,102,200,000 roubles—an increase of nearly 1,500 per cent. In France it decreased, but in Germany, Italy, Japan and the United States it increased enormously. The figures for the United States are: 641,600,000 dollars (about £130,000,000) in 1932-1933 to nearly 1,000,000,000 dollars (£200,000,000) in 1937-1938.

YOUR PERSONAL BILL FOR ARMAMENTS

In 1938 the annual cost of armaments per head of the population was £12 in Germany, £7 in Britain, £6 in Russia, £5 in France and Japan, £3 in Italy and £2 in the United States. In the same year Germany was spending on armaments £2 10s. and Soviet Russia was spending £3 for every £1 spent by Britain.

Between 1913 and 1938 the proportion of their national incomes that was spent on armaments by the European Great Powers increased considerably. The following table shows the varying percentages:—

	1913	1938
Russia	5 per cent	22 per cent
Germany	4 ,,	15 ,,
France	6 ,,	10 ,,
Italy	3 ,,	9 ,,
Britain	5 ,,	7 ,,

The slump in international trade which began in 1929 and still obtained in 1937 affected the traffic in arms much less than that in general merchandise. Between 1929 and 1937 the volume of the armaments traffic decreased by only thirteen per cent but the export trade in general decreased by fifty-five per cent.

AGREEMENTS FOR LIMITATION OF ARMAMENTS

One of the earliest agreements concerning the limitation of armaments is contained in the Definitive Treaty between Great Britain, Austria, Prussia, Russia and France, signed at Paris, November 20, 1815. Article III is as follows: " The fortifications of Huninguen having been constantly an object of uneasiness to the Town of Basle, the High Contracting Parties, in order to give to the Helvetic Confederacy a new proof of their good-will and of their solicitude for its welfare, have agreed among themselves to demolish the fortifications of Huninguen; and the French Government engages, from the same motive, not to re-establish them at any time, and not to replace them by other fortifications, at a distance of less than that of three leagues from the town of Basle."

Two years later (1871) came the agreement concerning Naval Forces on the Great Lakes, between the United Kingdom and the United States of America. The frontier between the United States and Canada is probably the most undefended in the world.

The treaty between the Argentine Republic and Chile defining the boundaries between the two countries, signed at Buenos Aires, July 23, 1881, contained the following article: " Magellan's Straits are neutralized for ever, and free navigation is guaranteed to the flags of all nations. To insure this liberty and neutrality no fortifications or military defences shall be erected that could interfere with this object."

SUEZ CANAL OPEN TO ALL

The year 1888 saw the signing, at Constantinople, of a convention between Great Britain, Austria-Hungary, France, Germany, Italy, the Netherlands, Russia, Spain and Turkey regarding the free navigation of the Suez Canal. Article I stipulated that: " The Suez Maritime Canal shall always be free and open, in time of war as in time of peace, to every vessel of commerce or of war, without distinction of flag. Consequently the High Contracting Parties agree not in any way to interfere with the free use of the canal . . . which shall never be subjected to the exercise of the right of blockade."

In 1894 Britain and China agreed together not to fortify the Burma-Tibet frontier. In 1895 Britain signed an agreement with Russia concerning certain territory on the North-West Frontier of India: " that it shall not be annexed to Great Britain and that no military posts or forts shall be established in it." In 1896 Britain and France agreed that neither of them would, " without the consent of the other, in any case or under any pretext, advance their armed forces " into certain areas of Siam.

BLOCKADE AND THE PANAMA CANAL

In 1901 Britain and the United States made a treaty "relative to the establishment of a communication by ship canal between the Atlantic and Pacific oceans (Canal of Panama). The canal shall never be blockaded, nor shall any right of war be exercised nor any act of hostility be committed within it."

In 1902 the Governments of the Argentine and Chile agreed: "to reduce their respective fleets, for which object they will continue to exert themselves until they arrive at an understanding which shall establish a just balance between the said fleets."

In 1905, at the conclusion of the war between the two countries, Russia and Japan: "mutually agreed not to construct in their respective possessions on the Island of Saghalien (Sakhalin) or the adjacent islands any fortifications or other similar military works."

In the same year (1905) Sweden and Norway, after the dissolution of the territorial union between them, agreed that: "In order to ensure pacific relations between the two states, a territory (neutral zone) which shall enjoy the advantages of perpetual neutrality, shall be established on either side of the common frontier."

In 1912 France and Spain agreed not to fortify the part of the Moroccan coast that lies immediately to the south of the Strait of Gibraltar.

Two days after the outbreak of the World War (August 6, 1914), Britain and France undertook not to erect fortifications in the New Hebrides. This protocol was not ratified until March, 1922.

GENERAL REDUCTION OF ARMAMENTS

The German disarmament clauses of the Versailles Treaty (1919) were preceded by the following statement: "In order to render possible the initiation of a general limitation of the armaments of all nations, Germany undertakes strictly to observe the military, naval and air clauses which follow."

The German representatives at the Peace Conference (1919) stated that their country was prepared to agree to the basic idea of disarmament, "provided that this was a beginning of a general reduction of armaments." To which Georges Clemenceau, who presided, replied on behalf of the Allies that German disarmament would be regarded as the first step towards a reduction or limitation of armaments on the part of the other Powers.

Neither pledge was carried out. Whereas in the five years immediately preceding the World War the six chief Allied Powers—Great Britain, France, Italy, Russia, the United States of America, and Japan—were spending about £306,500,000 a year on arms, they were spending £555,000,000 a year in 1930. Great Britain's expenditure had increased by 48 per cent, France's by 57 per cent, Italy's by 114 per cent, Russia's by 56 per cent, America's by 135 per cent, and Japan's by 143 per cent. At the same period Germany's expenditure showed a decrease of 50 per cent. It will be noticed that Britain's armaments bill showed a smaller increase than that of any of her former Allies, and it should be remembered that the purchasing power of money was a good deal less in 1930 than in 1913. British statesmen claim that the Empire led the way towards disarmament but that none of the other great Powers would follow her.

In the year 1931 the world's expenditure on armaments was £1,400 a minute, of which Great Britain was responsible for one-seventh. Since then there has been a vast increase in the armed strength of every country. The tonnage of the world's navies increased from 5,299,000 tons in 1932 to 6,677,000 tons in 1937. The corresponding figure for 1913 was 6,900,000 tons, but since then great improvements have been made in naval shipbuilding and armaments so that the figures are not really comparable.

PRE-WAR EXPENDITURE ON ARMAMENTS

" The enormous growth of armaments and the insecurity and fear caused by them—it was these made war inevitable." Thus Lord Grey of Fallodon, who, as Sir Edward, was British Foreign Secretary in August, 1914. In the twenty-five years immediately preceding the outbreak of the World War the armaments expenditure of the six great Powers of Europe—Great Britain, France, Germany, Austria-Hungary, Russia and Italy—rose from £130,000,000 to £450,000,000 per annum. During the same period British expenditure rose from less than £50,000,000 to over £200,000,000 a year. The whole amount expended by these Powers in the period 1889-1914 was about £6,100,000,000, or one-fifteenth of the sum spent on the War itself.

INDEX